Healthcare

Project Management

By

Kathy Schwalbe

and

Dan Furlong

Healthcare

Project Management

Back Cover Photos: Dan Schwalbe

©2013 Schwalbe Publishing

ISBN-13: 978-0982800355
ISBN-10: 0982800355

Materials from Kathy Schwalbe's *Information Technology Project Management, Sixth Edition*, are used with permission from Cengage Learning.

Microsoft and the Office logo are either registered trademarks or trademarks of Microsoft Corporation in the United States and/or other countries. All screenshots from Microsoft products are used with permission from Microsoft.

Information and screenshots from MindView Business are used with permission from MatchWare.

Some of the product names and company names used in this book have been used for identification purposes only and may be trademarks or registered trademarks of their respective manufacturers and sellers. PMI, PMP, and PMBOK are registered marks of the Project Management Institute, Inc.

Published by Schwalbe Publishing, Minneapolis, Minnesota, July 2013. Includes minor corrections.

Book stores should email schwalbe@augsburg.edu to place orders at a discount. This book can also be purchased from www.amazon.com. The Kindle version will be available soon.

Free companion Web site: *www.healthcarepm.com.*

Visit ***www.schwalbepublishing*** or ***www.kathyschwalbe.com*** for more information on this and other books by Kathy Schwalbe.

BRIEF TABLE OF CONTENTS

DETAILED TABLE OF CONTENTS

PREFACE

The recent recession has made organizations appreciate the need for good project, program, and portfolio management skills more than ever. Many organizations, including corporations, government agencies, non-profit organizations, and universities have responded to this need by establishing courses and programs in project management. Hundreds of books are now available on this topic, but very few are available that focus on one of the most important and changing industries today—healthcare.

The first book I (Kathy Schwalbe) wrote in 1999 was focused on managing projects involving information technology, with many examples taken from my own work experience. *Information Technology Project Management* is now in its seventh edition, published by Cengage Learning. I also wrote a more general book in 2006, *An Introduction to Project Management*, now in its fourth edition. Several instructors and practitioners have asked me to write additional books, especially this one, designed for people in healthcare fields. I was very fortunate to find several people to help me in writing this book, especially my co-author, Dan Furlong. I think it's very important to have someone with intimate knowledge of the field as an author, and Dan definitely provided the healthcare expertise in this book. We also had several excellent reviewers who all have experience managing various healthcare projects and/or teaching courses to students in the healthcare field.

We used *An Introduction to Project Management, Fourth Edition*, as the basis for this book, but we made a lot of changes to address the need for people in the healthcare field to understand and apply good project, program, and portfolio management. Dan Furlong took the lead in writing a new running case, Ventilator Associated Pneumonia Reduction (VAPR), which provides great examples of applying various project management tools and techniques to an important healthcare project that will help both patients and providers. This text also includes many real-world examples in the "What Went Right," "What Went Wrong," "Media Snapshot," "Best Practice," "Video Highlights," and "Healthcare Perspective" segments. People like to read about real projects to learn from the successes and failures of others. They also realize that there are a wide variety of projects in the healthcare field, from preventing hospital acquired conditions to remodeling a hospital to providing online services. We have collaborated with many experts in the healthcare field to provide examples that are easy to understand and relevant to challenges of today.

Many people learn best by example, so we've provided detailed examples of applying project management to a project from start to finish. We have never come across a textbook that presents project management concepts and then brings them to life in a fully developed sample project for the healthcare industry. We also provide template files for creating the sample documents and case studies that students can do based on real or fictitious projects. We believe this approach helps many people truly understand and apply good project management.

APPROACH

This text provides up-to-date information on how good project, program, and portfolio management can help you achieve organizational as well as individual success. Distinct features of this text include its:

- Emphasis on projects in the healthcare industry and comprehensive samples of applying tools and techniques to a realistic healthcare project

- Relationship to the Project Management Body of Knowledge (based on the PMBOK® Guide, Fifth Edition (2013))

- Instructions on using Microsoft Project 2013, the leading project management software in use today

- Inclusion of templates and seamless integration of various software applications

- Robust and free companion Web site (www.healthcarepm.com) with links to video highlights and other resources, interactive quizzes, and more; a secure instructor site is also available with lecture slides, test banks, etc.

Emphasis on the Healthcare Industry

Several chapters include sections with information unique to the healthcare industry. For example, the first chapter includes a section describing the context of healthcare projects, including a brief history of the U.S. healthcare industry, the nature of healthcare projects, characteristics of project team members, and recent trends in healthcare that can affect project management. Each chapter also includes features with healthcare perspectives as well as examples of projects that went right and wrong, best practices, media snapshots, and video highlights. Many of the examples are from healthcare projects. The running case throughout the book (Ventilator Associated Pneumonia Reduction) is also based on a healthcare project, describing work done to initiate, plan, execute, monitor and control, and close the project.

PMBOK® Guide Framework

The Project Management Institute (PMI) created the *Guide to the Project Management Body of Knowledge* (the *PMBOK® Guide*) as a framework for understanding project management. The *PMBOK® Guide* is, however, just that—a guide. This text uses the *PMBOK® Guide, Fifth Edition* as a foundation, but goes beyond it by providing more details, highlighting additional topics, and providing a real-world context for project, program, and portfolio management.

Instructions for using Microsoft Project 2013

Appendix A of the text includes basic information on project management software and detailed, step-by-step instructions on using the number one product, Micros*oft Project 2013*. You do not need to buy a separate book to learn how to use Project 2013 effectively.

Templates and Seamless Integration of Various Software Applications

You do not have to reinvent the wheel when it comes to much of the documentation required for managing projects. This text uses over 60 free template files for creating various documents, spreadsheets, diagrams, and charts. Various software applications are used throughout the text in a seamless fashion. We purposely created the templates in a simple format. Feel free to modify them to meet your needs.

Free Companion Web Site (www.healthcarepm.com)

A companion Web site provides you with a one-stop location to access informative links and tools to enhance your learning. This site will be a valuable resource as you access links mentioned in the text, take online quizzes, play Jeopardy games, and download templates and files for Microsoft Project. Instructors can access a protected instructor site, which includes copyrighted lecture slides, solution files, test banks, sample syllabi, and other information.

ORGANIZATION AND CONTENT

Healthcare Project Management is organized into ten chapters and two appendices. The first two chapters introduce project, program, and portfolio management and discuss different approaches for their selection. You'll read about Academic Healthcare Systems (AHS) and how they decided to pursue the Ventilator Associated Pneumonia Reduction (VAPR) project. The next seven chapters follow the five process groups of project management: initiating, planning (broken down into three chapters), executing, monitoring and controlling, and closing. These seven chapters apply various tools and techniques in each of these process groups to the VAPR project. Chapter ten describes more information and research on best practices. Appendix A provides general information on project management software and a step-by-step guide to using Microsoft Project 2013. Appendix B, which we decided to make available in its entirety online, includes resources information, such as a list of templates, running case studies, advice on using simulation software, and resources to help you learn more about project management certification.

PEDAGOGICAL FEATURES

Several pedagogical features are included in this text to enhance presentation of the materials so that you can more easily understand the concepts and apply them. Throughout the text, emphasis is placed on applying concepts to up-to-date, real-world project management.

Learning Objectives, Chapter Summaries, Quick Quizzes, Discussion Questions, Exercises, Team Projects, and Case Studies

Learning Objectives, Chapter Summaries, Quick Quizzes, Discussion Questions, Exercises, Team Projects, and Case Studies are designed to function as integrated study tools. Learning Objectives reflect what you should be able to accomplish after completing each chapter. Chapter Summaries highlight key concepts you should master. The Quick Quizzes help reinforce your understanding of important concepts in each chapter. The Discussion Questions help guide critical thinking about those key concepts. Exercises provide opportunities to practice important techniques, as do the Team Projects. The Case Studies in Appendix B (available online) provide a robust means to apply what you have learned from the text to realistic case studies, similar to the example used throughout the text.

Opening Case and Case Wrap-Up

To set the stage, each chapter begins with an opening case related to the materials in that chapter. These scenarios spark interest and introduce important concepts in a real-world context. As project management concepts and techniques are discussed, they are applied to the opening case and other similar scenarios. Each chapter then closes with a Case Wrap-Up—some problems are overcome and some problems require more effort—to further illustrate the real world of project management.

What Went Right? and What Went Wrong?

Failures, as much as successes, can be valuable learning experiences. You may have heard the anonymous quote, "We need to learn from people's mistakes because we'll never have time to make them all ourselves." Each chapter of the text includes one or more examples of real projects that went right as well as examples of projects that went wrong, with many taken from the healthcare industry. These examples further illustrate the importance of mastering key concepts in each chapter.

Media Snapshots, Best Practices, Video Highlights, and Healthcare Perspectives

The world is full of projects. Several television shows, movies, newspapers, Web sites, and other media highlight project results, good and bad. Relating project management concepts to projects mentioned in the media will help you understand and see the importance of this growing field. It is also important to study best practices so readers can learn how to implement project management in an optimum way. Many students also enjoy watching videos to enhance their understanding of topics, so each chapter includes summaries and links to relevant videos. The healthcare perspective feature in each chapter provides additional insight and examples relevant to the healthcare industry.

Cartoons

Each chapter includes a cartoon used with permission from the popular Web site xkcd.com. These cartoons use humor to illustrate concepts from the text.

Key Terms

The field of project management includes many unique terms that are vital to creating a common language and understanding of the field. Key terms are displayed in boldface and are defined the first time they appear. Definitions of key terms are provided in alphabetical order at the end of each chapter and in a glossary at the end of the text.

Application Software

Learning becomes much more dynamic with hands-on practice using the top project management software tools in the industry, Microsoft Project 2013, MindView Business, as well as other tools, such as spreadsheet software. Each chapter offers you many opportunities to get hands-on experience and build new software skills by applying concepts to problems posed for them. In this way, the text accommodates both those who learn by reading and those who learn by doing.

SUPPLEMENTS

The following supplemental materials are available when this text is used in a classroom setting. All of the teaching tools available with this text are provided to the instructor on a secure Web site. Instructors must contact Kathy Schwalbe at schwalbe@augsburg.edu to gain access.

- **Instructor's Manual:** The Instructor's Manual that accompanies this textbook includes additional instructional material to assist in class preparation, including suggestions for lecture topics and additional discussion questions.

- **PowerPoint Presentations:** The instructor site for this text includes lecture slides for each chapter created with Microsoft PowerPoint. These slides provide a teaching aid for classroom presentation, and they can be made available to students on the organization's secure network for online review or they can be printed for classroom distribution. Instructors can modify slides or add their own slides for additional topics they introduce to the class. Remember that these slides are copyrighted materials.

- **Solution Files:** Solutions to end-of-chapter questions can be found on the instructor site.

- **Text Banks:** In addition to the Quick Quiz questions in the text and interactive quizzes available from *www.healthcarepm.com*, the secure instructor site includes hundreds of additional test questions in various formats.

ACKNOWLEDGEMENTS

We thank our many colleagues and experts in the field who contributed information to this book. We especially thank Cindy LeRouge, Associate Professor of Health Management and Policy at St. Louis University, for pushing us to create this book and co-authoring the first chapter. Thank you Elan Dillner for helping us find great references and videos. We also thank our outstanding reviewers:

- Jody Smith, Ph.D., Professor and Chair, Department of Health Informatics and Information Management, Doisy College of Health Sciences, Saint Louis University, St. Louis, MO

- April Horn, Program Administrator, Center for the Science of Health Care Delivery, Mayo Clinic, Rochester, MN

- Dan Wallis, Managing Director of KP OnCall, LLC, a wholly owned subsidiary of Kaiser Permanente, and instructor at UC San Diego, CA

- Charles H.Andrus, MHA, Clinical Information Systems Coordinator, St. Louis Children's Hospital, St. Louis, MO.

We also thank our spouses and children for their support, as well as the many students and colleagues we interact with daily. We are eager to receive your feedback on this book. Please send all feedback to Kathy at schwalbe@augsburg.edu

ABOUT THE AUTHORS

Kathy Schwalbe, Ph.D., PMP, is a Professor in the Department of Business Administration at Augsburg College in Minneapolis, where she primarily teaches courses in project management and problem solving for business. Kathy's first job out of college was as a project manager/officer in the Air Force. She worked for 10 years in industry (Air Force, Boeing, and Clark Oil) before entering academia in 1991. Kathy is an active member of PMI, having served as the Student Chapter Liaison for the Minnesota chapter, VP of Education for the Minnesota chapter, Editor of the ISSIG Review, Director of Communications for PMI's Information Systems Specific Interest Group, member of PMI's test-writing team, and writer for the community posts. Kathy earned her Ph.D. in Higher Education at the University of Minnesota, her MBA at Northeastern University's High Technology MBA program, and her B.S. in mathematics at the University of Notre Dame. She was named Educator of the Year in 2011 by the Association of Information Technology Professionals (AITP) Education Special Interest Group (EDSIG). Kathy lives in Minnesota with her husband. They enjoy being empty-nesters after raising three children.

Dan Furlong, PMP, FHIMSS, CPHIMS manages the Project Management Office for the Medical University of South Carolina and also teaches healthcare project management and healthcare technology in their Master in Health Administration program. Dan has served on advisory councils for multiple universities initiating or undergoing accreditation for project management programs. He has been an active member of the PMI Charleston chapter, serving on the board for the past ten years in a variety of roles including VP Professional Development, VP Marketing & Public Relations, VP Community Outreach, President, and Chairman. Dan is a graduate of the PMI Leadership Institute Master Class, a year-long development program offered by PMI to select chapter leaders worldwide. Dan has served on the board of the South Carolina HIMSS chapter and has been a frequent speaker at state and national HIMSS conferences. He was recently named a HIMSS Fellow (FHIMSS) for his contributions to HIMSS and the industry. Dan has hosted multiple 8-hour project management workshops during the HIMSS pre-symposia, and has presented at many other regional, national and international conferences. He has also served on the board or as a board advisor to SC.GMIS, a statewide government technology professional organization, since 2003. He earned his undergraduate degree in Computer Science at the College of Charleston, his MBA at The Citadel, and is currently working on his dissertation for his Doctorate in Health Administration from the Medical University of South Carolina. Dan also owns PM One, LLC, a project management training and consulting company. Dan lives in beautiful Charleston, SC with his wife and three sons.

To all the wonderful people working in healthcare, especially those who cared for my Uncle Fran, my husband, and me this past year. (I broke my left wrist playing tennis a week before publication! Not the type of "break" I wanted!)
Kathy Schwalbe

To my wife, Julie, and our three ambitious and bright sons, Christopher, Matthew, and Michael, who had to put up with me working many late nights and weekends while working on this book. There would be no reason to achieve if not for you four.
Dan Furlong

Chapter 1

An Introduction to Project, Program, and Portfolio Management in Healthcare

---

LEARNING OBJECTIVES

After reading this chapter, you will be able to:

- Understand the growing need for better project, program, and portfolio management in the healthcare industry

- Investigate the context of healthcare projects, including a brief history of the U.S. healthcare industry, the nature of healthcare projects, characteristics of project team members, and recent trends in healthcare that can affect project management

- Explain what a project is, provide examples of healthcare projects, list various attributes of projects, and describe project constraints

- Describe project management and discuss key elements of the project management framework, including project stakeholders, the project management knowledge areas, common tools and techniques, and project success factors

- Discuss the relationship between project, program, and portfolio management and their contribution to enterprise success

- Describe the project management profession, including suggested skills for project, program, and portfolio managers, the role of professional organizations like the Project Management Institute, the importance of certification and ethics, and the growth of project and portfolio management software

---

OPENING CASE

Francis (Fran) Anthony, the Chief Executive Officer (CEO) of America's Best Healthcare, Inc., was discussing strategic plans with the board of directors. "Healthcare is currently in an environment of change that seems to be moving at the speed of light. Health information technology, policy changes, cost containment, re-admit penalties, meaningful use, evidence - based medicine, and forming health networks are bearing down on us, and hard. Not to mention our desire to improve quality measures, explore the medical home concept, improve our patient experience, and reach rural communities. Managing a healthcare organization as it existed a few years ago is no longer an option, and at times it is overwhelming."

Everyone in the room took an extra breath as Fran went through the list of strategic initiatives. One of the board members commended Fran on the success of the electronic health records (EHR) implementation completed the prior year as well as the rising success of the new telemedicine service line helping to address emergency department stroke care needs by providing specialist access across their network. Fran responded that the "big guns" were pulled out for those projects, but several new initiatives had not gone so well.

Dr. Kaheed had been on the board for the last ten years, and he understood the climate changes Fran was talking about as well as the various levels of project success. He asked Fran what was so different about these two major projects, particularly since similar projects seem to be struggling at some other organizations.

Fran thought for a few seconds, and then replied, "Excellent question. What has really helped us the last two years is that we have embraced project management and are working to make it a core competency. We now have a project management office staffed with professionals to assist our organization on major projects. We assigned a full-time project manager to work with each of those projects. Don't get me wrong, these projects had major challenges, but we were able to get ahead of the issues to make things work out in the end. "

Fran went on to explain that using good project management ensured that the projects had clear goals, a good plan to follow in order to meet those goals, and a good path for integrating the projects into the organization's regular operations and workflow. "Board members, we need to become a more project-based organization. And believe me, it will not be easy. It's never easy to implement changes. These skills and methodologies need to not just stay with a couple of project managers and selected projects. We need increased capability to successfully manage and execute projects across the organization. We already have the talent and skills to provide quality medical care and maintain operations. If we invest what it takes to further develop the skills and talent to plan and execute projects across America's Best Healthcare, I am very confident that we will be able to navigate the rapid change opportunities and challenges in the current healthcare climate and have continued success in years to come."

INTRODUCTION

The opening case highlights the fact that healthcare organizations have a growing interest in project management. In the past, project management primarily focused on providing schedule and resource data to top management in just a few industries, such as the military and construction industries. Today's project management involves much more, and people in every industry and every country manage projects. The facts below demonstrate the significance of project management:

- In 2011, the average annual salary (excluding bonuses, in U.S. dollars) for someone in the project management profession was $160,409 in Switzerland (the highest-paid country), $139,497 in Australia, $105,000 in the United States, and $23,207 in China (the lowest-paid country). This Project Management Institute (PMI) survey was based on self-reported data from more than 30,000 practitioners in 29 countries.[1]

- CareerBuilder.com found that 44% of U.S. employers listed project management as a skill they looked for in new college graduates, behind only communication and technical skills.[2] Employers throughout the world, especially in Australia and Canada, echo the same request.

- Project management certification continues to be one of the most popular certifications throughout the world, and pay is often higher for project managers who hold PMI's Project Management Professional (PMP) certification.

- The U.S. spends $2.3 trillion on projects every year, and the world as a whole spends nearly $10 trillion on projects of all kinds. Projects, therefore, account for about one fourth of the U.S. and the world's gross domestic product (GDP).[3]

- Projects in the healthcare industry continue to grow, and the global healthcare market for just information technology (IT) projects is expected to reach $162.2 billion by 2015, growing at a compound annual rate of over ten percent from 2010 to 2015.[4]

- Project management is also a vital skill for personal success. Managing a family budget, planning a wedding, remodeling a house, completing a college degree, and many other personal projects can benefit from good project management.

Organizations claim that using project management provides advantages, such as:

- Better control of financial, physical, and human resources
- Improved customer relations
- Shorter development times
- Lower costs
- Higher quality and increased reliability
- Higher profit margins
- Improved productivity
- Better internal coordination
- Higher worker morale
- Reduced stress

What Went Wrong?

In 2010, the American Health Information Management Association (AHIMA) worked with the American Medical Informatics Association to publish "H.I.T or Miss: Lessons Learned from Health Information Technology Implementations". This collection of 17 vignettes documents real-life situations of health IT projects that did not go well. An important lesson learned in these tales from the trenches is the need to use sound project management principles in health IT projects.

The Standish Group first published an often-quoted "CHAOS" study in 1995 which reported that the overall success rate of IT application development projects in the U.S. was only 16.2 percent. The researchers defined success as meeting project goals on time and on budget. The study also found that more than 31 percent of IT projects were canceled before completion, costing U.S. companies and government agencies more than $81 billion. The authors of this study were adamant about the need for better project management in the IT industry. They explained, "Software development projects are in chaos, and we can no longer imitate the three monkeys—hear no failures, see no failures, speak no failures." [5]

In another large study, PricewaterhouseCoopers surveyed 200 companies from 30 different countries about their project management maturity and found that over half of all projects (not just IT projects) fail, including those in healthcare. They also found that only 2.5 percent of corporations consistently meet their targets for scope, time, and cost goals for all types of projects. [6]

The healthcare industry has initiated and completed projects for a long time, but not necessarily using formal project management techniques. New technologies, health reform, evidence-based medicine, health networks, patient-centered care, medical homes, and improved patient experience are some of the many forces that are radically changing the healthcare environment, and where there is change, there are projects! This rate of change, as well as increasing interest in applying business best practices from other industries to healthcare, has prompted the healthcare industry to examine their practices in managing projects. Healthcare organizations are realizing that to remain competitive, they must develop skills to effectively select and manage the projects they undertake. They need to be conversant with and use modern project management techniques and embrace program and portfolio management to address enterprise-level needs.

The main emphasis of this book is to help people in the healthcare industry to improve the success rate of their projects, from adding new hospital wings to preventing hospital acquired conditions to introducing new technologies.

Video Highlights

The Yale School of Management and Change Observer created a Web site and several videos about the Mayo Clinic in Rochester, Minnesota, an organization known worldwide for its excellence in healthcare and innovation. One of the videos about project management includes interviews with key members of the Center for Innovation. Barbara Spurrier, Administrative Director, describes how much project management has taken off at Mayo. They prepare project charters, status reports, and other documents to help manage projects and improve communications. Barbara indicates that it is crucial to be very clear regarding project deliverables while also being flexible with stakeholders in executing projects. The project management team uses disciplined processes to co-create. Dan O'Neil, a project manager, explains that project managers are part of a triad with designers and physicians to develop realistic plans that guide the execution of projects.[7]

See *www.healthcarepm.com* for links to this and other videos. Additionally, the history of project management is available a series of videos on youtube.com by Mark Kozak-Holland, author of a book on the subject.

THE HEALTHCARE PROJECT MANAGEMENT CONTEXT

Projects are not run in isolation. They are part of a bigger system, and in order to be successful, project managers must understand that system. The U.S. healthcare system is extremely complex, and many books and articles are available to attempt to explain it. For this text, it is important to understand basic information about the context of healthcare projects, including a brief history of the U.S. healthcare industry, healthcare costs, the nature of healthcare projects, and recent trends in healthcare that can impact project management.

Brief History of the U.S. Healthcare Industry

For most of American history, the maternal figure was responsible for the health needs of the family, performing the duties today traditionally performed by nurses, physicians, and other healthcare professionals. The mother-as-caregiver health model gradually dissipated with the rise of the American physician, which was based on the English model. The physician was promoted as a profession of learned individuals specializing in medical treatment. The maternal figure in the family or the physician could approach each case of short-term illness or injury as a project.

The model for the current, expansive healthcare industry was partially the result of one hospital's reaction to declining revenue during the Great Depression in 1929. American households faced difficult financial choices during the Depression and many people chose to forgo healthcare. As a result, Baylor University's hospital in Dallas, Texas offered schoolteachers up to 21 days of compensated hospital care for $6 per year. Baylor's modest plan would grow into Blue Cross, one of the most well-known health insurance plans in the industry, which would later merge with Blue Shield in 1982. Adjusting administrative systems to meet changing rules, regulations, and reporting requirements of third-party payers is a classic driving force for healthcare projects.

The creation of "the Blues" is an important part of the healthcare industry because the pair served as the basis for arguably one of the most important pieces of federal healthcare legislation – Medicare. Medicare provides healthcare coverage for U.S. citizens 65 years of age and older as well as other special populations. The same day President Lyndon B. Johnson signed Medicare into law in 1965, he also signed Medicaid, which is a joint venture between federal and state governments to provide health coverage for low-income and disabled individuals. The Medicare and Medicaid systems were designed largely after WWII to treat episodes requiring short-term or acute medical care. Today, the vast majority of expenditures are associated with long-term or chronic care, which requires a more integrated care system between hospitals, providers, patients, and community services. This difference between acute and chronic care health services and meeting the respective needs of each situation is one of the root drivers behind a good number of process-oriented projects today.

Medicare and Medicaid represent the most significant federal legislation to impact the industry, although not for lack of effort. Presidents Theodore Roosevelt, Franklin D. Roosevelt, Harry Truman, and Bill Clinton proposed some form of national healthcare. However, it was not until March 2010 that the Patient Protection and Affordable Care Act (PPACA or just ACA) proved to be the most impactful federal legislation on the healthcare industry since Medicare and Medicaid. The ACA has resulted in incentives and enablers for the implementation of EHRs, associated meaningful use, resultant procedural changes, and Health Information Exchanges. All of these initiatives coupled with movements to patient-centered care, evidence-based medicine, centers of excellence, and other forces bearing down on the healthcare industry have spawned a current climate of what may be an unsurpassed number of healthcare projects going on within the US and globally.

These initiatives operate in an environment of cost control propelled by rising costs and anticipated increased reductions to Medicare and Medicaid as well as third-party payer reimbursements. To meet these challenges, health and healthcare leaders need to do the following:
- Ensure they are working on the right projects at the right time
- Make investments in IT, infrastructure, and quality changes that will allow them to reduce costs.

Healthcare Costs

Today, due primarily to Medicare and Medicaid, government spending in U.S. healthcare accounts for almost 45% of total expenses. How is this money spent, and where does it come from? Health expenditures were distributed as follows in 2010 (in billions of dollars):
- Hospital care: $814.0
- Physician/clinical services: $515.5
- Prescription drugs: $259.1

- Nursing care facilities & continuing care retirement communities: $143.1
- Home healthcare: $70.2
- Other personal healthcare: $384.2
- Other health spending: $407.6

Historically, healthcare spending largely originated from private sources, but government spending has increasingly constituted a higher percentage. The source of funds for national health expenditures were as follows:
- Private health insurance: 32.7%
- Medicare: 20.2%
- Medicaid: 15.5%
- Out-of-pocket: 11.6%
- Other third party payers/public health: 10.6%
- Investment: 5.7%
- Other public insurance programs: 3.7%

The following statistics from the 2012 Henry J. Kaiser Family Foundation demonstrate that the spending level in the US may not taper off any time soon.
- Healthcare spending accounted for 17.9% of U.S. GDP in 2010, an average of $8,402 per person.
- The Centers for Medicare and Medicaid Services (CMS) estimates that healthcare spending will grow to about 19.8% of GDP by 2020.
- Compared to other Organisation for Economic Co-operation and Development (OECD) countries, the U.S. spends 48% more on healthcare compared to the next highest country, Switzerland.
- Increases in health insurance premiums continue to outpace inflation and the growth in workers' earnings.
- Hospital care ($814 billion) and physician/clinical services ($515.5 billion) are the top two categories of healthcare expenditures in the U.S. [8]

The Nature of Healthcare Projects

So what, if anything, makes healthcare projects stand out from other types of projects? In addition to the diversity of projects, some frequent attributes of healthcare projects include the following:
- *Care quality, cost containment, and external review are key characteristics.* Unlike many other types of projects, healthcare projects normally include these three hallmarks.
- *Quality of care for the patient is crucial.* Many healthcare projects are initiated to help people prevent, improve, or deal with a health concern. The successful execution of some healthcare projects can mean the difference between life and death. This means that quality will most often be considered more important than time, cost

and other constraints. For example, the use of electronic health records continues to grow, modifying workflow and changing the way healthcare is practiced. First and foremost in managing these projects, however, should be the goal to improve the quality of patient care or, at minimum, not to compromise the existing levels of quality.

- *Government and regulatory agencies often plays a big role.* The government is often the sponsor or reason for a healthcare project (i.e. Medicaid reform, public health campaigns, meaningful use incentive design, etc.) or it creates laws or standards that must be followed in private healthcare projects. For example, International Classification of Diseases (ICD) changes or surveillance of reportable disease projects cannot be ignored. Part of the challenge of this regulatory environment is that changes regularly occur and can impact projects mid-stream. The Health Information Technology for Economic and Clinical Health (HITECH) Act and PPACA are two recent examples of how government intervention can drive project priorities in healthcare organizations.

- *Finances are complex.* In many healthcare organizations it is difficult to easily predict the financial value of projects or calculate projected return on investment for several reasons:
  - o Revenues are difficult to estimate. Many healthcare organizations cannot estimate their revenues because of the complex insurance system in the U.S. For example, emergency rooms cannot turn away patients who cannot pay, and most patients honestly do not know how much of their care will be paid for by their insurance companies.
  - o Project budgets may be subject to fluctuating conditions. Donations can be a major source of funding: As demonstrated by the Media Snapshot example, many public or community health projects are prompted by donations or rely on them for their continuation. Furthermore, one never knows what regulation is suddenly going to mandate a project or change the scope of a project.
  - o Many hospital organizations are not-for-profit and must strive to fulfill their mission in tandem with return on investment. Community assessments and a demonstration of benefits to the communities they serve are often required for this type of organization to retain their not-for-profit status.

- *Healthcare is very personal.* People have very different attitudes about healthcare, such as how private or open they are about discussing it, how much they are willing to spend on it, and what types of services they will use. Regulations such as the Health Insurance Portability and Accountability Act of 1996 (HIPAA) seek to protect privacy, maintain confidentiality, and ensure that patient data is stored and transported securely. Compliance with HIPAA and generally preserving patient confidentiality, privacy, and security can introduce particularly challenging constraints and creates a high degree of risk for any project that will access, use, or transfer patient information.

- *Healthcare mistakes historically have increased revenue.* No caregiver wants to harm a patient; they commit their lives to improving the health of the patient. However, in the past any mistakes made by caregivers, through oversight, inexperience, or lack of knowledge, resulted in the patient returning for follow up treatment and generating additional revenue. Starting with HITECH and continuing with the PPACA, healthcare providers now have to pay for their mistakes by covering the treatment required to correct errors they made previously. This change is driving projects that reduce errors throughout the system, but these projects are introducing more rigor into a profession that is largely considered more art than science by its practitioners. Therefore, not everyone will agree that a project is a good idea, even though it may seem reasonable to anyone not delivering care.

- *Deliverables and metrics are different.* The end goal cannot always be quantified in a healthcare project. The health of a human is not always measureable in terms of any value metric. In light of this, healthcare generally looks to two types of metrics for healthcare projects – outcomes and process, particularly for quality improvement projects. For example, did a project result in an increase in the percentage of patients who got a certain test on an annual basis (process) and did this result in fewer patients developing a particular complication (outcomes)?

- *Projects are becoming ever more complex.* There are very few projects that take place within a healthcare organization that do not require multiple disciplines serving together on the project team. Nurses, physicians, technology staff, therapists, administration staff, compliance staff, and training staff are all engaged in significant healthcare projects, and most are engaged in smaller projects as well.

- *Collaboration across entities is required.* Projects in the modern healthcare context are requiring increasing degrees of intra (within the organization) and inter (across organization) collaboration. For example, adding a new telemedicine service line (e.g., distance-based speech pathology encounters) may require the IT department, healthcare providers, and hospital administrators at both the hub (specialty care provider – speech pathologist) and spoke (patient location) sites to work together. This may be especially challenging when the hub and spoke sites are not in the same health network or even the same type of organization, such as a speech pathologist providing services remotely to a child in a school.

Media Snapshot

Many people can't wait to see the famous singer, actress, writer, director, and producer, Barbara Streisand. Although she admits that she is shy and likes to stay out of the limelight, Barbara appeared on Katie Couric's new talk show, Katie, on September 25, 2012. Viewers may have been expecting to hear a lot of singing, but Barbara and Katie spent most of the time talking about the new Barbara Streisand Women's Heart Center at the Cedars-Sinai Heart Institute in Los Angeles, California. Barbara is passionate about her latest project – leading the revolution in women's heart health. She was shocked when she discovered that *heart disease kills more women than all cancers combined.* Heart disease kills 30% of the population in the United States, and starting in 1984, more women than men died of heart disease. Barbara and her colleagues at the Women's Heart Center are on a mission to reverse the gender discrimination in research about women's heart disease. Additional information about this project is available at www.streisandwomensheartcenter.org.

Recent Trends in Healthcare

At a 2012 conference panel on "Transforming from Healthcare to Health," senior leaders of various healthcare organizations and academic programs discussed some of the changes happening in the industry. Three executives shared their views of the future.[9]

- Kenneth Paulus, President and CEO of Allina Hospital and Clinics: The healthcare industry is at a proverbial crossroads and needs to change. In five years things will look very different as organizations become more customer-focused. The new generation wants choices and lower costs, and safety and quality will be a commodity like it is for the airline industry. Healthcare organizations will need to attract customers and keep them loyal. A new kind of leader is needed who understands insurance principles, risk management, and population health. Organizations must become lean to reduce costs. They must embrace information technology and make decisions based on data. Healthcare organizations must learn how to do marketing and become patient service oriented.

- Ronald Smith, Principle and Co-founder of Frauenshuh Healthcare Real Estate Solutions: Mr. Smith explained that his company's products keep people out of the hospital. Ambulatory facilities are growing in popularity as patients receive treatment on an outpatient basis. Hospital and physician integration is accelerating, and organizations must use standardized clinical and business models. Important strategies for success include an optimal care environment, brand loyalty, collaborative care models, and partnerships,

- Scott Kozicki, Entrepreneur and Market Manager of mHealth at Verizon Wireless: Entrepreneurs and technologists see huge opportunities for healthcare projects. It's a big business and growing every year. About half of healthcare dollars are spent on chronic diseases such as diabetes, heart disease, and lung disease. People wait too long to see a primary care physician – almost twenty days on average. Better primary care can lower healthcare costs. Healthcare must be more preventive and proactive. Cell phones apps are available to track weight, blood pressure, and other data, and patients can have video chats with nurses or other medical professionals. The industry needs to embrace new technologies and a different type of customer.

Healthcare Perspective

Berwick, Nolan, and Whittington asserted in a HealthAffairs article that "Improving the U.S. health care system requires simultaneous pursuit of three aims: improving the experience of care, improving the health of populations, and reducing per capita costs of health care. Preconditions for this include the enrollment of an identified population, a commitment to universality for its members, and the existence of an organization (an "integrator") that accepts responsibility for all three aims for that population. The integrator's role includes at least five components: partnership with individuals and families, redesign of primary care, population health management, financial management, and macro system integration."[10]

The triple aim and views of the future of U.S. healthcare are further discussed in a video by Barry Bittman , M.D. available on www.healthcarepm.com.

Healthcare organizations are also realizing that they have to learn from other industries and use proven practices to identify and manage the many projects they face today and in the future. They also have to understand how to group projects into programs and use portfolio management, as described later in this chapter. However, leaders in this area realize that healthcare has its own unique elements that require a certain level of specification or customization to suit best practices in the healthcare context. There is a lot at stake, which is creating a rising need for the specific study of healthcare project management.

WHAT IS A PROJECT?

To discuss project management, it is important to understand the concept of a project. A **project** is "a temporary endeavor undertaken to create a unique product, service, or result."[11] Operations, on the other hand, is work done in organizations to sustain the business. In the case of healthcare, operations may include such things as admitting patients to a hospital, performing surgery or procedures, caring for patients at the bedside in a hospital, or performing annual patient wellness exams for a primary care provider. An organization that is new to project management may zealously describe all activities as a project and create a lot of organizational confusion and potentially extra work. Projects are different from operations in that they end when their objectives have been reached or the project has been terminated. Operations represent routine activities that are part of the recurring day-to-day routine.

Examples of Public Health and Healthcare Projects

Projects in the healthcare sector can be large or small and involve one person or thousands of people. They can be done in one day or take years to complete. They also can occur in various types of healthcare related entities. Examples of healthcare entities and related projects in various contexts include the following:

Patient/Health Consumer Level:

- A family makes modifications to their home including a ramp to allow entry into the house and remodeling the bathroom to accommodate a wheelchair-bound family member.

- A diabetic designs how she will initiate a structured self-management program using monitoring devices that electronically send her blood sugar level and blood pressure directly to her physician. (Once the program is in place it will hopefully become part of the routine operations in her life).

Sole Providers and Physician Groups

- A physician's office implements an electronic health record (EHR) system

- A physician group modifies its billing system from ICD9 to ICD10 in order to meet revised International Classification of Diseases (ICD) code sets used to report diagnoses and inpatient procedures

Community Clinics

- A community health center brings federally certified moderate complexity lab testing in house to expedite access to test results and minimize the cost of lab testing for uninsured patients.

Assisted Living/ Long-term Care:

- A long-term care organization servicing an elderly population remodels their oldest wing in response to a consumer quality index evaluation of experiences of residents.

Hospital/ Hospital Departments:

- A community hospital launches a women's health initiative.

- A university hospital designs and constructs a new neurology clinic.

- A hospital develops a physician evaluation program to comply with new standards issued by a regulatory agency, such as The Joint Commission.

- An emergency department develops a formal process for notifying patients of sexually transmitted disease test results in advance of Department of Health notification.

- A hospital develops a program to reduce readmission rates by identifying and monitoring high-risk patient discharges.

Health Networks

- A collection of healthcare providers form an accountable care organization.

- A hospital network begins a telemedicine service line for stroke patients.

Health Research:

- A research team performs an evaluation of a state health information exchange.

- A cancer center develops an internship program for pre-med students to assist with research studies.

- A research team develops a smart phone application to assist diabetics with self-management and performs usability and field testing.

- A team of medical researchers conducts a clinical trial of a new medical device.

Payers

- A health insurance company establishes a medical call center and web site to help subscribers make decisions regarding medical care options.

Government and Public Health

- A developing country's health department launches a maternal and child wellness program.

- The state public health department develops and launches an immunization campaign.

- A local health agency works with the public health department to develop an educational course to train the public health workforce and other first responders to improve their capacity to respond and provide essential services for natural disasters and bio-terrorists situations.

Not for Profit/Community Health

- A medically supervised camp program for overweight adolescents creates a summer program.

- A not-for-profit hospital conducts a community assessment to determine how to target community benefit activities.

- A tobacco control charity designs and executes a smoking cessation campaign.

- A kidney disease foundation holds a 10K race event.

- A health research-funding agency designs and launches a new grant program.

Healthcare Vendor/Consulting/Auditing

- A consulting company designs and implements a dashboard for hospital executives to monitor key operational indicators for the facility.

- A medical supply and distribution company installs new distribution software that will facilitate just in time inventory levels.

- An audit team conducts an audit of a health organization.

- A healthcare consulting company develops a workforce needs assessment tool that hospitals use to optimize and plan for clinical workforce needs.

As shown in the examples of healthcare projects, there are many types of projects done by many types of healthcare entities. An individual patient can develop a project, as can an entire health network or federal agency.

Project Attributes

As you can see, projects come in all shapes and sizes. The following attributes help to define a project further:

- *A project has a unique purpose.* Every project should have a well-defined objective. As described in the next chapter, it is important to work on projects for the right reasons, and to manage them well. It should not be difficult to explain the goals or purpose of a project. For example, a long-term care facility may choose to renovate a wing to improve patient experience and attract a market segment capable of paying higher fees. Let's call this project the Expanding Wing Project. Though the long-term care facility may have performed upgrade projects in the past, each renovation project is unique. Remodeling of this wing may involve activities (e.g., adding small social circle spaces), materials (e.g., installation of intelligent device technology to monitor and communicate with residents and their families), a section of the facility, or a magnitude (an entire wing as opposed to a one-room renovation) not previously undertaken as a single initiative.

- *A project is temporary.* A project has a definite beginning and a definite end. For the Expanding Wing Project, senior management of the long-term care facility will usually have a date in mind when they'd like the renovations to start and be completed.

- *A project is developed using progressive elaboration or in an iterative fashion.* Project leaders often define projects broadly when they begin and provide greater specificity as time passes and more information is known and the details become clearer. For example, there are many decisions that must be made in planning and remodeling the wing of a long-term care facility. It works best to draft preliminary plans for management to approve before more detailed plans are developed.

- *A project requires resources, often from various areas.* Resources include people, hardware, software, or other assets. The Expanding Wing Project will engage many different types of people, skill sets, and resources.

- *Projects succumb to the theory of scarcity.* Organizations have more wants than they have resources to fill those wants, so not all projects requested may be undertaken. The Expanding Wings Project was chosen because it opens a new market and increases revenue more than other project options at the time.

- *A project should have a primary customer or sponsor.* Most projects have many interested parties or stakeholders, but someone must take the primary role of sponsorship. The **project sponsor** usually provides the general direction for the project as well as funding for the project. In the case of the Expanding Wing Project, the operations manager or chief operating officer might serve as the project sponsor.

- *A project involves uncertainty.* Because every project is unique, it is sometimes difficult to define the project's objectives clearly, estimate exactly how long it will take to complete, or determine how much it will cost. External factors also cause uncertainty. Such things as weather conditions, a supplier going out of business, or a key project team member taking unplanned time off could affect the Expanding Wing Project. Uncertainty is one of the main reasons project management is so challenging, because uncertainty invokes risk.

Projects also have informal or formally designated project managers. **Project managers** work with the project sponsors, the project team, and the other people involved in a project to define, communicate, and meet project goals. A good project manager contributes to a project's success. For the Expanding Wing Project, the facilities manager may be a strong possible choice to serve as project manager to provide detailed project planning and monitor and control the project day-to-day during project execution.

Unfortunately, a surgeon cannot implant a device, as shown in Figure 1-1, to make you a great project manager. You'll have to work at it, or wait until someone completes a project to make this type of surgery an option!

Figure 1-1. Surgery won't help (www.xkcd.com)

Project Constraints

Every project is constrained in different ways. To create a successful project, project managers must consider scope, time, and cost (to name a few) as defined below.

- *Scope*: What work will be done as part of the project? What unique product, service, or result does the customer or sponsor expect from the project?
- *Time*: How long should it take to complete the project? What is the project's schedule?
- *Cost*: What should it cost to complete the project? What is the project's budget? What resources are needed?

These limitations are sometimes referred to in project management as the **triple constraint**, the project management triangle, or the iron triangle, as shown in the first diagram in Figure 1-2. Project managers must balance these three often-competing goals. The act of balancing these goals often results in trade-offs. For example to increase scope, the project's time and/or cost will also increase. To reduce the time, cost may need to increase or scope must decrease. To reduce the cost, scope may need to decrease or time must increase.

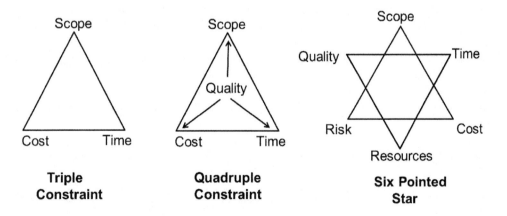

Figure 1-2. Growing Number of Project Constraints

Other people focus on the **quadruple constraint**, which adds quality as a fourth constraint to the model, as shown in the second diagram in Figure 1-2. For example, how good does the quality of the products or services need to be? What do we need to do to satisfy the customer? As described earlier, quality has a special place in healthcare projects. Almost all healthcare projects either directly or indirectly affect the improvement or decrement of the lives of health consumers. If a software developer provides poor coding in an electronic health record system, it could permanently impact an individual's life in a negative way. This high-risk environment creates a constraint and often a lot of bureaucratic processes for healthcare projects given the foremost concern for patient and health consumer safety. If an individual's life could be in danger because of a lack of quality, other constraints may need to be adjusted to support higher quality. In a healthcare project, if you don't take the time to do it right, you may have to do it over to maintain patient quality standards.

The *PMBOK® Guide, Fifth Edition* has expanded the quadruple constraint model to suggest a six point star model (or some people prefer a hexagon) that includes the addition of risk and resources, but recognizes that there may be others as well, depending on the project. The last diagram in Figure 1-2 shows these six project constraints.

The triple constraint goals—scope, time, and cost—often have a specific target at the beginning of the project. For example, the sponsor for the Expanding Wing Project might initially define the scope of the project to include adding new social spaces, visitor amenities, minor decorating changes, and moderate upgrades to existing furniture and bathroom fixtures in patient rooms. They might set a goal of completing the renovation in five months and spending about $300,000 on the entire project. The project team will have to make many decisions along the way that may affect meeting those goals. The project leaders might need to increase the budget to meet scope and time goals or decrease the scope to meet time and budget goals. The other three constraints—quality, risk, and resources—affect the ability to meet scope, time, and cost goals.

Projects by definition involve uncertainty and resources, and the customer defines quality. No one can predict with one hundred percent accuracy what risks might occur on a project. Resources (people) working on a project might produce different results than originally expected, and material resources may vary as well. It is very difficult, if not impossible for project planners to define their quality expectations in detail during project initiation when the project details and resource availability may be a bit fuzzy. Quality, risk, and resource constraints often affect each other as well as the scope, time, and cost goals of a project.

To illustrate the interrelationship among the constraints, assume the project budget included replacing the current bathtubs in the facility with new tubs with similar features (e.g., railing, hand shower, and room for a bath chair). The American Disability Act (ADA) Certified contractor may provide a compelling case for an alternatively designed ADA walk-in tub to reduce the potential for injury to either the patient or healthcare worker. The project manager and sponsor can see the potential benefit to increasing the quality of the bathtub. First, it can be a selling point to potential residents and their families. Second, it can increase patient and medical staff safety. The project sponsor and manager will need to make some decisions that can involve project constraint tradeoffs in response to this new information. Changing the planned type of bathtub in favor of an ADA walk-in tub may affect the cost of the project, the schedule (if more time is required to the purchase process or installation), and certainly the scope of the project as the scope includes product characteristics and deliverables. In addition, the project sponsor, manager, and team may encounter other options and issues that could affect project plans.

It is because of such situations and uncertainties that projects rarely finish according to the discrete scope, time, and cost goals originally planned. Instead of discrete target goals for scope, time, and cost, it is often more realistic to set a range of goals that allow for uncertainties. Early Expanding Wing Project plans may best serve the organization by targeting spending between $250,000 and $350,000 and having the renovation completed within five to eight months. These goals allow for inevitable changes due to risk, resources, and quality considerations.

Experienced project managers know that, due to the tradeoff inherently part of many project decisions, project leaders should decide which constraints are most important on each particular project very early in the project's life. These priorities will guide planning activities as well as decisions made as the project is executed. If time is most important, you may have to change the initial scope and/or cost goals to meet the schedule. Project leaders might have to accept more risk and lower quality expectations in a tight time constraint situation. If scope goals are most important, project leaders may need to adjust time and/or cost goals, decrease risk, and increase quality expectations.

Other constraints may come into play. Understanding and awareness is a critical factor for many healthcare projects. Adhering to a strong communications plan may be a constraint that may cause some schedule delays or introduce some additional costs, such as public awareness campaign materials for a project affecting the community. Procurement constraints include those imposed by Food and Drug Administration (FDA), state and local health department, or American with Disabilities Act (ADA) regulations. Healthcare projects in the U.S. invariably must also take into account the Health Insurance Portability and Accountability Act (HIPAA), The Joint Commission (formally Joint Commission on Accreditation of Healthcare Organizations, or JCAHO) standards, Institutes for Healthcare Improvement (IHI) best practices, and American Medical Association (AMA) guidelines.

Though unknowns exist as projects are conceived, sponsors must provide some type of target goals for a project's scope, time, and cost and define other key constraints for a project. How can you avoid the problems that occur when you meet a project's scope, time, cost, and other goals, but lose sight of customer satisfaction? The answer is *good project management, which includes more than meeting project constraints.*

WHAT IS PROJECT MANAGEMENT?

Project management is "the application of knowledge, skills, tools and techniques to project activities to meet the project requirements."[12] Project managers must not only strive to meet specific goals of projects, they must also facilitate the entire process to meet the needs and expectations of the people involved in or affected by project activities.

Figure 1-3 illustrates a framework to help explain project management. Key elements of this framework include the project stakeholders, project management process groups, knowledge areas, tools and techniques, project success, and the contribution of a portfolio of projects to the success of the entire enterprise. Each of these elements of project management is discussed in more detail in the following sections.

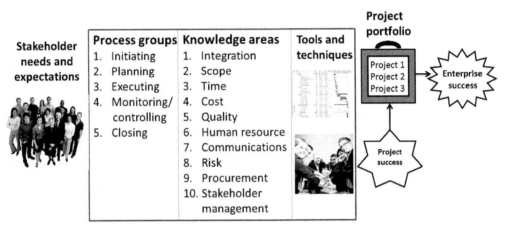

Figure 1-3. Project management framework

Project Stakeholders

Stakeholders are the people involved in or affected by project activities and include the project sponsor, project team, support staff, customers, users, suppliers, and even opponents to the project. These stakeholders often have very different needs and expectations. For example, there are several stakeholders involved in the Expanding Wing Project to renovate the long-term care facility.

- The project sponsor might be the divisional director of operations. The Operations Division would be the organizational unit funding the renovation to the long-term care facility and could be on a very tight budget. The project sponsor would have to make important decisions to keep the costs of the project within the budget approved by the CEO and CFO. As a result, the sponsor would expect the contractor to provide accurate estimates of the costs involved in renovating the wing. The sponsor would also need a realistic idea of when the remodeled wing will be ready for occupancy so the organization could begin marketing its availability, hiring staff if required, and ordering required furniture and equipment. Current residents of the wing would need to be either temporarily or permanently relocated.

- The project manager in this example might be the facilities manager, who is responsible for the maintenance and upgrade of the long-term care facility's structure, furniture, and fixtures. He or she needs to work with all the project stakeholders to meet their needs and expectations. If necessary, an assistant may be required to take over some of the operational work normally done by the facilities manager.

- The project team for the Expanding Wing Project would include an ADA certified general contractor, construction workers, electricians, carpenters, and so on to perform the actual remodeling. The administrative side of the team would include, but may not be limited to, a marketing manager (to brand and market the new facilities), the medical director (to provide patient care guidelines and needs for the new facility), and the director of nursing (to coordinate patient transition and relocation from the current facility to temporary or permanent new locations). Both the administration and construction stakeholders would need to know exactly what work they must do and when they need to do it. Each project team member's work would need to be coordinated with other team members' activities because there are many interrelated factors involved in remodeling the wing.

- Current and proposed long-term care facility residents are very important stakeholders in this project. The renovation design and project decisions need to consider their needs, physical conditions, and financial capabilities. The project team should use timely and well-crafted communications to explain how the renovation project may temporarily (e.g. relocation and noise) and permanently (e.g. upgraded room) affect existing residents. In the spirit of patient-centered care, project team members may seek feedback from targeted residents of the new facility at various points during the progress of the project as a factor in various project decisions.

- Support staff might include the regular maintenance staff, the general contractor's administrative assistant, and other people who support other stakeholders. The general contractor's administrative assistant would support the project by coordinating meetings between the buyers, the contractor, suppliers, and other stakeholders. The facilities manager might expect maintenance staff to focus on their routine operations work but allow some flexibility so they can visit the new wing site and provide their thoughts on progress or future maintenance needs.

- Renovating a long-term care facility wing will likely require many suppliers. The Expanding Wing Project suppliers may provide the furniture for new social spaces, materials for the bathroom (floor and wall tiles, bathtub, toilet, sink, lighting, etc.), and electronic monitoring equipment and software. Suppliers would expect exact details on what items they need to provide, where and when to deliver those items, and similar information.

- Healthcare is a regulated industry. A long-term care facility that holds a very high rating from the Centers of Medicare and Medicaid (CMS) would want to maintain this rating. As such, team members may communicate with a CMS regulatory auditor on the details of this project that involve increasing and maintaining resident care quality and the patient experience. They may also consult with patient experience and quality experts. There are also state and local health departments that oversee the construction work and issue the final certificate of occupancy before patients may move into the space.

- Additional stakeholders might include the healthcare providers that serve residents, third-party payers (insurance companies, AARP, Medicaid, and Medicare), and medical device safety officials. The providers would use any proposed communication or monitoring equipment, and their skill level and past experiences in working with patients could provide valuable information. In addition, there may be regulations to ensure the safety of the items installed as part of the renovation project that could affect equipment choices. The local housing inspector would also be a stakeholder, concerned with ensuring that everything meets specific codes and regulations.

- There may or may not be opponents to a project. In this example, some existing residents of the wing may not be able to afford occupancy in the remodeled wing and their families might band together to oppose the project to assure their family member is not displaced.

As you can see from the Expanding Wing Project example, there are many different stakeholders on projects, and they all have different interests. The following example describe a national public health project situation that demonstrates stakeholders' needs and expectations are important in the beginning and throughout the life of a project. Successful project managers develop good relationships with key project stakeholders to understand and meet their needs and expectations.

What Went Right?

The Center for Disease Control's (CDC's) Biosense project was jokingly referred to as Biononsense in some public health circles. Introduced in 2003, the CDC did not hold the first project stakeholder meeting until 2005. But the government agency has been working hard to improve on their hard lessons learned from this project. The Center revisited the struggling effort in 2010 and incorporated concepts from project management to promote open collaboration between stakeholders with the ultimate goal of delivering a more useful product. To date, the CDC has been largely successful in its efforts.

The CDC noted two key concepts as effective in redesigning the Biosense 2.0 program. First, stakeholder engagement involving input from federal, state, and local public health officials at the outset clarified what pertinent changes were required to add value for all stakeholders. And secondly, improved internal contract management allowed the government agency to reduce the program's operating costs and redistribute these savings to support state and local public health agencies.

Biosense 2.0 is an example of revisiting a failed project from a fresh perspective, salvaging useful components, and adopting relevant project management concepts to journey toward a better solution. By engaging stakeholder feedback from the outset and encouraging transparent collaboration, Biosense 2.0 will likely arrive at a satisfactory conclusion for all engaged parties[13].

Characteristic of Healthcare Project Team Members

A special group of project stakeholders are the team members that actually drive, plan, and execute the project. Instead of just one leader, different people, who play very important, yet very distinct roles, might lead projects:

- A designer/idea generator provides ideas to improve current processes, address a requirement, or seize an opportunity. These designers are often viewed as being very optimistic and freethinking, yet often unaffected directly by the results of projects that are implemented. Aside from idea generator this initial project leader may be instrumental in creating initial project momentum and interest. In some cases, the designer/ idea generator (particularly if in a management position) may evolve to become the project sponsor.

- A project manager works with all of the various stakeholders to develop a realistic scope, schedule, and budget for the project and facilitates its completion. In many healthcare environments, project managers must be especially sensitive to the needs of other team members and share the leadership role. The project manager should communicate with the sponsor throughout the project to make sure the project meets his or her expectations.

- A physician, nurse, therapist, technician, or other medical expert is required on many healthcare projects to make sure the project follows sound medical practices and will not cause harm to patients. Healthcare providers may feel overworked and overwhelmed by the many changes facing their field. If a project requires a physician leader (and those involving patient care often do), it is up to the project sponsor and project manager to make a clear connection and case for patient and/or physician benefit and the importance of physician involvement in the project process.

Best Practice

The Center for Innovation (CFI), established in 2008, serves a liaison between medical practice and human-centered design thinking. CFI uses a design thinking model inspired by the IDEO design consultancy firm philosophies. According to Tim Brown, CEO of IDEO, "Design thinking can be described as a discipline that uses the designer's sensibility and methods to match people's needs with what is technologically feasible and what a viable business strategy can convert into customer value and market opportunity." [14]

A major challenge for healthcare projects is ensuring the team operates as a cohesive unit to achieve its stated goal. The Center's interdisciplinary teams exemplify a design thinking (or creative problem solving) task force where team members come together to connect, prototype, adapt, explore, and solve in a Design Research Studio. Teams provide "sensibility to a problem" through empathy, creativity, ambidextrous thinking, and systems thinking. These teams may involve clinical professionals, non-clinical professionals (e.g., communications and user-centered design specialists), clerical staff, support staff, administrators, or external stakeholders, like a non-patient community member. A prime example of engaging internal and external stakeholders to achieve a stated goal is the Center's collaboration with primary care physicians, the payer, and patients to provide telemedicine consults for patients in remote areas of Minnesota.

Other team members who might be assigned to a project on an on-going or temporary basis might include:

- administrators, such as a hospital director
- a head nurse and nursing staff
- a lab manager, staff managers, and marketing managers
- information technology experts, such as systems analysts or programmers;
- other physicians
- patient advocates and patient representatives
- community relations or benefits staff
- a quality officer
- a medical informatics officer
- legal counselors
- accounting, purchasing, or operations staff
- equipment technologists, etc.

There is also often a need for multiple champions representing different roles (e.g. physician champion) or different units (e.g., champions from both a hospital and a clinic in a health network that a project may affect) to help healthcare projects succeed. Project champions may use their experience, resources, organizational rank, charisma, or reputation to facilitate the success of the project. These champions may have either a formal or an informal role on the project team.

Conflicts often arise as project team members and other stakeholders disagree on what should be done, when, and how. Given the diversity of stakeholders in most healthcare projects, project managers must be especially sensitive to the perspectives and needs of various stakeholders to create an environment where people can work together to achieve common goals. Although most projects include stakeholders with diverse backgrounds and skills, healthcare is somewhat unique in that each stakeholder group typically has its own reporting hierarchy. Physicians may report to an executive medical director and yet not actually work for the hospital. In an academic medical center, the physicians may serve as faculty members, working for the university, even though they treat patients in the hospital. They most likely also belong to practice plans, which bill their professional services. Physicians alone may introduce three different chains of command! Nurses typically work for the hospital and report to a chief nursing officer (CNO) while at the same time reporting to service line administrators. Administration staff often report to the chief operating officer (COO), accounting and finance report to the chief financial officer (CFO), and technology staff may report to the chief information officer (CIO). These last three professional groups are primarily there to support the staff providing direct patient care, often creating a pseudo-customer relationship. Last of all, throw in a chief medical information officer (CMIO) and a chief nursing information officer (CNIO), who may fit into more than one of the above chain of commands, and you have the perfect recipe for confusion. Healthcare is a complex industry!

Skilled project managers working in the healthcare domain know when to hand off control, enlist a champion that a particular group may favor, and negotiate differences among various factions to direct the project towards success. They also understand the five project management process groups and ten knowledge areas, as described next.

Project Management Process Groups and Knowledge Areas

The five **project management process groups** include initiating, planning, executing, monitoring and controlling, and closing activities. Chapter 3 provides more information on the process groups and how they relate to the ten project management knowledge areas. **Project management knowledge areas** describe the key competencies that project managers must develop. The center of Figure 1-3 shows the ten knowledge areas of project management. Project managers must have knowledge and skills in all ten of these areas, briefly described as follows:

- Project integration management is an overarching function that coordinates the work of all other knowledge areas. It affects and is affected by all of the other knowledge areas.
- Project scope management involves working with all appropriate stakeholders to define, gain written agreement for, and manage all the work required to complete the project successfully.
- Project time management includes estimating how long it will take to complete the work, developing an acceptable project schedule given cost-effective use of available resources, and ensuring timely completion of the project.
- Project cost management consists of preparing and managing the project budget.
- Project quality management ensures that the project will satisfy the stated or implied needs for which it was undertaken.
- Project human resource management is concerned with making effective use of the people involved with the project.
- Project communications management involves generating, collecting, disseminating, and storing project information.
- Project risk management includes identifying, analyzing, and responding to risks related to the project.
- Project procurement management involves acquiring or procuring goods and services for a project from outside the performing organization.
- Project stakeholder management focuses on identifying project stakeholders, understanding their needs and expectations, and engaging them appropriately throughout the project. Note that PMI added stakeholder management as a tenth knowledge area to the *PMBOK® Guide, Fifth Edition* in 2013.

Project Management Tools and Techniques

Thomas Carlyle, a famous historian and author, stated, "Man is a tool-using animal. Without tools he is nothing, with tools he is all." As the world continues to become more complex, it is even more important for people to develop and use tools, especially for managing important projects. **Project management tools and techniques** assist project managers and their teams in carrying out work in all ten knowledge areas. For example, some popular time-management tools and techniques include Gantt charts, project network diagrams, and critical path analysis. Figure 1-4 lists some commonly used tools and techniques by knowledge area. You will learn more about these and other tools and techniques throughout this text. Note that the *PMBOK® Guide* refers to some of these items as outputs.

A sample of project managers directed respondents to rate tools on a scale of 1–5 (low to high) based on the extent of their use of the tool and the potential of the tool to help them improve project success. "Super tools" were defined as those with high use and high potential for improving project success. The tools defined as "super tools" included:

1. project management software
2. scope statements
3. work breakdown structures
4. requirement analyses
5. lessons-learned reports
6. status and progress reports
7. well-planned kick-off meetings
8. Gantt charts
9. change requests

The last four items have long been found to improve project performance, while the others need to become more common. You will learn how to use all of these super tools plus several others throughout this text. The super tools are bolded in Figure 1-4.[15]

Project management best practices and tools may be new or just emerging in some healthcare industry contexts. In these contexts, project managers may want to introduce project management structure incrementally and focus on "super tools" that align with project needs and circumstances. As with any tool, there has to be a fit to the situation. Some tools may be better suited or have more of an impact in some situations than others. It is crucial for project managers and their team members to determine which tools will be most useful for their particular projects.

Despite its advantages, project management is not a "cure-all" that guarantees success on all projects. Some projects, such as those involving new technologies, have a higher degree of uncertainty, so it is more difficult to meet their scope, time, and cost goals. Project management is a very broad, often complex discipline. What works on one project may not work on another, so it is essential for project managers to continue to develop their knowledge and skills. It is also important to learn from the mistakes and successes of others.

Knowledge Area/Category	Tools and Techniques
Integration management	Project selection methods, project management methodologies, project charters, project management plans, **project management software, change requests**, change control boards, project review meetings, **lessons-learned reports**
Scope management	**Scope statements, work breakdown structures**, mind maps, statements of work, **requirements analyses**, scope management plans, scope verification techniques, and scope change controls
Time management	**Gantt charts**, project network diagrams, critical-path analyses, crashing, fast tracking, schedule performance measurements
Cost management	Net present value, return on investment, payback analyses, earned value management, project portfolio management, cost estimates, cost management plans, cost baselines
Quality management	Quality metrics, checklists, quality control charts, Pareto diagrams, fishbone diagrams, maturity models, statistical methods
Human resource management	Motivation techniques, empathic listening, responsibility assignment matrices, project organizational charts, resource histograms, team building exercises
Communications management	Communications management plans, **kickoff meetings**, conflict management, communications media selection, **status and progress reports**, virtual communications, templates, project Web sites
Risk management	Risk management plans, risk registers, probability/impact matrices, risk rankings
Procurement management	Make-or-buy analyses, contracts, requests for proposals or quotes, source selections, supplier evaluation matrices
Stakeholder management	Stakeholder registers, stakeholder analyses, issue logs, interpersonal skills, reporting systems

Figure 1-4. Common project management tools and techniques by knowledge area

Project Success

How do you define the success or failure of a project? There are several ways to define project success. The list that follows outlines a few common criteria for measuring project success as applied to the example Expanding Wing Project for remodeling the long-term care facility wing:

- *The project met scope, time, and cost goals.* If the planned renovation work was completed within five months and cost under $300,000, we could call it a successful project based on these criteria.
- *The project satisfied the customer/sponsor.* Even if the project met initial scope, time, and cost goals, the divisional director of operations sponsoring and funding the renovation might not be satisfied. Perhaps the project manager made important decisions without the sponsor's approval. Perhaps the quality of some of the construction or materials was not acceptable. If the targeted

residents to occupy the remodeled wing were not happy about important aspects of the project, it would be deemed a failure based on this criterion. Many organizations implement a customer/user satisfaction rating system for projects to measure project success.

- *The results of the project met its main business or clinical objective.* Business or clinical objectives in this example could include improving patient experience ratings or providing a good return on investment through increased occupancy or increased fees for rooms in the new wing. Scores on customer assessments of healthcare providers and systems are becoming increasingly important for healthcare organizations to maintain market share and avoid losing payer reimbursement. If the long-term care facility gained greater market share and increased its patient satisfaction scores as a result of the renovation, even if it cost more or took longer to build, it would be a successful project based on this criterion. As another example, suppose the owners of the long-term care facility wanted to sell the facility in the next three to four years and for a good return on investment (ROI). If that happened, the owners would deem the project a success, regardless of other factors involved.

For healthcare projects, all three measurement techniques are important. When dealing with projects that involve patient safety and outcomes, however, it is typically the last technique that matters most. That is not to say that projects may overrun their budget by 200% and be called successful! You may, though, assume that any project that harms a patient will be called a failure, regardless of it meeting all other typical success measurements. For many projects with ROI objectives, financial success cannot be determined until well after the project is completed. It is also true that success cannot be measured for many healthcare projects targeted to improve health outcomes until well after the project is complete.

Project managers play a vital role in helping projects succeed. Project managers work with the project sponsors, the project team, and the other people involved in a project to meet project goals. They also work with the sponsor to define success for that particular project. Good project managers do not assume their definition of success is the same as the sponsors' definition. They take the time to understand their sponsors' expectations. For example, if you are in charge of renovating a long-term care facility wing, find out what is most important:

- meeting scope, time, and cost goals of the project to renovate the wing
- satisfying other needs, such as target customer approval
- being sure the project delivers a certain result, such as increased occupancy or improved patient satisfaction scores

The success criteria should help you to develop key performance indicators needed to track project progress. It is important to document this information in enough detail to eliminate ambiguity.

PROGRAM AND PROJECT PORTFOLIO MANAGEMENT

As mentioned earlier, about one-quarter of the world's gross domestic product is spent on projects. Projects make up a significant portion of work in most business organizations or enterprises, and successfully managing those projects is crucial to enterprise success. Two important concepts that help projects meet enterprise goals are the use of programs and project portfolio management. Both of these extensions of project management have a place in the healthcare industry.

Programs

A **program** is "a group of related projects, subprograms, and program activities managed in a coordinated way to obtain benefits not available from managing them individually."[16] It is often more economical to group projects together to help streamline management, staffing, purchasing, and other work. The following are examples of programs in healthcare:

- A government agency has a program for children's services, which includes a project to provide pre-natal care for expectant mothers, a project to immunize newborns and young children, and a project for developmental testing for pre-school children, to name a few. Figure 1-5 illustrates the program structure.

- A health network is expanding its telehealth services. It will create a teledermatology service line, a telestroke service line, and a telepsychology service line. Each telemedicine service line is a separate project involving potentially different sets of providers and locations, but each service line is part of a program. There would be several benefits to managing these projects under one telehealth program. For example, the program manager could advertise the comprehensive telehealth services together and purchase equipment with functionality that could be used across the telemedicine service lines to save money.

- A healthcare consulting firm has a program to analyze healthcare customer-buying patterns for plastic surgery. Projects under this program might include one to send out and analyze electronic surveys, one to conduct several focus groups in different geographic locations with different types of buyers, and a project to develop an information system to help collect and analyze current healthcare customers' buying patterns.

A **program manager** provides leadership and direction for the project managers heading the projects within the program. Program managers also coordinate the efforts of project teams, functional groups, suppliers, and operations staff supporting the projects to ensure that project products and processes are implemented to maximize benefits. Program managers are responsible for more than the delivery of project results; they are change agents responsible for the success of products and processes produced by those projects.

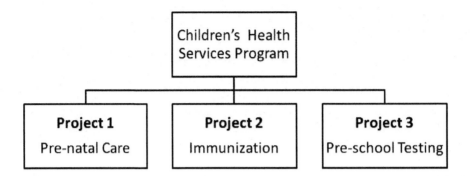

Figure 1-5. Example programs

      Program managers often have review meetings with all their project managers to share important information and coordinate important aspects of each project. Many program managers worked as project managers earlier in their careers, and they enjoy sharing their wisdom and expertise with their project managers. Effective program managers recognize that managing a program is much more complex than managing a single project. They recognize that technical and project management skills are not enough. In addition to skills required for project managers, program managers must also possess strong business knowledge, leadership capability, and communication skills.

Project Portfolio Management

In many organizations, project managers also support an emerging business strategy of **project portfolio management** (also called just **portfolio management** in this text), in which organizations group and manage projects and programs as a portfolio of investments that contribute to the entire enterprise's success. Pacific Edge Software's product manager, Eric Burke, defines project portfolio management as "the continuous process of selecting and managing the optimum set of project initiatives that deliver maximum business value."[17]

      PMI published the *Standard for Portfolio Management, Third Edition,* in 2013. PMI members can download this and other standards, such as the PMBOK® Guide, for free from www.pmi.org. Topics included in this standard include:

- Understanding the role of portfolio management in relation to an organization's structure and strategy
- Streamlining operations through portfolio management
- Improving the implementation and maintenance of corporate governance initiatives
- Designing and implementing metrics to demonstrate and improve return on investment through portfolio management.
- Reporting information to make the most of an organization's projects and programs

Portfolio managers need to understand how projects fit into the bigger picture of the organization, especially in terms of organizational strategy, finances, and business risks. Portfolio managers create portfolios based on meeting specific organizational goals, such as maximizing the value of the portfolio or making effective use of limited resources. In the case of a healthcare organization, the organization's mission and regulatory mandates would also influence the composition of the portfolio. Portfolio managers may or may not have previous experience as project or program managers. It is most important that they have strong financial and analytical skills and understand how projects and programs can contribute to meeting strategic goals.

The main distinction between project or program management and portfolio management is that project and program managers are focused on meeting tactical versus strategic goals. Individual projects and programs often address tactical goals, whereas portfolio management addresses strategic goals. Tactical goals are generally more specific and short-term than strategic goals, which emphasize long-term goals or mission of an organization.

Project and program management address questions like:
- Are we carrying out projects well?

- Are projects on time and budget?

- Do project stakeholders know what they should be doing?

Portfolio management addresses questions like:

- Are we working on the right projects?

- Are we investing in the right areas?

- Do we have the right resources to be competitive?

- Are we doing projects that help to fulfill our organizational mission?

There can be portfolios for all types of projects. For example:
- A government agency for children's services could group projects into a portfolio based on key strategies such as improving health, providing education, and so on to help make decisions on the best way to use available funds and resources.

- In a healthcare consulting firm, strategic goals might include increasing profit margins on large projects, decreasing travel costs, and improving skill levels of key workers. Projects could be grouped into these three categories for portfolio management purposes.

- In a hospital, strategic goals might include expanding to rural communities, improving patient experience, decreasing costs, and being recognized as a center of excellence for primary areas of specialty care. These might be the main categories for their portfolio of projects.

Organizations group projects into portfolios to help them make better investment decisions, such as increasing, decreasing, discontinuing, or changing specific projects or programs based on their financial performance, risks, resource utilization, quality impact, and similar factors that affect business value. For example, if an electronic health record vendor has much higher profit margins with private hospitals than university hospitals, for example, it might choose to pursue more private hospitals. The firm might also create a new project to investigate ways to increase profits for university hospital projects. On the other hand, if the organization has too many projects focused on financial performance and not enough focused on improving its work force, the portfolio manager might suggest initiating more projects to support the strategic goal to improve its workforce. As with a personal financial portfolio, a project portfolio should be diversified to account for risk and balance the organization.

Project and portfolio management work hand-in-hand. By grouping projects into portfolios, organizations can better tie their projects to meeting strategic goals both before the project launches as well as during project execution. Portfolio management can also help organizations do a better job of managing its human resources by hiring, training, and retaining workers to support the projects in the organization's portfolio. For example, if the healthcare consulting firm needs more people with experience with health IT, they can make necessary adjustments by hiring or training current workers in the necessary skills.

THE PROJECT MANAGEMENT PROFESSION

As you can imagine, good project managers should have a variety of skills. Good program and portfolio managers often need additional skills and experience in managing projects and understanding organizational strategies. This section describes some of the skills that help you manage projects, and you will learn many more throughout this text. If you are serious about considering a career in project management, you should consider earning one or more project management certifications, as described later in this section. You should also be familiar with some of the project management software products available on the market today.

Suggested Skills for Project, Program, and Portfolio Managers

Project managers and their teams must develop knowledge and skills in the following areas:
- All ten project management knowledge areas
- The application area (domain, industry, market, etc.)
- The project environment (politics, culture, change management, etc.)
- General management (financial management, strategic planning, etc.)
- Human relations (leadership, motivation, negotiations, etc.)

An earlier section of this chapter introduced the ten project management knowledge areas, as well as some tools and techniques that project managers use. The application area refers to the application to which project management is applied. For example, a project manager responsible for building houses or apartment buildings should understand the construction industry, including standards and regulations important to that industry and those types of construction projects. A project manager leading a large software development project must know a lot about that application area. A project manager in education, entertainment, the government, healthcare, and other fields must understand those application areas.

The project environment differs from organization to organization and project to project, but there are some skills that will help in most project environments. These skills include understanding change, and understanding how organizations work within their social, political, and physical environments. Project managers must be comfortable leading and handling change, since most projects introduce changes in organizations and involve changes within the projects themselves. Project managers need to understand the organizations they work in and how products are developed and services are provided. Furthermore, healthcare is a field with its own terminology and acronyms. Health IT projects further complicates the potential for language barriers by adding host of computer terminology and acronyms to the communication mix. If you plan to work on a lot of projects in the healthcare field, you should make sure you understand the language and culture of healthcare and potentially basic IT terminology as well.

Project managers should also possess general management knowledge and skills. They should understand important topics related to financial management, accounting, procurement, sales, marketing, contracts, manufacturing, distribution, logistics, the supply chain, strategic planning, tactical planning, operations management, organizational structures and behavior, personnel administration, compensation, benefits, career paths, and health and safety practices. On some projects, it will be critical for project managers to have substantial experience in one or several of these general management areas. On other projects, project managers can delegate detailed responsibility for some of these areas to a team member, support staff, or even a supplier. Even so, the project managers must be intelligent and experienced enough to know which of these areas are most important and who is qualified to do the work. They must also make and/or take responsibility for all key project decisions.

Achieving high performance on projects requires human relations skills, also known as soft skills. Some of these soft skills include effective communication, influencing the organization to get things done, leadership, motivation, negotiation, conflict management, and problem solving. Healthcare is uniquely filled with very distinct silos of subspecialized clinicians, administrators, others that must come together for a common purpose, the patient. However, they often do not initially come together easily and it is the job of the project manager to bring everyone together. This is the only way projects succeed and are well implemented in health care is with good communication. Project managers must lead their project teams by providing vision, delegating work, creating an energetic and positive environment, and setting an example of appropriate and effective behavior. Project managers must focus on teamwork skills in order to use their people effectively. They need to be able to motivate different types of people and develop *esprit de corps* within the project team and with other project stakeholders.

Importance of Leadership Skills

In a popular study, one hundred project managers listed the characteristics they believed were critical for effective project management and the characteristics that made project managers ineffective. Figure 1-6 lists the results. The study found that effective project managers provide leadership by example, are visionary, technically competent, decisive, good communicators, and good motivators. They also stand up to top management when necessary, support team members, and encourage new ideas. The study also found that respondents believed *positive leadership contributes the most to project success.*[18]

Effective Project Managers	Ineffective Project Managers
Lead by example	Set bad examples
Are visionaries	Are not self-assured
Are technically competent	Lack technical expertise
Are decisive	Avoid or delay making decisions
Are good communicators	Are poor communicators
Are good motivators	Are poor motivators

Figure 1-6. Most significant characteristics of effective and ineffective project managers

Leadership and *management* are terms often used interchangeably, although there are differences. Generally, a **leader** focuses on long-term goals and big-picture objectives, while inspiring people to reach those goals. A **manager** often deals with the day-to-day details of meeting specific goals. Some people say that, "Managers do things right, and leaders do the right things." "Leaders determine the vision, and managers achieve the vision." "You lead people and manage things."

Project managers often take on the role of both leader and manager. Good project managers know that people make or break projects, so they must set a good example to lead their team to success. They are aware of the greater needs of their stakeholders and organizations, so they are visionary in guiding their current projects and in suggesting future ones.

As mentioned earlier, program managers need the same skills as project managers. They often rely on their past experience as project managers, strong business knowledge, leadership capability, and communication skills to handle the responsibility of overseeing the multiple projects that make up their programs. It is most important that portfolio managers have strong financial and analytical skills and understand how projects and programs can contribute to meeting strategic goals.

Organizations that excel in project, program, and portfolio management grow project leaders, emphasizing development of business and communication skills. Instead of thinking of leaders and managers as specific people, it is better to think of people as having leadership skills, such as being visionary and inspiring, and management skills, such as being organized and effective. Therefore, the best project, program, and portfolio managers have leadership and management characteristics; they are visionary yet focused on the bottom line. Above all else, they focus on achieving positive results!

Ethics in Project Management

Ethics, loosely defined, is a set of principles that guide our decision making based on personal values of what is "right" and "wrong." Making ethical decisions is an important part of our personal and professional lives because it generates trust and respect with other people. Project managers often face ethical dilemmas, as do medical professionals. For example, several projects involve different payment methods. If a project manager can make more money by doing a job poorly, should he or she do the job poorly? No! If a project manager is personally opposed to certain types of life support, should he or she refuse to manage a project that promotes extended life support measures? Yes! Ethics guide us in making these types of decisions.

PMI approved a new Code of Ethics and Professional Conduct effective January 1, 2007. This new code applies not only to PMPs, but also to all PMI members and individuals who hold a PMI certification, apply for a PMI certification, or serve PMI in a volunteer capacity. It is vital for project management practitioners to conduct their work in an ethical manner. Even if you are not affiliated with PMI, these guidelines can help you conduct your work in an ethical manner, which helps the profession earn the confidence of the public, employers, employees, and all project stakeholders. The PMI Code of Ethics and Professional Conduct includes short chapters addressing vision and applicability, responsibility, respect, fairness, and honesty. A few excerpts from this document include the following:

"As <u>practitioners</u> in the global project management community:

2.2.1	We make decisions and take actions based on the best interests of society, public safety, and the environment.
2.2.2	We accept only those assignments that are consistent with our background, experience, skills, and qualifications.
2.2.3.	We fulfill the commitments that we undertake—we do what we say we will do.
3.2.1	We inform ourselves about the norms and customs of others and avoid engaging in behaviors they might consider disrespectful.
3.2.2	We listen to others' points of view, seeking to understand them.
3.2.3	We approach directly those persons with whom we have a conflict or disagreement.
4.2.1	We demonstrate transparency in our decision-making process.
4.2.2	We constantly reexamine our impartiality and objectivity, taking corrective action as appropriate.

4.3.1   We proactively and fully disclose any real or potential conflicts of interest to appropriate stakeholders.

5.2.1   We earnestly seek to understand the truth.

5.2.2   We are truthful in our communications and in our conduct."[19]

In addition, PMI added a new series of questions to the PMP certification exam in March 2002 to emphasize the importance of ethics and professional responsibility.

The topic of ethics may be more comprehensive for those the work in the healthcare sector. Medical doctors take oaths that assign moral, psychological, social, and cultural responsibilities to protect patients from harm and injustice. Healthcare projects that involved patient care must acknowledge this ethical bond. Projects should be vetted based on whether or not they are ethically appropriate for patient care, in addition to profitability. If projects are unethical but produce a high profit margin, the organization is likely not being true to its mission to care for patients. Issues of patient privacy and quality of care are not always readily identifiable and clear. It is well worth the effort of those who wish to engage in healthcare projects to review the words of the Hippocratic Oath as well as the World Medical Association's Physician's Oath to use as an ethical pillar for guiding ethically challenging healthcare project decisions.

Project Management and Related Certifications

Professional certification is an important factor in recognizing and ensuring quality in a profession. For example, there are many professional societies and certifications for people working in healthcare. The **Project Management Institute (PMI)** is a global professional society for project and program managers. PMI has a Healthcare Community of Practice (www.healthcare.vc.pmi.org) with over 2,500 members, which demonstrates the growing interest in project management in the healthcare community.

PMI provides certification as a **Project Management Professional (PMP)**— someone who has documented sufficient project experience, agreed to follow the PMI code of professional conduct, and demonstrated knowledge of the field of project management by passing a comprehensive examination. The number of people earning PMP certification continues to increase. In 1993, there were about 1,000 certified project management professionals. By the end of December, 2012 there were 510,434 active certified project management professionals. There were also over 20,157 CAPMs (Certified Associate in Project Management.[20]

Figure 1-8 shows the rapid growth in the number of people earning project management professional certification from 1993 through 2012. Although most PMPs are in the U.S. and Canada, the PMP credential is growing in popularity in several countries, such as Japan, China, and India.

Project management certification is also enabling professionals throughout the world to share a common base of knowledge. For example, any person with PMP certification can list, describe, and use the ten project management knowledge areas, as described in PMI's Guide to the Project Management Body of Knowledge (*PMBOK® Guide*). Sharing a common base of knowledge is important because it helps advance the theory and practice of project management. Some organizations require that all project managers be PMP certified. "When Western companies come into China they are more likely to hire individuals who have PMP certification as an additional verification of their skills. In our salary survey, the salary differences in IT, for example, was dramatic. A person with certification could make five to six times as much salary, so there is a terrific incentive to get certified and work for these Western companies."[21]

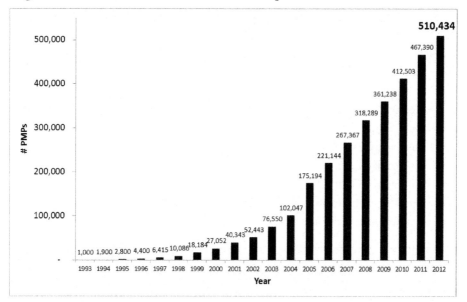

Figure 1-8. Growth in PMP certification, 1993–2012

Many colleges, universities, and organizations around the world now offer courses related to various aspects of project management and specialized courses, such as healthcare project management. You can even earn bachelors, masters, and doctoral degrees in project management. See the companion Web site for more information.

PMI Student Membership and Certification Information

As a student, you can join PMI for a reduced fee ($40 vs. $129 in 2013). Consult PMI's Web site (*www.pmi.org*) for more information. You can network with other students studying project management by joining the New Practitioners Community of Practice. There are many other communities of practice, include one for healthcare professionals. Also check to see about a local chapter. Many welcome students to attend free events, including job networking. You can also volunteer to help develop your skills and serve your community.

Also consider earning the Certified Associate in Project Management (CAPM) credential from PMI or the Project+ certification from CompTIA. See the last section of Appendix B for more details. If you complete a bachelor's degree, you do not need any work experience to earn either of these two certifications.

Project Management Software

The project management and software development communities have definitely responded to the need to provide more software to assist in managing projects. Gartner estimates the size of the project and portfolio management (PPM) solutions market to be about $1 billion, and they created a magic quadrant showing cloud-based PPM providers categorized as leaders, visionaries, niche players, and challengers. For example, they list Innotas, Instantis, AtTask, Daptiv, and PowerSteering as market leaders.[22]

In 2013, TopTenReviews ranked Clarizen as the number one online or cloud-based tool, followed by Genius Project, as shown in Figure 1-9. A few features of PPM tools include:

- Team management
- Issue tracking
- Request management
- Budgeting
- Risk analysis
- Customized reports
- Interactive Gantt charts
- Baseline comparisons
- Critical path method[23]

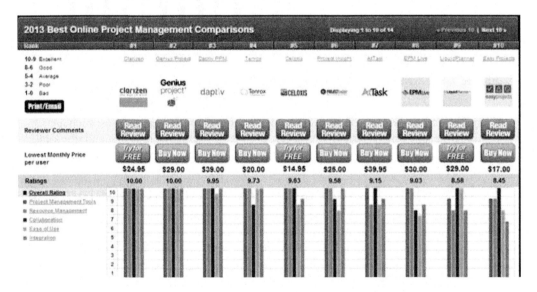

Figure 1-9. Top ten online project management product comparisons

Note that both the Gartner and TopTenReviews information were published before Microsoft released their new version of Project 2013. Microsoft is a key player in the project management software market, and Project 2013 can be used totally online along with other familiar Office applications. Microsoft, along with many other software companies, are developing and tailoring products to the large healthcare market.

There are hundreds of PPM tools available, ranging from free online or smart phone apps to enterprise tools costing thousands of dollars to implement and high monthly fees per user. Deciding which project management software to use has become a project in itself. Software does not take the place of strong project management skills and processes. The software is a tool that can make certain project management tasks and communications easier or more efficient in the hands of a skilled project manager and project team members. Inexperienced project managers who try to let the software "manage their projects" may be very disappointed in the project results.

Project needs and the project management culture and sophistication of the organization should drive the selection and adoption of project management software. A requirements list suited to the organization should be the guiding light to seeking suitable project management software. In a market space of hundreds of options, it is very easy to let the sizzle of bells and whistles or the attractiveness of low costs lure the purchaser into a sale. Organizations should not use technology for technology's sake; they should select technology that can drive productivity.

In Appendix A, you will learn how to use Microsoft Project 2013, the most widely used project management software tool today. Figure 1-10 shows a Gantt chart you can create using the instructions in Appendix A. You will also see screen shots of a few other tools throughout the text.

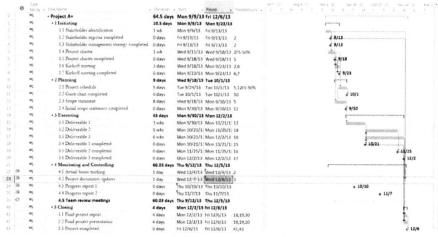

Figure 1-10. Gantt chart created in Microsoft Project 2013

Free Trials and Information on Using Project 2013

A 60-day evaluation copy of Microsoft Project is available from Microsoft's Web site at *www.microsoft.com/project*. See Appendix A of this text, Brief Guide to Microsoft Project 2013, for more information so you can develop hands-on skills using this popular product.

By the end of the twentieth century, people in virtually every industry around the globe began to investigate and apply different aspects of project, program, and portfolio management. The sophistication and effectiveness with which organizations use these concepts and tools today is influencing the way they do business, use resources, and respond to market needs with speed and accuracy. Many colleges, universities, and organizations now offer courses related to various aspects of project, program, and portfolio management, including healthcare project management courses. The growing number of projects and the evidence that good project management really can make a difference continue to contribute to the growth of this field.

CASE WRAP-UP

Another board member asked Fran, the CEO of America's Best Healthcare, to describe specific actions they could take to help their organization become more successful at managing projects. Fran began to explain his vision. "Overall, we have to dramatically improve our ability to quickly select and implement projects that help us succeed and cancel or redirect others. We have to respond quickly to market changes and take advantage of new technologies. Health systems that are not able to do this simply will not last."

Fran went on to explain how he would like to formalize a corporate Project Management Office (PMO), with a strong person at the VP level. The new Chief Project Officer (CPO) would oversee the many smaller PMOs currently dispersed throughout the organization. Fran said this new group could be formed at no additional cost by consolidating and reorganizing the current PMOs, and he got board approval to move forward with creating this new group.

"We also need to set goals and then develop timelines with deliverables and people committed to getting things done. Three key initiatives of the corporate PMO should include education, incentives, and tools. First, we need to educate employees in project management and develop a mentoring program for part-time or full-time project managers. For example, a nurse is leading a major phase of a project at one of our academic hospitals to reduce the occurrence of ventilator associated pneumonia. She is being mentored by a senior PMO member, and the project is going great. Second, we also need to develop project-based reward systems to get everyone fully engaged in changing our approach to projects. Third, we need to find and implement a user-friendly, web-based PPM tool across the enterprise."

After a review of on-going and completed major projects over the last two years, board members were convinced that effectively selecting and managing projects was crucial to their future. The board and the organization's shareholders were ready to move forward with Fran's ideas and extending project management best practices throughout the organization.[24]

CHAPTER SUMMARY

There are many reasons to study project, program, and portfolio management, especially in the healthcare field. The number of projects continues to grow, the complexity of these projects continues to increase, and the profession of project management continues to expand and mature. Using a more disciplined approach to managing all types of projects can help organizations succeed. The healthcare industry has to make changes to meet government and markets demands as well as seize opportunities to increase the quality of patient care and decrease costs; applying good project management is an important step in meeting the many challenges ahead.

The context of healthcare project management has unique characteristics. It is important to understand the healthcare environment, the nature of healthcare projects, and recent trends in healthcare that can affect project management for project management practices to achieve the greatest impact in advancing healthcare projects towards success.

A project is a temporary endeavor undertaken to create a unique product, service, or result. Projects are developed incrementally; they require resources, have a sponsor, and involve uncertainty. The triple constraint of project management refers to managing the scope, time, and cost dimensions of a project. The quadruple constraint adds quality, and additional constraints include risk and resources.

Project management is the application of knowledge, skills, tools, and techniques to project activities to meet the project requirements. Stakeholders are the people involved in or affected by project activities. A framework for project management includes the project stakeholders, project management knowledge areas, and project management tools and techniques. The ten knowledge areas are project integration management, scope, time, cost, quality, human resource, communications, risk, procurement, and stakeholder management.

A program is a group of related projects, subprograms, or program activities managed in a coordinated way to obtain benefits not available from managing them individually. Project portfolio management involves organizing and managing projects and programs as a portfolio of investments that contribute to the entire enterprise's success. Portfolio management emphasizes meeting strategic goals while project management focuses on tactical goals.

The profession of project management continues to grow and mature. Project, program, and portfolio managers play key roles in helping projects and organizations succeed. They must perform various duties, possess many skills, and continue to develop skills in project management, general management, and their application area, such as healthcare. Soft skills, especially leadership, are particularly important for project, program, and portfolio managers. The Project Management Institute (PMI) is an international professional society that provides certification as a Project Management Professional (PMP), upholds a code of ethics, and has a recognized community of practice in healthcare. Today, hundreds of project management software products are available to assist people in managing projects.

QUICK QUIZ

1. Approximately what percentage of the world's gross domestic product is spent on projects?
    A. 10%
    B. 25%
    C. 50%
    D. 75%

2. Healthcare spending accounted for 17.9% of U.S. GDP in 2010, an average of over _____ per person.
    A. $10,000
    B. $5,000
    C. $8,000
    D. $3,000

3. Which of the following is not a potential advantage of using good project management?
    A. Shorter development times
    B. Higher worker morale
    C. Lower cost of capital
    D. Higher profit margins

4. A _____ is a temporary endeavor undertaken to create a unique product, service, or result.
    A. program
    B. process
    C. project
    D. portfolio

5. Which of the following is not an attribute of a project?
    A. projects are unique
    B. projects are developed using progressive elaboration
    C. projects have a primary customer or sponsor
    D. projects involve no uncertainty

6. Which of the following is not part of the triple constraint of project management?
    A. meeting scope goals
    B. meeting time goals
    C. meeting quality goals
    D. meeting cost goals

7.   _____ is the application of knowledge, skills, tools and techniques to project activities to meet project requirements.
      A.   Project management
      B.   Program management
      C.   Project portfolio management
      D.   Requirements management

8.   Project portfolio management addresses _____ goals of an organization, while project management addresses _____ goals.
      A.   strategic, tactical
      B.   tactical, strategic
      C.   internal, external
      D.   external, internal

9.   What is the most significant characteristic or attribute of an effective project manager?
      A.   is a strong communicator
      B.   is decisive
      C.   is visionary
      D.   leads by example

10.   What is the certification program called that the Project Management Institute provides?
      A.   Microsoft Certified Project Manager (MCPM)
      B.   Project Management Professional (PMP)
      C.   Project Management Expert (PME)
      D.   Project Management Mentor (PMM)

Quick Quiz Answers

1. B, 2. C, 3. D, 4. C, 5. D, 6. C, 7. A, 8. A, 9. D, 10. B

DISCUSSION QUESTIONS

1. Why is there a new or renewed interest in the field of project management, especially in the healthcare industry?

2. What is a project, and what are its main attributes? How is a healthcare project different from routine operational activities in a healthcare organization?

3. What is the triple constraint? What is the quadruple constraint? What are other project constraints? Which of these constraints seems to have special meaning for the healthcare context?

4. What is project management? Briefly describe the project management framework, providing examples of stakeholders, knowledge areas, tools and techniques, and project success factors that are often found in the healthcare setting.

5. Describe the context of project management in the healthcare industry. How do things like history, costs, or recent trends affect healthcare project management?

6. Discuss the relationship between project, program, and portfolio management and their contribution to enterprise success.

7. What are the roles of the project, program, and portfolio managers? What are suggested skills for project managers? What additional skills do program and portfolio managers need to be successful in the healthcare industry?

8. What role does the Project Management Institute (PMI) play in advancing the profession? What role can PMI's Healthcare Community of Practice play in advancing project management in the healthcare industry?

9. What are some of the features of project and portfolio management (PPM) software? What are some of the popular and recommended tools on the market?

EXERCISES

Note: These exercises can be done individually or in teams, in-class, as homework, or in a virtual environment. Learners can either write their results in a paper or prepare a short presentation or video to show their results.

1. Find at least three Web sites that provide interesting information about project management in general and in the healthcare industry, including the Project Management Institute's Web site (*www.pmi.org*). Summarize key information about these three Web sites, including at least two articles you find on the sites. See the companion Web site for some suggested sites and articles.

2. Find an example of a real project with a real project manager in the healthcare industry. Describe the project in terms of its scope, time, and cost goals and each of the project's attributes. Try to include information describing what went right and wrong on the project and the role of the project manager and sponsor. Also describe whether you consider the project to be a success or not and why. Include at least one reference and proper citations.

3. Review information from.toptenreviews.com about online project management software. Read at least four reviews and visit the supplier Web sites for their products. Also investigate examples of how healthcare organizations are using project management software, and summarize your findings.

4. Watch the videos mentioned in the Video Highlights. The direct links are available on the companion Web site. Summarize key points from the videos. How does May Clinic use project management? What are some famous projects in the history of project management? Summarize your responses and impressions of the videos.

TEAM PROJECTS

Note: These team projects can be done in-class, as homework, or in a virtual environment. Learners can either write their results in a paper or prepare a short presentation or video to show their results.

1. Interview people who work as project managers or team members on at least two different project teams in a healthcare environment. Use the following interview guidelines, and then ask the questions in person, via the phone, or via the Internet. Discuss the results with your team, and then prepare a paper, presentation, or video to summarize and compare your findings.

Project Manager Interview Guidelines

Please note that these are guidelines and sample questions only. Use only the questions that seem appropriate, and feel free to add your own.

Note: If the interviewee wants to remain anonymous, that's fine. If not, please include his/her name and place of employment as a project manager in your paper. Let him/her know that you are doing this interview for a class assignment and that the information may be shared with others.

The main purpose of these interviews is for students to gain more insight into what project managers really do, what challenges they face, what lessons they've learned, what concepts/tools you're learning about that they really use, and what suggestions they have for you and other students as future team members and project managers. People often like to tell stories or relate particular situations they were in to get their points across. To this end, here are a few sample questions.

1) How did you get into project management or on a project team?
2) If you had to rate the job of project manager on a scale of 1-10, with 10 being the highest, how would you rate it?
3) Briefly explain the reason for your rating. What do you or would you enjoy most and what do you or would you like least about being a project manager?
4) Did you have any training or special talents or experiences that qualified you to be a project manager or team member? Are you certified or have you thought about becoming certified as a PMP?
5) What do you feel is the most important thing project managers do in the healthcare industry? On what task do you spend the most time each day?
6) What are some of the opportunities and risks you have encountered on projects? Please describe any notable successes and failures and what you have learned from them.
7) What are some of the tools, software or otherwise, that you use, and what is your opinion of those tools?

8) How have you introduced project management skills, tools, and techniques to healthcare stakeholders?

9) What are some steps a project manager can take to improve the effectiveness and efficiency of a team? How does a new project manager gain the respect and loyalty of team members? Can you share any examples of situations you faced related to this topic?

10) What suggestions do you have for working with sponsors and senior managers? Can you share any examples of situations you faced related to this topic?

11) What suggestions do you have for working with clinical providers? Can you share any examples of situations you faced related to this topic?

12) Do you have any suggestions for someone who may manage future healthcare projects, such as any specific preparations they should make, skills they should learn, etc.?

2. Go to *www.monster.com* or a similar site and search for jobs as a "project manager" or "program manager" in three geographic regions of your choice. If possible, focus on jobs in the healthcare industry. Summarize what you found, especially related to position in healthcare organizations.

3. As a team, discuss projects that you are currently working on or would like to work on to benefit yourself, your employers, your family, or the broader community. Come up with at least ten projects, and then determine if they could be grouped into programs. Summarize your results.

4. Review information on project management certification. As a team, discuss your findings and opinions on earning PMP, CAPM, or other certification for someone intending to work in the healthcare industry. Document your findings, citing your references.

KEY TERMS

ethics — A set of principles that guide our decision making based on personal values of what is "right" and "wrong".

leader — A person who focuses on long-term goals and big-picture objectives, while inspiring people to reach those goals.

manager — A person who deals with the day-to-day details of meeting specific goals.

portfolio — A collection of projects or programs and other work that are grouped together to facilitate effective management of that work to meet strategic business objectives.

program — A group of projects, subprograms, or program activities managed in a coordinated way to obtain benefits not available from managing them individually.

program manager — A person who provides leadership and direction for the project managers heading the projects within the program.

project — A temporary endeavor undertaken to create a unique product, service, or result.

project management — The application of knowledge, skills, tools, and techniques to project activities to meet the project requirements.

project management process groups — Initiating, planning, monitoring and controlling, and closing.

project manager — The person responsible for working with the project sponsor, the project team, and the other people involved in a project to meet project goals.

Project Management Institute (PMI) — International professional society for project managers.

project management knowledge areas — Project integration management, scope, time, cost, quality, human resource, communications, risk, and procurement management.

Project Management Professional (PMP) — Certification provided by PMI that requires documenting project experience, agreeing to follow the PMI code of ethics, and passing a comprehensive exam.

project management tools and techniques — Methods available to assist project managers and their teams; some popular tools in the time management knowledge area include Gantt charts, network diagrams, critical path analysis, and project management software.

project portfolio management — The grouping and managing of projects and programs as a portfolio of investments that contribute to the entire enterprise's success.

project sponsor — The person who provides the direction and funding for a project.

stakeholders — People involved in or affected by project activities.

triple constraint — Balancing scope, time, and cost goals.

END NOTES

[1]Project Management Institute. *Project Management Salary Survey, Seventh Edition*, (2011).

[2]CareerBuilder. "Employers Plan to Hire More Recent College Graduates in 2011, Finds CareerBuilder's Annual Forecast," (April 27, 2011).

[3]Project Management Institute (PMI). *The PMI Project Management Fact Book. Second Edition* (2001).

[4]Sarah Fister Gale, "The Human Element," PM Network (December 2012).

[5]The Standish Group, "The CHAOS Report," (1995).

[6]PricewaterhouseCoopers, "Boosting Business Performance through Programme and Project Management," (June 2004).

[7]Yale School of Management and Change Observer, "Mayo Clinic - Project Management Video," (2010).

[8]The Henry J. Kaiser Family Foundation, "Healthcare Costs: A Primer, Key Information on Healthcare Costs and Their Impact," (2012).

[9]Association of University Programs in Health Administration (AUPHA) Annual Meeting & Global Symposium, "Transformation Panel & Reception," Minneapolis, (June 1, 2012).

[10]Donald M. Berwick, Thomas W. Nolan, and J. Whittington, "The Triple Aim: Care, Health, And Cost," HealthAffairs (2008;27(3):759-69).

[11]Project Management Institute I. *A Guide to the Project Management Body of Knowledge (PMBOK Guide). Fifth Edition* (2013).

[12]Ibid.

[13]Centers for Disease Control and Prevention, "BioSense", USA.gov (accessed April 19, 2013).

[14]Center for Innovation, "Design Thinking," Mayo Clinic (2013).

[15]Besner C, Hobbs B, editors. "The Perceived Value and Potential Contribution of Project Management Practices to Project Success," PMI Research Conference Proceedings (July 2006).

[16]Project Management Institute I. *A Guide to the Project Management Body of Knowledge (PMBOK Guide), Fifth Edition* (2013).

[17]Eric Burke, "Project Portfolio Management," PMI Houston Chapter Meeting (July 10, 2002).

[18]Thomas Zimmerer and Mahmoud M. Yasin, "A Leadership Profile of American Project Managers," Project Management Journal (March 1998.

[19]Project Management Institute, "PMP Credential Handbook," (August 31, 2011).

[20]Project Management Institute, "PMI Fact File," PMI Today (February 2013).

[21]Vanessa Wong, "PMI On Specialization and Globalization," Projects@Work, (June 23, 2008).

[22]Daniel B. Stang and Robert A. Handler, "Magic Quadrant for Cloud-Based Project and Portfolio Management Services", Gartner (June 27, 2012).

[23]TopTen Reviews, "Online Project Management Review," TechMediaNetwork (2013).

[24]Note: Chapter 1 was co-authored with Cynthia LeRouge, Ph.D.

Chapter 2

Project, Program, and Portfolio Selection

LEARNING OBJECTIVES

After reading this chapter, you will be able to:

- Discuss the systems view of project management and how it applies to healthcare projects
- Describe the importance of aligning projects with business strategy, the strategic planning process, and using a SWOT analysis
- Explain the four-stage planning process for project selection and provide examples of applying this model to ensure the strategic alignment of projects
- Summarize the various methods for selecting projects and demonstrate how to calculate net present value, return on investment, payback, and the weighted score for a project
- Discuss the program selection process and distinguish the differences between programs and projects
- Describe the project portfolio selection process and the five levels of project portfolio management

---

OPENING CASE

Marie Scott, the new Chief Project Officer (CPO) for the corporate Project Management Office (PMO) at America's Best Healthcare, Inc., was facilitating a meeting with several senior managers throughout the company. The purpose of the meeting was to discuss their processes for selecting projects, grouping them into programs, and determining how they fit into the organization's portfolio of projects. She knew there were silos within the company, and unified communication and project selection could help the company as a whole. She had invited an outside consultant to the meeting to provide an objective view of the theory and practice behind project, program, and portfolio selection.

She could see that several managers were getting bored with the presentation, while others looked concerned that their pet projects might be cancelled if the company implemented a new, unified approach for project selection. After the consultant's presentation, Marie had each participant write down his or her questions and concerns and hand them in anonymously for her group to review. She was amazed at the obvious lack of understanding of the need for projects to be viewed as part as a whole system and align with the company's mission and business strategy. She was also surprised to see the lack of concern for meeting recent federal laws. What should Marie do next?

A SYSTEMS VIEW OF HEALTHCARE PROJECT MANAGEMENT

Even though projects are temporary and intended to provide a unique product or service, you cannot run projects in isolation, especially in the complex environment of health care. If project managers lead projects in isolation, it is unlikely that they will ever truly serve the needs of the organization. To handle complex situations effectively, project managers need to use **systems thinking**, which involves taking a holistic view of a project and understanding how it relates to the larger organization.

A Systems Approach

The term **systems approach** emerged in the 1950s to describe a holistic and analytical approach to solving complex problems that includes using a systems philosophy, systems analysis, and systems management. A **systems philosophy** is an overall model for thinking about things as systems. **Systems** are sets of interacting components that work within an environment to fulfill some purpose. For example, the human body is a system composed of many subsystems—the nervous system, the skeletal system, the circulatory system, the digestive system, and so on. **Systems analysis** is a problem-solving approach that requires defining the scope of the system, dividing it into components, and then identifying and evaluating its problems, opportunities, constraints, and needs. Once this is completed, the systems analyst then examines alternative solutions for improving the current situation; identifies an optimum, or at least satisfactory, solution or action plan; and examines that plan against the entire system. **Systems management** addresses the business, technological, and organizational issues associated with creating, maintaining, and modifying a system. Note that business issues include concerns related to an organization's entire mission, not just financial aspects of the organization.

Using a systems approach is critical to successful project management in all fields, particularly in healthcare. Top management and project managers must follow a systems philosophy to understand how projects relate to the whole organization. They must use systems analysis to address needs with a problem-solving approach. They must use systems management to identify key business, technological, and organizational issues related to each project in order to identify and satisfy key stakeholders and do what is best for the entire organization.

The Three-Sphere Model for Systems Management

Many projects fail because project and portfolio managers do not use a systems approach. A common example is an information technology (IT) project failing because members of the IT department did all of the planning without engaging key stakeholders. Even though the project managers may have sent an email to all stakeholders about the project, they often do not address many of the organizational issues involved. Most employees at healthcare organizations are very busy, and they may not pay attention to every email they get. They might also have had bad experiences on past projects, especially those pushed on them by the IT department. Many project managers are unaware of the effects that their projects would have on other parts of the organization. They may not clearly define the business, technological, and organizational issues associated with the project and instead work on the project in isolation.

In order to avoid this common cause of project failure, it is important to understand systems management. The simple idea of addressing the three spheres of systems management— business, organization, and technology—can have a huge impact on selecting and managing projects successfully.

Figure 2-1 provides a sample of business, organizational, and technological issues that could be factors in many healthcare projects. In many cases, technological issues, though not simple by any means, are probably the least difficult to identify and resolve. Projects must address issues in all three spheres of the systems management model. Although it is easier to focus on the immediate and sometimes narrow concerns of a particular project, project managers and other staff must recognize the effects of any project on the interests and needs of the entire system or organization. CEOs of healthcare organizations, medical staff, and senior administrators must focus on whether or not a project will add value to the organization as whole. Project managers must do the same.

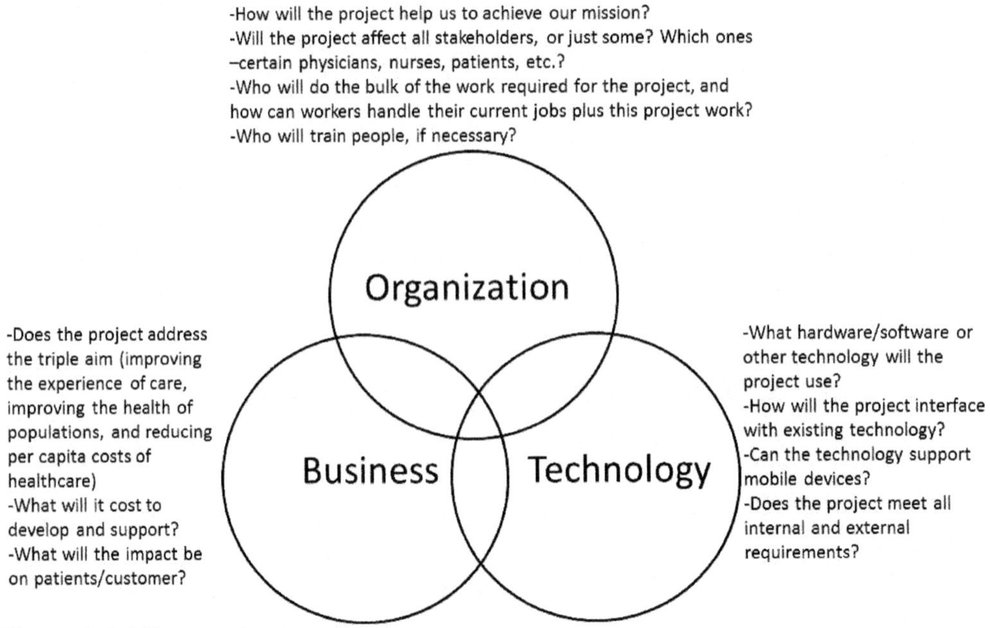

-How will the project help us to achieve our mission?
-Will the project affect all stakeholders, or just some? Which ones
–certain physicians, nurses, patients, etc.?
-Who will do the bulk of the work required for the project, and
how can workers handle their current jobs plus this project work?
-Who will train people, if necessary?

-Does the project address
the triple aim (improving
the experience of care,
improving the health of
populations, and reducing
per capita costs of
healthcare)
-What will it cost to
develop and support?
-What will the impact be
on patients/customer?

-What hardware/software or
other technology will the
project use?
-How will the project interface
with existing technology?
-Can the technology support
mobile devices?
-Does the project meet all
internal and external
requirements?

Organization

Business   Technology

Figure 2-1. Three-sphere model for systems management

Many project managers become captivated with the technology and day-to-day problem solving involved in working on projects, as shown in the technology sphere for systems management. Project managers may become frustrated with many of the "people problems" or politics involved in most organizations. Project managers must address organizational questions, such as, "Will the project affect all stakeholders, or just some?" In addition, many project managers ignore important business questions, such as, "What will the impact be on patients/customer?" Using a more holistic approach and systems management helps project managers integrate business and organizational issues along with technology into their planning. Chapter 3, Initiating, provides suggestions on identifying stakeholders and using a good change management process as part of project management.

ALIGNING PROJECTS WITH MISSION AND BUSINESS STRATEGY

Most healthcare organizations face hundreds of problems and opportunities for improvement and consider potential projects to address them. These organizations—both large and small—cannot undertake most of the potential projects identified because of resource limitations and other constraints. Therefore, an organization's overall mission and business strategy should guide the project selection process and prioritization of those projects.

Mission

The mission of the organization is often the driving force in project selection. Two examples of mission statements are provided below based on information found on the organizations' Web sites at the time of publication. You can imagine the wide variety of projects that might be done related to each aspect of these mission statements.

- The mission of The Johns Hopkins Hospital is to improve the health of our community and the world by setting the standard of excellence in patient care. Specifically, we aim:
  o To be the world's preeminent health care institution
  o To provide the highest quality care and service for all people in the prevention, diagnosis and treatment of human illness
  o To operate cooperatively and interdependently with the faculty of The Johns Hopkins University to support education in the health professions and research development into the causes and treatment of human illness
  o To be the leading health care institution in the application of discovery
  o To attract and support physicians and other health care professionals of the highest character and greatest skill
  o To provide facilities and amenities that promote the highest quality care, afford solace and enhance the surrounding community (The Johns Hopkins Hospital, Baltimore, Maryland)
- The mission of Medtronic is:
  o To contribute to human welfare by application of biomedical engineering in the research, design, manufacture, and sale of instruments or appliances that alleviate pain, restore health, and extend life.
  o To direct our growth in the areas of biomedical engineering where we display maximum strength and ability; to gather people and facilities that tend to augment these areas; to continuously build on these areas through education and knowledge assimilation; to avoid participation in areas where we cannot make unique and worthy contributions.
  o To strive without reserve for the greatest possible reliability and quality in our products; to be the unsurpassed standard of comparison and to be recognized as a company of dedication, honesty, integrity, and service.
  o To make a fair profit on current operations to meet our obligations, sustain our growth, and reach our goals.
  o To recognize the personal worth of employees by providing an employment framework that allows personal satisfaction in work accomplished, security, advancement opportunity, and means to share in the company's success.
  o To maintain good citizenship as a company. (Medtronic, Minneapolis, Minnesota)

What Went Wrong?

Unfortunately, when deciding to approve projects, many organizations lack a structured process and do not align projects to their mission or key business objectives. Mike Peterson, project management professional (PMP) and director with PricewaterhouseCoopers' Advisory Services, described an organization that decided it needed to implement a new financial system, which is often a very expensive, challenging project. "With little in the way of analysis, they selected a big-name enterprise resource planning package, and hired a boutique firm to assist with the implementation. At no time did they formally define the benefits the new system was meant to usher in; nor did they decide, exactly, which processes were to be redesigned. Their own assumptions were not articulated, timelines were never devised, nor were the key performance indicators needed to track success ever established."[2]

What was the result of this project? It was completed over budget and behind schedule. Instead of helping the company, it prevented it from closing its books for over 12 months. The company undertook a long and costly project, and ultimately failed to improve the organization's effectiveness. The company could have avoided many of the problems it encountered if it had followed a formal, well-defined process to identify and select projects.

Strategic Planning

Successful leaders look at the big picture or strategic plan of the organization to determine what projects will provide the most value. The same can be said for successful individuals. No one person can do everything, so individuals must pick projects to pursue based on their talents, interests, limitations, and other criteria. **Strategic planning** involves determining long-term objectives by analyzing the strengths and weaknesses of an organization, studying opportunities and threats in the business environment, predicting future trends, and projecting the need for new products and services. Strategic planning provides important information to help organizations identify and select potential projects.

Most organizations have a written strategic plan. This plan usually includes the organization's mission, vision, and goals for the next 3-5 years. For example, the following information is from Nemours Strategic Plan for 2008-2012.[1] U.S. News & World Report ranked Nemours as one of the best children's hospitals in their 2012-2013 edition. Nemours uses its strategic goals along with other tools, such as a SWOT analysis and balanced scorecard, as described in the following sections, select project.

Mission: To provide leadership, institutions, and services to restore and improve the health of children through care and programs not readily available, with one high standard of quality and distinction regardless of the recipient's financial status.

Vision: Freedom from disabling conditions.

Goals:

1. Be a leader in improving children's health through our integrated health system; becoming a pre-eminent voice for children
2. Care for each and every child as if they were our own
3. Be a great place to work
4. Be effective stewards of all of our assets, continually improving them to advance our mission

SWOT Analysis

Many people are familiar with **SWOT analysis**—analyzing **S**trengths, **W**eaknesses, **O**pportunities, and **T**hreats—which is used to aid in strategic planning. For a large organization, a SWOT analysis can be very complex. Figure 2-2 provides an example of a SWOT analysis done by Nemours as part of their strategic plan. Notice that they broke down the SWOT into categories for stewardship, customers, process, and people, which are used in their balanced scorecard approach, described later in this chapter. The SWOT analysis is then used to identify strategic initiatives, which Nemours defines as one-time projects with a defined beginning, tasks, and conclusion, to which resources are allocated.

	STRENGTHS	WEAKNESSES	OPPORTUNITIES	THREATS
Stewardship	Financial strength	Slowdown in managed care rate increases	External funding of biomedical research	Cost pressures (labor & professional liability)
	Support from the Trust	Declining state revenues	Charitable giving to Nemours	Bad debt particularly related to growing uninsured & underinsured population
	Debt capacity	Declining revenue sources for community organization partners	Approaching 2008 elections to be able to educate candidates	Medicaid reimbursement
	Triple A credit rating & low cost of capital	Office of Development infancy		Significant capital needs
				Change in DE Governor in 2008
Customers	Prevention & Advocacy programs unique among providers	Decline in inpatient admissions	Advocate changes in policies, programs & practices to support child health	Unreimbursed preventative services
	Focus on children's health	Patient and family dissatisfaction as relates to access i.e., phone, scheduling, website navigation	Increase market share in Delaware & Florida	Intense competition in Delaware Valley
	Respected as an expert in child health & health matters		Branding Nemours & other social marketing	Declining birth rate & flat demographics in Delaware
				Litigious environment
Process	Integrated child health system	Infrastructure needs at AIDHC	Distinguishing ourselves in clinical quality, patient safety & child health promotion	Consumer-driven health plans
	Robust electronic environment, commitment to use IS in clinical care		Improve service excellence	Pay-for-performance
	Priority on patient safety & quality			Price transparency
	Special programs: Kidshealth, NHPS & BrightStart!		Address access issues (phone, appointments, bundling)	Inflation on capital projects
	Community & government partnerships to advance policy & practice change in prevention		Integration of clinical treatment and community-based prevention	Technology obsolescence
People	Quality health care professionals & delivery	Competitive pay & benefits package particularly for physicians	Culture change initiatives	Pediatric specialist & nursing shortages
	Low vacancy rates	Organizational culture		Aging workforce
	Below industry turnover rate	Performance management		"Whitewater" change
		Staffing requirements in Orlando		Erosion of trust

Figure 2-2. Sample SWOT analysis (Nemours)

Some people like to perform a SWOT analysis by using mind mapping. **Mind mapping** is a technique that uses branches radiating out from a core idea to structure thoughts and ideas. The human brain does not work in a linear fashion. People come up with many unrelated ideas. By putting those ideas down in a visual mind map format, you can often generate more ideas than by just creating lists. You can create mind maps by hand, by using sticky notes, using presentation software like PowerPoint, or by using mind mapping software. Mind mapping can be a more structured, focused, and documented approach to brainstorming individually or in small groups.

Figure 2-3 shows a sample mind map for part of the SWOT analysis presented earlier. This diagram was created using MindView Business software by MatchWare Inc. Notice that this map has four main branches representing strengths, weaknesses, opportunities, and threats. It is simplified to only address items that fall under the "people" perspective. You can then add branches to develop potential project ideas that could address specific items. For example, Nemours identified four strategic initiatives or potential projects for the people perspective as follows:

1. Benefits assessment: Hire an external consultant to conduct a comprehensive benefits and retirement review. Benchmark current benefits and retirement plans to ensure best practices are used and workers are fairly compensated.

2. LeadQuest implementation: Hire an organizational development consultant to assist with the culture change of Nemours. Build high-performing leaders and teams to ensure personal accountability and provide tools for effective feedback, coaching, mentoring, and teambuilding.

3. Values rollout: Develop workshops on each of Nemours core values that will be given every quarter throughout the organization. Ensure that these values are used in recruiting, performance management, delivery of service, etc.

4. Performance management rollout: Develop and rollout a framework for a consistent, objective performance management process. Provide managers with tools to identify clear performance expectations and provide regular development feedback.

By using the SWOT information, you can ensure that project ideas are tied to the organization's strategic plan.

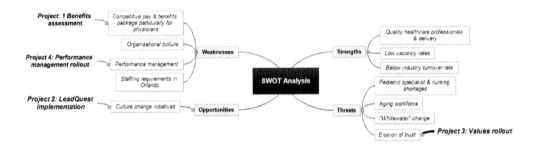

Figure 2-3. Mind map of a SWOT analysis to help identify potential projects (Created with MatchWare's MindView 4 Business Edition)

Video Highlights

Many companies and individuals provide video tutorials to teach a new concept or software tool. Mind mapping is no exception. There are several good videos that show you how to create mind maps. For example, youtube.com includes videos by Tony Buzan, author of *The Mind Map Book: How to Use Radiant Thinking to Maximize Your Brain's Untapped Potential*. Other good videos on mind mapping are available by MacGrercy Consultants, ukbraintrainer, and many others.

You can also learn how to use MindView Business software by watching their online tutorials from *www.matchware.com* or *youtube.com*. You can download a special 60-day trial of this software from *www.matchware.com/intropm*. Their videos include an introduction to mind mapping software, a quickstart tutorial of their software, using mind maps to create a business plan, and how to use MindView Business for project management.

FOUR-STAGE PLANNING PROCESS FOR PROJECT SELECTION

One of the most important factors in project success is selecting the best projects to undertake. In addition to using a SWOT analysis, organizations often follow a detailed planning process for project selection. Figure 2-4 shows a four-stage planning process for selecting projects. Note the hierarchical structure of this model and the results produced from each stage. *It is very important to start at the top of the pyramid to select projects that support the organization's mission and business* strategy. *It is also important to update plans and estimates based on the changing business environment.* The four stages of this process include:

1. *Strategic planning*: The first step of the project selection process is to determine the organization's mission, strategy, goals, and objectives. This information should come from the strategic plan or strategy planning meetings. Senior executives, such as the CEO, chief medical officer, senior physicians, senior administrators, etc., should all be involved in strategic planning and project selection. For example, if an organization's competitive strategy is providing the highest quality of care for a certain medical specialty, it should focus on selecting projects that will help it retain its position in that area. Of course there will be projects that must be done to meet other needs, but the organization should remember to focus on its competitive strategy.

2. *Business area analysis*: The second step is to analyze business processes that are central to achieving strategic goals. For example, could the organization make improvements in facilities, information technology (IT), research and development, or other areas to support the strategic plan?

3. *Project planning*: The next step is to start defining potential projects that address the strategies and areas identified. Managers should discuss the potential projects' scope, time, and cost goals; projected benefits; and constraints as part of this process.

4. *Resource allocation*: The last step in the project planning process is choosing which projects to do and assigning resources for working on them. The amount of resources the organization has available or is willing to acquire will affect decisions on how many projects it can support.

Figure 2-4. Pyramid for the project planning process

METHODS FOR SELECTING PROJECTS

Although people in organizations identify many potential projects as part of their strategic planning process, they also identify projects by working on day-to-day operations. For example, a nurse working in one section of a hospital might notice that some workers are much more efficient than others are. He or she might suggest a project to provide standardized training on specific skills. A marketing analyst for a healthcare company might notice that competitors are using new forms of advertising and suggest a project to respond to this competition. It is important for organizations to encourage workers at all levels as well as customers to submit project ideas because they know firsthand what problems they are encountering and what opportunities might be available.

How do senior managers decide which of the many potential projects their organization should pursue? Some projects directly support competitive strategy and are easy choices, but other project ideas require additional thought and analysis. However, organizations need to narrow down the list of potential projects due to resource and time constraints and focus on projects that will be most beneficial. Most large organizations go through a preliminary project prioritization process annually. For example, early each fall one major corporation's IT organizations work with all of their internal client organizations worldwide to identify potential IT projects and resource requirements for the coming year. This process takes about three weeks, followed by meetings to discuss and prioritize potential projects and agree to cut-off lines based on the availability of funds and other resources. Senior management then reviews the prioritized list of potential projects as part of the corporation's fall company planning and budgeting process.

Selecting projects is not an exact science, but it is a critical part of project, program, and project portfolio management. Many methods exist for selecting from among possible projects. Common techniques include:

- Focusing on mission and broad organizational needs

- Performing net present value analysis or other financial projections

- Using a weighted scoring model

- Implementing a balanced scorecard

- Addressing problems, opportunities, and directives

- Considering project time frame

- Considering project priority

In practice, organizations usually use a combination of these approaches to select projects. Each approach has advantages and disadvantages, and it is up to management to decide the best approach for selecting projects based on their particular organization. In any case, projects should first and foremost address business needs.

Focusing on Mission and Broad Organizational Needs

When deciding what projects to undertake, when to undertake them, and to what level, managers must focus on meeting their organizations' many needs. Projects that fit well with the organization's mission and broad organizational needs are much more likely to be approved. For example, some healthcare organizations include performing research as part of their mission. Some research projects are funded by outside sources, but many must be funded with internal funds. Organizations approve them because it is part of their mission and can often result in higher quality products and services.

In addition to projects that directly tie to the mission, organizations might pursue projects that everyone agrees will meet broad organizational needs. These needs might involve improving social value, minimizing legal or financial risks, improving the firm's IT infrastructure, improving safety or morale, or providing faster customer service. It is often impossible to estimate the financial value of such projects, but everyone agrees that they do have a high value. As the old proverb says, "It is better to measure gold roughly than to count pennies precisely."

One method for selecting projects based on broad organizational needs is to determine whether they meet three important criteria: need, funding, and will. Do people in the organization agree that the project needs to be done? Does the organization have the capacity to provide adequate funds to perform the project? Is there a strong will to make the project succeed? For example, many visionary CEOs can describe a broad need to improve certain aspects of their organizations, such as communications. Although they cannot specifically describe how to improve communications, they might allocate funds to projects that address this need. As projects progress, the organization must reevaluate the need, funding, and will for each project to determine if the projects should be continued, redefined, or terminated.

Performing Financial Projections

Financial considerations are often an important aspect of the project selection process, especially during tough economic times. As authors Dennis Cohen and Robert Graham put it, "Projects are never ends in themselves. Financially they are always a means to an end, cash."[2] Many organizations require an approved business case before pursuing some projects, and financial projections are a critical component of the business case. Three primary methods for determining the projected financial value of projects include net present value analysis, return on investment, and payback analysis. Because project managers often deal with business executives, they must understand how to speak their language, which often boils down to understanding these important financial concepts. Although many healthcare professionals have an advantage by already having strong people skills, they often have a disadvantage by not having strong business knowledge and skills. You will be happy to know that you can use a template file called business case financials created in Excel that is provided with this book to assist you. Even though the template file is easy to use, you should still understand these concepts! Some business managers focus on NPV, some on ROI, and some on payback period. The template provides all three measures.

Net Present Value Analysis

Net present value (NPV) analysis is a method of calculating the expected net monetary gain or loss from a project by discounting all expected future cash inflows and outflows to the present point in time. Money earned today is worth more than money earned in the future, so you need to use NPV to perform equal comparisons. Even if a project supports strategic goals, there is often more than one way to implement the project, and NPV analysis helps you decide the best approach from a financial perspective. An organization should consider only projects with a positive NPV if financial value is a key criterion for project selection. A positive NPV means the return from a project exceeds the **opportunity cost of capital**—the return available by investing the capital elsewhere. For example, is it best to put money into Project A or Project B? Many healthcare projects involve decisions on where to assign people versus money. Is it best to commit people to Project A or Project B? Projects with higher NPVs are preferred to projects with lower NPVs if all other factors are equal. Likewise, a lower negative NPV is best for projects that you know will have a negative financial impact on the organization.

Figure 2-5 illustrates the NPV concept for two different projects. Note that this example starts discounting right away in Year 1 and uses a 10% discount rate for both projects. You can use the NPV function in Microsoft Excel to calculate the NPV quickly. Detailed steps on performing this calculation manually are provided in Figure 2-6. Note that Figure 2-5 lists the projected benefits first, followed by the costs, and then the calculated cash flow amount. Notice that the sum of the **cash flow**—benefits minus costs, or income minus expenses—is the same for both projects at $5,000. The net present values are different, however, because they account for the time value of money. Project 1 had a negative cash flow of $5,000 in the first year, whereas Project 2 had a negative cash flow of only $1,000 in the first year.

Although both projects had the same total cash flows without discounting, these cash flows are not of comparable financial value. NPV analysis, therefore, is a method for making equal comparisons between cash flow for multiyear projects. Although this example shows both projects having the same length, NPV also works for projects of different lengths.

	A	B	C	D	E	F	G
1	Discount rate	10%					
2							
3	**PROJECT 1**	**YEAR 1**	**YEAR 2**	**YEAR 3**	**YEAR 4**	**YEAR 5**	**TOTAL**
4	Benefits	$0	$2,000	$3,000	$4,000	$5,000	$14,000
5	Costs	$5,000	$1,000	$1,000	$1,000	$1,000	$9,000
6	Cash flow	($5,000)	$1,000	$2,000	$3,000	$4,000	**$5,000**
7	NPV ——→	**$2,316**					
8		Formula =npv(b1,b6:f6)					
9							
10	**PROJECT 2**	**YEAR 1**	**YEAR 2**	**YEAR 3**	**YEAR 4**	**YEAR 5**	**TOTAL**
11	Benefits	$1,000	$2,000	$4,000	$4,000	$4,000	$15,000
12	Costs	$2,000	$2,000	$2,000	$2,000	$2,000	$10,000
13	Cash flow	($1,000)	$0	$2,000	$2,000	$2,000	**$5,000**
14	NPV ——→	**$3,201**					
15		Formula =npv(b1,b13:f13)					
16							
17							

Note that totals are equal, but NPVs are not because of the time value of money

Figure 2-5. Net present value example (Schwalbe, Information Technology Project Management, Sixth Edition, 2010)

Discount rate	10%					
PROJECT 1	**1**	**2**	**3**	**4**	**5**	**TOTAL**
Costs	$5,000	$1,000	$1,000	$1,000	$1,000	$9,000
Discount factor*	0.91	0.83	0.75	0.68	0.62	
Discounted costs	$4,545	$826	$751	$683	$621	**$7,427**
Benefits	$0	$2,000	$3,000	$4,000	$5,000	$14,000
Discount factor*	0.91	0.83	0.75	0.68	0.62	
Discounted benefits	0	$1,653	$2,254	$2,732	$3,105	**$9,743**
Discounted benefits - discounted costs, or NPV ⟶						**$2,316**
*Note: The discount factors are NOT rounded to two decimal places.						
They are calculated using the formula discount factor = 1/(1+discount rate)ˇyear.						
You can access this spreadsheet on the companion Web site under Sample Documents.						

Figure 2-6. Detailed NPV calculations (Schwalbe, Information Technology Project Management, Sixth Edition, 2010)

There are some items to consider when calculating NPV. Some organizations refer to the investment year for project costs as Year 0 instead of Year 1 and do not discount costs in Year 0. Other organizations start discounting immediately based on their financial procedures; it is simply a matter of preference for the organization. The discount rate can also vary, based on the prime rate and other economic considerations. Financial experts in your organization will be able to tell you what discount rate to use. Some people consider it to be the rate at which you could borrow money for the project. You can enter costs as negative numbers instead of positive numbers, and you can list costs first and then benefits. For example, Figure 2-7 shows the financial calculations a consulting firm provided in a business case for an intranet project. Note that the discount rate is 8%, costs are not discounted right away (note the Year 0), the discount factors are rounded to two decimal places, costs are listed first, and costs are entered as positive numbers. The NPV and other calculations are still the same; only the format is slightly different. Project managers must be sure to check with their organization to find out its guidelines for when discounting starts, what discount rate to use, and what format the organization prefers. Chapter 3 includes a NPV analysis as part of the business case written to help justify investing in a project.

Discount rate	8%					
Assume the project is completed in Year 0			Year			
	0	1	2	3	Total	
Costs	140,000	40,000	40,000	40,000		
Discount factor	1	0.93	0.86	0.79		
Discounted costs	140,000	37,200	34,400	31,600	243,200	
Benefits	0	200,000	200,000	200,000		
Discount factor	1	0.93	0.86	0.79		
Discounted benefits	0	186,000	172,000	158,000	516,000	
Discounted benefits - costs	(140,000)	148,800	137,600	126,400	272,800	←NPV
Cumulative benefits - costs	(140,000)	8,800	146,400	272,800		
ROI ─────────────→	112%					
	Payback in Year 1					

Figure 2-7. Intranet project NPV example (Schwalbe, Information Technology Project Management, Sixth Edition, 2010)

To determine NPV, follow these steps:

1. Determine the estimated costs and benefits for the life of the project and the products it produces. For example, the intranet project example assumed the project would produce a system in about six months that would be used for three years, so costs are included in Year 0, when the system is developed, and ongoing system costs and projected benefits are included for Years 1, 2, and 3.

2. Determine the discount rate. A **discount rate** is the rate used in discounting future cash flows. It is also called the capitalization rate or opportunity cost of capital. In Figures 2-5 and 2-6, the discount rate is 10% per year, and in Figure 2-7, the discount rate is 8% per year.

3. Calculate and interpret the net present value. There are several ways to calculate NPV. Most spreadsheet software has a built-in function to calculate NPV. For example, Figure 2-5 shows the formula that Excel uses: =npv(discount rate, range of cash flows), where the discount rate is in cell B1 and the range of cash flows for Project 1 are in cells B6 through F6. To use the NPV function, there must be a row in the spreadsheet (or column, depending on how it is organized) for the cash flow each year, which is the benefit amount for that year minus the cost amount. The result of the formula yields an NPV of $2,316 for Project 1 and an NPV of $3,201 for Project 2. Because both projects have positive NPVs, they are both good candidates for selection. However, because Project 2 has a higher NPV than Project 1 (38%

higher), it would be the better choice between the two. If the two numbers are close, other methods should be used to help decide which project to select.

The mathematical formula for calculating NPV is:

$$NPV = \sum_{t=0...n} A_t / (1+r)^t$$

where t equals the year of the cash flow, n is the last year of the cash flow, A_t is the amount of cash flow in year t, and r is the discount rate. If you cannot enter the data into spreadsheet software, you can perform the calculations by hand or with a simple calculator. First, determine the annual **discount factor**—a multiplier for each year based on the discount rate and year—and then apply it to the costs and benefits for each year. The formula for the discount factor is $1/(1+r)^t$, where r is the discount rate, such as 8%, and t is the year. For example, the discount factors used in Figure 2-5 are calculated as follows:

Year 0: discount factor = $1/(1+0.08)^0 = 1$

Year 1: discount factor = $1/(1+0.08)^1 = .93$

Year 2: discount factor = $1/(1+0.08)^2 = .86$

Year 3: discount factor = $1/(1+0.08)^3 = .79$

After determining the discount factor for each year, multiply the costs and benefits by the appropriate discount factor. For example, in Figure 2-7, the discounted cost for Year 1 is $40,000 * .93 = $37,200, where the discount factor is rounded to two decimal places. Next, sum all of the discounted costs and benefits each year to get a total. For example, the total discounted costs in Figure 2-7 are $243,200. To calculate the NPV, take the total discounted benefits and subtract the total discounted costs. In this example, the NPV is $516,000 – $243,200 = $272,800. (Don't forget, you can use the business case financial template file to avoid entering all of these formulas yourself.)

Return on Investment

Another important financial consideration is return on investment. **Return on investment (ROI)** is the result of subtracting the project costs from the benefits and then dividing by the costs. For example, if you invest $100 today and next year your investment is worth $110, your ROI is ($110 – 100)/100, or 0.10 (10%). Note that the ROI is always a percentage. It can be positive or negative. It is best to consider discounted costs and benefits for multiyear projects when calculating ROI. Figure 2-7 shows an ROI of 112%. You calculate this number as follows:

ROI = (total discounted benefits – total discounted costs)/discounted costs

ROI = (516,000 – 243,200) / 243,200 = 112%

The higher the ROI, the better; an ROI of 112% is outstanding. Many organizations have a required rate of return for some projects. The **required rate of return** is the minimum acceptable rate of return on an investment. For example, an organization might have a required rate of return of at least 10% for some projects. The organization bases the required rate of return on what it could expect to receive elsewhere for an investment of comparable risk.

You can also determine a project's **internal rate of return (IRR)** by finding what discount rate results in an NPV of zero for the project. You can use the Goal Seek function in Excel (use Excel's Help function for more information on Goal Seek) to determine the IRR quickly. Simply set the cell containing the NPV calculation to zero while changing the cell containing the discount rate. For example, in Figure 2-5, you could set cell B7 to zero while changing cell B1 to find that the IRR for Project 1 is 27%. (Note: The Excel file for Figure 2-5 is provided on the companion Web site if you want to try this out. Consult additional sources for more information on IRR and other financial concepts.)

Payback Analysis

Payback analysis is another financial tool to use when selecting projects. **Payback period** is the amount of time it will take to recoup—in the form of net cash inflows—the total dollars invested in a project. In other words, payback analysis determines how much time will lapse before accrued benefits overtake accrued and continuing costs. Payback, if there is one, occurs in the year when the cumulative benefits minus costs reach zero.

For example, assume a project cost $100,000 up front with no additional costs, and its annual benefits were $50,000 per year. Payback period is calculated by dividing the cost of the project by the annual cash inflows ($100,000/$50,000), resulting in 2 years in this simple example. If costs and benefits vary each year, you need to find where the lines for the cumulative costs and benefits cross, or where the cumulative cash inflow is equal to zero. The data used to create the chart in Figure 2-8 is provided above the chart.

Template Files Available

A template file called payback period chart is provided on the companion Web site for this text, as well as one for calculating NPV, ROI, and payback for a project (called business case financials). See Appendix B for a list of all template files.

Year	Costs	Benefits	Cum Costs	Cum Benefits	Cum Cash Inflows
0	100,000	0	100,000	0	-100,000
1	0	50,000	100,000	50,000	-50,000
2	0	50,000	100,000	100,000	0
3	0	50,000	100,000	150,000	50,000

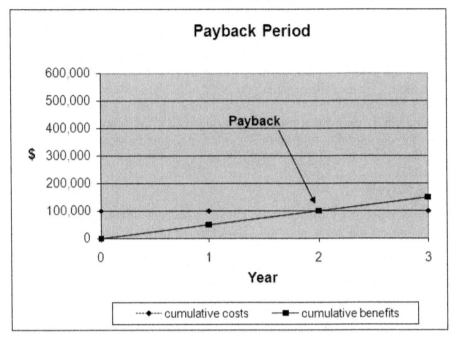

Figure 2-8. Charting the payback period

Many organizations have certain recommendations for the length of the payback period of an investment. For example, they might require all IT projects to have a payback period of less than two years or even one year, regardless of the estimated NPV or ROI. Rhonda Hocker, CIO at San Jose–based BEA Systems, Inc. (now owned by Oracle), notes that the general rule at the company is that its IT projects should have a payback period of less than one year. The company also tries to limit project teams to no more than 12 people, who perform the work within four months. Given the economic climate and rapid pace of change in businesses and technology, the company has to focus on delivering positive financial results quickly.[4] However; organizations must also consider long-range goals when making major investments. Many crucial projects, such as drug development or medical research projects, cannot achieve a payback that quickly, if ever, or be completed in such a short time period.

To aid in project selection, it is important for project managers to understand the organization's financial expectations for projects. It is also important for management to understand the limitations of financial estimates, because they are just estimates.

Using a Weighted Scoring Model

A **weighted scoring model** is a tool that provides a systematic process for selecting projects based on many criteria. These criteria include such factors as meeting strategic goals or broad organizational needs; addressing specific problems or opportunities; the amount of time it will take to complete the project; the overall priority of the project; and the projected financial performance of the project. Another criterion that is often used for healthcare projects is social value. Will the project help an individual patient, a group of patients, or all of humanity? Social value often outweighs the other criteria.

The first step in creating a weighted scoring model is to identify criteria important to the project selection process. It often takes time to develop and reach agreement on these criteria. Holding facilitated brainstorming sessions or using software to exchange ideas can aid in developing these criteria.

For example, suppose your family wants to take a trip. (You might need a vacation after trying to understand the previous section!) Some possible criteria for selecting which trip to take include the following: total cost of the trip; probability of good weather; fun activities nearby; and recommendations.

Next, you assign a weight to each criterion. Once again, determining weights requires consultation and final agreement. These weights indicate how much you value each criterion or how important each criterion is. You can assign weights based on percentage, and the sum of all the criteria's weights must total 100%. You then assign numerical scores to each criterion (for example, 0 to 100) for each project (or trip in this example). The scores indicate how much each project (or trip) meets each criterion. At this point, you can use a spreadsheet application to create a matrix of projects, criteria, weights, and scores. Figure 2-9 provides an example of a weighted scoring model to evaluate four different trips. After assigning weights for the criteria and scores for each trip, you calculate a weighted score for each trip by multiplying the weight for each criterion by its score and adding the resulting values.

For example, you calculate the weighted score for Trip 1 in Figure 2-9 as:

$$25\%*60 + 30\%*80 + 15\%*70 + 30\%*50 = 64.5$$

Note that in this example, Trip 3 is the obvious choice for selection because it has the highest weighted score. Creating a bar chart to graph the weighted scores for each project allows you to see the results at a glance. If you create the weighted scoring model in a spreadsheet, you can enter the data, create and copy formulas, and perform a "what-if" analysis. For example, suppose you change the weights for the criteria. By having the weighted scoring model in a spreadsheet, you can easily change the weights to update the weighted scores and charts automatically. This capability allows you to investigate various options for different stakeholders quickly. Ideally, the result should be reflective of the group's consensus, and any major disagreements should be documented. A template file for creating a weighted scoring model is provided on the companion Web site for this text.

Criteria	Weight	Trip 1	Trip 2	Trip 3	Trip 4
Total cost of the trip	25%	60	80	90	20
Probability of good weather	30%	80	60	90	70
Fun activities nearby	15%	70	30	50	90
Recommendations	30%	50	50	60	90
Weighted Project Scores	**100%**	**64.5**	**57.5**	**75**	**66.5**

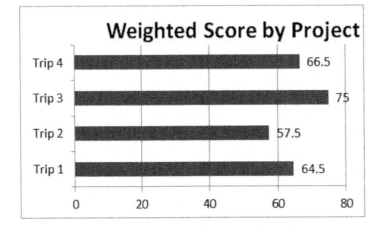

Figure 2-9. Sample weighted scoring model for project selection

Many readers of this text are probably familiar with a weighted scoring model because teachers often use them to determine grades. Suppose grades for a class are based on two homework assignments and two exams. To calculate final grades, the teacher would assign a weight to each of these items. Suppose Homework One is worth 10% of the grade, Homework Two is worth 20% of the grade, Test One is worth 20% of the grade, and Test Two is worth 50% of the grade. Students would want to do well on each of these items, but they would focus on performing well on Test Two because it is 50% of the grade.

You can also establish weights by assigning points. For example, a project might receive 100 points if it definitely supports key business objectives, 50 points if it somewhat supports them, and 0 points if it is totally unrelated to key business objectives. With a point model, you can simply add all the points to determine the best projects for selection without having to multiply weights and scores and sum the results.

You can also determine minimum scores or thresholds for specific criteria in a weighted scoring model. For example, suppose an organization decided that it should not consider a project if it does not score at least 50 out of 100 on every criterion or at least 80 on the most important criterion. The organization can build this type of threshold into the weighted scoring model to automatically reject projects that do not meet these minimum standards. As you can see, weighted scoring models can aid in project selection decisions.

Implementing a Balanced Scorecard

Dr. Robert Kaplan and Dr. David Norton developed another approach to help select and manage projects that align with business strategy. A **balanced scorecard** is a methodology that converts an organization's value drivers—such as customer service, innovation, operational efficiency, and financial performance—to a series of defined metrics. The Nemours SWOT example presented earlier in this chapter used this approach. Organizations record and analyze these metrics to determine how well projects help them achieve strategic goals.

The Balanced Scorecard Institute, which provides training and guidance to organizations using this methodology, quotes Kaplan and Norton's description of the balanced scorecard as follows:

"The balanced scorecard retains traditional financial measures. But financial measures tell the story of past events, an adequate story for industrial age companies for which investments in long-term capabilities and customer relationships were not critical for success. These financial measures are inadequate, however, for guiding and evaluating the journey that information age companies must make to create future value through investment in customers, suppliers, employees, processes, technology, and innovation."[5]

The balanced scorecard approach is often a good fit for healthcare organizations because they must address additional factors beyond financial measures in order to fulfill their missions and goals. "The Nemours Strategy Management System (SMS) uses the Balanced Scorecard architecture to articulate the strategy and link key processes, behaviors, and personal accountability, enabling Nemours to close the gap between where it currently is and where it wishes to be."[6] Figure 4-10 shows Nemours' highest order strategy map. You can read Nemours detailed strategic plan in the reference provided in the End Notes.

Nemours uses four perspectives in their balanced scorecard approach:

1. People and Learning: What resources, skills, training and support must staff have in order to work effectively? What organizational culture is conducive to strong people performance?
2. Process Perspective: What must we excel at in order to satisfy our customers? How do we meet their needs consistently?
3. Customer Perspective: How do we meet customer needs and exceed expectations? What do we want the community to say about us?
4. Stewardship Perspective: What resources are required to achieve the mission? How are revenue generating strategies balanced with expense management?

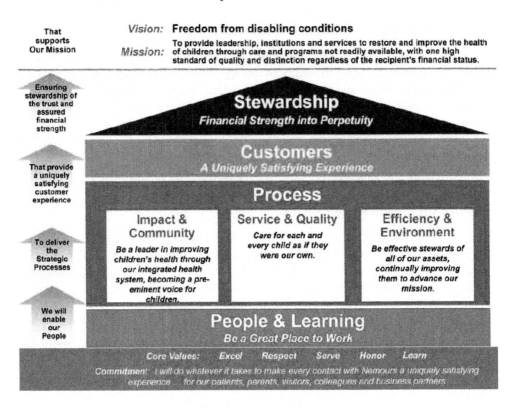

Figure 2-10. Sample balanced scorecard strategy map (Nemours)

Visit www.balancedscorecard.org for more information on using this approach for project selection. This site includes several examples of how organizations use this methodology. You can also visit www.thepalladiumgroup.com to read about the many organizations, including a few in the healthcare industry, who won the Palladium Balanced Scorecard Hall of Fame Award for Executing Strategy. The following quotes are from past award winners, including Nemours:

- Nemours President and CEO David J. Bailey, MD, MBA: "In developing Nemours's strategy, our objective was to create a credible and relevant direction that is distinguished both by its simplicity and its power to assist leadership in making tough decisions in order to achieve the desired future state. Going forward, Nemours" Strategy Management System will be the business model guiding our operation... Ultimately, success will depend upon our employees' willingness to remain on course, lean and focused, adjusting our initiatives but not our aspirations."

- St. Mary's/Duluth Clinic CEO Dr. Peter Person: "Building the strategy map was a turning point for the executive team in fully understanding the organization as a business, defining our customers, and translating this into a clearly focused strategy. This resulted in a performance management tool to focus the entire health care system. Our monthly scorecard review sessions are incredibly valuable to me as CEO. The scorecard enables us to easily scan and digest overall organizational performance and to identify any necessary course corrections. The balance of our discussion time has definitely shifted from day-to-day operations to strategic issue decision-making."

- Chief Medical Director Dr. Jon Meliones: "As an academic institution, we were interested in a solution that could function as a teaching and learning tool and report how we were doing. The Balanced Scorecard provides that monitoring and conscience and assists us in improving our practice patterns. We look at the scorecard as the evolving brain of our organization. In practicing smarter, we dramatically reduced our cost per patient case and patient length-of-stay, and significantly increased our customer satisfaction. Our results at Duke Children's prove the Balanced Scorecard approach can be the catalyst for positive change in healthcare."[7]

Addressing Problems, Opportunities, and Directives

Another method for selecting projects is based on their response to a problem, an opportunity, or a directive, as described in the following list:

- Problems are undesirable situations that prevent an organization from achieving its goals. These problems can be current or anticipated. For example, if an important piece of medical equipment stops working, that problem must be addressed as soon as possible. If the equipment is known to need repairs to prevent a problem, a project should be initiated soon to take care of it.

- Opportunities are chances to improve the organization. For example, a company might want to revamp its Web site to attract more visitors to the site. Or there might be new markets an organization could pursue.

- **Directives** are new requirements imposed by management, government, or some external influence. For example, many healthcare organizations have created projects in to meet requirements based on new federal laws. The government often offers incentives or applies penalties to prompt organizations to take actions to meet new laws.

Organizations select projects for any of these reasons. It is often easier to get approval and funding for projects that address problems or directives because the organization must respond to these categories of projects to avoid hurting the business and, in the case of healthcare, patients. For example, several hospitals initiated projects to meet the Hospital Readmission reduction (HRR) Program, a provision of the Patient Protection and Affordable Care Act (PPACA). The Department of Health & Human Services (HHS) said it would invest up to $1 billion in federal funding toward this program. "$500 million of that funding was made available through the Community-based Care Transition Program. Up to $500 million more will be dedicated from the Centers for Medicare & Medicaid Services (CMS) Innovation Center to support new demonstrations related to reducing hospital-acquired conditions. The funding will be invested in reforms that help achieve two shared goals:

- Keep hospital patients from getting injured or sicker…

- Help patients heal without complication." [8]

Many problems and directives must be resolved quickly. For example, an inspection by the Joint Commission's Office of Quality Monitoring often results in project ideas. Organizations often find the funds and resources for these projects fairly quickly to avoid litigation and other negative side-effects. However, managers must also consider projects that seek opportunities for social value, especially those that improve patient care.

Project Time Frame

Another approach to project selection is based on the time it will take to complete a project or the date by which it must be done. For example, some potential projects must be finished within a specific time period, such as projects that were done to meet Year 2000 issues. If they cannot be finished by this set date, there may be serious consequences. Likewise, if there is a potential project that is only valid if it can be done by a certain time and there is no way your organization can meet the deadline, it should not be considered. Some projects can be completed very quickly—within a few weeks, days, or even minutes. However, even though many projects can be completed quickly, it is still important to prioritize them.

Project Priority

Another method for project selection is the overall priority of the project. Many organizations prioritize projects as being high, medium, or low priority based on the current business environment. For example, if it were crucial to cut operating costs quickly, projects that have the most potential to do so would be given a high priority. The organization should always complete high-priority projects first, even if a lower priority project could be finished in less time. Usually, there are many more potential projects than an organization can undertake at any one time, so it is very important to work on the most important ones first.

As you can see, organizations of all types and sizes can use many approaches to select projects. Many project managers have some say in which projects their organizations select for implementation. Even if they do not, they need to understand the motive and overall business strategy for the projects they are managing. Project managers and team members are often asked to justify their projects, and understanding many of these project selection methods can help them to do so.

PROGRAM SELECTION

Many healthcare organizations create programs to address specific needs, such as delivering healthcare remotely. They know that there will be several projects required to meet these needs, and then go through a selection process for that program. On the other hand, specific projects might be proposed and deemed important, and the organization must decide if it is advantageous to manage them separately or as part of a new or existing program. Recall that a program is a group of projects managed in a coordinated way to obtain benefits and control not available from managing them individually.

Focusing on Coordination and Benefits

What does it mean to manage a group of projects in a coordinated way? Project managers focus on managing individual projects. Project managers and their teams have to do many things to achieve individual project success. For example, for projects to build a new office, clinic, hospital, or other building, some of the activities include:

- Working with local government groups to obtain permits

- Finding and managing a land excavation firm to prepare the land

- Coordinating with an architect to understand the house or building design

- Screening and hiring various construction workers or a construction firm

- Finding appropriate suppliers for the materials

If a construction firm is in charge of several buildings in the same geographic area, it makes sense to coordinate these common activities for all the projects instead of doing them separately.

What benefits and control would be possible by managing projects as part of a program? There are several. For example, potential benefits in a building construction program scenario include the following:

- *Saving money*: The construction firm can often save money by using economies of scale. It can purchase materials, obtain services, and hire workers for less money if it is managing the construction of 100 buildings instead of just one.

- *Saving time*: Instead of each project team having to perform similar work, by grouping the projects into a program, one person or group can be responsible for similar work, such as obtaining all the permits for all the buildings. This coordination of work usually saves time as well as money.

- *Increasing authority*: A program manager responsible for 100 buildings will have more authority than a project manager responsible for one. The program manager can use this authority in multiple situations, such as negotiating better prices with suppliers and obtaining better services in a more timely fashion.

Healthcare Perspective

Janice Weaver, PMP, was the program manager responsible for building the Norton Brownsboro Hospital, the first hospital built in Louisville, Kentucky in over 20 years. This five-story hospital is licensed for 127 beds, includes 16 critical care rooms, a 24-hour emergency room, 22 treatment rooms, eight operating rooms, two endoscopy suites, a catheterization lab, and an interventional radiology suite. The hospital features a patient- and family-centered model of care. For example, every room in the hospital is a private room with sleeping accommodations for family members. The hospital was designed using enhanced environmental and health principles that follow the Green Guide for Health Care. For example, there is natural light throughout the facility, including the operating rooms.

When Janice and her team started defining all of the work that needed to be done to build the hospital, they decided to break it down into fourteen separate projects with fourteen different project managers. Janice made sure that all of these projects "crossed the finish line" together by including a project called integrated testing, which she described as being like a final exam. They wanted to make sure that the hospital was ready for the first patient to walk through the door. Everything was done in a concurrent versus a linear fashion. They also built mock rooms, including a full-scale emergency room treatment room, a medical-surgical patient room, an Intensive Care Unit (ICU) patient room, and a fully equipped operating room.

You can watch a short video about this program from the companion Web site for this text. The Norton Brownsboro Hospital was a finalist in PMI's Project of the Year Award in 2010.

Approaches to Creating Programs

Some new projects naturally fall into existing programs, such as buildings being built in a certain geographic area. As another example, many companies use IT, and they usually have a program in place for IT infrastructure projects. Projects might include purchasing new hardware, software, and networking equipment, or determining standards for IT. If a new office, clinic, or hospital opens up in a new location, the project to provide the hardware, software, and networks for that facility would logically fall under the infrastructure program.

Other projects might spark the need for developing a new program. For example, a company might win a large contract to build a medical office complex in a foreign country. Instead of viewing the contract as either one huge project or part of an existing program, it would be better to manage the work as its own program that comprises several smaller projects. For example, there might be separate project managers for each building. Grouping related projects into programs helps improve coordination through better communications, planning, management, and control. Organizations must decide when it makes sense to group projects together. When too many projects are part of one program, it might be wise to create a new program to improve their management. Remember that the main goal of programs is to obtain benefits and control not available from managing projects separately.

Media Snapshot

Many people enjoy watching the extra features on a DVD that describe the creation of a movie. For example, the extended edition DVD for *Lord of the Rings: The Two Towers* includes detailed descriptions of how the script was created, how huge structures were built, how special effects were made, and how talented professionals overcame numerous obstacles to complete the three movies. Instead of viewing each movie as a separate project, the producer, Peter Jackson, decided to develop all three movies as part of one program.

"By shooting all three films consecutively during one massive production and post-production schedule, New Line Cinema made history. Never before had such a monumental undertaking been contemplated or executed. The commitment of time, resources, and manpower were unheard of as all three films and more than 1,000 effects shots were being produced concurrently with the same director and core cast."[9]

At three years in the making, *The Lord of the Rings* trilogy was the largest production ever to be mounted in the Southern Hemisphere. The production assembled an international cast, employed a crew of 2,500, used over 20,000 days of extras, featured 77 speaking parts, and created 1,200 state-of-the-art computer-generated effects shots. Jackson said that doing detailed planning for all three movies made it much easier than he imagined producing them, and the three movies were completed in less time and for less money by grouping them together. The budget for the three films was reported to be $270 million, and they grossed over $1 billion before the end of 2004.

In 2012, New Line Cinema announced that *The Hobbit* will also be a trilogy. Jackson said that after wrapping up shooting in New Zealand that the story was rich enough to create three films instead of the two that were originally planned.

PROJECT PORTFOLIO SELECTION

Projects and programs have existed for a long time, as has some form of project portfolio management. Many people are familiar with stock portfolios, and the concept of project portfolios is similar. There is no simple process for deciding how to create stock or project portfolios, but the goal of project portfolio management is clear: to maximize business value to ensure enterprise success. It is also important to develop and follow a sound process for project portfolio management. Just as financial planners work with clients to develop an investment strategy that meets their specific needs, such as having a certain percentage of investments in stocks and bonds based on the client's age and risk tolerance, project portfolio managers must also develop and follow a sound strategy.

Gaining a deep understanding of the project portfolio management process is beyond the scope of this text, but project managers should have a basic understanding of the process used in their organizations. This is especially true in the healthcare industry where so much is at stake and so many projects need to be done. As stated in a PMI's 2012 Pulse of the Profession Portfolio Management report, "Project portfolio management can be a potent weapon to ensure an organization's investments work together and deliver true business results...organizations with little variation in their project portfolio management practices see 64 percent of their projects meet expected ROI—17 percentage points more than those companies with high variability."[10]

You can measure an organization's value in several ways, such as in market share, profit margins, growth rates, share prices, patient outcomes, and customer or employee satisfaction ratings. Organizations, especially those in healthcare, cannot pursue only projects that have the best financial value. They must also consider resource availability (including people, equipment, and cash); risks that could affect success; and other concerns, such as potential mergers, public relations, balancing investments, social value, and other factors that affect enterprise success.

Focusing on Enterprise Success

Project managers strive to make their projects successful and naturally focus on doing whatever they can to meet the goals of their particular projects. Likewise, program managers focus on making their programs successful. Project portfolio managers and other senior managers, however, must focus on how *all* of an organization's projects and programs fit together to help the entire enterprise achieve success. That might mean canceling or putting several projects on hold, reassigning resources from one project to another, suggesting changes in project leadership, or taking other actions that might negatively affect individual projects or programs to help the organization as a whole. Running any large organization is complex, as is project portfolio management.

What Went **Right?**

Many companies have seen great returns on investment after implementing basic ideas of project portfolio management. For example, Jane Walton, the project portfolio manager for IT projects at Schlumberger, saved the company $3 million in one year by simply organizing the organization's 120 IT projects into one portfolio. Before then, all IT projects and their associated programs were managed separately, and no one looked at them as a whole. Manufacturing companies used project portfolio management in the 1960s, and Walton anticipated the need to justify investments in IT projects just as managers have to justify capital investment projects. She found that 80% of the organization's projects overlapped, and 14 separate projects were trying to accomplish the same thing. By looking at all IT projects and programs together, Schlumberger could make better strategic business decisions. The company canceled several projects and merged others to reduce the newly discovered redundancy.[11]

Leaders are turning to project portfolio management tools to better capture, manage, prioritize, and align investments and resources with the hopes of increasing the amount of business value they can provide. Many vendors promise triple-digit returns on their products. Is that possible? A recent study found that a comprehensive project portfolio management tool "is likely to provide an ROI of more than 250%."[12]

Recall that project portfolio management focuses on strategic issues while individual projects often focus on tactical issues. Portfolios should be formed and continuously updated to help the organization as a whole make better strategic decisions. Organizations can put all projects into one enterprise portfolio, but they often break it down into more detailed sub-portfolios, often set up by major facilities, departments, or other categories. For example, America's Best Healthcare, Inc., like many healthcare organizations, is very large and includes major facilities throughout the country. They found it more effective to manage project portfolios at lower levels. Academic Health Systems (AHS), for example, one of their main teaching hospitals, had its own strategic plan, budget, PMO, and project portfolio manager focused on meeting their strategic goals.

As shown in the Best Practice example, it is one thing to prepare a strategic plan; it is another, and more difficult thing, to follow it. It is crucial to allocate resources based on the most important projects in a portfolio.

Best Practice

Many organizations rely on effective new product development (NPD) to increase growth and profitability, yet according to Robert Cooper of McMaster University and the New Product Development Institute in Ontario, Canada, only one in seven product concepts comes to fruition. Why is it that some companies, like Proctor & Gamble, Johnson and Johnson, Hewlett Packard, and Sony are consistently successful in NPD? Because they use a disciplined, systematic approach to NPD projects based on best practices, including focusing NPD on business strategy.

Cooper's study compared companies that were the best at performing NPD with those that were the worst. For example:

- 65.5% of best performing NPD companies align projects with business strategy compared to 46% of companies performing the worst.
- 65.5% of best performing NPD companies align their resource breakdown to business strategy compared to only 8% of worst performing companies do.

It's easy for a company to say that its projects are aligned with business strategy, but assigning its resources based on that strategy is a measurable action that produces results. Best performing NPD companies are also more customer-focused in identifying new product ideas and put a project manager in charge of their NPD projects:

- 69% of best performing NPD companies identify customer needs and problems based on customer input, while only 15% of worst performing companies do.
- 80% of best performing companies have an identifiable NPD project manager, while only 50% of worst performing companies do.[13]

These best practices apply to all projects:

- Align projects *and* resources with business strategy.
- Focus on customer needs when identifying potential projects.
- Assign project managers to lead the projects.

Sample Approach for Creating a Project Portfolio

Figure 2-11 illustrates one approach for project portfolio management in which there is one large portfolio for an organization. Sections of the portfolio are then broken down to improve the management of projects in each particular sector. For example, an organization like AHS might use the main portfolio categories shown in the left part of Figure 2-11 (marketing, materials, IT, and HR (human resources)) and divide each of those categories further to address their unique concerns. The right part of this figure shows how the IT projects could be categorized in more detail. For example, there are three basic IT project portfolio categories:

1. *Venture*: Projects in this category would help transform the business. For example, AHS might have an IT project to provide remote patient care after patients left their facility. They might develop an app that patients could run on existing devices like tablets or smartphones to report important medical information and videoconference with medical staff. This project could help transform the business by developing longer and more trusting partnerships with patients and caregivers.

2. *Growth*: Projects in this category would help the company grow in terms of revenue. For example, an organization might have an IT project to provide information on its corporate Web site in a new language, such as Spanish. This capability could help the company grow its business to customers fluent in that language.

3. *Core*: Projects in this category must be accomplished to run the business. For example, an IT project to provide computers for new employees would fall under this category, as would projects required to meet new regulations.

Note that the core category of IT projects is labeled as **nondiscretionary costs**. This means that the organization has no choice in whether to fund these projects; it must fund them to stay in business. Projects that fall under the venture or growth category would be **discretionary costs** because the organization can use its own discretion in deciding whether to fund them. Also note the arrow in the center of Figure 2-11. This arrow indicates that the risks, value, and timing of projects normally increase as you go from core to growth to venture projects. However, some core projects can also be high risk, have high value, and require good timing.

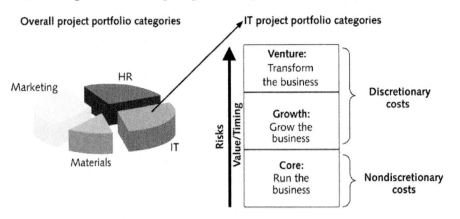

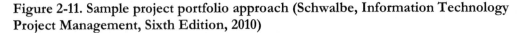

Figure 2-11. Sample project portfolio approach (Schwalbe, Information Technology Project Management, Sixth Edition, 2010)

Five Levels of Project Portfolio Management

As you can imagine, it takes time to understand and apply project portfolio management. You can develop and manage a project portfolio in many ways. Just as projects are unique, so are project portfolios.

An organization can view project portfolio management as having five levels, from simplest to most complex, as follows:

1. Put all of your projects in one list. Many organizations find duplicate or unneeded projects after they identify all the projects on which they are working.

2. Prioritize the projects in your list. It's important to know which projects are most important to an organization so that resources can be applied accordingly.

3. Divide your projects into several categories based on types of investment. Categorizing projects helps you see the big picture, such as how many projects are supporting a growth strategy, how many are helping to increase profit margins, how many relate to marketing, and how many relate to materials. Organizations can create as many categories as they need to help understand and analyze how projects affect business needs and goals.

4. Automate the list. Managers can view project data in many different ways by putting key information into a computerized system. You can enter the project information in spreadsheet software such as Excel. You might have headings for the project name, project manager, project sponsor, business needs addressed, start date, end date, budget, risk, priority, key deliverables, and other items. You can also use more sophisticated tools to help perform project portfolio management, such as enterprise project management software, as described in Chapter 1.

5. Apply modern portfolio theory, including risk-return tools that map project risks. Figure 2-12 provides a sample map to assist in evaluating project risk versus return, or business value. Each bubble represents a project, and the size of the bubble relates to its approved budget (that is, the larger bubbles have larger budgets). Notice that there are not and should not be projects in the lower-right quadrant, which is the location of projects that have low relative value and high risk.

As described in Chapter 1, many software products are available on the market today to help analyze portfolios. Consult references on portfolio theory and project portfolio management software for more details on this topic.

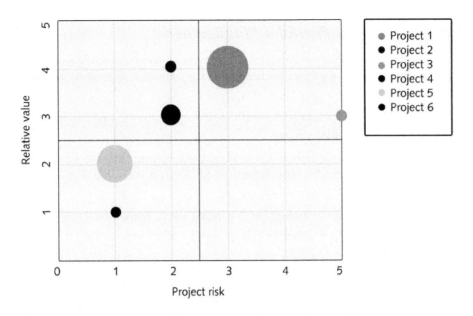

Figure 2-12. Sample project portfolio risk map (Schwalbe, Information Technology Project Management, Sixth Edition, 2010)

Figure 2-13 shows a humorous example of a portfolio chart listing various fruits, charting them based on their taste and ease of eating. In this example, people would eat a lot more seedless grapes, strawberries, blueberries and peaches and not many grapefruit!

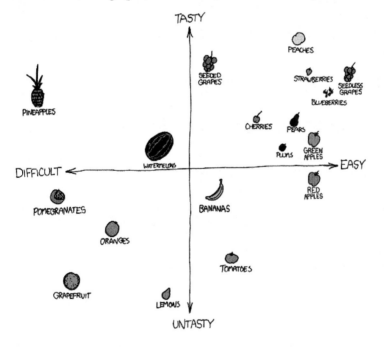

Figure 2-13. Deciding what fruit to eat (www.xkcd.com)

It is important for organizations to develop a fair, consistent, and logical process for selecting projects, programs, and portfolios. Studies show that one of the main reasons people quit their jobs is because they feel they do not make a difference. After employees understand how their work fits into the big picture, they can work more effectively to help themselves and their entire organizations succeed.

CASE WRAP-UP

Marie Scott and her team summarized the inputs from the meeting and discussed them with their CEO, Francis Anthony, along with the chief medical officer and other senior managers. They felt people were nervous that the company might not be doing well and that their jobs were in jeopardy. They discussed options for how to proceed and decided that it was important for senior management to explain the importance of aligning projects with business strategy.

Fran and his staff put together a memo and presentation to explain that the company was doing very well, and that they had no intentions of either letting anyone go or cutting major programs. On the contrary, they had far more projects to pursue than they possibly could, and they believed that using project portfolio management would help them select and manage projects better. After everyone heard this information, they were much more open to working with Marie's group to improve their project, program, and portfolio management processes.

CHAPTER SUMMARY

The healthcare industry is very complex. To handle complex situations effectively, project managers need to use systems thinking, which involves taking a holistic view of a project and understanding how it relates to the larger organization. Project managers must understand and consider business, technology, and organizational issues when defining and selecting projects.

An organization's overall mission and business strategy should guide the project selection process and management of those projects. Many organizations perform a SWOT analysis to help identify potential projects based on their strengths, weaknesses, opportunities, and threats.

The four-stage planning process helps organizations align their projects with their business strategy. The four stages of this model, from highest to lowest, are strategic planning, business area analysis, project planning, and resource allocation.

Several methods are available for selecting projects. Financial methods include calculating and analyzing the net present value, return on investment, and payback period for projects. You can also use a weighted scoring model; implement a balanced scorecard; address problems, opportunities, and directives; and consider project time frame and project priority to assist in project selection.

After determining what projects to pursue, it is important to decide if projects should be grouped into programs. The main criteria for program selection are the coordination and benefits available by grouping projects together into a program.

There is no simple process for deciding how to create project portfolios, but the goal of project portfolio management is to help maximize business value to ensure enterprise success. There are five levels of complexity for project portfolio management, ranging from simply putting all projects in one list to applying portfolio theory to analyze risks and returns of a project portfolio.

QUICK QUIZ

1. The three spheres of systems management are business, technology, and _____.

    A. process

    B. organization

    C. opportunities

    D. people

2. Which of the following is not part of a SWOT analysis?

    A. strengths

    B. weaknesses

    C. opportunities

    D. tactics

3. The last step in the four-stage planning process for projects is _____.

    A. resource allocation

    B. project planning

    C. business area analysis

    D. strategic planning

4. It is very important to start at the top of the four-stage planning process pyramid to select projects that support the organization's _____.

    A. vision

    B. business strategy

    C. financial position

    D. culture

5. Which of the following statements is false concerning the financial analysis of projects?

    A. The higher the net present value the better.

    B. A shorter payback period is better than a longer one.

    C. The required rate of return is the discount rate that results in an NPV of zero for the project.

    D. ROI is the result of subtracting the project costs from the benefits and then dividing by the costs.

6.   A _____ is a methodology that converts an organization's value drivers—such as customer service, innovation, operational efficiency, and financial performance—into a series of defined metrics.

   A. balanced scorecard

   B. weighted scoring model

   C. net present value analysis

   D. directive

7.   Which of the following is not a major benefit of grouping projects into programs?

   A. increasing revenues

   B. increasing authority

   C. saving money

   D. saving time

8.   The Hospital Readmission Reduction Program is an example of a(n) _____ from the Patient Protection and Affordable Care Act.

   A. venture

   B. opportunity

   C. problem

   D. directive

9.   The goal of project portfolio management is to help maximize business value to ensure _____.

   A. profit maximization

   B. enterprise success

   C. risk minimization

   D. competitive advantage

10.   Many organizations find duplicate or unneeded projects after they perform which step in project portfolio management?

   A. prioritizing the projects in their list

   B. dividing the projects into several categories based on type of investment

   C. putting all projects in one list

   D. applying modern portfolio theory, including risk-return tools that map project risk

Quick Quiz Answers

1. B; 2. D; 3. A; 4. B; 5. C; 6. A; 7. A; 8. D; 9. B; 10. C

DISCUSSION QUESTIONS

1.   What does it mean to take a systems view of a project? How can you use systems management to help understand how projects will affect a healthcare organization?

2.   Why is it important to align projects to an organization's mission and business strategy? What is SWOT analysis? How can you use a mind map to create a SWOT analysis and generate project ideas?

3.   What are the stages called in the four-stage planning process for project selection? How does following this process assist in selecting projects that will provide the most benefit to organizations?

4.   How do you decide which projects to pursue using net present value analysis? Explain how healthcare organizations use a balanced scorecard approach for project selection.

5.   What are three main benefits of grouping projects into programs?

6.   What are the five levels of project portfolio management?

EXERCISES

Note: These exercises can be done individually or in teams, in class, as homework, or in a virtual environment. Students can either write their results in a paper or prepare a short presentation to show their results.

1.   Perform a financial analysis for a project using the format provided in Figure 2-7. Assume the projected costs and benefits for this project are spread over four years as follows: Estimated costs are $100,000 in Year 1 and $25,000 each year in Years 2, 3, and 4. (*Hint*: Just change the years in the template file from 0, 1, 2, 3, and 4 to 1, 2, 3, and 4. The discount factors will automatically be recalculated.) Estimated benefits are $0 in Year 1 and $80,000 each year in Years 2, 3, and 4. Use an 8% discount rate. Use the business case financials template provided on the companion Web site to calculate and clearly display the NPV, ROI, and year in which payback occurs. In addition, explain whether you would recommend investing in this project based on your financial analysis.

2.   Create a weighted scoring model to determine which project to select. Assume the criteria are quality, strategic value, risk, and financials, with weights of 15%, 40%, 20%, and 25%, respectively. Enter values for Project 1 as 90, 70, 85, and 50; Project 2 as 75, 80, 90, and 70; and Project 3 as 80 for each criterion. Use the weighted scoring model template provided on the companion Web site to create the model, calculate the weighted score, and graph the results.

3. Search the Internet to find a real example of how a healthcare organization uses a structured process to aid in project, program, and/or project portfolio selection. See the End Note by Nemours for their strategic plan if you cannot find one on your own. Summarize your findings and cite your references.

4. Search the Internet for software that helps organizations perform strategic planning, project selection, or project portfolio management. Summarize at least three different tools and discuss whether or not you think these tools are good investments. Cite your references.

5. Watch two different videos about creating and using mind maps, as described in the Video Highlights feature in this chapter. You can find your own videos, or use the direct links available from *www.healthcarepm.com* under Student Resources, Links, for this chapter. Summarize key points of the videos.

6. Watch the video about the Brownsboro Hospital Project described in this chapter. You can find the link to it from www.healthcarepm.com. Find at least one article describing the project as well. Summarize key points of the video and article.

TEAM PROJECTS

1. Find someone who has been involved in the project selection process within a healthcare organization. Prepare several interview questions, and then ask him or her the questions in person, via the phone, or via the Internet. Be sure to ask if he or she uses any of the project selection tools discussed in this chapter (for example, ROI, weighted scoring models, balanced scorecards, or other methods). Discuss the results with your team, and then prepare a short paper or presentation summarizing your findings.

2. Search the Internet to find two good examples of how healthcare organizations group projects into programs and two examples of how they create project portfolios. Prepare a short paper or presentation summarizing your results, being sure to cite your references.

3. Develop criteria that your class could use to help select what projects to pursue for implementation by your class or another group. For example, criteria might include benefits to the organization, interest level of the sponsor, interest level of the class, and fit with class skills and timing. Determine a weight for each criterion, and then enter the criteria and weights into a weighted scoring model, similar to that shown in Figure 2-9. (You can use the template for a weighted scoring model provided on the companion Web site.) Then review the list of projects you prepared in Chapter 1, Team Project 3, and enter scores for at least five of those projects. Calculate the weighted score for each project. Prepare a short paper or presentation summarizing your results.

4. As a team, discuss other methods you could use to select class projects. Be sure to review the other methods described in this chapter (besides a weighted scoring model). Document your analysis of each approach as it applies to this situation in a short paper or presentation.

5.   Using your college, university, or an organization your team is familiar with, create a mind map of a SWOT analysis, including at least three branches under each category. Also add sub-branches with at least four potential project ideas. You can create the mind map by hand, or try using software like MindView (60-day free trial available at *www.matchware.com/intropm*. You can watch video tutorials to learn how to use the software, as described in the Video Highlights feature in this chapter.

KEY TERMS

balanced scorecard — A methodology that converts an organization's value drivers to a series of defined metrics.

cash flow — Benefits minus costs, or income minus expenses.

directives — The new requirements imposed by management, government, or some external influence.

discretionary costs — costs that organizations have discretion in deciding whether to fund them.

discount factor — A multiplier for each year based on the discount rate and year.

discount rate — The rate used in discounting future cash flows.

internal rate of return (IRR) — The discount rate that results in an NPV of zero for a project.

mind mapping — A technique that uses branches radiating out from a core idea to structure thoughts and ideas.

net present value (NPV) analysis — A method of calculating the expected net monetary gain or loss from a project by discounting all expected future cash inflows and outflows to the present point in time.

nondiscretionary costs — costs that organizations must fund to stay in business

opportunity cost of capital — The return available by investing the capital elsewhere.

payback period — The amount of time it will take to recoup, in the form of net cash inflows, the total dollars invested in a project.

required rate of return — The minimum acceptable rate of return on an investment.

return on investment (ROI) — (Benefits minus costs) divided by costs.

strategic planning — The process of determining long-term objectives by analyzing the strengths and weaknesses of an organization, studying opportunities and threats in the business environment, predicting future trends, and projecting the need for new products and services.

systems — Sets of interacting components working within an environment to fulfill some purpose.

systems analysis — A problem-solving approach that requires defining the scope of the system to be studied, and then dividing it into component parts for identifying and evaluating its problems, opportunities, constraints, and needs.

systems approach — A holistic and analytical approach to solving complex problems that includes using a systems philosophy, systems analysis, and systems management.

systems management — Addressing the business, technological, and organizational issues associated with creating, maintaining, and modifying a system.

systems philosophy — An overall model for thinking about things as systems.

systems thinking — A holistic view of an organization to effectively handle complex situations.

SWOT analysis — Analyzing **S**trengths, **W**eaknesses, **O**pportunities, and **T**hreats.

weighted scoring model — A technique that provides a systematic process for basing project selection on numerous criteria.

END NOTES

[1]Nemours, "Blueprint for the Future: Nemours Strategic Plan 2008-2012," Nemours, (2007).

[2]Mike Peterson, "Why Are We Doing This Project?" Projects@Work, (*www.projectsatwork.com*) (February 22, 2005).

[2]Dennis J. Cohen and Robert J. Graham, *The Project Manager's MBA.* San Francisco: Jossey-Bass (2001), p. 31.

[3]Marc L. Songini, "Tight Budgets Put More Pressure on IT," *Computer World* (December 2, 2002).

[5]The Balanced Scorecard Institute, "What Is a Balanced Scorecard?" (*www.balancedscorecard.org*) (accessed April 2012).

[6] Nemours, "Blueprint for the Future: Nemours Strategic Plan 2008-2012," Nemours, (2007).

[7] Paladium Group, Inc., "Hall of Fame Organizations," Paladium Group, Inc., (accessed January 22, 2013).

[8] Center for Medicare & Medicaid Services. Details for: Partnership for Patients to Improve Care and Lower Costs for Americans (Aril 12, 2011).

[9]The Compleat Sean Bean Web Site, "Lord of the Rings" (February 23, 2004).

[10]Project Management Institute, "thePulse," PM Network (June 2012).

[11]Scott Berinato, "Do the Math," *CIO Magazine* (October 1, 2001).

[12]Craig Symons, "The ROI of Project Portfolio Management Tools," Forrester Research (May 8, 2009).

[13]Robert G. Cooper, "Winning at New Products: Pathways to Profitable Intervention," PMI Research Conference Proceedings (July 2006).

Chapter 3
Initiating Projects

LEARNING OBJECTIVES

After reading this chapter, you will be able to:

- Describe the five project management process groups, map them to the project management knowledge areas, discuss other project management methodologies, and understand the importance of top management commitment and organizational standards in project management
- Discuss the initiating process used by Academic Health Systems, including pre-initiating tasks and breaking large projects down into phases
- Prepare a business case to justify the need for a project
- Identify project stakeholders and perform a stakeholder analysis
- Create a project charter to formally initiate a project
- Describe the importance of holding a good project kick-off meeting

---

OPENING CASE

Academic Health Systems (AHS), a teaching hospital under America's Best Healthcare, Inc., had a defined process for adding and prioritizing projects for their portfolio. In a nutshell, projects could be requested online by anyone at any level, and they were then forwarded to a committee that met bi-weekly to score project requests based on pre-defined criteria, including meeting strategic goals and improving patient outcomes and satisfaction.

However, project initiatives related to federal government regulations were now a high priority. In 2005 Congress passed the Deficit Reduction Act, aimed squarely at reducing America's debt. Because the U.S. government is the source of almost half of all healthcare spending, included in those cost cutting measures was a type of "pay for performance." This bill gave the Centers for Medicare and Medicaid Systems (CMS) the ability to define conditions that the healthcare provider caused through poor or erroneous medical care, commonly known as Hospital Acquired Conditions (HAC). If a patient acquired a condition after admission, CMS would not reimburse the hospital for any of the patient's hospital stay or treatment.

Like many hospitals, AHS responded to federal initiatives by focusing their attention on projects that would improve the quality of care while also reducing the cost of the care provided. Dr. Marilyn Shoemaker, RN, Ph.D., was the Chief Nursing Officer at AHS. She noticed that AHS spent $3.6 million last year treating patients with Ventilator Associated Pneumonia (VAP) due to CMS no longer paying for the treatment. Without treatment for the pneumonia, patients could die.

Dr. Shoemaker believed that this project would most likely be approved, but she needed more information to support her position. She would serve as the sponsor, but she wanted a physician from the quality group to oversee its implementation, as it would require developing current- and future-state workflows, implementing a system for collecting and reporting the data, and working with both nurses and physicians. The Chief Quality Officer, Dr. Danielle Sheerer, was a physician respected by all, and she would be the best person to serve as project champion.

After a short meeting, Dr. Sheerer agreed with Dr. Shoemaker that it this was a good time to look at VAP, and she agreed to start collecting information that would support this project when it went before the project selection committee. The project needed a name: "VAP Reduction" or perhaps VAPR ("vapor"), as they wanted it to disappear!

PROJECT MANAGEMENT PROCESS GROUPS

Recall from Chapter 1 that project management consists of ten project management knowledge areas: project integration, scope, time, cost, quality, human resource, communications, risk, procurement, and stakeholder management. Another important concept to understand is that projects involve five project management process groups: initiating, planning, executing, monitoring and controlling, and closing. Applying these process groups in a consistent, structured fashion increases the chance of project success. This chapter briefly describes each project management process group and then describes the initiating process in detail through a case study based on the VAPR project. Subsequent chapters describe the other process groups and apply them to the same project.

Project management process groups progress from initiating activities to planning activities, executing activities, monitoring and controlling activities, and closing activities. It is important to understand that a project does not move from one to other in a linear fashion, as in most projects you revisit each process group multiple times in a cycle. Within each process group you will find a set of processes, each defined to manipulate certain pieces of information using a set of defined tools, with the intent on creating one or more specific project management deliverables.

More succinctly, a **process** is a series of actions directed toward a particular result. All projects use the five process groups as outlined in the following list:

- **Initiating processes** include actions to define and authorize new projects and project phases as well as identifying those who will be impacted by the project. A project charter and a kick-off meeting are often used during initiation. This chapter will describe initiating processes in detail.

- **Planning processes** include devising and maintaining a workable scheme to ensure that the project meets its scope, time, and cost goals as well as organizational needs. There are often many different plans to address various project needs as they relate to each knowledge area. For example, as part of project scope management for the VAPR project, the project team will develop a scope statement to identify the work that needs to be done to meet the project objectives (such as reducing VAP incidence rates). As part of project time management, the project team will create a detailed schedule that lets everyone know when specific work will start and end. As part of procurement management, the project team will plan for work that will be done by external organizations to support the project. Each of the ten knowledge areas has processes within the planning process group, and chapters 4, 5, and 6 describe them in detail.

- **Executing processes** include coordinating people and other resources to carry out the project plans and produce the deliverables of the project or phase. A **deliverable** is a product or service produced or provided as part of a project. For example, a project to construct a new building would include deliverables such as blueprints, cost estimates, progress reports, the building structure, windows, plumbing, and flooring. The VAPR project would include deliverables such as identification of a VAP best-practices bundle, current and future workflows, development of new bedside procedures, training and training aids for clinicians, data collection systems, and compliance reporting systems. Chapter 7 describes executing processes in detail.

- **Monitoring and controlling processes** measure progress toward achieving project goals, monitor deviation from plans, and take corrective or preventative action to match progress with plans and customer expectations. For example, the main objective of the VAPR project is to reduce the VAP incidence rate at AHS. The project team must identify the way in which ventilated patients are currently receiving care, define how patients should be receiving care based on best practices, and then develop a plan to move from their current state to the desired future state. If they cannot identify best practices by the deadline in their schedule, then they would have to delay identifying how to move to the desired future state. This delay may result in a schedule change or the allocation of additional resources to identify the best practices. Chapter 8 describes monitoring and controlling processes in detail.

- **Closing processes** include formalizing completion and acceptance of the project or phase and bringing it to an orderly end. Administrative activities are often involved in this process group, such as archiving project files, closing out contracts, documenting lessons learned, and receiving formal acceptance of the deliverables. It is also important to plan for a smooth transition of the results of the project to the responsible operational group. For example, after the VAPR project is completed, there would be a formal hand-off to the training department of the VAP best practices and training curriculum for new clinicians. Chapter 9 describes closing processes in detail.

The process groups are not isolated events. For example, project managers must perform monitoring and controlling processes throughout the project's life span, beginning on day one of the project. With the VAPR project, the project manager (with support from the champion and sponsor) would make sure that the project scope did not grow from just VAP to include VAP and other Ventilator Associated Events (VAE), which although they may include similar algorithms for detection, follow different protocols for prevention.

The level of activity and length of each process group varies for every project, with the project manager deciding on the level of tailoring required. Normally, executing processes require the most resources and time, followed by planning processes. Initiating and closing processes are usually the shortest, and they also require the least amount of resources and time. However, every project is unique, so there can be exceptions.

Many people ask for guidelines on how much time to spend in each process group. In his book, *Alpha Project Managers: What the Top 2% Know That Everyone Else Does Not*, Andy Crowe collected data from 860 project managers in various companies and industries in the United States. He found that the best or "alpha" project managers spent more time on every process group than their counterparts *except for execution*, as follows:[1]

Process Group	Alpha PM	Average PM	Alpha Difference (%)
Initiating	2%	1%	100% more
Planning	21%	11%	91% more
Executing	69%	82%	16% less
Monitoring & Controlling	5%	4%	25% more
Closing	3%	2%	50% more
Total	100%	100%	

Figure 3-1. Time spent on each project management process group

This breakdown suggests that the most time should be spent on executing, followed by planning. However, it also suggests, as do several studies since, that most project managers jump in and spend too much time executing the project and not enough time preparing for and then monitoring and controlling the work itself. Because most of project costs are spent during executing, one could conclude that projects that are better planned and controlled will be less costly to complete.

The process groups apply to entire projects as well as to project phases. A **phase** is a distinct project cycle that produces deliverables; think of it as a mini-project, and most projects have distinct phases. For example, the VAPR project includes phases such as "Identify Current State Workflows," "Develop Data Collection System," and "Pilot New Process," each of which would be managed as a mini-project. To ensure that they continue to meet current organizational needs, projects should pass successfully through each phase before continuing. At the end of each phase project leadership will determine if the project should move to the next phase. This process is sometimes referred to as **phase-gating**, and it can be either formal or informal depending upon the scope and impact that the project will have on the organization.

Mapping the Process Groups to the Knowledge Areas

You can map the process groups into the ten project management knowledge areas. For example, the first process group, initiating, includes only two processes:

- Develop project charter (part of the project integration management knowledge area).

- Identify stakeholders (part of the project stakeholder management knowledge area).

The first knowledge area, project integration management, includes the following processes:

- Develop project charter (part of the initiating process group).

- Develop project management plan (part of the planning process group).

- Direct and manage project work (part of the executing process group).

- Monitor and control project work and perform integrated change control (part of the monitoring and controlling process group).

- Close project or phase (part of the closing process group).

Based on the *PMBOK® Guide, Fifth Edition*, the international standard for project management and basis for the PMP and other certifications, there are 47 total processes in project management. Figure 3-2 provides a big-picture view of the relationships among these processes, the process group in which they are typically completed, and the knowledge areas into which they fit. The numbering is based on the chapter and section numbers in the *PMBOK® Guide*. This list of processes by knowledge area is a framework that PMI suggests most projects, with a bit of tailoring, may require.

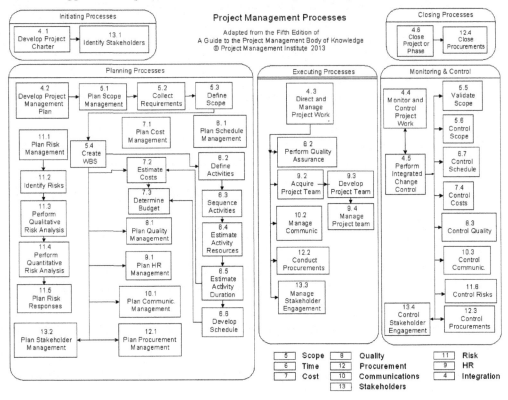

Figure 3-2. Project management processes (Source: PMO To Go LLC, 2013)

This chapter describes in detail the processes followed and the outputs produced while initiating the VAPR project. The *PMBOK® Guide, Fifth Edition*, suggests that the main outputs of initiating include a stakeholder register, stakeholder management strategy, and a project charter. In addition to these three outputs, this chapter also includes a kick-off meeting as an initiating output as well as some outputs produced during a pre-initiating process. The *PMBOK® Guide* is just that — a guide. This text includes some additional ideas from other sources and the authors' personal experiences as well.

You can access templates to help create many of the documents created in project management on the companion Web site for this text, as summarized in Appendix B. A **template** is a file with a preset format that serves as a starting point for creating various documents so that the format and structure do not have to be re-created. A template can also ensure that critical information is not left out or overlooked. The remaining chapters of this text follow a similar format to describe the processes and outputs used for the VAPR project for planning, executing, monitoring and controlling, and closing. To help you visualize outputs for each process group, Figure 3-3, shown later in the chapter, summarizes the outputs for the initiating process group. Similar figures or tables are provided in the following chapters as well.

Several organizations use PMI's information as a foundation for developing their own project management methodologies, as described in the next section. Notice in Figure 3-2 that the majority of project management processes occur as part of the planning process group. Because each project is unique, project teams are always trying to do something that has not been done before. To succeed at unique and new activities, project teams must adequately plan, doing the best they can to effectively and efficiently utilize resources during project execution.

It is good practice for organizations to determine how project management will work best in *their own* organizations. They must not only develop their own methodology based on their culture and environment, but they must also encourage project managers to tailor the methodology to meet their specific projects.

Project Management Methodology Options

Some organizations spend a great deal of time and money on training efforts for general project management skills, but after the training, a project manager might still not know how to tailor their project management skills to the organization's particular needs. As this is a common situation, most organizations develop their own internal project management methodologies or adopt one that will work for them. As previously noted, the *PMBOK® Guide* is a **standard** that describes best practices for *what* should be done to manage a project. A **methodology** describes *how* things should be done.

It is important to understand that the *PMBOK® Guide* does not include the entire project management body of knowledge, as they concede in section 1.1. PMI acknowledges that there are many valid methodologies to manage projects, and their guide includes what they consider to be a good framework that can be incorporated into most project methodologies. So, although many organizations do use the *PMBOK® Guide* as a basis for a project management methodology, many organizations use others, such as the following:

- *Six Sigma*: Many healthcare organizations have projects underway that use Six Sigma methodologies. The work of many project quality experts contributed to the development of today's Six Sigma principles. In their book, *The Six Sigma Way*, authors Peter Pande, Robert Neuman, and Roland Cavanagh define Six Sigma as "a comprehensive and flexible system for achieving, sustaining and maximizing business success. Six Sigma is uniquely driven by close understanding of customer needs, disciplined use of facts, data, and statistical analysis, and diligent attention to managing, improving, and reinventing business processes."[2] Six Sigma's target for perfection is the achievement of no more than 3.4 defects, errors, or mistakes per million opportunities. Six Sigma carries its own set of certifications, aligning themselves with martial arts terms such as Green Belt, Black Belt, and Master Black Belt. Within healthcare, Six Sigma is commonly used by the quality or performance improvement teams for relatively short projects (90 days or less) designed to improve a very specific process. Often larger projects managed by more traditional methods, such as the implementation of a new Electronic Medical Record (EMR) system, may include sub-projects that are managed by the Six Sigma teams. In the case of installing the EMR, there may be many sub-projects spawned for redesigning workflows within a nursing unit, pharmacy, or procedural area that are perfect for the Six Sigma teams to manage. There are two main methodologies used on Six Sigma projects:

- o DMAIC (Define, Measure, Analyze, Improve, and Control) is used to improve an existing business process, and

- o DMADV (Define, Measure, Analyze, Design, and Verify) is used to create new product or process designs to achieve predictable, defect-free performance.

- *Agile*: Many software development projects use agile methods, meaning they use an iterative workflow and incremental delivery of software in short iterations. Popular agile approaches include extreme programming, Scrum, feature driven development, and lean software development. Although agile projects typically run in short sprints (such as two weeks in duration), each that produces a given deliverable, that does not preclude a project manager from incorporating sound practices from the *PMBOK® Guide*. For example, you would still be required to gather requirements at the start and verify scope when the work is done, but the period between these two processes may only be two weeks long. (See an article called "Managing a Project Using an Agile Approach and the PMBOK® Guide" on the companion Web site.) Agile is growing in popularity in the healthcare industry because it requires ongoing stakeholder/user engagement. This smaller commitment of several two- to four- week "projects" that may be separated by weeks or months, rather than a two-year project, is more flexible for clinicians and allows them to commit time when it is most needed. In 2011, PMI introduced a new certification called Agile Certified Practitioner (ACP) to address the growing interest in agile project management.

- *Rational Unified Process (RUP) framework*: RUP is an iterative software development process that focuses on team productivity and delivers software best practices to all team members. According to RUP expert Bill Cottrell, "RUP embodies industry-standard management and technical methods and techniques to provide a software engineering process particularly suited to creating and maintaining component-based software system solutions."[3] Cottrell explains how you can tailor RUP to include the *PMBOK* process groups, because several customers asked for that capability. There are several other project management methodologies specifically for software development projects such as Joint Application Development (JAD) and Rapid Application Development (RAD).

- ***PRojects IN Controlled Environments (PRINCE2)***: Originally developed for information technology projects, PRINCE2 was released in 1996 as a generic project management methodology by the U.K. Office of Government Commerce (OCG). It is the defacto standard in the U.K. and is used in over 50 countries. It is not commonly used within the US, where the PMBOK is considered the premiere standard, but in fact the two standards are not in conflict, as you can see from their definition of the PRINCE2 process groups. PRINCE2 defines 45 separate sub-processes and organizes these into eight process groups as follows:

  1. Starting Up a Project
  2. Planning
  3. Initiating a Project
  4. Directing a Project
  5. Controlling a Stage
  6. Managing Product Delivery
  7. Managing Stage Boundaries
  8. Closing a Project

Developing Your Project Management Methodology

Many organizations tailor one of the above, or sometimes a combination of the above, standards or methodologies to meet their unique needs. The may use Agile as their basis for small technology projects and the PMBOK as their basis for longer projects. Or, they may use Agile for all projects or the PMBOK for all projects. There are no hard and fast rules, but regardless of which standard they begin with, they will still have to do a fair amount of work to adapt it to their culture and work environment.

For example, the *PMBOK® Guide, Fifth Edition* lists *what* information a project charter, as described later in this chapter, should address:

- Project purpose or justification
- Measureable project objectives and related success criteria
- High-level requirements
- High-level project description
- High-level risks
- Summary milestone schedule
- Summary budget
- Stakeholder list

- Project approval requirements

- Assigned project manager, responsibility, and authority level

- Name and authority of the sponsor or other person(s) authorizing the project charter

However, the *PMBOK® Guide* does not provide information on *how* the previously listed project charter requirements should be created, when, or by whom.

Successful organizations have found that they need to develop and follow a customized, formal project management methodology that describes not only what needs to be done, but also how it should be done in their organizations. Without a defined methodology they must depend on individual project manager skills for project success. With a defined methodology they can define best practices as a group and let everyone benefit from a broader set of knowledge and experience, much like caregivers do when defining and following best practices in patient care.

To facilitate this process, often organizations create or adopt templates and include them within their methodology. Companies that excel in project management know that it does not make sense to reinvent the wheel by having every project manager decide how to create standard documents, such as project charters and business cases, so templates are often used to ensure that basic, required information is included. They also know that top management commitment and organizational standards are crucial for project success.

What Went Right?

William Ibbs and Justin Reginato completed a five-year study to help quantify the value of project management. Among their findings are the following points:

- Organizations with more mature project management practices have better project performance, which result in projects being completed on time and within budget much more often than most projects.
- Project management maturity is strongly correlated with more predictable project schedule and cost performance.
- Organizations that follow good project management methodologies have lower direct costs of project management (6 - 7 percent) than those that do not (11 - 20 percent).[4]

Several experts have warned against cutting back on project and portfolio management during tough economic times. "Portfolio management can help focus on the projects that are most profitable, while project management can help you execute those projects more efficiently. For example, According to David Muntz, CIO at Baylor Health Care System, "Making informed decisions about which projects to work on is critical at a time when Baylor Health is being especially fiscally prudent."[5]

The Importance of Top Management Commitment

Without top management commitment, many projects will fail. Some projects have a senior manager called a **champion** who acts as a key proponent for a project. Having a project champion is critical within healthcare as there are many chains of command, and typically the project manager has no control over any of them. Further, since projects are part of the larger organizational environment, which includes business administration, physicians, nursing, and perhaps research, there will be many factors that might affect a project that are out of the project manager's control. An experienced project manager will seek out a champion at the highest levels within their organization, and they should attempt to get a champion who has influence over the most critical faction within the project.

As an example, within the VAPR project there are primarily two groups who will be impacted by this project: nurses and physicians. Nurses will have to change the way they care for patients by following the best practices identified, and they will have to deal with any patient backlash (because they spend the most time with the patient). However, physicians will be required to enter orders into a Computerized Physician Order Entry (CPOE) system for things that are listed within the best practices, and that will take them more time to complete, meaning more time spent with each patient. This is good from the patient viewpoint, but it is not good from the physician perspective where they still need to see all of their patients before they can go home.

Because physicians are not the ones who are dealing with patients most of the time, they are less concerned with whether or not the nurses have more duties in order to follow best practices, but they are very concerned about having to write more orders. Physicians are paid for treating a disease, not by the order or by the hour, so adding extra orders will result in less patients being seen per day or more hours spent at the hospital.

What Went Wrong?

A 2012 survey of Chief Information Officers (CIOs of healthcare organizations found that independent physicians are the stakeholders most resistant to projects that bring about change. More than half (52 percent) of survey respondents identified non-employed physicians as the group most resistant to change, followed by staff physicians (22 percent) and nurses (17 percent). Almost half of CIOs said the hardest part of change management is changing individual behaviors, but they also emphasized the role of leadership in creating a culture conducive to change. Computerized Physician Order Entry (CPOE) and electronic physician documentation projects pose the biggest challenges in terms of change management. Projects related to the emergency department are most receptive to change.

The majority (74 percent) of CIOs believed that health systems are being pushed to the brink by having too much change forced on them all at once. Some respondents were concerned that patients would be lost in the shuffle, while others expressed concern about the ability to align incentives to qualify for Meaningful Use and participate in Accountable Care Organizations. Many stressed the importance of having strong leadership to effectively manage change.[6]

However, if a patient develops VAP physicians will not get paid for their services during the recovery period, while nurses will continue to be paid their hourly rate. You can see how complex it can become, even for a simple project, to choose the correct champion for a healthcare project. For VAPR the physicians probably have the most to gain from project success, and at the same time will be the most likely to resist change as following best practices is often considered taking the "art" out of medicine (it removes some of their decision making ability).

So who would *you* consider the best champion for the VAPR project? It depends a great deal on your organizational structure, but for most healthcare organizations the Chief Medical Officer (CMO) would be a great choice as he or she can help gain physician buy-in. Another good choice would be the Chief Nursing Officer (CNO), who can lead the nurses to comply, although they have limited influence on physicians. If you had to choose one, the CMO is often the better choice for projects that impact both nurses and physicians, as nurses tend to follow defined processes more readily than physicians, so gaining physician buy-in is more critical to your success. Can you have co-champions? Absolutely, and often this is the case for inpatient projects that impact all clinicians or for projects that impact clinicians and administration, technology, or other non-clinical areas.

Regardless of who is chosen as champion, it is important that you secure top management commitment to the project. Top management commitment is crucial for the following reasons:

- Project managers need adequate resources. The best way to hurt a project is to withhold the required money, human resources, and/or visibility required. If project managers have top management commitment, they will also have adequate resources and be able to focus on completing their specific projects.

- Project managers often require approval for unique project needs in a timely manner. For example, a project team might encounter unexpected issues and need additional resources halfway through the project, or the project manager might need to offer special pay and benefits to attract and retain key project personnel. With top management commitment, project managers can meet these specific needs in a timely manner.

- Project managers must have cooperation from people in other parts of the organization. Most projects cut across functional areas and often involve political issues requiring top management to aid in their resolution. Although any industry has functional silos such as accounting, information technology, sales, marketing, production, and so forth, healthcare has those silos plus more. When dealing with healthcare organizations, there are always several chains of command, and although they work together they exhibit a great deal of independence from one another. These chains include administration (which has the typical silos listed above), physicians, nursing, ancillaries (labs, radiology, etc.), and often research. In healthcare if a functional managers is not responding to a project manager's requests for necessary information, top management must step in to encourage the functional managers to cooperate. That can be difficult if top leadership does not work in a collegial manner.

- Project managers often need someone to mentor them to improve their leadership skills. Many project managers come from technical positions and are inexperienced as leaders. Senior managers should take the time to pass on advice on how to be good leaders. They should encourage new project managers to take classes to develop leadership skills and allocate the time and funds for them to do so. In many situations top leadership can assign a subject matter expert (SME) to your project, who may serve as a mentor while you learn the terms, workflows, and other things unique to a healthcare project. Although physicians are hard to get assigned to projects due to their time constraints, nurses (or even nursing students) are great to include on many clinical projects.

The Need for Organizational Standards

Another deficiency in most organizations is the lack of standards or guidelines to follow that could help in performing project management functions. These standards or guidelines might be as simple as providing forms or templates for common project documents, examples of good project documentation, or guidelines on how the project manager should perform certain activities, such as holding a kick-off meeting or providing status information. Providing status information might seem like common sense to seasoned project managers, but many new project managers have never given a project status report and are not used to communicating with a wide variety of project stakeholders. Top management must support the development of these standards and guidelines and encourage or even enforce their use.

Some organizations invest heavily in project management by creating a project management office or center of excellence. A **project management office (PMO)** is an organizational entity created to assist project managers in achieving project goals. Some organizations develop career paths for project managers. Some require that all project managers have some type of project management certification and that all employees have some type of project management training. The implementation of all of these standards demonstrates an organization's commitment to project.

A 2010 study found that 84% of U.S. companies have PMOs, growing significantly from prior surveys, as shown in Figure 3-3. For large organizations, 91% have PMOs, while only 48% of small organizations do. This makes sense as large organizations are typically more complex, resulting in more complex projects and therefore require more formalized project management functions. They also have more funding available to support a PMO role, and the PMO can support a wide variety of projects across the organization which further enhances its value. When smaller organizations create a PMO, it is often a part-time role of one of the most experienced project managers. Although this can work for some companies, the PMO must take care to be unbiased, which may mean that they step back and let other project managers serve in oversight functions on projects that the PMO himself is managing. There are different ways to structure a PMO, and they can have various roles and responsibilities. PM Solutions identified three key factors that are playing major roles in the growth of PMOs:

1. The growing strategic value of the PMO
2. The increased role of the PMO in training
3. The ever-present challenge of resource management[7]

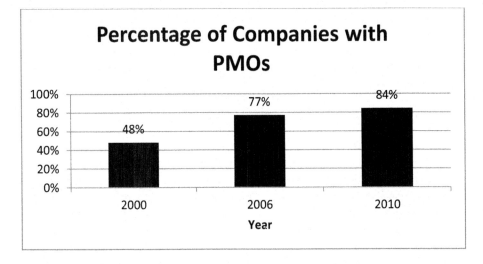

FIGURE 3-3 Growth in the number of project management offices (Source: PM Solutions, "The State of the PMO 2010" (2010))

Below are possible goals of a PMO:

- Collect, organize, and integrate project data for the entire organization

- Research, develop, and share best practices in project management

- Develop and maintain templates, tools, standards, and methodologies

- Develop or coordinate training in various project management topics

- Develop and provide a formal career path for project managers

- Provide project management consulting services

- Provide a structure to house project managers while they are acting in those roles or are between projects

- Manage all projects within the organization, or some subset of projects (such as those over a certain cost level)

Many people learn best by example. The following section describes an example of how AHS applied initiating processes to the VAPR project. It uses some of the ideas from the *PMBOK® Guide* and additional ideas to meet the unique needs of this project and organization. Several templates illustrate how project teams prepare various project management documents. You can download these templates from the companion Web site for this text.

Best Practice

It is important to follow best practices while initiating projects, especially to avoid rapid scope expansion. Senior management must take an active role in following these best practices:

- Keep the scope realistic. Don't make projects so large that they can't be completed. Break large projects down into a series of smaller ones, with reviews at the end of each smaller project or phase to determine if it still makes sense to continue (phase-gating).
- Involve users from the start. Assign key users to the project team, invite them to important meetings, and require their signatures on key documents.
- Identify a skilled project manager, perhaps from within the PMO if you have one, or from a technical area if one is involved in the project. In healthcare it is not advised that you choose a leader from the operations side to serve as the project manager, unless they have experience as a project manager. For the most part our users are experts in caring for patients, billing patients, managing compliance issues, etc. – these are all very complex issues that take years of specialized education to master. Many may have the aptitude to be good project managers, but this is not where they have focused their education and career.
- Assign a champion to help promote the project. Sometimes the champions are the same people as the sponsors, but often they are floor clinicians who have the respect of other clinicians and can help you gain support from across the many healthcare disciplines.
- Identify someone on the user side who can serve as your customer owner and who will work side-by-side with your project manager.
- Use off-the-shelf hardware and software whenever possible. Many people enjoy using the latest and greatest technology, but business needs, not technology trends, must take priority.
- Follow good project management processes. As described in this chapter and others, there are several standards and methodologies for managing projects. Senior managers should define them and enforce their use as appropriate on their projects.

PRE-INITIATING PROCESS

Figure 3-4 illustrates the process for getting a project started. Notice that several processes are completed *before* the project actually starts, called pre-initiating. First, the project is approved through a formal project selection process and is then given the go-ahead. Second, senior managers perform several activities as part of pre-initiating. Finally, initiating begins, as described in the following section.

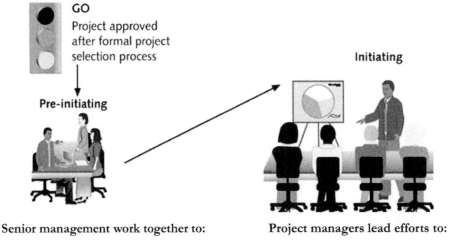

Senior management work together to:

- Determine scope, time, and cost constraints

- Identify the project sponsor

- Select the project manager

- Review processes/expectations

- Determine if the project should be divided into phases or smaller projects

- Develop a business case for the project

Project managers lead efforts to:

- Identify and understand project stakeholders

- Create the project charter

- Hold a kick-off meeting

Figure 3-4. Initiating process summary

PRE-INITIATING PROCESSES AND OUTPUTS

It is good practice to lay the groundwork for a project before it officially starts. After a project is approved, senior managers should meet to:

- Determine the scope, time, and cost constraints for the project. It is very important to develop a clear understanding of the high-level definition of the project. This information is often included in the business case and project charter.

- Identify the project sponsor. As described earlier, project sponsors are crucial to project success. The project sponsor is usually involved in proposing the project as part of the selection process.

- Select the project manager. Often a project manager is not identified until the charter is issued, but there is a growing practice where a project manager is suggested shortly after the project is conceptualized. Assigning project managers before creating the business case and project charter is extremely helpful. Their knowledge, skills, and experience will influence the way the project is organized, managed, and executed.

- Meet with the project manager to review processes and expectations. For example, will there be formal management reviews for the project, and if so, how often will they be held? Will the PMO have oversight on this project, or will the project manager have full control? Are there any regulations, standards, or guidelines related to the project? There are very few clinical projects that are not influenced directly by the Centers for Medicare and Medicaid Systems (CMS) and The Joint Commission (JC), and a great deal are influenced by studies, best practices, or evidenced-based care published by the Institutes of Medicine (IOM), Institutes for Healthcare Improvement (IHI), Centers for Disease Control (CDC), or a host of other public and private healthcare oversight organizations. Is there historical information, or lessons learned, from past projects that might apply to the project?

- Determine if the project should be divided into phases or smaller projects. Some projects are very broad in scope, and it often makes sense to break them down into distinct phases or even into separate projects. Many healthcare projects are broken down into a technical phase and a clinical phase, as you'll see in the VAPR project.

- Develop a business case for the project, if required. Some projects require a detailed business case before they can be officially launched and funded. For many healthcare projects, it is also important to determine which components of a project should be communicated to stakeholders early in order to gain their buy-in, especially those that concern:

    o Compliance with federal, state, or local regulations

    o Compliance with CMS, the Joint Commission, or other regulations and standards

    o Patient safety

    o Financial impact

    o Business continuity

The first four processes above seem obvious, but the last two (determining if a project should be divided into phases or smaller projects and developing a business case) are often more challenging. Examples of each are provided in the following sections.

Breaking a Project into Phases

Many people know from experience that it is easier to successfully complete a small project than a large one. It often makes sense to break large projects down into two or more smaller projects or into distinct phases. For AHS's VAPR project, senior management decided to break the project down into a technical and a clinical phase, as each involved different resources and needed different approaches to be successful. They knew that when it was unclear if they had the technical information needed for caregivers to change their workflows, it made sense to break the project down into first proving the technical component, and if that was successful, engaging caregivers in a workflow modification project.

Casey Lidwell, the Chief Analytics Officer at AHS, would champion the technical phase, now named the *VAPRware* project, or "VAP Reduction Phase I, Proof of Concept & Data Sourcing Project" by those who insist on using its formal name. Note that many projects take on a name that plays off the initials or abbreviation of the work being done. This gives the team an identity, is more fun to use when making posters or Web sites representing the project, and is easier to say when discussing the project. In this case VAPRware is also a play on the notion that vapor-ware is software that vendors sell that does not yet exist, and because this data may or may not yet exist in the format required, the technical staff decided it was an ideal name.

Dr. Scheerer, the Chief Quality Officer, would serve as the champion of the clinical phase, now referred to as VAPRflow because it will impact the workflow for patients on a ventilator. Like VAPRware, VAPRflow also has its proper name, "VAP Reduction Phase II Clinical Workflow Improvements." Dr. Scheerer has the respect of her peers and reports directly to the hospital's CMO. Having worked with the PMO on several successful technology projects, she has suggested that the PMO provide project managers for both project phases, and Casey agreed.

In order to implement the VAPR project quickly, Dr. Scheerer also asked if the two phases could overlap a bit. The PMO reviewed the required major deliverables and agreed that there could be a good deal of phase overlap. However, having overlapping phases requires that the two project managers, who are each managing their own phase, work together closely throughout the life of the project. Communication is key to every project's success, but even more so when working on phased projects.

Figure 3-5 shows how even the first phase of the project is meeting two major objectives: validating that AHS has the data and the technology to accomplish their VAPR objectives in the proof of concept (POC), and collecting the data required to identify adherence to best practices. However, once the POC is completed, Phase II can begin because most of the effort will require workflow analysis, marketing, and gaining buy-in from clinicians. Of course Phase II can only get so far until the data collection part of Phase I is completed, because you cannot test, train, or go live without the adherence to best practices data.

Figures 3-6 and 3-7 provide more details on these two phases, summarizing the scope, cost, and schedule as well as key assumptions. These high level project definitions will ultimately become part of the business case and then the project charter itself.

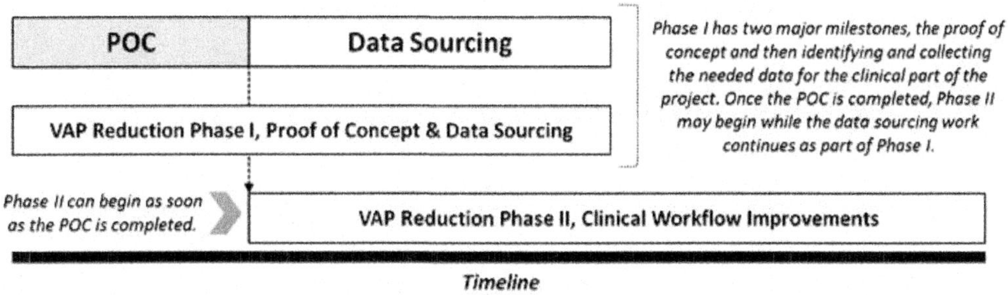

| POC | Data Sourcing | Phase I has two major milestones, the proof of concept and then identifying and collecting the needed data for the clinical part of the project. Once the POC is completed, Phase II may begin while the data sourcing work continues as part of Phase I. |

VAP Reduction Phase I, Proof of Concept & Data Sourcing

Phase II can begin as soon as the POC is completed.

VAP Reduction Phase II, Clinical Workflow Improvements

Timeline

Figure 3-5. Two phases of the VAPR project

Phase I – VAPRware – Proof of Concept & Data Sourcing

Scope
- Identify required information for the VAP best practices
- Determine if the required data exists in current electronic systems
- For data available, determine if the data is in the data warehouse
- For data not-available, determine the work required to collect the data
- Develop data structure for optimal reporting of the best practices
- Implement process to import data into the structure
- Implement and prove process to ensure data is no more than six hours old
- Implement online reporting solution
- Create reporting options for best practices based on requirements prepared in Phase II

Cost
- $700,000, with estimates as follows: $500,000 capital, $150,000 internal labor, $50,000 contract labor

Schedule
- Eight months, with estimated milestones as follows
    - Two months to identify data and determine availability
    - Four months to create data structure, develop import scripts as needed, and develop process to store data
    - Two months to implement reporting solution

Assumptions
- Our current data warehouse server will require additional CPUs and memory
- Additional licenses will be required for our enterprise reporting tool for online access
- Contract labor will only be needed for complex dashboards
- All data required for best practices is either available or can be collected through the nursing documentation system (ClinDoc)
- The ClinDoc oversight committee will fast-track any required changes to ClinDoc

---

Figure 3-6. Phase I scope, cost, and schedule

Phase II – VAPRflow – Clinical Workflow Improvements

Scope
- Identify current workflows for patients on ventilators
- Review best practices
- Identify required changes to workflow to align with best practices
- Develop new workflows, taking into account patient acuity and staffing
- Develop training program, to include online, face-to-face, and quick reference materials
- Identify, train, and test new workflow and system with a pilot nursing unit
- Develop rollout plan for all nursing units
- Train and implement across the hospital

Cost
- $175,000, with estimates as follows: $100,000 internal labor, and $75,000 temporary nursing staff labor

Schedule
- Three to four months, with estimated milestones as follows
  - One month to develop new workflows
  - One month to develop training program
  - Two to four weeks for pilot program
  - Two to four weeks for roll out across the organization

Assumptions
- The data warehouse team will still be available for last minute changes during the pilot and roll out
- Chief Medical Officer and Chief Nursing Officer will enforce the "not documented, not done" rule so that we can use the data as "the gospel"
- The ClinDoc oversight committee will fast-track any required changes to ClinDoc
- The Chief Quality Officer will support the best practices bundle and encourage its usage

---

Figure 3-7. Phase II scope, cost, and schedule

Note that the assumptions in Figure 3-7 refer to the, "*Not documented, not done,*" rule. This is a common healthcare policy that states that a nurse or doctor may not say that they delivered care to the patient but just failed to document it (regardless of whether the documentation method is paper or electronic). The policy infers that only those things documented were actually performed, whether they are talking about medications administered, nursing care delivered, or procedures performed. Aside from being required for billing, the documentation is what the other caregivers depend upon when treating the patient, so it is imperative that it is accurate. In the case of a lawsuit, the documentation is the only evidence that the appropriate care was given by an organization.

Another statement, not common in some industries but important in healthcare, can be found in the assumptions in Figure 3-7. The last assumption states that the Chief Quality Officer will support the use of the best practices for ventilated patients. This is important because often physicians and nurses will push back on best practices or evidenced-based-medicine if it does not align with their philosophy or approach to treatment. It is imperative that the clinical leadership supports this project. Because most physicians are not employed by hospitals, but instead work with hospitals in a collaborative partnership, projects that improve care often have to find ways to gain the support by finding physicians who support the project goals. These informal champions can then help gain support from other doctors, and thus the pool of informal champions can grow until the new processes are adopted by all.

The project leadership reviewed their work so far in defining the VAPR project and its two distinct phases. They were satisfied with the stated objectives of the Phase I project, but after reviewing the objectives of both phases they decided they wanted someone from the clinical staff running Phase II with a seasoned project manager from the PMO serving as a coach. It would be critical that the project manager for Phase II understand clinical workflows and clinical language, and the end users (doctors and nurses) would be more accepting of suggestions coming from other caregivers.

Dr. Danielle Scheerer, the project champion, suggested that Pat Wager, RN, be named as the Phase II project manager. Wager served as a floor nurse for fifteen years, spent ten years as an Intensive Care Unit (ICU) nurse, and was currently working in the clinical analytics department, responsible for the collection and reporting of CMS measures. Wager understood all facets of the VAPR project and had a good relationship with the PMO from past projects. Because she had never managed a project, she was a bit nervous, but agreed to take on the challenge as long as the PMO could assist with the project management details.

The PMO assigned Jeff Birdwell, PMP, to work with Pat, knowing his mentoring style would be perfect in this situation. For Phase I, the PMO talked with Casey and agreed that Jeff would be a good choice as he had worked with the analytics group previously. As shown in Figure 3-8, the project's organizational chart was starting to take shape as the primary leadership roles had been identified.

Dr. Scheerer knew it was a good practice to have experienced leaders from the clinical area lead projects that impacted the caregivers or their patients. She also knew that they needed support from leadership in the physician, nursing, and analytics groups, as well as other areas, such as IT. So she recommended that key managers from several divisions serve on a project steering committee to oversee the project. As its name implies, a project steering committee *steers* a project in the right direction by overseeing it and providing guidance to the project manager. The people on the steering committee are important stakeholders on the project.

Figure 3-8. VAPR project organizational chart

Developing a Business Case

A key document often produced during the pre-initiation phase of project is a business case. As the name implies, a **business case** is a document that provides financial justification for investing in a project. Some organizations list different project management requirements based on the value of a project. For example, a project estimated to cost less than $50,000 might not require a business case. A project estimated to cost more than $1 million might need an extensive business case signed off by the CFO, CMO, or perhaps by the entire executive leadership staff.

Successful business organizations, including many healthcare organizations, initiate projects to meet business needs, such as improving efficiency, increasing revenue, or reducing costs. However, healthcare has a very different set of needs – patient care – where common measures such as return on investment (ROI), payback period, and net present value (NPV) have much less relevance. The VAPR project is also somewhat unusual for healthcare in that it serves both needs – business and clinical – as it improves patient care and patient outcomes, but also reduces unnecessary costs and inefficiencies.

Like most project documents, the contents of a business case will vary to meet both the organizational and individual project needs. However, typical information in a business case includes the following:

- Executive Summary
    - o Typically a single page (or less) overview that only includes the highlights of the following sections. For many leaders, this is the only part of the business case that they will read.

- Introduction/Background
  - Usually brief, but it helps to give the reader a frame of reference for the project objectives.

- Clinical and/or Business Objective
  - What is the desired measurable outcome of this project?

- Current Situation and Problem/Opportunity Statement
  - Projects are initiated to solve problems or take advantage of opportunities. Describe the situation in enough detail that it is clear to the reader why the project objectives are desirable.

- Critical Assumptions and Constraints
  - Assumptions are those things that you *believe* are true today. They are not things that you wish were true or hope are true. They must be based on sound reasoning or judgment.
  - Constraints are those things that *constrain* the project. Most projects are constrained by time, money, and people, but you can also have other constraints such as facilities, equipment, regulations, strict quality requirements, etc.

- Analysis of Options and Recommendations
  - You should include a brief overview of the alternatives that were considered that could have also addressed the need, along with your final recommendation and justification for that recommendation.

- Preliminary Project Requirements
  - High level requirements as defined by the sponsor and other leaders. This will be refined during project planning.

- Budget Estimate and Financial Analysis
  - High level funding requirements that may include a year by year overview and a total cost of ownership (TCO).
  - If a financial analysis was performed (not common on purely clinical projects), the method used should be described briefly along with a summation of the results.

- Schedule Estimate
  - High level schedule, often defined by quarters or even years, with major milestones sometimes included.

- Potential Risks

  o High level project risks can be defined now since risks should be evident from the time the project is first considered for approval. More specific risks will be defined throughout the project's life.

- Exhibits

  o Any supporting documents are best appended so that the business case itself can be as brief as possible, with the supporting detail available if needed.

Because this project is relatively small and is for an internal sponsor, the business case is not as long as many other business cases. The following section shows the initial business case for the VAPR project.

Sample Business Case

Jeff, and Pat worked together to develop the business case for the VAPR project, including both phases. Although projects with large phases may have a business case for each phase, this project did not require that level of work. Once completed, the project management team, composed of the project managers and the champions for both phases, reviewed it with the sponsor, Dr. Marilyn Shoemaker (the CNO). She suggested that they add projected cost savings into the proposal, even though this was primarily a patient care project, as budgets were getting very tight since the PPACA took effect. Saving money, on top of improving patient care, would ensure this project got the attention it deserved.

Updated after their review, the resulting business case, including a financial impact analysis, is provided in Figure 3-9 (executive summary) and Figure 3-10 (full business case).

Business Case Executive Summary

- **Background**
  - Ventilator Associated Pneumonia (VAP) has been identified by the IHI as a preventable condition
    - The IHI has developed a bundle of five care elements, that when followed in their entirety, has been proven in independent studies to reduce the incidence of VAP by at least 50%
  - CMS has adopted the CDC's method for identifying patients with VAP and will no longer pay for the treatment of VAP, considering it a Hospital Acquired Condition (HAC)
    - Takes effect in 19 months
    - All major third party payers are expected to follow suite immediately thereafter
  - AHS identified 212 cases of VAP last calendar year
  - VAP rates have increased 8% over the past 5 years at AHS
  - VAP, or complications as a result of VAP, can result in death
    - for 17% of VAP patients over 65
    - for 8% of VAP patients under the age of 2
  - VAP is expensive to treat
    - The cost to treat VAP averages $17,000 per patient
    - The reimbursed charges to treat VAP averages $23,000 per patient
    - At 212 cases last year, we were paid $4.9M by payers, incurred $3.6M in costs, resulting in $1.3M in profit
  - If AHS has 212 cases again next year
    - 11 patients may die under our care (based on our patient demographic and the stated averages)
    - we will not receive $4.9M in revenue
    - it will cost us $3.6M in costs
    - it will result in AHS losing a total of $8.5M (cost to treat plus lost reimbursement)
    - we may be exposed to litigation if we can't prove we are following the IHI ventilator best practices bundle
- **Solution**
  - Implement a reporting system that will alert caregivers on the floor when the IHI best practices are not being followed
  - Institute work flow changes that will hardwire the best practices into clinical care
  - Hold clinicians accountable for adhering to the best practices
  - Hold clinicians accountable for documenting adherence to the best practices
- **Cost**
  - $875,000 to $980,000 year 1
  - $0 subsequent years (support absorbed by current labor)
- **Payback**
  - Seven month payback period
- **Schedule**
  - Implemented in all units in one year

AHS **Academic Health Systems**
We Are Your Community Healthcare Practice

Figure 3-9. VAPR project business case (executive summary)

Business Case

INTRODUCTION & BACKGROUND

In 2009 Congress passed the Patient Protection and Affordable Care Act. In order to pay for coverage for more Americans, the bill introduced new taxes, a reduction in allowed charges for some patient care, and a plan to base payments more on outcomes than on services. Also included was a plan to not pay for conditions that healthcare provider themselves caused due to medical error, poor clinical judgment, or failure to follow best clinical practices.

Healthcare facilities can now be held responsible to pay for the care of patients who are readmitted once treated for certain diagnosis, as well as covering the treatment cost of ailments categorized as Hospital Acquired Conditions (HAC). One such HAC that AHS believes we can quickly improve upon is Ventilator Associated Pneumonia (VAP). VAP can be deadly to patients, especially the elderly and the young. Nationally nearly 17% of those over 65 years of age and 8% of those under the age of 2 die as a result of VAP or its complications. At AHS, this could translate into 11 unnecessary deaths in the next twelve months. CMS has also ruled that they will not pay for HAC treatments, but all third party payers are expected to follow suite, as they have in the past.

AHS currently has over 200 cases of VAP per year (using the CDC guidelines for identification), costing AHS over $3.6M per year for treatment, but generating $4.9M in revenue. Since we will no longer be able to bill for VAP, we will lose approximately $4.9M per year in revenue and spend $3.6M treating it, if we do not reduce VAP at AHS.

BUSINESS OBJECTIVES

A major part of AHS' mission is to deliver the best healthcare possible, at reasonable prices, to the citizens of North Dakota. We can only meet this mission if we are truly doing all that we can do to not only treat, but to protect, the patient from undue harm. Certainly no patient deserves to leave our facility less healthy than when they came, at least not from something we did or did not do correctly. We can improve patient care, reduce mortality, reduce costs, and improve patient satisfaction by reducing our VAP incidence rate at AHS.

CURRENT SITUATION AND PROBLEM / OPPORTUNITY

AHS, being an academic medical center, has a high degree of control over some of our clinical staff. Residents work under our direction, and it is here that we can help them learn that although medicine is part art, that art should learn from those who have devoted years to study and prove that the application of certain practices can improve patient outcomes. However, AHS also has some of the most experienced physicians in the country on our faculty, and as such they prefer to depend upon their many years of experience when determining how to treat their patients. Our attending physicians currently do not, for example, believe that it is desirable to adhere to the IHI Ventilator Bundle (best practices) when it comes to a sedation vacation for patients. They believe it puts undue stress on the patient, their family, and the nursing staff, so they prefer that the patient be allowed to remain sedated for longer periods of time than recommended by the IHI.

It will take a great deal of internal marketing / selling to gain buy-in from our attending physicians, but we can't ignore this problem due to the risk it puts on our patients and our institution.

We also have a problem with accurate nursing documentation, with each unit documenting patient care differently. In order to prove that we are following the IHI best practices for ventilated patients, we must standardize ventilator-related documentation, and enforce the "not documented, not done" rule. Critical to success of this project, we must hold all caregivers accountable for adherence to the IHI Ventilator Bundle.
Before we can present bundle compliance rates to the clinicians, we must improve our ability to collect this information. Some of the data is collected through nursing documentation, some through the pharmacy, and others through respiratory therapist documentation. We have no system that has data from all three systems in one place, so we will have to determine the most efficient method of collecting data from these three systems so that it can be translated into bundle compliance information. Last of all, a method of presenting this information back to the clinicians must be developed, and the presentation must be timely in order to impact patient care.

We have the chance to save 11 patients per year while under our care, save $4.9M annually, and improve the health and welfare of our patients by adhering to the IHI Ventilator Bundle.

CRITICAL ASSUMPTIONS AND CONSTRAINTS

The Chief Nursing Officer and Chief Medical Officer have agreed that this is a critical project, and as such have promised full support. There is no expectation that CMS or other payers will reverse their decision to not pay for VAP, or their no-pay deadline of July 1 of next year. Due to the growth of healthcare IT, it will be difficult to acquire new IT staff so the work will be done by current staff. This project will require collaboration between clinical, IT, and data analytics staff and should be sponsored by a senior clinical leader in order gain clinician support.

ALTERNATIVES ANALYSIS & RECOMMENDATION

There are three possible ways we can improve our VAP incidence rate:

1. Promote usage of the IHI Ventilator Bundle on a voluntary basis, allowing each nursing unit to determine the best way to pull their compliance information.

2. Develop a single system to provide caregivers with IHI ventilator compliance information, and encourage clinicians to follow the bundle.

3. Develop a single system to provide caregivers with IHI ventilator compliance information, put processes into place to monitor compliance by clinician, and hold caregivers accountable for non-compliance.

After reviewing the three available options, we believe that only the third method will be successful. Option #1 is essentially the current state, as we have left it to nursing units to develop their own process and our VAP rate is over double the national average. This option has not worked.

We do not believe Option #2 will work either, as having the data available will not ensure compliance. All units currently have the data available, albeit in three different systems, and do not feel it is important enough to pull the data. Simply providing the data to them in a more readily available format will most likely not improve compliance.

Option #3 is the only solution that not only provides the information they need, but also holds caregivers accountable. By holding caregivers accountable they will understand the value the organization places on bundle compliance. As we have proven in the past, we can't manage what we don't measure.

PRELIMINARY PROJECT REQUIREMENTS

This project is being undertaken to meet the following high level requirements:

1. Ensure that the IHI Ventilator Bundle is being applied consistently across the organization for ventilated patients.

2. Develop consistent protocols for managing vented patients.

3. Identify and collect data that supports compliance with the bundle.

4. Develop a method for delivering the compliance data, by patient, to their caregivers on a schedule that would allow caregivers to correct non-compliance.

5. Develop and deliver training for caregivers on the new procedures, protocols, and reporting system.

BUDGET ESTIMATE AND FINANCIAL ANALYSIS

Preliminary cost estimates for this project, which is split into two phases, with a total project cost of $875,000 (baseline) to $980,000 (including contingency). Project cost per phase is as follows:

Phase	Cost Estimate	Contingency Estimate	Contingency Notes
I – Proof of Concept & Data Sourcing	$700,000	$70,000	10% due to possible 3rd party software required to connect the disparate systems.
II – Clinical Workflow Improvements	$175,000	$35,000	20% set aside to pay for additional time from a physician to serve in a secondary champion role in the event the doctors do not "buy into the process".
Total	$875,000	$105,000	

This project is primarily about patient care as it will improve the health and well-being of our ventilated patients by preventing VAP. However, there is a financial benefit to the prevention of VAP. We currently average 200 cases of VAP per year and collect revenue of $4.9M for the treatment of their VAP condition. Going forward we will not be reimbursed for this treatment, so AHS will lose $4.9M per year in revenue. However, if we do nothing to reduce VAP, we will also lose another $3.6M due to the unreimbursed cost that we will incur for VAP treatment. If we can reduce the VAP incidence rate by 50%, which is realistic based on studies conducted, the project cost will be recovered within 7 months. Due to the short payback period, and the low cost of money (borrowing), the only financial analysis listed here is based on the payback period. However, as required, Exhibit A includes a three year, total cost of ownership (TCO) analysis taking into account the value of money.

Description	Cost
Average cost per patient to treat for VAP	$17,000
Number of patients prevented from VAP (assuming 50% reduction)	x 106
Total Annual Cost Savings	$1,800,000

SCHEDULE ESTIMATE

Due to the federal regulations taking effect in 19 months, the sponsor needs the project to be completed within one year so that the new workflows can be hard-wired before the change in reimbursement goes into effect.

RISKS

This project has two primary risks. The first is that the data, which exists in three disparate systems, will not be available for extract into a combined reporting system in the required near real-time basis. This is why the project begins with a proof of concept. The second risk is that the caregivers will not embrace the IHI Ventilator Bundle and do not integrate it into their care plans. A third, but less probable risk, is that the bundle is followed by all without any impact on VAP incidence rates at AHS. This is unlikely, but possible, since the bundle effectiveness has been validated by both independent research and other organizations.

EXHIBIT A: TOTAL COST OF OWNERSHIP (TCO) ANALYSIS

The table below includes the return on investment (ROI) and NPV, based on a three year TCO (the AHS standard for technology-based projects).

Project Costs

Element	Year 1	Year 2	Year 3	Total
Project Cost	$980,000	0	0	$980,000
Discount Factor	1.00	0.99	0.99	
Discounted Costs	$975,124	0	0	$975,124

Project Benefits

Element	Year 1	Year 2	Year 3	Total
Benefits	$0	$1,800,000	$1,800,000	$3,600,000
Discount Factor	1.00	0.99	0.99	
Discounted Costs	$0	$1,782,000	$1,782,000	$3,564,000

Discounted Benefit-Costs

Element	Year 1	Year 2	Year 3	Total
Discounted, Annual Benefits – Costs	($975,124)	$1,782,000	$1,782,000	$2,588,876
Discounted, Accumulative Benefits – Costs	($975,124)	$806,876	$2,588,876	

NPV = $2,588,876 (see above)   ROI = 265% ($2,588,876 discounted return / $975,124 discounted cost)

Figure 3-10. VAPR project full business case

Now that important pre-initiating activities were completed, Jeff Birdwell, from the PMO, was ready to tackle important processes to initiate the VAPR project. Since this was a two-phased project, with each phase being managed by a different project manager, it was important that Jeff and the project manager of the second phase, Pat Wager, work together throughout, even though Phase II would not officially begin for several months.

INITIATING PROCESSES AND OUTPUTS

The main processes normally involved in project initiation include:

- Identifying project stakeholders
- Creating the project charter
- Holding a kick-off meeting

Key outputs of initiating, as described in the *PMBOK® Guide, Fifth Edition*, include a stakeholder register and project charter, as shown in Figure 3-11. Even though it is not part of the *PMBOK® Guide*, AHS also required a formal kick-off meeting as part of the initiating process. The following sections of this chapter describe each of these outputs in detail for the entire VAPR project.

Knowledge area	Initiating process	Outputs
Project integration management	Develop project charter	Project charter
Project stakeholder management	Identify stakeholders	Stakeholder register

Figure 3-11. Initiating processes and outputs

Identifying Stakeholders

Recall from Chapter 1 that project stakeholders are the people who have a vested interest in the project and its outcomes. The *PMBOK® Guide, Fifth Edition*, expands on this definition as follows: "Project stakeholders are individuals, groups, or organizations who may affect, be affected by, or perceive themselves to be affected by a decision, activity, or outcome of a project." Stakeholders can be internal to the organization or external.

- Internal project stakeholders generally include the project sponsor, project team, support staff, and internal customers for the project. Because organizations have limited resources, projects affect top management, other functional managers, and other project managers by using some of the organization's limited resources.

- External project stakeholders include the project's customers (if they are external to the organization), competitors, suppliers, and other external groups that are potentially involved in or affected by the project, such as government officials and concerned citizens.

It is important to consider all project stakeholders, especially those that might be negatively impacted, or perceive to be impacted, by the project. If a project is working to improve efficiencies, reduce labor costs, or reduce the inventory of medical supplies in a hospital, then there are many people who will consider themselves stakeholders. If your job may be cut if a project succeeds, then you are interested! If an inventory reduction project plans to reduce the count and variety of a medical supply, like a catheter, then all physicians would be stakeholders as they might have their own preferences of catheters that will be eliminated from the stockroom as part of that project.

How does a project manager identify key project stakeholders and find out more about them? The best way is by asking around. There might be formal organizational charts or biographies that can provide some information, but the main goal is to help project managers manage relationships with key stakeholders. Talking to other people who have worked with those stakeholders usually provides the best information. For example, in this case, Jeff and Corey may know that clinicians would surely be in the stakeholder list, but they might not know which ones carried the most influence or which ones would be the most opposed to the VAPR project. Pat, on the other hand, is a nurse who works with caregivers daily, and she could help identify those key clinical stakeholders. By working together, they can identify a good starting group of stakeholders.

Because the purpose of project management is to meet project requirements and satisfy stakeholders, it is critical that project managers take adequate time to identify, understand, and manage relationships with all project stakeholders. As discussed in Chapter 1, PMI created a new knowledge area, project stakeholder management, to emphasize this area. The main initiating output for this knowledge area is a stakeholder register, and a key technique for understanding stakeholders is a stakeholder analysis.

Sample Stakeholder Register and Stakeholder Analysis

A **stakeholder register** is a document that includes details related to the identified project stakeholders. It can take various forms and include the following information:

- Identification information: The stakeholders' names, positions, locations, roles in the project, and contact information

- Assessment information: The stakeholders' major requirements and expectations, potential influences, and phase(s) of the project where there is the most interest

- Stakeholder classification: Internal/external, supporter/resistor, etc.

Figure 3-12 provides an example of a part of the stakeholder register for the VAPR project. Notice it includes only basic stakeholder information, such as name, position, if they are internal or external to the organization, role on the project, and contact information. Because this document would be available to other people in their organization, Jeff was careful not to include information that might be sensitive, such as how strongly the stakeholders supported the project or how much power they had. He would keep these and other issues in mind discretely and use them in performing the stakeholder analysis.

Name	Title	Internal/ External	Project Role	Contact Information
Marilyn Shoemaker, RN, PhD	CNO	Internal	Project Sponsor	shoemaker_m@ahs.edu
Casey Lidwell	CAO	Internal	Project Champion, Phase I	lidwell_c@ahs.edu
Danielle Scheerer, MD	CQO	Internal	Project Champion, Phase II	scheerer_d@ahs.edu
David Whichard, MD	ICU Med Director	Internal	User	whichard_d@ahs.edu
Melissa Fortnight	Bed Mgmt	Internal	Impacted	white_m@ahs.edu

Figure 3-12. Sample stakeholder register

In Figure 3-12 it is clear who the first three stakeholders are, as they compose the top level of project leadership. David Whichard, the ICU Medical Director, is listed because the ICUs have the highest percentage of ventilated patients, so his staff will have to change their protocols to align with the new IHI Ventilator Bundle, a key component of the project. The last stakeholder listed is Melissa Fortnight, the bed management manager. She would not be a user of the new process, but she might be impacted as bed turnover may increase if VAP incidence is reduced.

Stakeholder analysis is a technique for analyzing information to determine which stakeholders' interests to focus on and how to increase stakeholder support throughout the project. After identifying key project stakeholders, you can use different classification models to determine an approach for managing relationships with them. For example, you can create a power/interest grid to group stakeholders based on their level of authority (power) and their level of concern (interest) for project outcomes, as shown in Figure 3-13. You should manage relationships with stakeholders 1 and 2 in this example very closely because they have high interest and high power, especially stakeholder 1.

You should keep stakeholders 3 and 4 informed because they have high interest but low power. Stakeholders 5 and 6 should be kept satisfied, perhaps by brief updates on the project, because they have low interest but high power. You should spend the least amount of effort by simply monitoring stakeholders 7 and 8, where both have low interest and low power. For the stakeholders listed in the above stakeholder register, where do you think each of them should be placed on the power/interest grid? Who would you ensure was kept satisfied? Who would you be least concerned with satisfying?

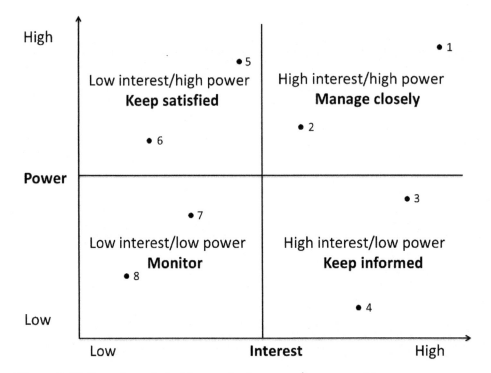

Figure 3-13. Sample stakeholder analysis power/interest grid

It is also important to measure the engagement level of stakeholders throughout the project. You can categorize stakeholders as being one of the following:

- *Unaware:* Unaware of the project and its potential impacts on them
- *Resistant:* Aware of the project yet resistant to change
- *Neutral:* Aware of the project yet neither supportive nor resistant
- *Supportive:* Aware of the project and supportive of change
- *Leading:* Aware of the project and its potential impacts and actively engaged in helping it succeed

The project team should take corrective action as soon as possible if they find that a stakeholder with high interest and high power is also categorized as resistant or unaware. It is very difficult to manage a project under those circumstances, and most project managers do not have the required influence (or access) to change the minds of the resistant stakeholders. This is where you should utilize your sponsor, champion(s), and any supporting or leading stakeholders who have influence or power. They are in a much better position to turn around a negative stakeholder, especially if they are in the same discipline. *Remember that nurses listen to nurses, doctors to doctors, therapists to therapists, etc.* They all respect the skills the others bring to patient care, but if you want to win over a physician, you will need another physician to turn them around. Likewise for the other disciplines!

Healthcare Perspective

Dr. Michael Marcaccio shared his perspective on Ontario, Canada's highly successful Wait Time Information System (WTIS) project. This project helped reduce wait times for millions of surgical procedures and MRI/CT scans throughout hospitals in Ontario. One of the success factors included engaging stakeholders who served as role models on expert panels, including Dr. Marcaccio.

Dr. Marcaccio was not surprised at the initial resistance to the project, especially from surgeons. The expert panel identified common resistance issues, such as the impact on the administrative workload for surgeons and their staff, cost, general distrust of administrative and government initiatives, and concern about the loss of autonomy. The panel incorporated feedback while setting finite deadlines for implementation to provide a good balance between consultation and action. For example, the project team initially planned to target five areas of high priority for the government, but front-line surgeons made it clear that they did not support a strategy that propagated their perception of two-tier care within surgery, creating a "have and have not" environment. The project team took their advice. Another important decision was using priority assessment tools that required clinician judgment in the priority decision for each patient. Engaging key stakeholders early in the project definitely helped the WITS project become a success. [8]

After identifying and analyzing stakeholders, the project manager and team should develop a stakeholder management plan, as described in more detail in Chapter 6.

Figure 3-14 provides a humorous example of analyzing a stakeholder's needs. Many healthcare professionals and patients are familiar with rating pain on a scale of one to ten, but each person interprets these numbers differently.

Figure 3-14. Analyzing stakeholder needs (www.xkcd.com)

Creating a Project Charter

After top management determines which projects to pursue, it is important to let the rest of the organization know about these projects. Management needs to create and distribute documentation to authorize project initiation. This documentation can take many different forms, but one common form is a project charter. A **project charter** is a document that formally recognizes the existence of a project and provides a summary of the project's objectives and management. Most importantly, it authorizes the project manager to use organizational resources to complete the project. Ideally, the project manager will play a major role in developing the project charter.

Instead of project charters, some organizations use a simple letter of agreement, whereas others use much longer documents or formal contracts. When AHS initiates a project using outside professional services or purchases such as software, it still creates a separate charter and attaches it to the contract, which is usually a much longer, more complex document. *A crucial part of the project charter is the sign-off section, where key project stakeholders sign the document to acknowledge their agreement on the need for the project.* Remember that healthcare disciplines tend to most respect those within their own discipline, so if you have a project that impacts nurses, try to get the highest level nurse to sign off on the charter. You must know who the project will most impact, and who will require the most convincing to be on board before you can identify the best leader to sign the charter.

Contents of a Project Charter

Contents of a project charter will also vary to meet individual organizational and project needs. Typical information included in a project charter includes the following:

- The project's title and date of authorization

- The project manager's name and contact information

- A summary schedule or timeline, including the planned start and finish dates; if a summary milestone schedule is available, it should also be included or referenced

- A summary of the project's estimated cost and budget allocation

- A brief description of the project objectives, including the business need or other justification for authorizing the project

- Project success criteria, including project approval requirements and who signs off on the project

- A summary of the planned approach for managing the project, which should describe stakeholder needs and expectations, important assumptions and constraints, and should refer to related documents, such as a communications management plan, as available

- A roles and responsibilities matrix of key project leadership

- A sign-off section for signatures of key project stakeholders

- A comments section in which stakeholders can provide important comments related to the project

Project charters are normally short documents. Some are only one-page long, whereas others might be several pages long. For a large project, such as the implementation of an Electronic Medical Record (EMR), the charter could be up to one hundred pages long, as it may include project governance, detailed scope information, etc. Some charters include signatures of team members, although most do not because the project team is rarely chosen at that point in the project. The following section shows the project charter for the VAPR project.

Sample Project Charter

Jeff, working with Pat's input, drafted a project charter and had the project champions review it before showing it to Dr. Marilyn Shoemaker, the sponsor. Dr. Shoemaker made a few minor changes, which Jeff incorporated, and then she, the two champions, and the two project managers involved signed the project charter. Figure 3-15 shows the final project charter. Note that Dr. Shoemaker noted a concern she had with making sure nursing didn't get burdened with following the new protocols in the event that physicians did not engage. Pat Wager knew that she would have to consider these concerns when managing Phase II, as this was when workflow changes would be developed and implemented.

Media Snapshot

Many people enjoy watching television shows like Trading Spaces, where participants have two days and $1,000 to update a room in their neighbor's house. Because the time and cost are set, it is the scope that has the most flexibility. Designers often have to change initial scope goals due to budget or time constraints. For example, designers often go back to local stores to exchange items for less expensive ones to meet budget constraints. Or they might describe a new piece of furniture they'd like, but the carpenter changes the design or materials to meet time constraints.

Another important issue related to project scope management is meeting customer expectations. Who wouldn't be happy with a professionally designed room at no cost to them? Although most homeowners on Trading Spaces are very happy with work done on the show, some are obviously disappointed. Unlike most projects where the project team works closely with the customer, homeowners have little say in what gets done and cannot inspect the work along the way. They walk into their newly decorated room with their eyes closed. What happens when the homeowners don't like the work that's been done? Part of agreeing to be on the show includes signing a release statement acknowledging that you will accept whatever work has been done. Too bad you can't get sponsors for your projects to sign a similar release statement! Not only will they not sign such an agreement, but they may be invited to many project meetings and not attend, as they are too busy. This is especially true for healthcare projects.

When choosing stakeholders in a clinical environment you must be aware of the demands placed upon physicians, nurses, and surgeons. Each already has a variety of stakeholders related to their primary job—patient care. Your project, no matter how important to you and the organization, is often just a distraction for caregivers. Surgeons are often the most difficult to pull from their work, as spending two hours in a meeting can cost tens of thousands of dollars in lost revenue. Pulling a physician from a clinic may mean that patients have to reschedule their visits or wait for them to catch up on their patient load after attending your meeting. This is a poor way to gain physician buy-in. One way to reduce this problem is to pay for clinician time under your project budget, which will result in the project gaining a higher level of participation from these busy (and expensive) people. It will also provide a truer picture of project cost!

Project Charter
May 21

PROJECT TITLE
Ventilator Associated Pneumonia (VAP) Reduction – "VAPR"

PROJECT TIMELINE
Start: July 1   **Projected Finish Date:** June 30

PURPOSE
VAP costs AHS over $3.6M per year in costs, and puts our patients at risk for severe and sometimes fatal consequences. VAP is considered preventable by CMS, having worked with the Institute for Healthcare Improvement to develop a set of best practices that, if followed, has been proven to reduce VAP by 50% in other healthcare facilities. AHS will implement a system to collect and report compliance with the best practices in order to better manage VAP in order to better serve our patients healthcare needs. Since VAP is considered preventable, it is no longer reimbursable by CMS or major payers as of July 1, which will also put a financial burden on our organizations.

BUDGET
The VAPR project is expected to cost $980,000 over one year, with a total TCO of $980,000 over three years.

PROJECT MANAGER
VAPR has been broken down into two phases. The first phase is a proof of concept and the data collection/reporting system and will be managed by Jeff Birdwell, PMP from the PMO's office. The second phase includes clinical process reengineering, training, and monitoring and will be managed by Pat Wager, RN, from the analytics department.

SUCCESS CRITERIA
This project will be considered successful if the sponsor rating is at least 8/10 upon project completion and VAP incidence rate drops by at least 50% within six months of implementation. Incidence rates will be determined based on the number of VAP events per 1000 ventilator days.

APPROACH
- All work to be completed by internal staffing, where possible.
- Project to be broken up into two major phases that will overlap their work, requiring the two project managers to work closely together throughout the project.

AHS Academic Health Systems
We Are Your Community Healthcare Practice

- Phase I, VAPRware, is concerned with the proof of concept, data collection and data reporting. It is primarily a technology project but will require the cooperation of and collaboration with analytics and nursing in order to identify the required data elements and their source systems.
- Phase II, VAPRflow, is concerned with clinical workflow reengineering, and is primarily a clinical project that will require working with the Nursing Documentation Committee and Medical Executive Committee in order to gain their input and support.
- Training to be developed and delivered by the Nurse Educator Team under the direction of the Phase II project manager. All training will be computer-based training (CBT) and will be included in annual training requirements for all clinicians.
- The cost of any work conducted on behalf of the project will be paid by the project budget, with the exception of the time nurses spend in training.

PROJECT LEADERSHIP

Name	Title	Project Role	Contact Information	Signature/Date
Marilyn Shoemaker, RN, PhD	CNO	Project Sponsor	shoemaker_m@ahs.edu	M. Shoemaker May 3
Casey Lidwell	CAO	Ph. 1 Project Champion	lidwell_c@ahs.edu	Casey J Lidwell May 6
Danielle Scheerer, MD	CQO	Ph. II Project Champion	scheerer_d@ahs.edu	Danielle Scheerer May 4
Jeff Birdwell, PMP	Sr. Project Mgr	Ph. I Project Manager	Birdwell_j@ahs.edu	Jeff Birdwell May 8
Pat Wager, RN	CMS Analytics Mgr	Ph. II Project Manager	Wager_p@ahs.edu	Pat Wager May 5

AHS Academic Health Systems
We Are Your Community Healthcare Practice

Figure 3-15. Sample project charter

Because many projects fail due to unclear requirements and expectations, starting with a clearly defined project charter makes good business sense. If project managers are having difficulty obtaining support from project leadership, for example, they can refer to what everyone agreed to in the project charter. After the charter is completed, it is good practice to hold an official kick-off meeting for the project.

Holding a Project Kick-Off Meeting

Experienced project managers know it is crucial to get projects off to a great start. Holding an effective kick-off meeting is an excellent way to do this. A **kick-off meeting** is a meeting held at the beginning of a project so that stakeholders can meet each other, review the goals of the project, and discuss future plans. It is often held after the business case and project charter are completed, but it could be held sooner, if needed.

Project kick-off meetings are often used to get end-user and project team support for a project, as well as to clarify roles and responsibilities within the project. If there is a project champion, as there is for this project, he or she should speak first at the kick-off meeting and introduce the project sponsor and project manager. If anyone seems opposed to the project or unwilling to support it, the project champion—an experienced senior manager—should be able to handle the situation.

As discussed earlier in the chapter, there is normally a fair amount of work done before an official kick-off meeting for a project. At a minimum, the project manager, sponsor, and champion should have met several times, and other key stakeholders should have been involved in developing the project charter. The project manager should make sure the right people are invited to the kick-off meeting and send out an agenda in advance. For a small project, a kick-off meeting might be an informal meeting of the project team held in a social environment. The main idea is to get the project off to a good start. Ideally the kick-off meeting should be held face-to-face so stakeholders can physically meet each other and be able to pick up on each other's body language.

Video Highlights

There are many training videos to help you learn about various aspects of project management. For example, *www.projectmanager.com* provides several free videos, including one on how to kick-off a project. The instructor in the video emphasizes the importance of getting everyone on the same page, holding one-on-one meetings to get to know everyone, sorting out the administrative documents, and having a formal kick-off event.

The same site also has a video on starting a new project. Key points include knowing your project, setting a vision, creating and communicating the project charter, getting formal sign offs, creating a project notebook, and building relationships. Additional video topics include how to run team meetings, how to manage stakeholders during crisis, and many others.

Sample Kick-Off Meeting Agenda

All project meetings with major stakeholders should include an agenda. Figure 3-16 provides the agenda that Jeff provided for the VAPR project kick-off meeting. Notice the main topics in an agenda:

- Meeting objective

- Agenda (lists in order the topics to be discussed)

- A section for documenting action items, who they are assigned to, and when each person will complete the action

- A section to document the date and time of the next meeting

---

Ventilator Associated Pneumonia Reduction (VAPR)
Project Kick Off
9:00 am – 10:30 am

Meeting Objective: Introduction of key stakeholders, meet the project team, review the project objectives (scope, time, costs), and discuss the relevance of this project to organizational objectives.

Agenda

Topic	Who	Time (minutes)
Welcome!	Marilyn Scheerer, RN, PhD	5
Introduction of Attendees	Jeff Birdwell, PMP	10
Project Background	Danielle Scheerer, MD Casey Lidwell	7
Review of Business Case & Charter	Jeff Birdwell, PMP Pat Wager, RN	15
Overview of Project Organizational Structure	Marilyn Scheerer, RN, PhD	5
Review of Project Scope	Pat Wager, RN	5
Discuss Project Schedule & Phases	Jeff Birdwell, PMP	8
Review of Project Costs & Financial Impact	Jeff Birdwell, PMP	5
Open Floor for Discussion	Danielle Scheerer, MD Casey Lidwell	20
Review of Action Items	Jeff Birdwell, PMP	5
Set Next Meeting Date/Time	Jeff Birdwell, PMP	5

Action Items

Action Item	Assigned To?	Due Date?

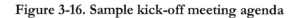
AHS Academic Health Systems
We Are Your Community Healthcare Practice

Figure 3-16. Sample kick-off meeting agenda

Note that the agenda includes the name of the person responsible for that portion of the agenda. This helps the attendees put the name with the face later. Times are added as guidelines to help keep the meeting on track. It also gives the project manager an opportunity to talk about how they will all be working against deadlines until the project is completed. A significant, and intentional, mix of project leadership was given speaking (and leading) roles in the kick-off meeting.

The sponsor begins the meeting, being at the top of the project hierarchy, and introduces the key project leadership (champions and project managers). Then Jeff, the project manager for Phase I, takes over and introduces all the attendees in the room. For very large kick-off meetings individual introductions may be skipped or limited to just the key attendees such as department heads, service line directors, etc. Next, the two project champions give a bit of history about why this project is important. Remember, they are the ones who will be the face of this project to the users. Most kick-off meetings include key users, so the champions need to get stage time to show their support of the project.

Next in the agenda, the two project managers review the project documents (the business case and project charter), and then the sponsor returns to talk about how the project leadership is structured (and why). By the time the structure is introduced the attendees would have heard from the leadership team already. The scope is covered by Pat, as she is closest to understanding the impact to the clinical workflows. When the meeting turns back to project management, Jeff takes over again. The meeting is turned back over to the champions for the question and comment period, but the two project managers could also run this part of the meeting. It really depends upon the relationship between the attendees and the project managers and the attendees and the champions.

It is important to think about the people running each section of your kick-off meeting. Put the proper person at the front of the room for that part of the meeting. Don't be afraid to switch people for different sections of the meeting. It keeps it interesting and lets the attendees know that this is a team effort.

It is good practice to focus on results of meetings, and having sections for documenting action items and deciding on the next meeting date and time on the agenda helps to do so. It is also good practice to document meeting minutes, focusing on key decisions and action items, and to send them to all meeting participants and other appropriate stakeholders within a day or two of a meeting. Meeting minutes are valuable to people who could not attend a meeting since they summarize key discussions and results of the meeting. If there is a project Web site or other place for storing project information, the meeting minutes should be stored there.

CASE WRAP-UP

Jeff and Pat were pleased with the work completed while initiating the VAPR project, as were the project sponsor, both champions, and several key stakeholders who found the time to attend the project kick-off meeting. During Phase I, Jeff planned to meet weekly with the project steering committee to review project progress. He found the committee to be very helpful, especially when dealing with several challenges the project team encountered. For example, they had a difficult time getting physicians to accept the meeting invitation for the kick-off meeting, so the steering committee helped Jeff get a resource from the AV department who recorded the entire meeting and made it available via a webcast for the doctors to view from their offices or homes.

Pat was also a bit nervous knowing that she had to get up in front of the group at the meeting, but Dr. Marilyn Scheerer, the project sponsor, agreed to always be at her side, and Jeff agreed to coach her beforehand by having her practice her speaking parts for him. The project champions helped to diffuse a few touchy moments in the meeting when the pediatrics chief resident and an ICU nurse manager got into an on-again off-again debate over why the IHI Ventilator Bundle is not followed by caregivers. Jeff and Pat could see how important senior management support was on this project, in particular for obtaining buy-in from all parts of the organization.

CHAPTER SUMMARY

The five project management process groups are initiating, planning, executing, monitoring and controlling, and closing. These process groups occur at varying levels of intensity throughout each phase of a project, and specific outcomes are produced as a result of each process. The most time and money is normally spent on executing.

Mapping the main activities of each project management process group into the ten project management knowledge areas provides a big picture of what activities are involved in project management. Some organizations develop their own project management methodologies, often using the standards found in the *PMBOK® Guide* as a foundation. It is important to tailor project management methodologies to meet the organization's particular needs.

AHS' VAPR project demonstrates the process of initiating a project. After a project is approved, senior managers often meet to perform several pre-initiating activities, as follows:

- Determining the scope, time, and cost constraints for the project

- Identifying the project sponsor

- Selecting the project manager

- Developing a business case for the project, if required

- Meeting with the project manager to review the process and expectations for managing the project

- Determining if the project should be divided into phases or smaller projects

The main processes normally involved in project initiation are the following:

- Identifying stakeholders

- Creating the project charter

- Holding a kick-off meeting

Descriptions of how each of these processes was accomplished and samples of related outputs are described in the chapter.

QUICK QUIZ

1.   In which of the five project management process groups is the most time and money usually spent?

    A.   initiating

    B.   planning

    C.   executing

    D.   monitoring and controlling

    E.   closing

2.   In which of the five project management process groups are activities performed that relate to each knowledge area?

    A.   initiating

    B.   planning

    C.   executing

    D.   monitoring and controlling

    E.   closing

3.   The best or "alpha" project managers spend more time on every process group than other project managers except for which one?

    A.   initiating

    B.   planning

    C.   executing

    D.   monitoring and controlling

4.   What document provides justification for investing in a project?

    A.   project charter

    B.   business case

    C.   net present value analysis

    D.   stakeholder register

5.   What document formally recognizes the existence of a project and provides direction on the project's objectives and management?

   A.   project charter

   B.   business case

   C.   stakeholder register

   D.   stakeholder management strategy

6.   What is a crucial part of the project charter—a section in which key project stakeholders acknowledge their agreement on the need for the project?

   A.   project objectives

   B.   approach

   C.   roles and responsibilities

   D.   sign-off

7.   Which project document should not be made available to all key project stakeholders due to its sensitive nature?

   A.   project charter

   B.   business case

   C.   stakeholder register

   D.   stakeholder analysis

8.   All project meetings with major stakeholders should include _____.

   A.   an agenda

   B.   food

   C.   name tags

   D.   all of the above

9.   Preparing a stakeholder register and performing a stakeholder analysis are part of which knowledge area?

   A.   project integration management

   B.   project human resource management

   C.   project stakeholder management

   D.   project communications management

10.   Which of the following is recommended in this text but is not an output of initiating in the *PMBOK® Guide, Fifth Edition*?

    A. project charter

    B. stakeholder register

    C. kick-off meeting

    D. none of the above

Quick Quiz Answers

1. C; 2. B; 3. C; 4. B; 5. A; 6. D; 7. D; 8. A; 9. C; 10. D

DISCUSSION QUESTIONS

1.   Briefly describe what happens in each of the five project management process groups (initiating, planning, executing, monitoring and controlling, and closing). On which process should team members spend the most time? Why? Why is it helpful to follow a project management methodology?

2.   What pre-initiating tasks were performed for the VAPR project? Does it make sense to do these tasks? What are the main initiating tasks?

3.   Describe the purpose of a business case and its main contents.

4.   What is the main purpose of developing a stakeholder analysis? What information in it might be sensitive and kept confidential?

5.   Why should projects have a project charter? What is the main information included in a project charter?

6.   Discuss the process for holding a project kick-off meeting. Who should attend? What key topics should be on the agenda?

EXERCISES

Note: These exercises can be done individually or in teams, in-class, as homework, or in a virtual environment. Learners can either write their results in a paper or prepare a short presentation or video to show their results.

1.   Find an example of a large healthcare project that took more than a year to complete. Why was the project initiated? Describe some of the pre-initiating and initiating tasks completed for the project.

2.   Review the business case for the VAPR project. Do you think there is solid business justification for doing this project? Why or why not? What parts of the business case do you think could be stronger? How? Rewrite a section that you believe can be improved.

3.   Search the Internet for "project charter." Find and critique at least three references that describe project charters and summarize your findings.

4.   Review the project charter for the VAPR project. How does this document help clarify what work will be done on the project? Is the success criteria clear for this project? What questions do you have about the scope of the project?

5.   Watch the videos called "How to Kickoff a Project" and "Starting a New Project" from *www.projectmanager.com*. Summarize key points in these videos and your opinion of them.

6.   Find two additional videos related to any of the topics in this chapter, focusing on examples in the healthcare industry. Summarize your findings.

TEAM PROJECTS

Note: These team projects can be done in-class, as homework, or in a virtual environment. Learners can either write their results in a paper or prepare a short presentation or video to show their results

1.   Your organization has decided to initiate a project to raise money for an important charity. Assume that there are 1,000 people in your organization. Use the pre-initiating tasks described in this chapter to develop a strategy for how to proceed. Be creative in describing your organization; the charity; the scope, time, and cost constraints for the project; and so on.

2.   You are part of a team in charge of a project to help people in your company (500 people) lose weight. This project is part of a competition, and the top "losers" will be featured in a popular television show. Assume that you have six months to complete the project and a budget of $10,000. Develop a project charter for this project using the sample provided in this chapter. Be creative in developing detailed information to include in the charter.

3.   Using the information you developed in Team Project 1 or 2, role-play the kick-off meeting for this project. Follow the sample agenda provided in this chapter.

4.   Perform the initiating tasks for one of the case studies provided in Appendix B. If you are working on a real team project, perform the applicable pre-initiating and initiating tasks for that project. Be sure to work closely with your project sponsor to get the project off to a good start.

5.   As a team, research two different project management methodologies (other than using the *PMBOK® Guide*), such as PRINCE2, RUP, Six Sigma, etc. Summarize your findings, and include examples of projects managed using each methodology.

KEY TERMS

agile — Popular software development method that use an iterative workflow and incremental delivery of software in short iterations.

business case — A document that provides justification for investing in a project.

champion — A senior manager who acts as a key proponent for a project.

closing processes — The actions that involve formalizing completion and acceptance of the project or phase and bringing it to an orderly end.

deliverable — A product or service produced or provided as part of a project.

executing processes — The actions that involve coordinating people and other resources to carry out the project plans and produce the deliverables of the project.

initiating processes — The actions to define and authorize new projects and project phases as well as identifying those who will be impacted by the project.

kick-off meeting — A meeting held at the beginning of a project so that stakeholders can meet each other, review the goals of the project, and discuss future plans.

methodology — A plan that describes how things should be done to manage a project.

monitoring and controlling processes — The actions taken to measure progress toward achieving project goals, monitor deviation from plans, and take corrective or preventative action to match progress with plans and customer expectations.

phase — A a distinct project cycle that produces deliverables.

phase gating — A process whereby project leadership reviews progress on a project after each phase to determine if it should move on to the next phase.

planning processes — The actions that involve devising and maintaining a workable scheme to ensure that the project meets its scope, time, and cost goals as well as organizational needs.

process — A series of actions directed toward a particular result.

project charter — A document that formally recognizes the existence of a project and provides a summary of the project's objectives and management.

project management office (PMO) — An organizational entity created to assist project managers in achieving project goals.

PRojects IN Controlled Environments (PRINCE2) — A project management methodology with eight process groups developed in the U.K.

Rational Unified Process (RUP) framework — A project management methodology that uses an iterative software development process that focuses on team productivity and delivers software best practices to all team members.

Six Sigma — A comprehensive and flexible system for achieving, sustaining, and maximizing business success; uniquely driven by close understanding of customer needs, disciplined use of facts, data, and statistical analysis, and diligent attention to managing, improving, and reinventing business processes.

stakeholder register — A document that includes details related to the identified project stakeholders

stakeholder analysis — A a technique for analyzing information to determine which stakeholders' interests to focus on and how to increase stakeholder support throughout the project.

standard — A document that describes best practices for what should be done to manage a project.

template — A file with a preset format that serves as a starting point for creating various documents so that the format and structure do not have to be re-created.

END NOTES

[1]Andy Crowe, *Alpha Project Managers: What the Top 2% Know That Everyone Else Does Not*, Velociteach Press (2006).

[2]Peter S. Pande, Robert P. Neuman, and Roland R. Cavanagh, *The Six Sigma Way*. New York: McGraw-Hill (2000), p. xi.

[3]Bill Cottrell, "Standards, compliance, and Rational Unified Process, Part I: Integrating RUP and the *PMBOK*," *IBM Developerworks* (May 10, 2004).

[4]William Ibbs and Justin Reginato, *Quantifying the Value of Project Management*, Project Management Institute (2002).

[5]Meridith Levinson, "Why Project and Portfolio Management Matter More At Recession Time," CIO.com (November 10, 2008).

[6]Kate Gamble, "Survey Finds Independent Docs Most Resistant to Change," healthsystemcio.com, May 30, 2012).

[7]PM Solutions, "The State of the PMO 2010" (2010).

[8]Michael Marcaccio, "Stakeholder Engagement: Thoughts from a Clinician," Healthcare Quarterly Vol. 12 Special Issue (2009).

Chapter 4

Planning Projects, Part 1
(Project Integration and Scope Management)

LEARNING OBJECTIVES

After reading this chapter, you will be able to:

- Describe the importance of creating plans to guide project execution, and list several planning processes and outputs for project integration and scope management
- Discuss the project integration management planning process
- Explain the purpose and contents of a team contract and a project management plan
- Describe the four project scope management planning processes
- Explain the purpose and contents of a scope management plan and requirements management plan
- Discuss different ways to collect project requirements, and prepare requirements documentation and a requirements traceability matrix
- Create a scope statement and project documents updates to define project scope
- Create a work breakdown structure (WBS) and a WBS dictionary to clearly describe all of the work required for a project

---

OPENING CASE

Jeff Birdwell continued to work with his Phase I project team and other key stakeholders on the Ventilator Associated Pneumonia Reduction (VAPR) project. Although this was the technical phase of the project, he knew that he would need Pat Wager to work with him, as she was the one who could best identify the data elements required for the Institute for Healthcare Improvement (IHI) Ventilator Bundle.

He knew that it was crucial to do a good job in planning all aspects of the project, and he strongly believed that execution would be much smoother if they had good plans to follow. He also knew that it was important to involve the people who would be doing the work in actually planning the work, and that planning was an iterative process. Involving key people in the planning process and keeping the plans up to date had been his main challenges on past projects, so Jeff focused proactively on those areas.

Jeff and his team were fortunate to have many templates to use in developing several planning documents. They could also review examples of planning documents from past and current projects available on the Academic Health Systems (AHS) intranet site and use project management software to enter key planning data. Jeff also found that the project steering committee that had been set up during project initiation gave him very helpful advice. Several experienced clinician members warned him that he may have to work around physician schedules if he wanted their input during planning, and their time would be limited. They suggested that he be thorough in planning but to not become bogged down in too much detail.

INTRODUCTION

Many people have heard the following sayings:

- If you fail to plan, you plan to fail.

- If you don't know where you're going, any road will take you there.

- What gets measured gets managed.

All of these sayings emphasize the fact that planning is crucial to achieving goals. Successful project managers know how important it is to develop, refine, and follow plans to meet project goals, and they know how easy it is to become sidetracked if they do not have good plans to follow. They also know that people are more likely to perform well if they know what they are supposed to do and when.

PROJECT PLANNING SHOULD GUIDE PROJECT EXECUTION

Planning is often the most difficult and unappreciated process in project management. Often, people do not want to take the time to plan well, but theory and practice show that good planning is crucial to good execution. *The main purpose of project planning is to guide project execution.* To guide execution, plans must be realistic and useful, so a fair amount of effort must go into the project planning process.

What Went Wrong?

Many people make great plans, but they don't realize the importance of using those plans as their roadmap. For example, a transplant nurse, Sally (BSN, MSN), had moved up to the position as the lead technical person in her department and was named the project manager for a new transplant implementation. Because of her inexperience managing projects, the PMO Director, Mike "Mikey" Matthews, was asked to help her plan the project. Mikey set up a meeting with the Sally for the following week, and she studied everything she could find about project management over the weekend.

The following week Mikey and Sally sat down with her team and developed a project management plan, including schedules, budgets, and other required documents. It seemed like a great start. Sally thanked Mikey, and he went back to his other projects while Sally's project chugged along, appearing in status reports to be doing fine. After about three months someone approached Mikey and asked if he would attend an upcoming transplant project meeting.

The meeting started off great, with each team member giving their updates. One by one they each told the nurse project manager of obstacles, setbacks, lack of stakeholder participation, and unclear requirements from users. Sally listened to each person intently, jotted notes, and then said, "That's great. Thanks everyone. I'll see you next week!" The meeting ended. Just like that! After the room cleared Mikey asked Sally how the project was going, and after a slight pause, she replied that it was going very well. Mikey then asked where they were in the schedule. Sally paused again, this time for what seemed like minutes, looking back at Mikey blankly. He then rephrased the question, "What activity are you working on right now, as a team? Are you ahead of schedule? Behind schedule? You know, compared to the schedule we laid out three months ago." After another slight pause, Sally replied with a very simple and honest reply: "You didn't say that we needed to use that schedule again."

Sally had never considered the plan to be her roadmap, and as a result the project ended up being 100% over schedule and nearly that much over budget.

Recall from Chapter 3 that project planning involves devising and maintaining a workable scheme to ensure that the project meets its scope, time, and cost goals as well as other constraints and organizational needs. Also, recall that planning includes tasks related to each of the ten project management knowledge areas. This chapter describes the types of planning performed in two of the knowledge areas—project integration and scope management—and summarizes the planning done for AHS' VAPR project. Chapter 5 focuses on planning in the time, cost, and quality knowledge areas, and Chapter 6 addresses planning for the other five knowledge areas—human resource, communications, stakeholder, risk, and procurement management.

SUMMARY OF PLANNING PROCESSES AND OUTPUTS

The *PMBOK® Guide, Fifth Edition* lists over 50 documents that project teams can produce as part of project planning. Other experts suggest even more potential planning documents. Every project is unique, so project managers and their teams must determine which planning outputs are needed for their projects and how they should be created.

Figure 4-1 summarizes the project planning processes and outputs for integration and scope management listed in the *PMBOK® Guide, Fifth Edition*. This chapter provides samples of some of these outputs, as well as a few additional ones, such as a team contract. All of these planning documents, as well as other project-related information, will be available to all team members on a project Web site. AHS had used project Web sites for several years, and everyone agreed that they significantly facilitate communications.

Knowledge area	Planning process	Outputs
Project integration management	Develop project management plan	Project management plan
Project scope management	Plan scope management	Scope management plan
		Requirements management plan
	Collect requirements	Requirements documentation
		Requirements traceability matrix
	Define scope	Project scope statement
		Project documents updates
	Create WBS	Scope baseline
		Project documents updates

Figure 4-1. Planning processes and outputs for project integration and scope management

The following sections describe planning processes and outputs in these first two knowledge areas and then provide examples of applying them to the VAPR project at AHS. You can consider some of the planning processes as following a chronological order, especially for the scope, time, and cost tasks. You need to plan the project scope and determine what activities need to be done before you can develop a detailed project schedule. Likewise, you need a detailed project schedule before you can develop a cost baseline. Of course, human resource planning and assignment to the project team must also be accomplished as part of project human resource management, as described in the next chapter. As noted earlier, there are many interdependencies between various knowledge areas and process groups.

PROJECT INTEGRATION MANAGEMENT

Project integration management involves coordinating all the project management knowledge areas throughout a project's life span. The one planning process performed as part of project integration management, according to PMI, is called "develop project management plan." Some project teams also create a team contract (not mentioned in the *PMBOK® Guide*) in addition to developing the project management plan.

Team Contracts

Because of the multiple disciplines that often work on AHS projects, the PMO had adopted using **team contracts** to help promote teamwork, ensure all team members understand the commitment required of them, and to clarify team communications. After core project team members have been selected, they meet to prepare a team contract. The process normally includes reviewing a template and then working in small groups of three to four people to prepare inputs for the team contract. Creating smaller groups makes it easier for everyone to contribute ideas. Each group then shares their ideas on what the contract should contain, and then they work together to form one project team contract. Ideally, the contract should be finished in a one- to two-hour meeting. The project manager should attend the meeting and act as a coach or facilitator, observing the different personalities of team members and seeing how well they work together. It is crucial to emphasize the importance of the project team throughout the project's life cycle. The team contract should provide the groundwork for how the project team will function, and as such it should be the work of the team, not the work of just the project manager.

In some organizations the project manager contributes to the team contract, but as a team equal and not as the project manager. This is can best be accomplished by bringing in another project manager or trained facilitator to run the session. It is critical that the facilitator runs the meeting, as everyone in the room must be allowed to contribute equally to the team contract.

Sample Team Contract

Figure 4-2 shows the team contract created for the VAPR project. Notice that the main topics covered include the following: code of conduct, participation, communication, problem solving, and meeting guidelines.

Everyone involved in creating the team contract should sign it. As new project team members are added, the project manager should review ground rules with them and have them read and sign the contract as well.

Team Contract

Project Name: VAPR (Ventilator Associated Pneumonia Reduction)

Project Team Members Names and Sign-off:

<u>Name</u>   <u>Date</u>

Jeff Birdwell   *May 21*
Other team members

Code of Conduct: As a project team, we will:
- Work proactively, anticipating potential problems and preventing their occurrence.
- Keep other team members informed of information related to the project.
- Focus on what is best for the entire project team.

Participation: We will:
- Be honest and open during all project activities – never varnish the truth.
- Provide the opportunity for equal participation by all members, all disciplines.
- Be open to new approaches and consider new ideas.
- Let the project manager know well in advance if a team member has to miss a meeting or may have trouble meeting a deadline for a given activity.

Communication: We will:
- Keep discussions on track and have one discussion at a time.
- Use the telephone, e-mail, a project Web site, instant messaging, texts, and other technology to assist in communicating.
- Have the project manager or designated person facilitate all meetings and arrange for phone and videoconferences, as needed.
- Work together to create the project schedule and related information and enter actuals, issues, risks, and other information into our enterprise project management system by 4 p.m. every Friday.

Problem Solving: We will:
- Only use constructive criticism and focus on solving problems, not blaming people.
- Strive to build on each other's ideas.
- Bring in outside experts when necessary.

Meeting Guidelines: We will:
- Avoid the use of mobile devices during meetings, unless required for meeting discussion.
- Respect the skills, experience, and schedules of the diverse disciplines on the project.
- Plan to have a face-to-face meeting of the entire project team every Tuesday morning.
- Arrange for telephone or videoconferencing for participants as needed.
- Hold other meetings as needed.
- Develop and follow an agenda for all meetings.
- Record meeting minutes and send an announcement within 24 hours stating that the minutes are posted on the project Web site. Minutes will focus on decisions made and action items and issues from each meeting.

AHS Academic Health Systems

Figure 4-2. Sample team contract

Project Management Plans

To coordinate and integrate information across all project management knowledge areas and across the organization, there must be a good project management plan. A **project management plan** is a document used to coordinate all project planning documents and to help guide a project's execution and control. Plans created in the other knowledge areas are subsidiary parts of the overall project management plan. Project management plans facilitate communication among stakeholders and provide a baseline for progress measurement and project control, as discussed in detail in Chapter 8. A **baseline** is a starting point, a measurement, or an observation that is documented so that it can be used for future comparison. The project management plan briefly describes the overall scope, time, and cost baselines for the project. Specific plans in each of those knowledge areas provide more detailed baseline information. For example, the project management plan might provide a high-level baseline for the work required for the entire project, whereas the scope baseline prepared as part of the project scope management knowledge area (explained later in this chapter) provides detailed scope information.

Project management plans should be dynamic, flexible, and receptive to change when the environment or project changes. These plans should greatly assist the project manager in leading the project team and assessing project status. Just as projects are unique, so are project plans. For a small project involving a few people over a couple of months, a project charter, team contract, scope statement, and Gantt chart might be the only project planning documents needed; there would not be a need for a separate project management plan. A large project involving 100 people over three years would benefit from having a detailed project management plan and separate plans for each knowledge area. It is important to tailor all planning documentation to fit the needs of specific projects. Because all project plans should help guide the completion of the particular project, they should be only as detailed as needed for each project.

There are, however, common elements to most project management plans, as follows, and as shown in Figure 4-3:

- Project Title
- Project Purpose
- Project Organization
- Project Governance
- Scope Management
- Budget Management
- Schedule Management
- Approach
- References to other project planning documents, as needed

Project Management Plan
Version 1.0   May 23, 20xx

PROJECT TITLE

Ventilator Associated Pneumonia (VAP) Reduction – "VAPR"

PURPOSE

VAP costs AHS over $3.6M per year in costs, and puts our patients at risk for severe and sometimes fatal consequences. VAP is considered preventable by CMS and has worked with the Institutes for Healthcare Improvement (IHI) to develop a set of best practices that, if followed, has demonstrated a reduction of VAP by 50% in other healthcare facilities. AHS will implement a system to collect and report compliance with the best practices to better manage VAP.

PROJECT ORGANIZATION

The basic organization of the project is provided in Figure 1. The project sponsor, Marilyn Shoemaker, RN, PhD, will have the final say on major decisions, with consultation from the project steering committee and project champions, Casey Lidwell and Dr. Danielle Scheerer. The project sponsor should have time to thoroughly review important project information and provide timely feedback to the project manager.

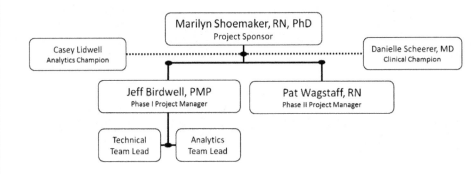

PROJECT GOVERNANCE

1. Management Review Process: The project steering committee will meet at least monthly to provide inputs and review progress on this project.

2. Progress Measurement Process: The project steering committee will review project progress during project review meetings, and they can also review information as needed by viewing reports on the enterprise project management system.

3. Change Approval Process: See Attachment 1 based on AHS standards.

4. VAPR has been broken down into two phases. The first phase is a proof of concept and the data collection/reporting system and will be managed by Jeff Birdwell, PMP from the PMO's office. The second phase will be managed by Pat Wager, RN from analytics.

Scope Management

Key stakeholders will be interviewed to gather their requirements. Key stakeholders include the patient intensive care director, at least one nurse from each intensive care unit (ICU), the chair of the Clinical Quality Improvement Council, the manager of Infection Control, and any other key stakeholders identified by those in this list. The team will also use observation to review current workflows in order to determine the impact on caregivers. Requirements provided by all methods will be reviewed by the steering committee. All requirements will be prioritized and scored by the project steering committee. Once the scope, budget, and timeline are approved, then any change to requirements must be approved by the sponsor and both champions.

Budget Management

The budget will be developed using three standard labor rates: $45/hr for general staffing; $65/hr for licensed clinicians other than physicians, and $125/hr for physicians. External IT labor will be estimated at $175/hr based on recent contract labor rates used by AHS. No external clinical labor is expected to be required.

The VAPR project is expected to cost $980,000 over one year, with a total cost of ownership (TCO) of $980,000 over three years (internal support costs are absorbed).

Schedule Management

The schedule will be developed based, when practical, on our staff's experience working with similar projects. All time estimates will be provided by the staff charged with doing the work.
Once the schedule has been approved by the steering committee, no schedule changes can be made without approval from the sponsor. The project is expected to take twelve months and be live by July 1.

Approach

- Project to be broken up into two major phases that will overlap their work, requiring the two project managers to work closely together throughout the project.
- Phase I, VAPRware, is concerned with the proof of concept, data collection and data reporting. It is primarily a technology project but will require the cooperation of and collaboration with analytics and nursing in order to identify the required data elements and their source systems.
- Phase II, VAPRflow, is concerned with clinical workflow reengineering, and is primarily a clinical project that will require working with the Nursing Documentation Committee and Medical Executive Committee in order to gain their input and support.
- Training to be developed and delivered by the Nurse Educator Team under the direction of the Phase II project manager. All training will be computer based training (CBT) and will be included in annual training requirements for all clinicians.
- The cost of any work conducted on behalf of the project will be paid by the project budget, with the exception of the time nurses spend in training.

AHS Academic Health Systems

Figure 4-3. Sample Project Management Plan

Sample Project Management Plan

Figure 4-3 provides partial information from the initial project management plan for the VAPR project. Of course, the actual document would be longer because this is a one-year, nearly $1 million project involving and impacting a variety of stakeholders including nurses, physicians, respiratory therapists, pharmacists, data analysts, and report writers. Like all project management documents, the project management plan is a living document and will be updated as needed. It is important to mark the date, version number, and a summary of the changes on the document to avoid confusion. (20xx is used instead of the actual year in this example.) Also note that project organization varies on projects, so it is helpful to provide a high-level project organizational chart in the project management plan.

On some projects, the project sponsor and project champion are the same person, but not always. Projects that cross functional boundaries, as the VAPR project, often benefit from having a high-level project sponsor, such as the CNO, and also having several project champions over each of the functional areas. The VAPR project has one champion (Casey Lidwell) leading the first phase, which primarily deals with data and technology, and a second champion (Dr. Danielle Scheerer) for the second phase, which deals primarily with the clinical aspects of reducing ventilator associated pneumonia.

PROJECT SCOPE MANAGEMENT

Project scope management involves defining and controlling what work is and is not included in a project. The main planning processes performed as part of project scope management include planning scope management, collecting requirements, defining scope, and creating the WBS. The main documents produced are requirements documents, a requirements management plan, a requirements traceability matrix, and a **scope baseline**, which is composed of an approved scope statement, a WBS, and a WBS dictionary.

Planning Scope Management

The purpose of the process of planning scope management is to determine how the project scope will be defined, validated, and controlled. Project teams usually have several meetings with key stakeholders and experts to help them develop a scope management plan and requirements management plan.

A scope management plan, and all other knowledge area plans (except for integration management, where the overarching project management plan is created), are components of the project management plan. Contents of the scope management plan include descriptions of how you will perform the following:

- preparing a detailed project scope statement
- creating, maintaining, and approving the WBS
- obtaining acceptance of the completed project deliverables
- controlling how requests for changes to the project scope statement will be processed

The *PMBOK® Guide, Fifth Edition*, defines a **requirement** as "conditions or capabilities that must be met by the project or present in the product, service, or result to satisfy an agreement or other formally imposed specification." Before you collect requirements you must develop a **requirements management plan,** which describes how project requirements will be collected, analyzed, documented, and managed throughout the project.

Sample Requirements Management Plan

There were many requirements involved in the VAPR project. Some requirements, such as which ventilator protocol to use, were identified in the project charter. However, Jeff knew from past experience that it was important to do a good job managing requirements or this project would expand to include other quality of care improvements that were outside of the scope of VAP reduction. Once a project starts to look at how to improve patient care, both the stakeholders and the project team themselves will start to see many other ways they can improve care. Jeff knew to resist this temptation if the work is not directly related to VAP reduction.

He worked with the team to develop a requirements management plan. Important contents of this plan include information related to:

- Planning, tracking, and reporting requirements

- Performing configuration management activities, such as initiating, analyzing, authorizing, tracking, and reporting changes to requirements

- Prioritizing requirements

- Identifying requirement metrics

- Tracing requirements

Figure 4-4 shows a sample requirement management plan.

Requirements Management Plan
Version 1.0 May 29, 20xx

PROJECT TITLE: VENTILATOR ASSOCIATED PNEUMONIA (VAP) REDUCTION – "VAPR"

Planning, tracking, and reporting requirements

Information provided in the business case and project charter will provide valuable information in determining requirements for this project, as will the IHI Ventilator Bundle itself. All requirements will be documented within the project management system and will be reviewed for progress weekly as part of the regular project meetings. Each requirement will be assigned a customer owner, designated initially as the provider of the requirement, but in some cases as the staff member who is considered the expert on the requirement itself.

Performing configuration management activities

Requirements can be identified through a variety of methods. Executive clinical leadership will be interviewed individually, committees such as the Med Exec and Clinical Quality Improvement Council will be asked for requirements through our sponsor, and our champions will conduct focus groups with their peers and customers to gather input. Requirements will also be extracted from the IHI Ventilator Bundle, and both CMS and Joint Commission measures will be reviewed for additional requirements. Appropriate project stakeholders will analyze, authorize, track, and report changes to requirements. The project manager must be informed in advance of potential changes to requirements and be involved in the decision process to approve those changes. Any change that will impact the project's cost by more than 2% or extend the schedule past the identified go live date must be approved by the project steering committee.

Prioritizing requirements

All requirements will be designated as 1, 2 or 3, for mandatory, desirable, or nice-to-have, respectively. Emphasis will be placed on meeting all mandatory requirements, followed by desirable and then nice-to-have requirements. All IHI, CMS, and Joint Commission requirements will be assigned a value of 1. Other requirements will be prioritized and scored by the project steering committee, using an anonymous method of scoring (Delphi method).

Identifying requirements metrics

Requirements will be reviewed on an ongoing basis to determine their accuracy and completeness. This will be done by tracking the number of requirement changes required and compliance with the IHI Ventilator Bundle of the project deliverable.

Tracing requirements

All mandatory requirements will be included in the requirements traceability matrix. Desirable and nice-to-have requirements will be documented but addressed only as time and resources allow. The matrix will be created using AHS' requirements matrix template.

AHS Academic Health Systems

Figure 4-4. Sample requirements management plan

Collecting Requirements

It is important to document requirements in enough detail so that they can be measured during project execution. After all, meeting scope goals is often based on meeting documented requirements. However, some project managers go into extreme detail with the result of having too many requirements to manage efficiently. In cases where the project truly has hundreds or thousands of requirements, it is best to break the project down into multiple phases, where groups of requirements can be more easily managed.

The main outputs of collecting requirements include:

- requirements documents, which can range from a single-page checklist to a room full of notebooks that may include a variety of text narrative, diagrams, images, process flows, workflows, system layouts, blueprints, regulations, standards, best practices, etc.

- a **requirements traceability matrix (RTM)**, which is a table that lists the actual requirements, various attributes of each requirement, and the status of the requirements to ensure that all of them are addressed. The attributes you track vary by project, but they normally include the category and source of the requirement. An RTM might also include the priority, the deliverable from the WBS that is required to meet this requirement, and the version of the requirement (as requirements may change over time).

There are several ways to collect requirements. Interviewing stakeholders one-on-one is often very effective, although it can be very expensive and time-consuming. This method is often the only possibility for collecting requirements from physicians and executive leadership, and you must be fully prepared to ask pre-determined questions before entering an interview. Often they are squeezing you in between meetings, patient visits, or surgical procedures, so you may only get ten to fifteen minutes to conduct your interview. Be concise, and they will appreciate your respect of their time.

For many staff, including nurses, therapists, and people in clinical support positions, operations, finance, patient billing, claims, etc., holding focus groups, facilitated workshops, and using group creativity and decision-making techniques to collect requirements are normally faster and less expensive than one-on-one interviews. Questionnaires and surveys can also be very efficient ways to collect requirements as long as key stakeholders provide honest and thorough information. There is also a tendency to ask leading questions on surveys, so be sure to have others review the survey before it is sent out to ensure it is unbiased. For clinical projects, especially those involving changes to nursing, physician, or therapy workflows, observation is often the most effective technique for collecting requirements. Observation is most powerful when used after initial requirements are collected using other methods, as observations can then be used to verify the accuracy of the data collected earlier.

Another method used to collect requirements is prototyping. A prototype is a less than fully functional model of the expected final product, used to allow the stakeholders to get a feel for how the final product will look., often used in software development, engineering, and construction. However, if you are building a new wing in a hospital, the architects will most likely prepare a scale model of the wing so that staff can get a clearer perspective than a 2-D blueprint provides. For software projects, prototypes are often used to allow the customer to verify that the look and feel of the user interface is correct, before any actual code is produced. With the advancement of software development tools increasing the speed of development, and with the spreading use of Agile project management techniques, prototypes are becoming less common for software projects.

The project's size, complexity, importance, and other factors will affect how much effort is spent on collecting requirements. For example, a team working on a project to upgrade their entire electronic health record (EHR) system for a multi-hospital healthcare system with 28,000 employees would allocate a great deal of time to collecting requirements. However, a project initiated to upgrade the EHR system at a small family practice with just eight employees would need a much smaller effort. In any case, it is important for a project team to decide how to collect and manage requirements. It is crucial to gather inputs from key stakeholders and align the scope, a key aspect of the entire project, with business strategy, as described in Chapter 2. There are also many software products available to assist in the requirements management process, like the one described in the What Went Right example.

What Went Right?

Requirements management is a challenge on many healthcare informatics projects. Mia McCroskey, an IBM Champion (someone recognized for helping others make the best use of IBM software) and project and requirements manager at Emerging Health, described two key challenges they faced. "Deriving meaningful information from the electronic medical record is essential to justifying the cost of those systems. We're piloting the use of predictive analytics—combining statistical methods with the mass of patient data collected every day at our parent medical center—to predict outcomes at the population level. To do it you need a very wide range of data: blood pressure, height, and weight, smoking patterns, history of heart disease, current blood sugar level, and on and on. Just bringing all this data together is the first challenge…Another area of critical concern is patient information. The need to pool patient data for direct care as well as population research is supported by legislature and funding sources. But we are bound, both legally and ethically, to protect patient identity in every circumstance."[1]

Emerging Health started using a tool by IBM called Rational DOORS to help manage requirements. As a result, they saw a 69 percent reduction in the cost of test preparation, testing, and rework in the software development process and a 25 percent reduction in the time it took to customize their Clinical Looking Glass application for unique client requirements. According to McCroskey, "Time to market is always a critical benchmark, but especially so in the fast-paced healthcare industry. Because our industry is so competitive, being able to deliver the product faster enhances our reputation and the confidence our customers have in us. Faster time to market is vital to our success, and we've now achieved that with the more responsive environment Rational DOORS has allowed us to establish."[2]

Sample Requirements Traceability Matrix

Figure 4-5 provides an example of a few requirements traceability matrix (RTM) entries for the VAPR project. Remember that the main purpose of an RTM is to maintain the linkage from the source of each requirement through its decomposition to implementation and verification. For example, the first entry, R26, states that the project team must identify the electronic (or paper) sources of the data at AHS that indicates whether or not the IHI Ventilator Bundle is being complied with for vented patients. Note this requirement has been completed, and the three data sources were noted in the comments section. The other requirements listed have not yet been addressed as it is too early in the project.

Req ID	Name	Category	Source	Status	Comments
R26	Identify source systems that document compliance with the IHI vent bundle	Technical	Chief Medical Information Officer	Complete	Three sources were identified: ClinDoc, Pharmacy Administration, and RT Documentation.
R91	Online report to indicate compliance, by patient, with IHI bundle	Analytics	Chief Quality Officer	Not started	Data must be no more than 6 hours old.
R123	Design new ventilator protocol for nursing	Clinical Workflow	Chief Nursing Officer	Not started	Must be reviewed and approved by the nursing oversight committee.

Figure 4-5. Sample requirements traceability matrix

Defining Scope

Good scope definition is crucial to project success because it helps improve the accuracy of time, cost, and resource estimates; defines a baseline for performance measurement and project control; and aids in communicating clear work responsibilities. Work that is not included in the scope statement should not be done, and any work that may potentially be considered a "gray area" should explicitly be excluded in the scope statement. The main techniques used in defining scope include expert judgment, product analysis, alternatives identification, and facilitated workshops. The main outputs of scope definition are the scope statement and updates to project documents.

The project charter, requirements documentation, and **organizational process assets** (i.e. policies and procedures related to project management, past project files, and lessons-learned reports from previous, similar projects or with similar customers) are all inputs for creating the initial scope statement. The scope statement should be updated as more information becomes available. Although content varies, scope statements should include, at a minimum, a product scope description, product user acceptance criteria, and detailed information on all project deliverables. It is also helpful to document project boundaries, constraints, and assumptions. The scope statement should also reference supporting documents, such as product specifications and corporate policies, which often affect how products or services are produced.

It is important to note the difference between the *project* and the *product*. The project is the effort required to create the product, and each has its own requirements and scope. For example, the project scope defines what the project is expected to accomplish, while the product scope defines the qualities of the ultimate deliverable. In the case of the VAPR project, the project scope is to develop systems and processes to reduce the VAP incidence rate at AHS. The product scope includes specifics about those systems and processes, such as online reports, data no more than six hours old, and modified ventilator protocols to include the IHI best practices.

Sample Scope Statement

Jeff and Pat worked closely together while planning the project work for Phase I. Because their two phases were so closely tied together, it was crucial that they collaborate, especially during planning. Jeff engaged his key team members as well as the project champion and other key stakeholders within AHS, such as the head of nursing education and the director of Infection Control, whose jobs included collecting data and reporting VAP incidence rates at AHS.

Jeff wanted to be sure the scope would be clear to anyone who read it, so the scope statement was several pages long, as it was based on over one hundred requirements. Pat, who worked with clinicians frequently, insisted that the scope statement define the project boundary lines or what the project would *not* do. She knew that if they did not define what was out of scope that the work would expand once they started reviewing and modifying nursing workflows.

Part of the scope statement is shown in Figure 4-6. Both Jeff and Pat knew that this document would change as they finalized more details of the project scope, but they were satisfied that it was a good start. Note that some details have been added and changes have been made since the project charter was completed. For example, the actual IHI Ventilator Bundle elements are now listed, and the success criteria have been modified slightly. In additional to the product-oriented deliverables, the team would also produce several project management-related deliverables, like a WBS, project schedule, and so on. Because AHS project teams understood the scope of those deliverables, they did not include them on scope statements.

Ventilator Associated Pneumonia Reduction (VAPR) Project
Scope Statement, Version 1.0, June 1

Product Characteristics and Requirements

This project will introduce the IHI Ventilator Bundle (best practices) into our AHS clinical protocols and workflows. We must identify which, if any, AHS system currently collects data that would indicate compliance with the five elements in the bundle. If the data is not currently collected electronically at AHS, a data collection point must be identified. All data must be integrated into a single online report so that they may correct the patient's care during the required time period. To minimize the amount of corrective actions required, the nursing and respiratory therapy workflows will be modified to include the best practices, and the ventilator protocols will be modified to automatically include orders for the bundle elements. The following best practices are included in the IHI Ventilator Bundle:

- Patient Head of Bed (HOB) elevation, 30 to 45 degrees
- Sedation vacation every 24 hours
- Daily oral/mouth care with Chlorhexidine
- Venous Thrombosis Embolism (VTE) prophylaxis
- Peptic ulcer prophylaxis

Out of Scope

This project will not consider any other patient care, best practices, evidenced based medicine, or other patient care improvements discovered during the project work. Any additional potential patient care improvement projects will be submitted to the project request system and reviewed, approved, and managed separately based on their own merits.

Product User Acceptance Criteria

This project will be considered successful if the following measures are met:

- Project completed by the end of the next fiscal year (June 30)
- Project completed for $980,000 or less
- VAP incidence is reduced by 25% within 90 days of go live
- VAP incidence rate is reduced by 35% within 180 days of go live
- VAP incidence rate is reduced by 50% within 270 days of go live

Product-Oriented Deliverables

1. Data Interfaces from source systems, including registration, bed management, clinical documentation, and respiratory therapy documentation systems.
2. Database to store IHI bundle data elements collected on AHS patients.
3. Online report to present IHI bundle compliance to caregivers using standard AHS reporting tools.
4. Convenient and timely report delivery method, including availability on mobile devices.
5. Modified clinical workflows to integrate IHI Ventilator Bundle best practices.
6. Modified ventilator protocols to integrate IHI Ventilator Bundle best practices.

Figure 4-6. Sample scope statement

As more information becomes available and decisions are made related to project scope—such as the adoption of additional ventilator elements to include or changes to the way the data will be presented to the users—the project team would update the project scope statement. Subsequent iterations of the draft scope statement should be identified as Version 1.1, Version 1.2, and so on. Minor versions are typically those that do not change the direction of the project dramatically, while major versions (the number to the left of the decimal) are thought of as substantial changes to project scope. At any given time the project scope statement should accurately portray the project scope, regardless of the number of changes that have been introduced and approved. The project scope statement is, like most project documents, a living document.

Once the scope baseline is established (approved by the steering committee as being the official project scope), further updates will require that the steering committee, or some subset of that committee, approve those changes before they are included in the scope. These updates might also require changes to the project management plan. For example, if the team decides to purchase products or services for the project from a supplier with whom it has never worked, the project management plan should include information on working with that new supplier.

An up-to-date project scope statement is an important document for developing and confirming a common understanding of the project scope. Deliverables should be described in as much detail as required to ensure that the resulting deliverable is correct. For example, it is helpful to estimate the length of a report or presentation so the person responsible for that work has a good understanding of what is expected. The scope statement describes in detail the work to be accomplished on the project and is an important tool for ensuring customer satisfaction and preventing **scope creep**, which is the tendency for project scope to continually increase.

Figure 4-7 shows a humorous example of scope creep no surgeon wants to encounter. The initial estimate of the work did not include a buzzing noise!

Figure 4-7. Scope creep during surgery (www.xkcd.com)

Creating the Work Breakdown Structure

A **work breakdown structure (WBS)** is a deliverables-oriented grouping of the work involved in a project that defines the total scope of the project. In other words, the WBS is a document that breaks *all* the work required for the project into discrete deliverables, and groups those deliverables into a logical hierarchy. Because most projects involve many people and many different deliverables, it is important to organize and divide the work into logical components that make sense to the project team. Although some, especially academics, believe that there is only one way to build a correct WBS, in practice there are many ways to decompose deliverables. Project managers and their teams will decide which method they want to use, and if it works for them, then it is an acceptable WBS.

A WBS begins at the top with the largest deliverable of the project, often defined as the entire project, or simply the project name itself. Then each subsequent level, while moving downward, breaks down, or decomposes, the deliverables that are listed above it, much like an outline for a research paper. Creating a research paper outline is a practice most of you have been required to do since middle school, so you should already have a clear understanding of the process. At some point you will have decomposed the deliverables down enough to be able to assign each of the sub-deliverables to a specific group or person. When project managers can do this for each and every sub-deliverable, they are done with the WBS.

A deliverable or sub-deliverable at the lowest level of the WBS, where it can be appropriately assigned to and managed by a single accountable person, is called a **work package.** Each work package should be defined in enough detail to estimate what it would cost and how long it would take to create. If you try to assign it to a group or person, and they tell you that they will have to work with another group to complete this work, then you should consider splitting that sub-deliverable down into two or more sub-deliverables so that you can assign them to the areas that will do the work. This practice allows you to hold one person, or group, accountable for the work completion.

The WBS is a foundation document in project management because it provides the basis for planning and managing project schedules, costs, resources, and changes. Because the WBS defines the total scope of the project, work should not be done on a project if it is not included in the WBS. This is a critical point in the definition of the WBS: The WBS contains 100% of the deliverables (often called "work") of the project—not 95%, not 102%, but 100%. The WBS puts the project team, and its stakeholders, on the same page as it is the first time that everyone can look at the work that will be completed. If something is missing, it should be apparent. If something is added in error, it should be apparent. Therefore, it is crucial to develop a good WBS.

A WBS is often depicted in a graphical format, similar to an organizational chart. The name of the entire project is the top box, called Level 1, and the main groupings for the work are listed in the second tier of boxes, called Level 2. This level numbering is based on PMI's *Practice Standard for Work Breakdown Structure, Second Edition (2006)*. Each of those boxes can be broken down or decomposed into subsequent tiers of boxes to show the hierarchy of the work. Project teams often organize the WBS around project products, project phases, system modules, geographical regions, or other logical groupings. People often like to create a WBS in a graphical format first to help them visualize the whole project and all of its main parts. You can also show a WBS in tabular form as an indented list of elements.

Healthcare Perspective

A project team had been working for several months attempting to identify where they could electronically pull CMS measures data in order to reduce chart abstraction time at their hospital. The sponsor knew that they were only trying to pull data for three CMS measures and one Joint Commission measure. Although he met with the project team weekly, he could not understand why it was taking so long to identify and pull data for just four "little measures." The project manager and her team had a difficult time trying to get the sponsor to understand how complex this project was and how those four measures required a great deal of data to be submitted to CMS and JC. Week after week the sponsor was patient, but he was growing less patient. Perhaps worse, his lack of patience was causing the project team to start losing their motivation to complete the project.

After a particularly stressful meeting with the sponsor, the project manager met with the team to brainstorm options to help the sponsor understand the breadth and depth of this project. One person suggested that the sponsor be shown the thousands of lines of software written to pull the data. Another frustrated team member even suggested that they let the sponsor show them how to do it more quickly. Then someone suggested that they create a WBS for the data elements required for the four measures, and to include indicators on the WBS itself to show the availability and accuracy of the data. Everyone agreed it was a great idea, and so the project manager assigned a staff member to this work. By the next sponsor meeting the detailed WBS was ready for presentation, and the team brought it to the meeting. This WBS was 36 inches tall and 20 feet wide, with 1392 data elements represented on it!

The project sponsor and physician champion were facing the WBS, side by side, both with hands behind their backs, and about every 10 seconds they would both step to the right. There was no discussion in the room and no discussion between the two leaders. When the project manager came into the room the team immediately gave him the signal to "be quiet and watch," and he did, taking a seat at the table. After about another 10 minutes the two leaders turned around, smiled broadly, and the sponsor said, "I think I just realized that I am a graphically-oriented person. This is incredible. I had no idea this project was so complex! Can I show this to the Executive Medical Director?"

At the next all staff meeting the sponsor made a 20-minute presentation about this project, showed off the WBS and the project work completed to date (indicated on the WBS itself), and thanked the project team for their amazing work to date. At that point the project team would have done anything for this sponsor, as they knew that he had their backs as well. The WBS is a powerful tool. Use it to ensure that everyone is on the same page.

Example WBSs

Understanding how to create a WBS is difficult. Many people learn by example, so this section includes several of them. The first involves a very simple demonstration of the basic reason for a WBS—it includes a breakdown of major project deliverables into smaller deliverables. Figure 4-8 is a WBS designed to represent a project to bake a Birthday Cake! The cake is decomposed into the cake itself, the frosting, toppings added to the top of the cake, and candles. Note that there is no oven, no pans, no mixer, no utensils, and no mixing bowl in the WBS. Furthermore, it does not indicate how to mix the ingredients, the amount of the ingredients, the order of the construction, the baking temperature or time, or any other steps required to actually make this cake. Why? Because the WBS should represent the project deliverables, not the tools, techniques, or actions required to create those deliverables.

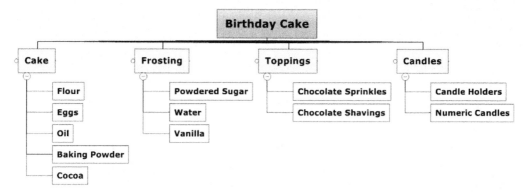

Figure 4-8. WBS for a birthday cake

Of course no one would create a WBS for a birthday cake, but many of us have created documents that are very similar in construction to a WBS, such as a shopping list for a birthday party. You begin with your party's concept and then define the things that you must have in order to make the party happen (food, drinks, decorations, etc.). A WBS is not unlike that shopping list, except you are defining the things that your project must deliver to be successful. It is important to understand that the project does not have to create each of the deliverables (the boxes on the WBS), but it must create, purchase, or in some other way provide those items.

One basic method to verify that your WBS is complete is to look at the lowest level of deliverables and ask yourself, "If I have these deliverables will they, in combination, give me everything I need to create the higher level deliverable?" In the Birthday Cake example, consider the Cake deliverable. The Cake deliverable is decomposed into five smaller deliverables: flour, eggs, oil, baking powder, and cocoa. The question you would then ask the team is, "If I have flour, eggs, oil, baking powder, and cocoa, will I have everything I need to create a cake?" Of course the answer is no, as you forgot about the salt and water! You would then correct the WBS by adding salt and water as two other sub-deliverables under the Cake deliverable. Every box on the WBS is referred to as a deliverable in context of itself, but it is called a sub-deliverable when talking about it in reference to the larger deliverable above it.

Because project managers rarely create Birthday Cakes as projects (with the popular Cake Boss television show as a possible exception), the following examples are more representative of projects that most project managers can understand. For example, building a house is a common project, but there are many ways to create a WBS for it.

Figure 4-9 and 4-10 show two different WBSs for building a house from examples provided by two companies that design software to help manage projects—MatchWare and Microsoft. MatchWare creates a software product called MindView Business, mentioned in Chapter 2. You can use this software to create a mind map for many different purposes, including creating a WBS. Microsoft creates Project 2013, mentioned in Chapter 1 and described in detail in Appendix A. Notice that the second tier, or Level 2, WBS items in Figure 4-9 includes *six* major deliverables: the foundation, external construction, internal construction, roof, services, and yard & access. (For this example, only the internal construction and services categories are broken down further, but for a real house project they would all be broken down several more levels.) However, in Figure 4-10, there are *ten* different categories for the Level 2 items: general conditions, site work, foundation, framing, dry in, exterior finishes, utility rough-ins and complete concrete, interior finishes, landscaping and grounds work, and final acceptance. Some categories are similar, while others are not. The main thing to understand is that you are organizing the main deliverables based on *what* work needs to be done and *not how* the work will be done. Neither of these examples for building a house includes obtaining financing or moving items from a former residence to the new house. If this work is in the scope of the project, then you could include WBS Level 2 deliverables called "financing" and "relocation." If it was important to you to include outdoor recreational items in the scope of the project, you might also include a Level 2 category called "outdoor recreation" with Level 3 sub-deliverables called "swimming pool," "tennis court," and "hot tub."

The key concept is that the WBS includes 100% of the work required to complete the project. If your project will create something, it should be shown in the WBS. Nothing should be created that is not in the WBS. This concept is also true for interim deliverables that will not end up in the hands of the customer. For example, when a firm built a patient walkway that connected two buildings separated by wetlands, the project team had to first build a temporary wooden causeway that stood above the marsh, protecting it from equipment and giving the workers a platform from which to work. When the project was completed, they removed the temporary causeway. This temporary causeway would be included in the WBS as it was required for the project, even though it was not the final deliverable.

These three examples, the birthday cake and two different house projects, show a WBS in a graphical or tree view, resembling the format of an organizational chart. You can also create or display a WBS in a tabular or list view that is text- based. Figure 4-11, described in the next example, shows both a graphical and tabular view of a WBS.

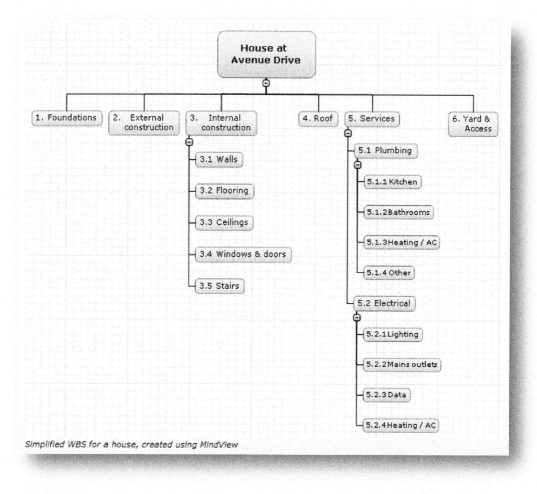

Simplified WBS for a house, created using MindView

4-9. WBS for a house showing 6 main deliverables (www.matchware.com)

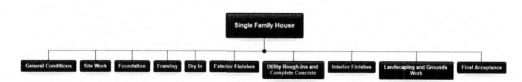

4-10. WBS for a house showing 10 main deliverables (Microsoft Project 2013)

When do you use one format versus the other? It depends upon the audience, the complexity of the WBS, and the medium that you are using to represent the WBS. The graphical format is often preferred but can be hard to follow once you get past several hundred deliverables and sub-deliverables, and it often requires a large format printer (36" wide or wider) to be able print in its entirety. The tabular format can be printed on regular letter sized paper (often many pages), but may not show the relationship between the deliverables as clearly.

Figure 4-11 shows a WBS in both graphical and tabular views for a project to create a new patient sign-in kiosk for a small physician practice. The title of the project is Kiosk Project, shown in the top box or Level 1 of the WBS, and the Level 2 deliverables are location, patient kiosk, staff training and marketing. Level 3 deliverables are also included.

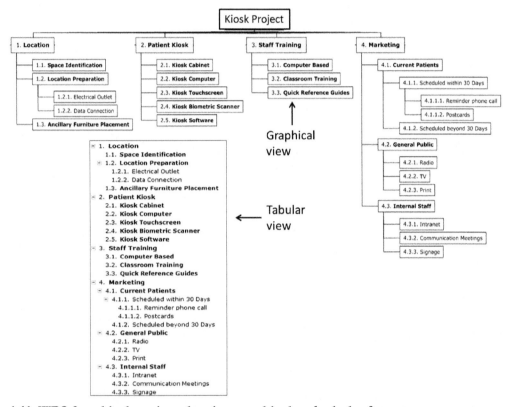

4-11. WBS for a kiosk project showing graphical and tabular formats

Notice that both of these formats in Figure 4-11 show the same information. Many documents, such as contracts, use the tabular format. Project scheduling software also uses this format, although there often are options to provide graphical formatting, if desired. Also note that work packages exist on different levels, depending on which deliverable thread you follow downward. For example, under the "2. Patient Kiosk" deliverable, the work packages are all listed at the next level as 2.1, 2.2, 2.3, 2.4, and 2.5. However, Marketing is decomposed down to a fourth level for "Current Patients" that are "Scheduled within 30 Days." For this thread the work packages are numbered 4.1.1.1 and 4.1.1.2. Remember, work packages are the lowest level deliverable or sub-deliverable for a given thread, and each deliverable thread can decompose to the level required to manage the project work without regard for how deep the other deliverables are decomposed. The depth at which you decompose a deliverable is based upon the complexity of the work, the uniqueness of the work, the experience of the team, and whether or not you are outsourcing the work.

Best Practice

If you look closely at the WBS examples shown you will notice that there are no verbs, as verbs represent action, and a WBS is not about action, but rather about deliverables. According to PMI, a WBS only contains deliverables, as it is a deliverables-based representation of the work required. As the definition of a WBS has fluctuated over the decades, sometimes you may still come across a definition that shows activities on the WBS.

However, it is incorrect to show activities on the WBS, according to PMI and modern project management practices, so try to consistently use deliverables on your WBS. *After* creating the WBS you then define activities that are required to create those work packages. These activities should be shown on the schedule and not on the WBS itself. Several project management software packages use the WBS to create the activities, which may also cause some confusion.

When PMI refers to project work, it is not talking about activities. Work refers to what the project must complete—deliverables. Think of it as the result, not the effort, required of the project. Merriam-Webster's online dictionary (2013) includes a similar definition of the noun, work, as follows: "Something produced or accomplished by effort, exertion, or exercise of skill <this book is the work of many hands>."

Sometimes teams struggle with finding a way to state something as a deliverable. If you have trouble defining deliverables, consider the activity or action required to create the deliverable, and then swap the verb-noun order, and it becomes a deliverable. For example, if you must clear the site for a house, and your team wants to call it "Clear Site" (an activity), your deliverable can be listed instead as "Site Clearing" or "Site Work," which are both nouns.

A work package represents the level of work that the project manager monitors and controls. You can think of work packages in terms of accountability and reporting. If a project has a relatively short time frame and requires weekly progress reports, a work package might represent work completed in one week or less. On the other hand, if a project has a very long time frame and requires quarterly progress reports, a work package might represent work completed in one month or more. A work package might also be the procurement of a specific product or products, such as an item or items purchased from an outside source. If you can manage a deliverable, which means you are able to estimate the time and resources required to complete it, without more detail, and you can assign that deliverable to one person, you most likely are already at the work package level.

The WBS provides the structure and contents for the Task Name column in tools like Microsoft Project and MindView Business, and the hierarchy is shown by indenting and numbering items within the software. Note that PMI's *Practice Standard for Work Breakdown Structures, Second Edition*, numbers all WBS items starting with the number 1. For example, the Kiosk Project would be numbered as follows:

    1 Kiosk Project
      1.1 Location
        1.1.1 Space Identification
        1.1.2 Location Preparation
          1.1.2.1 Electrical Outlet

            1.1.2.2 Data Connection
          1.1.3 Ancillary Furniture Placement
     1.2 Patient Kiosk
     1.3 Staff Training
     1.4 Marketing

Be sure to check with your organization to see what numbering scheme it prefers to use for work breakdown structures.

The sample WBSs shown here seems somewhat easy to construct and understand. *Nevertheless, it is very difficult to create a good WBS.* To create a good WBS, you must understand both the project and its scope, and incorporate the needs and knowledge of the stakeholders. The project manager and the project team must decide as a group how to organize the work and how many levels to include in the WBS. Many project managers have found that it is better to focus on getting the top levels done well to avoid being distracted by too much detail.

Many people confuse deliverables on a WBS with specifications. Items on a WBS represent work that needs to be completed to finish the project, but do not include detailed characteristics of those deliverables. For example, for the Kiosk Project, the WBS did not include the color or material of the cabinet, the type of CPU in the computer, the size of the monitor, etc. That information would be part of the *product* requirements found in the scope statement and, if you created one, within the WBS dictionary.

A **WBS dictionary** is a document that describes the deliverables on the WBS in more detail. Any attribute, characteristic, or quality that better defines the deliverable should be in the WBS dictionary. It may also include who owns the work package, estimated cost and schedule information, contract information if outsourced, specific quality requirements, technical and performance requirements, etc. Recall that the project scope statement, WBS, and WBS dictionary join together to create the project scope baseline, as all three are required to paint the complete project picture.

Another frequent concern when creating a WBS is how to organize it so that it provides the basis for the project schedule. You should focus on what work needs to be delivered, not when or exactly how it will be done. In other words, the WBS items do not have to be developed as a sequential list of deliverables, and although they may be started that way, they do not typically follow that method beyond the second level.

If you do want some time-based flow for the work, you can create a WBS using the project management process groups of initiating, planning, executing, monitoring and controlling, and closing as Level 2 in the WBS, as shown in Appendix A using Project 2013. By using this approach, not only does the project team follow good project management practice, but the WBS tasks can be mapped more easily against time. The executing deliverables are what vary most from project to project. In teaching an introductory project management class, this approach seems to work well, even though it is not that common in practice.

You can also create a WBS that is somewhat time-based in that the deliverables listed follow a required chronological order or work flow, as shown below in Figure 4-12. Construction projects will also sometimes follow a chronological order for the second level, moving from site work to foundation work to framing to exterior work to landscaping. Cautionary note: In most cases, and certainly in both of these examples, a deliverable from the far right side of Level 2, such as Testing in Figure 4-12, may have work that needs to be completed during earlier parts in the project, such as System Design. For example, the testing plan may be developed when the system is being designed, as testing should be performed against design and not against the final software that is developed.

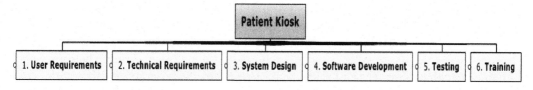

Figure 4-12. WBS showing work flow or chronological order (somewhat)

Media Snapshot

Few events get more media attention than the Olympic Games. Imagine all the work involved in planning and executing an event that involves thousands of athletes from around the world with millions of spectators. The 2002 Olympic Winter Games and Paralympics took five years to plan and cost more than $1.9 billion. PMI awarded the Salt Lake Organizing Committee (SLOC) the Project of the Year award for delivering world-class games that, according to the International Olympic Committee, "made a profound impact upon the people of the world."[3]

Four years before the Games began, the SLOC used a Primavera software-based system with a cascading color-coded WBS to integrate planning. A year before the Games, they added a Venue Integrated Planning Schedule to help the team integrate resource needs, budgets, and plans. For example, this software helped the team coordinate different areas involved in controlling access into and around a venue, such as roads, pedestrian pathways, seating and safety provisions, and hospitality areas, saving nearly $10 million.[4]

Approaches to Developing Work Breakdown Structures

Because it is so important to create a good WBS, this section describes several approaches you can use to develop them. These approaches include:

- Using guidelines or templates
- The analogy approach
- The top-down approach
- The bottom-up approach
- The mind-mapping approach

Using Guidelines

If organizational, industry, or professional guidelines for developing a WBS exist, it is very important to follow them. Some organizations—for example, the U.S. Department of Defense (DOD)—prescribe the form and content for WBSs for particular projects. Some industries have guidelines or standards that are commonly used to drive project deliverables, and some professions (engineering fields, especially) have their own guidelines that suggest certain deliverables for all projects. If there are guidelines, there are also often templates available that can be used as the WBS starting point, with project specific deliverables added as required. Templates are especially useful for common or repeatable types of work, such as outfitting patient rooms, installing PCs in procedural areas, or creating training classes for staff. Some software products, like Microsoft Project 2013, include templates for WBSs for various types of projects that can be used as a starting point for creating a new WBS, such as building a house, as shown earlier. There are very limited templates available for healthcare projects, primarily because formal project management is still new in the industry.

The Analogy Approach

Another approach for constructing a WBS is the analogy approach, where you use a similar project's WBS as a starting point. For example, many organizations have WBSs from past projects and make them available for other project managers to use. While starting with a WBS from a similar project can save a lot of time, it is important that project managers and their teams address their unique project needs and understand how work will be done when creating their own WBS. The project manager must also understand the constraints and assumptions that the previous project worked under, as that may have impacted how they constructed their WBS. There are no two projects that are exactly the same, and using a WBS from another project without understanding how it differs from your project can be risky. One advantage to using this approach, at least as a starting point, is that it is less likely that you will accidently leave deliverables off the WBS since you are copying the WBS of a successful project.

The Top-down Approach

Most project managers consider the top-down approach of WBS construction to be the conventional approach to building a WBS. To use the top-down approach, start with the largest items or deliverables of the project and break them into their subordinate items. This process involves refining the work into greater and greater levels of detail. After breaking down or decomposing the top-level items, resources should then be assigned at the work-package level. The top-down approach is best suited to project managers and teams who have the technical, clinical, and business insight required (expert judgment) and a big-picture perspective.

The Bottom-up Approach

In the bottom-up approach, team members first identify as many specific activities related to completing the project as possible. They then aggregate the specific activities and organize them into groups based on what they are creating (the work package). They then take groups of work packages and determine what they, as a group, will create (the next higher level in the WBS), and so forth. This method is often easier when staff members understand the detailed work but are not necessarily thinking of the project from the broader perspective.

For example, a group of people might be responsible for creating a WBS to open a new neighborhood clinic for an organization that has never had a remote clinic. They could begin by listing detailed activities required in order to open a clinic (get building permits and DHEC approval, hire contractors, design the building, pick color schemes, etc.). They may list these activities in the order they believe they will be performed, or they may suggest them based on their limited knowledge of opening a new clinic. They would then start grouping the activities into what that group of activities, when completed, would create. For example, picking paint colors, choosing furniture fabrics, choosing carpet style, etc. may be grouped into a deliverable called, "Interior Design."

Some people have found that writing all possible activities down on sticky notes and then placing them on a wall helps them see all the work required for the project and develop logical groupings for performing the work. The bottom-up approach can be very time consuming, but it can also be a very effective way to create a WBS. Project teams often use the bottom-up approach for projects that represent entirely new products or approaches to doing a job, or to help create buy-in and synergy with a project team.

Mind Mapping

Some project managers like to use mind mapping to help develop a WBS. As described in Chapter 2, mind mapping is a technique that uses branches radiating out from a core idea to structure thoughts and ideas. This more visual, less structured approach to defining and then grouping activities can unlock creativity among individuals and increase participation and morale among teams. You can create mind maps by hand, by using sticky notes, using presentation software like PowerPoint, or by using mind mapping software.

Figure 4-13 shows a mind-mapping diagram for the Kiosk Project described earlier. This diagram's radiating arms were created as team members identified required deliverables. The facilitator added it to the map, in no particular order. Note there are no numbers associated on the deliverables yet, as they have not yet been organized into a WBS.

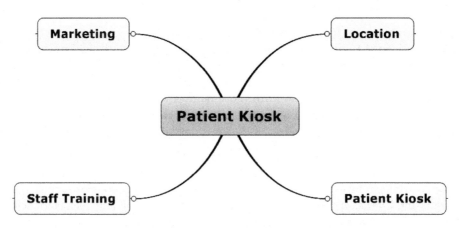

Figure 4-13. Patient kiosk WBS initial mind map

Once the major deliverables, which will comprise Level 2 of the WBS, are identified, the team creates sub-deliverables for each of them, as shown in Figure 4-14. They can keep them in the above format or move them into the more common graphical WBS format. The value of leaving the WBS in the mind-map format is that implies there is no order to the deliverables, which often encourages out-of-the-box thinking by the team. The detailed mind map requires more brainstorming. The threads may be focused on one at a time, or they can be assigned to sub groups within the group based on who best knows the deliverables required for that thread. Remember that the people creating the WBS should include the project team along with other stakeholders, so you may have someone from facilities, marketing, training, and IT involved. Let those identify the work who knows the work the best.

At this point the team may decide that the WBS is 100% complete, and with the click of a button they can change the format to the tabular format (shown previously), and with another click they can add numbering to each WBS element. Some tools, such as MindView Business, also let you easily change the WBS mind map into a Gantt chart, as described in the Video Highlights. There are several good mind-mapping applications available. Some are open source such as X-Mind and FreeMind, while some are purchased such as MatchWare MindView Business or MindJet MindManager.

Figure 4-14. Patient kiosk WBS detailed mind map

Video Highlights

MindView Business software allows you to create a WBS with a mind map. You can access a special 60-day trial of their software at www.matchware.com/intropm. You can also watch several videos about creating a WBS using a mind map. For example, the 14-minute "Quickstart" video gives you a great overview of what you can do with MindView Business software. There is also a 12-minute "Work Breakdown Structure" video. See the companion site for this text at www.healthcarepm.com for links to these and other video highlights.

Sample WBS for the VAPR Project

The VAPR project team decided to use the two project phases for the Level 2 categories in its WBS, following a top-down approach. Because there were no other projects at AHS that they could use as examples, they had to depend on the expert judgment of the team to determine the deliverables. They believed that between Jeff's project management experience, Pat's nursing experience and CMS knowledge, and Dr. Scheerer's physician and quality experience they could do a good job breaking down the required elements. Of course they invited other key stakeholders, from both project phases, as creating the WBS is a job best done with a diverse group of bright minds.

Figure 4-15 shows part of the initial WBS Jeff, Pat, and their team created. You will see this information in the next chapter when creating the Gantt chart. Jeff and Pat were wise to include others in creating the WBS, as you must involve the entire project team and other stakeholders in creating and reviewing the WBS if you want it to be a truly useful tool. *People who will do the work should help to plan the work* by creating the WBS. It is also important to let workers be creative in their approach to the work and to let them know that they have a say in how their work is done. It also helps to identify where coordination between different work packages will be required, and when working on clinical technology projects, there is frequently cross-discipline integration of work required.

You may review this WBS and decide that you would have broken things down differently, and that is fine. This team broke the work down this way because it made sense to the way they, and their organization, work best.

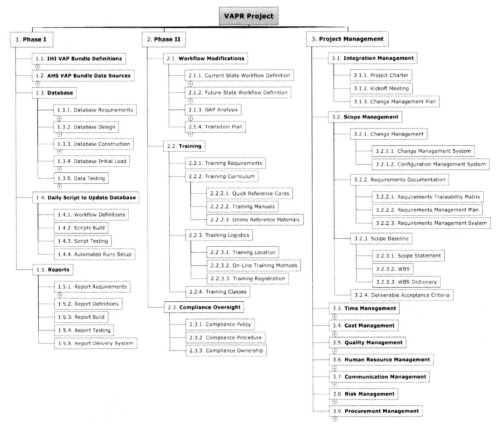

Figure 4-15. VAPR project WBS

Creating the WBS Dictionary

Due to the small space available for naming a deliverable, many of the activities listed on a WBS can appear vague. Would anyone who read the VAPR WBS know what 2.3.1 Compliance Policy meant? The person responsible for this deliverable, the manager of the quality department, might think that it does not need to be broken down any further if he or she understood it enough to estimate time and costs for it. However, the WBS items should be described in more detail so that everyone has the same understanding of what they involve. What if someone else had to be assigned to perform the work? What would you tell them to do? Would they be able to create a good estimate of the hours, costs, and resources required to complete the work? More detailed information is needed to answer these and other questions, and that information must be readily available to those that need it. Like all project work, you must use common sense in deciding how much documentation is needed, but if the deliverable is worth putting on the WBS, it is worth documenting what you know about it.

As mentioned previously, a WBS dictionary is a document that describes the deliverables on the WBS in more detail. The format of the WBS dictionary can vary based on project needs. It might be appropriate to have just a short paragraph describing each work package. For a more complex project, an entire page or more might be needed for the work-package descriptions. You will most likely maintain your WBS dictionary in your project management software or another tool. Depending on your project and your organization, the WBS dictionary can include some or all of the following elements, and of course you are free to add others as you deem fit. Some of these elements may not be known now, but they will be filled in as they become known at a later date:

- WBS item number (e.g., 2. 3.1)

- WBS item name

- Requirement trace

- Responsible person

- Estimated cost

- Estimated duration

- Resource requirements

- Description (detailed)

Sample WBS Dictionary Entry

Project manager should work with their teams and sponsors to determine the level of detail needed in the WBS dictionary. Project teams often review WBS dictionary entries from similar activities to get a better idea of how to create these entries. They should also decide where this information will be entered and how it will be updated. For the VAPR project, Jeff and his team will enter all of the WBS dictionary information into their enterprise project management system. Figure 4-16 provides an example of one of the entries.

The approved project scope statement and its associated WBS and WBS dictionary form the scope baseline, as mentioned earlier. Performance in meeting project scope goals is based on the scope baseline, so it is critical that is correct and complete.

WBS Item Number: 2.3.1

WBS Item Name: Compliance Policy

Requirement Trace: R12 – Enforce VAP Best Practices

Responsible Person: Danielle Scheerer, MD, Chief Quality Officer

Estimated Cost: $0, executive leadership costs not charged to the project

Estimated Duration: 3 months, due to committee schedules and approvals required

Resource Requirements: Executive Quality Oversight Committee (CQO, CNO, CMO, CMIO, CNIO), Compliance Officer

Description: Caregivers treat patients based on their own experiences, education, and research. However, there are many best-practices that have been proven to be superior to those based on individual judgment as they take into account large numbers of patients studied over extended periods of time. Although these best practices are proven, the organizations who publish these practices are not sitting in front of the patient and therefore do not understand the patient as a whole. A policy must be created that encourages and holds accountable physicians and nurses for complying with the IHI Ventilator Bundle that has been designed and proven to reduce the incidence of VAP. The policy must include the ability to deviate from the best practices if the caregiver believes it is in the best interest of the patient's health, but the policy should also require that the caregiver documents the deviation and reasoning so that AHS may study the patient outcomes of these patients compared to those who follow the best practices. The policy must be co-issued by the highest level clinicians (Chief Medical Officer and Chief Nursing Officer) and communicated, supported, and enforced by clinical leadership.

Figure 4-16. Sample WBS dictionary entry

CASE WRAP-UP

Pat learned a lot by working with Jeff, an experienced project manager, while planning the scope of the VAPR project. As a clinician, she was more effective than Jeff at getting other clinicians to get involved, but Jeff was more successful talking technology with the IT staff. It was a good partnership, and Pat was wondering if maybe they should work together on both phases. She was sure that she could help Jeff in Phase I, and she knew that Jeff could help her in Phase II.

Pat was surprised that even in the IT group, who work with projects all the time, some of the staff wanted to plan to the bottom-most detail, while others were adamant that they were wasting time planning and wanted to jump in and start the work. She thought Jeff did a good job getting both groups to come to the middle.

Both Jeff and Pat continued to consult members of the project steering committee for their advice, especially in helping everyone see how crucial it was to understand and document the scope of the project to provide a good baseline for measuring progress. It was a challenge, of course, as even the steering committee just wanted the project to be done, but she was starting to see the advantages of a good plan and, as a team, they were able to convince leadership that the time they spent planning would result in a more successful project. Jeff made it clear—good planning results in less rework, less cost overruns, and increased user satisfaction.

CHAPTER SUMMARY

Successful project managers know how important it is to develop, refine, and follow plans to meet project goals. It is important to remember that the main purpose of project plans is to guide project execution. Planning is done in all ten project management knowledge areas. This chapter summarizes the planning processes and outputs for project integration and scope management.

Planning for integration management includes developing a project management plan. Plans in the other knowledge areas are considered to be subsidiary parts of the project management plan. You can also create a team contract to help set the stage for good teamwork and communications.

Planning processes for scope management include planning scope management, collecting requirements, defining scope, and creating a WBS. A WBS is a very important document in project management because it provides the basis for planning and managing project schedules, costs, resources, and changes.

Approaches for developing a WBS include using guidelines, an analogy approach, a top-down approach, a bottom-up approach, and mind mapping. Several examples are provided. A WBS dictionary provides more detail on WBS items.

Samples of several planning documents are provided for the VAPR project.

QUICK QUIZ

1. What can project teams create to help promote teamwork and clarify team communications?

    A. a project Web site

    B. a team-building plan

    C. a team roster

    D. a team contract

2. The main purpose of project planning is to:

    A. obtain funding for the project

    B. guide project execution

    C. clarify roles and responsibilities

    D. keep senior managers informed

3. Project teams develop a _____ to coordinate all other project plans.

    A. strategic plan

    B. project management plan

    C. master plan

    D. project Web site

4. A requirements _____ _____ is a table that lists requirements, various attributes of each requirement, and the status of the requirements to ensure that all of them are addressed.

    A. traceability matrix

    B. management plan

    C. management matrix

    D. tracking tool

5. A _____ is a deliverable-oriented grouping of the work involved in a project that defines the total scope of the project.

    A. contract

    B. Gantt chart

    C. WBS

    D. network diagram

6.   A _____ is a deliverable at the lowest level of the WBS that represents the level of work that the project manager uses to monitor and control the project.

A. WBS dictionary

B. budget item

C. line item

D. work package

7.   The entire project is considered to be Level ___ in the WBS.

A. 0

B. 1

C. 2

D. 3

8.   A WBS is often depicted in a _____ format, similar to an organizational chart

A. tabular

B. mind-map

C. block

D. graphical

9.   According to PMI, which of the following would not be good wording for a WBS item?

A. install software

B. software

C. software installation

D. software training

10.   A WBS _____ is a document that describes the deliverables on the WBS in more detail.

A. glossary

B. statement

C. dictionary

D. appendix

Quick Quiz Answers

1. D; 2. B; 3. B; 4. A; 5. C; 6. D; 7. B; 8. D; 9. A; 10. C

DISCUSSION QUESTIONS

1. Why does having good plans help project teams during project execution? Why is it difficult to develop good plans?

2. What are the main planning processes performed as part of project integration management? What are the main documents created, and what are some of their main contents?

3. What are the main planning processes performed as part of project scope management?

4. What are some approaches for creating a WBS? Why is it important to develop a good WBS?

5. What do you think about the scope planning documents prepared by the VAPR project team? Do they seem too broad or too detailed in certain areas? Be specific in suggesting possible improvements.

EXERCISES

Note: These exercises can be done individually or in teams, in-class, as homework, or in a virtual environment. Learners can either write their results in a paper or prepare a short presentation or video to show their results.

1. Find an example of a large healthcare project that took more than a year to complete. Describe some of the planning work completed for the project as part of project integration and scope management. Summarize your findings.

2. Review the sample scope statement for the VAPR project. Assume you are responsible for planning and then managing the deliverable called "data interfaces from source systems." What additional information would you want to know to develop a good schedule and cost estimate for this deliverable?

3. Create a partial requirements traceability matrix for a project to build a house. Assume you or one of your classmates would use this information to plan his or her dream home. Include at least ten requirements.

4. Go to www.matchware.com and search for "what is a WBS." Watch the online tutorials and read the example provided for building a house. Find a similar video on another site, and summarize similarities and differences. Also document any questions you have about creating a WBS.

5. Create your own WBS for a project (preferably one related to healthcare) by using the mind-mapping approach. Break at least two Level 2 items down to Level 4. Try to use MindView software from www.matchware.com/intropm, if possible. You can also create the mind map by using similar mind-mapping software or a tool like PowerPoint.

6. Find at least four samples of WBSs different from the ones in this chapter. Microsoft Project, MindView, and other project management software tools include templates that you can use as examples. Analyze the similarities and differences between the WBSs. Also review them for completeness. Do they seem to include all the work required for the project? Does the hierarchy make sense? Summarize your findings, and be sure to cite references.

TEAM PROJECTS

Note: These team projects can be done in-class, as homework, or in a virtual environment. Learners can either write their results in a paper or prepare a short presentation or video to show their results.

1. Your organization initiated a project to raise money for an important charity. Assume that there are 1,000 people in your organization. Also assume that you have six months to raise as much money as possible, with a goal of $100,000. Develop a scope statement, WBS, and partial WBS dictionary for the project. Be creative in deciding how you will raise the money and the deliverables and sub-deliverables required to complete the project.

2. You are part of a team in charge of a project to help people in your company (500 people) lose weight. This project is part of a competition, and the top "losers" will be featured in a popular television show. Assume that you have six months to complete the project and a budget of $10,000. Develop a scope statement, WBS, and partial WBS dictionary for the project. Be creative in deciding how you will raise the money and the deliverables and sub-deliverables required to complete the project.

3. Using the information you developed in Project 1 or 2 above, role-play a meeting to review one of these planning documents with key stakeholders. Determine who will play what role (project manager, team member from a certain department, employees, senior managers, and so on). Be creative in displaying different personalities (i.e. a senior manager who questions the importance of the project to the organization, a team member who is very shy or obnoxious, etc.).

4. Perform the planning tasks (only for the knowledge areas covered in this chapter) for one of the case studies provided in Appendix B. Remember to be thorough in your planning so that your execution goes smoothly.

5. As a team, find at least four examples of WBSs for various types of healthcare projects (different from the examples in this chapter). Discuss the similarities and differences between how the WBSs are structured. Also discuss the quality of the

examples you find and if the organization used specific software or provided guidelines for its creation. Include screen shots of the examples and citations.

KEY TERMS

baseline — A starting point, a measurement, or an observation that is documented so that it can be used for future comparison; also defined as the original project plans plus approved changes.

organizational process assets — Policies and procedures related to project management, past project files, and lessons-learned reports from previous, similar projects.

project management plan — A document used to coordinate all project planning documents and to help guide a project's execution and control.

requirement — A condition or capability that must be met or possessed by a system, product, service, result, or component to satisfy a contract, standard, specification, or other formal document.

requirements management plan — A plan that describes how project requirements will be analyzed, documented and managed.

requirements traceability matrix (RTM) — A table that lists requirements, various attributes of each requirement, and the status of the requirements to ensure that all of them are addressed.

scope baseline — The approved project scope statement and its associated WBS and WBS dictionary.

scope creep — The tendency for project scope to continually increase.

team contract — A document created to help promote teamwork and clarify team communications.

work breakdown structure (WBS) — A deliverable-oriented grouping of the work involved in a project that defines the total scope of the project.

work breakdown structure (WBS) dictionary — A document that describes detailed information about WBS deliverables, sub-deliverables, and work packages.

work package — A deliverable at the lowest level of the WBS, where it can be appropriately assigned to and managed by a single accountable person.

END NOTES

[1]IBM, "Emerging Health IT achieves fast ROI with IBM Rational DOORS," IBM Case Studies (March 31, 2011).

[2]Vijay Sankar, "Meet our new IBM Champion Mia McCroskey," IBM Requirements Management Blog (Mar 27, 2013).

[3]Ross Foti, "The Best Winter Olympics, Period," *PM Network* (January 2004) p. 23.

[4]Ibid, p. 23.

Chapter 5
Planning Projects, Part 2
(Project Time and Cost Management)

LEARNING OBJECTIVES

After reading this chapter, you will be able to:

- List several planning processes and outputs for project time and cost management
- Describe the six project time management planning processes, and prepare an activity list and attributes, milestone list, project schedule network diagram, activity resource requirements, activity duration estimates, and project schedule
- Understand how to find the critical path and its implications on timely project completion
- Explain the concept of critical chain scheduling and how it can be used in healthcare organizations
- Discuss the three project cost management planning processes
- Create a cost estimate, cost baseline, and project funding requirements

---

OPENING CASE

Jeff and Pat continued developing the VAPR project plans. Although Jeff always tried to engage those doing the actual work in the planning, he felt it was especially critical when estimating time and cost because it was difficult to hold people accountable if they had no input on the estimates.

Therefore, Jeff suggested they collaborate with work package owners to identify the activities required to create them, and the owners could then estimate the time required to complete each activity as well as their associated costs. Aggregated together these activity estimates would determine the cost of each work package. Aggregated further, they would provide estimated costs and time required for each deliverable, and aggregated further, the cost and time required to complete the entire project.

Pat had estimated costs and activity durations before while working as a staff member on other projects, but she did not know how to create a schedule as that had always been done by the PMO staff. She was eager to learn, and Jeff coached her on analyzing the activities defined for each work package and determining if any of them would have to be completed prior to other activities starting (i.e. a finish-to-start dependency). Although there are other dependency types, Jeff suggested they stick with this one because they are easier to manager for new project managers.

Pat was proud when she put in activity durations and dependencies and had a project schedule. Jeff cautioned her, however, that it was a rough draft. They would have to apply multiple tools and techniques before they could call it a true schedule that would serve as a baseline for completing project work on time.

INTRODUCTION

In the previous chapter you read about the importance of doing a good job in planning for project integration and scope management. This chapter focuses on planning the next two knowledge areas—time and cost—which are also important, as are the others described in the next chapter. Recall that doing a thorough job in planning all applicable knowledge areas is fundamental to guiding project execution.

SUMMARY OF PLANNING PROCESSES AND OUTPUTS

Figure 5-1 summarizes the project planning processes and outputs for project time and cost management listed in the *PMBOK® Guide, Fifth Edition*. The following sections describe these processes and outputs further and then provide examples of applying them to the VAPR project at AHS. After planning the project scope and determining what deliverables need to be produced you can start developing a detailed schedule and cost baseline. Of course, quality and human resource planning affect the scope, time, and cost planning, as do the other knowledge areas. As noted earlier, there are many interdependencies between various knowledge areas and process groups, and planning for project integration management is needed to coordinate all of these plans.

Knowledge area	Planning process	Outputs
Project time management	Plan schedule management	Schedule management plan
	Define activities	Activity list
		Activity attributes
		Milestone list
	Sequence activities	Project schedule network diagrams
		Project documents updates
	Estimate activity resources	Activity resource requirements
		Resource breakdown structures
		Project documents updates
	Estimate activity durations	Activity duration estimates
		Project documents updates
	Develop schedule	Schedule baseline
		Project schedule
		Schedule data
		Project calendars
		Project management plan updates
		Project documents updates
Project cost management	Plan cost management	Cost management plan
	Estimate costs	Activity cost estimates
		Basis of estimates
		Project documents updates
	Determine budget	Cost baseline
		Project funding requirements
		Project documents updates

Figure 5-1. Planning processes and outputs for project time and cost management

PROJECT TIME MANAGEMENT

Project time management includes the processes required to ensure timely completion of a project. The planning processes performed as part of project time management are conducted in order to develop the project schedule. The project manager, with the project team's input, plans how they will manage the schedule, defines activities required to create the work packages, sequences those activities, estimates resource requirements for the activities, estimates activity durations, and in the end develops the project schedule baseline. The main documents produced are a schedule management plan, an activity list and activity attributes, a milestone list, a project schedule network diagram, the activity resource requirements, the activity duration estimates, and a project schedule. Samples of these documents are provided later in this section.

Planning Schedule Management

The purpose of this process is to determine the policies, procedures, and documentation for planning, developing, managing, executing, and controlling the project schedule. The project team holds meetings, consults with experts, and analyzes data to help produce a schedule management plan, which becomes a component of the project management plan.

Contents of the schedule management plan can include the following:
- scheduling methodology and tools used to create a schedule model, if required
- level of accuracy required for activity duration estimates
- units of measure, such as staff hours, days, or weeks
- variance thresholds for monitoring schedule performance, such as a percentage deviation from the baseline plan
- rules of performance measurement, especially if earned value management is used (see Chapter 8, Monitoring and Controlling, for more information on earned value management)
- formats and frequency for schedule reports
- descriptions of each of the other schedule management processes

Defining Activities

Project schedules grow out of the basic documents that initiate a project. The project charter often identifies desired project start and end dates, which serve as the starting points for a more detailed schedule. The project manager starts with the project charter and then develops a project scope statement and WBS, as discussed in the previous section. Using this information with the scope statement, WBS, WBS dictionary, project management plan, and other related information, the project team begins to develop a schedule by first clearly defining all the activities it needs to perform. As defined in the PMBOK® Guide, Fifth Edition (2013), an **activity** is a distinct, scheduled portion of work performed during the course of a project.

Creating the Activity List and Attributes

The **activity list** is a tabulation of activities to be included on a project schedule. The list should include the activity name, an activity identifier or number, and a brief description of the activity. The **activity attributes** provide schedule-related information about each activity, such as predecessors, successors, logical relationships, leads and lags, resource requirements, constraints, imposed dates, and assumptions related to the activity. The activity list is created by identifying the activities required to create each work package on the WBS, and any activity and its attributes must be in alignment the WBS and WBS dictionary. As an example, if the WBS dictionary indicates that the VAPR reporting system must be available online using Internet Explorer, Google Chrome, and Mozilla Firefox, then the activities defined for creating that reporting system must include work to ensure the software runs on all three browsers equally well.

Why are activities only created for the work packages, and not all deliverables on the WBS? Recall from Chapter 4 that a work package is the lowest level item or work in a WBS, and that a WBS includes all project work. Further, when a deliverable is decomposed into smaller deliverables (and eventually the work packages), all work required for a deliverable is included in its sub-deliverables, known as the WBS 100% rule. Therefore, if you complete all activities required to complete all work packages, then you complete all work required for the project. Figure 5-2, a small section of the Kiosk Project WBS from the previous chapter, demonstrates this principle. In this example, if the kiosk cabinet, kiosk computer, kiosk touchscreen, kiosk biometric scanner, and kiosk software are all completed, then the patient kiosk will be completed. Remember, only the work packages (2.1, 2.2, 2.3, 2.4, and 2.5 in this example) have activities assigned to them.

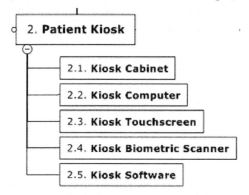

Figure 5-2: WBS 100% rule

The goal of the activity definition process is to ensure that project team members have a *complete* understanding of all the work they must do so that they can start scheduling the work. For example, one of the work packages in the WBS for the VAPR project is "Training Manuals." The project team would have to understand who will be getting the training, the format of the training (i.e. face-to-face, self-paced, synchronous online, etc.), the length of time that users will be available for training, the training budget, printing capabilities within the organization (assuming some manuals had to be printed), and so on before they could determine the activities required to complete the training manuals. By better understanding the work package the team can better define what activities are required to create that specific deliverable.

The WBS is often expanded during the activity definition process as the project team members may identify other deliverables required in order to complete the project. This is especially true of interim deliverables, which are those deliverables required to create the final product, but are then discarded once the project is completed. For the VAPR project, the project team may decide that they need a temporary data staging server for internal team testing, with the server being repurposed for another project once VAPR is implemented. This text has repeatedly stated that the WBS is deliverables based, and that is true. However, once you define the activities required to create each work package, those activities essentially hang off the end of the work packages, and therefore off the bottom of the WBS. If you were asked to present the WBS at a meeting, you would hide the activities as the WBS technically does not include them. With so many great software tools that allow you to connect the work packages to the activities, it is tempting to include them on the WBS proper, but they should *not* be if you are following PMI's standards. It is fine to include *all* the activity data in one place, but you should be consistent in how you represent the WBS. You should also present the information at whatever level of detail is required for the audience.

The project team should review the activity list and activity attributes with appropriate project stakeholders. If they do not, they could produce an unrealistic schedule and deliver unacceptable results. For example, assume the VAPR project team estimated that it would take one day to create the deliverable "1.5.1 Report Requirements," and they assigned its related activities to an intern who spent a full day developing requirements for the reports. However, if the team had shown the WBS and its related activities to the most affected project stakeholders, they would have pointed out that the report is very complex. Because so many different disciplines needed to have input, it would take weeks to complete the set of activities required to complete that work package.

Clearly defining the work and having a realistic schedule for all activities is crucial to project success.

Sample Activity List and Attributes

Jeff and his team developed dozens of activities that would be used later for creating the project schedule. Figure 5-3 provides an example of how they reviewed a work package, "1.5.1 Report Requirements," and developed a list of activities required to build that work package. Note that unlike the deliverables described within the WBS, which are listed as nouns, activities are all listed using a verb and then a noun, using verbs such as *review, determine, analyze, distribute, write,* and *conduct.*

After the project team creates the activities for each work package, they can begin to fill in the attributes. Not all attributes will be known at this point, but the team will record what is known and update information as it becomes available. For example, the team may know what activities must be completed before this activity, but they may only know this for activities within this single work package. They may later find out that there are activities for other work packages that also must be completed before this activity can start, or vice-versa.

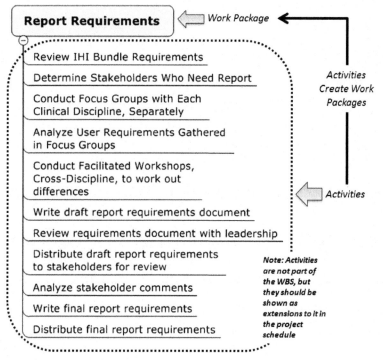

Figure 5-3. Report requirements activity list

Figure 5-4 shows an example of activity attributes for WBS item "1.5.1.5 Conduct Facilitated Workshops." Notice the detailed information provided, such as the predecessors, successors, resource requirements, and assumptions. As you can see from this sample, Jeff and his team would have to work closely with other stakeholders to define this information. These are just a few of the many activity attributes that you may decide to collect for your project. As with all project management tools, techniques, and processes, you must tailor it to your needs. For example, you may decide to include who is assigned this activity, how it will be tested or verified, whether or not it requires sign off upon completion, etc.

Creating a Milestone List

To ensure that all major activities are accounted for, project teams often create a milestone list. A **milestone** is a significant event on a project. It usually includes many activities, and therefore a lot of work, to complete a milestone. Unlike a deliverable, which is the output of activities, and unlike an activity, which is the actual project work, a milestone is simply a marker to help in identifying necessary activities. *There is usually no cost or duration associated with a milestone.* Milestones are like the mile markers on a highway. Either you pass them or you do not.

ACTIVITY LIST AND ATTRIBUTES

Project Name	**VAPR Project**
Activity Number	1.5.1.5
Activity Name	Conduct facilitated workshops
Details	Cross-discipline workshop to work out differences in user report requirements.
Predecessors	1.5.1.4 Analyze user requirements gathered in focus groups
Successors	1.5.1.6 Write draft report requirements document
Logical Relationships	finish-to-start (FS)
Leads and Lags	None
Resource Requirements	Clinical analyst, trained facilitator, data analyst
Constraints	Must be conducted before 7am or after 5pm to accommodate physician schedules
Imposed Dates	None
Assumptions	Physicians and nurses and respiratory therapists will have different and incongruent requirements. It will require a facilitated work to align and integrate their needs.

Figure 5-4. Sample activity list and attributes

Milestones are useful tools for setting schedule goals and monitoring progress, and project sponsors and senior managers often focus on major milestones when reviewing projects. For example, milestones for many projects include sign-off of key documents, completion of specific products, or completion of important process-related work, such as awarding a contract to a supplier. *Milestone names are generally written in past tense*, such as "Contract awarded" and are indicated on a Gantt chart as diamond shapes with no cost, duration, or resources.

Sample Milestone List

Jeff, Pat, and their team reviewed the draft WBS and activity list to develop an initial milestone list. They reviewed the list with their sponsor and other key stakeholders. Project teams often estimate completion dates for milestones early in the scheduling process and adjust them after going through additional time management planning steps such as activity sequencing, activity resource estimating, duration estimating, and schedule development. Figure 5-5 shows part of the milestone list for the VAPR project. This section focuses on the milestones related to the training program that is required to train the staff on the new workflow and system (WBS item 2.2). Pat would be running this project phase, with Jeff assisting as needed, and they worked together to determine logical milestones for both phases.

VAPR MILESTONES

Milestone	Estimated Date
Project kickoff meeting held	June 1
IHI bundle & data sources identified	July 15
Database developed	August 20
Report requirements identified	October 1
Online reports completed	December 30
Clinical workflows designed	February 15
Training curriculum developed	April 15
Training delivered	May 30
Go live	June 15

Figure 5-5. Sample milestone list

Pat and Jeff decided that the first milestone was critical to the rest of the project, so they would report its status to the sponsor and champions. They also identified a few smaller, less critical milestones that the leadership would not be interested in monitoring, and a few major milestones that they would also report to leadership. Using project management software, such as Project 2013, makes it easy to filter information and create reports so that different people can focus on their own activities and milestones. See Appendix A for more details on using Project 2013.

Best Practice

Many people use the SMART criteria to help define milestones. The SMART criteria are guidelines suggesting that milestones should be:

- **S**pecific – anyone with a basic knowledge of the project should understand the milestone
- **M**easureable – the milestone must be something you can measure (objective)
- **A**ttainable – the milestone and the due date must be attainable
- **R**elevant – the milestone must be relevant to the project and the organization
- **T**ime-framed – it must be date driven

For example, completing the online reports, as listed in Figure 5-5, is specific (understandable, clear), measurable (are the reports completed or not?), attainable (the timeline appears to be accurate), relevant (the project will not be successful without the reporting aspects of it), and time-framed (date based).

You can also use milestones to reduce schedule risk by following these best practices:

- Define milestones early in the project and include them in the Gantt chart to provide a visual guide.
- Create milestones of manageable size and duration. If they are too large in size they will not help you manage the project effectively.
- The set of milestones must be all-encompassing.
- Each milestone must be binary, meaning it is either complete or incomplete.
- Carefully monitor the milestones on the critical path (described later in this chapter).[1]

Sequencing Activities

After defining project activities, the next step in project time management is activity sequencing. Activity sequencing involves reviewing the activity list and attributes, project scope statement, and milestone list to determine the relationships or dependencies between activities. It also involves evaluating the reasons for dependencies and the different types of dependencies.

A **dependency**, or **relationship**, relates to the sequencing of project activities. For example, does a certain activity have to be finished before another one can start? Can the project team do several activities in parallel? Can some overlap? Determining these relationships or dependencies between activities has a significant impact on developing and managing a project schedule.

There are three basic reasons for creating dependencies among project activities:

- **Mandatory dependencies** are inherent in the nature of the work being performed on a project. They are sometimes referred to as hard logic because their relationships are unavoidable. For example, you cannot hold training classes until the training materials are ready, and the training materials cannot be created until the objectives of the course are determined.

- **Discretionary dependencies** are defined by the project team. For example, a project team might follow good practice and not start detailed design work until key stakeholders sign off on all of the analysis work. Discretionary dependencies are sometimes referred to as soft logic and should be used with care because they might limit later scheduling options.

- **External dependencies** involve relationships between project and non-project activities. The installation of new software might depend on delivery of new hardware from an external supplier. Even though the delivery of the new hardware might not be in the scope of the project, it should have an external dependency added to it because late delivery will affect the project schedule. External dependencies can be either mandatory or discretionary.

As with activity definition, it is important that project stakeholders work together to define the activity dependencies that exist on their project. If you do not define the sequence of activities and estimate their durations, you cannot use some of the most powerful schedule tools available to project managers: schedule network diagrams and critical path analysis. The main output of activity sequencing is a network diagram.

Project Schedule Network Diagrams

Schedule network diagrams are the preferred technique for showing activity sequencing for project schedules. A project schedule network diagram or simply **network diagram** is a schematic display of the logical relationships among, or sequencing of, project activities. Some people refer to network diagrams as PERT charts. PERT is described later in this section. Figure 5-6 shows a sample network diagram for Project X, which is shown using the arrow diagramming method (ADM), or activity-on-arrow (AOA) approach. (Note: This approach is shown first because the diagrams are easier to understand and create. Its main limitations are that it can only show finish-to-start dependencies, as described later in this section, and that no major project management software supports it.)

Note the main elements on the network diagram in Figure 5-6. The letters A through I represent activities with dependencies that are required to complete the project. These activities come from the activity definition process described earlier. The arrows represent the activity sequencing, or relationships between activities. For example, Activity A must be done before Activity D, and Activity D must be done before Activity F.

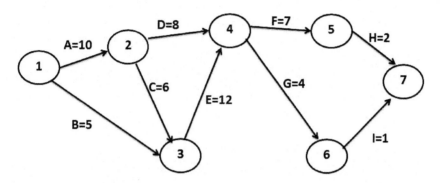

Note: Assume all durations are in days;
A=10 means Activity A has a duration of 10 days.

Figure 5-6. Activity-on-arrow (AOA) network diagram for Project X

The format of this network diagram uses the **activity-on-arrow (AOA)** approach, or the **arrow diagramming method (ADM)**—a network diagramming technique in which activities are represented by arrows and connected at points called nodes to illustrate the sequence of activities. In AOA, a **node** is simply the starting and ending point of an activity. The first node signifies the start of a project, and the last node represents the end of a project. If you are in a meeting and using a whiteboard to sequence a subset of project activities, AOA is frequently used due to its simplicity.

Keep in mind that the network diagram represents activities that must be done to complete the project. It is not a race to get from the first node to the last node. *Every activity on the network diagram must be completed for the project to finish.* It is also important to note that not every single activity needs to be on the network diagram; only activities with dependencies need to be shown on the network diagram. However, some people like to have start and end milestones and to list every activity. It is a matter of preference. For projects with hundreds of activities, it might be simpler to include only activities with dependencies on a network diagram.

Assuming you have a list of the project activities and their start and finish nodes, follow these steps to create an AOA network diagram:

1.   Remember that the circles only represent activity boundaries, or connection points, and that the activities themselves are represented by the lines.

2.   Draw a circle to represent the start of the project. Refer to this as Node 1.

3.   Find all of the activities that have no predecessor, and draw a node for each of these activities to the right of Node 1. Draw arrows connecting Node 1 to each of these new nodes, and put the activity name on each line that connects the node pairs. If you have a duration estimate, write that next to the activity letter or name, as shown in Figure 5-6. For example, A = 10 means that the duration of Activity A is ten days, weeks, or other standard unit of time. Although AOA always read left to right, be sure to put arrowheads on all arrows to signify the direction of the relationships.

4.   Continue drawing the network diagram, working from left to right. Look for bursts and merges. A **burst** occurs when two or more activities follow a single node. A **merge** occurs when two or more nodes precede a single node. For example, in Figure 5-6, Node 1 is a burst because it goes into Nodes 2 and 3. Node 4 is a merge preceded by Nodes 2 and 3.

5.   Continue drawing the AOA network diagram until all activities are included.

6.   As a rule of thumb, all arrowheads should face toward the right, and no arrows should cross on an AOA network diagram. You might need to redraw the diagram to make it look presentable.

Even though AOA network diagrams are generally easy to understand and create, a different method is more commonly used: the precedence diagramming method. The **precedence diagramming method (PDM)** (also called activity on node, or AON) is a network diagramming technique in which boxes represent activities. It is particularly useful for visualizing different types of time dependencies, as the AOA diagram can only show the most common type of dependency—finish-to-start (FS), described later in this section. If presented with a network diagram created by someone else, there are a few ways to distinguish an AOA from an AON network diagram, shown below in Figure 5-7.

Distinguishing Factor	Activity on Arrow	Activity on Node
Line information	Represents activities & precedence	Represents precedence
Node shape	Circle shape	Box shape
Activity information	Only duration typically shown	Often includes duration, start date, end date, and assigned resource
Line shape	Straight	Utilize right angles
Line direction	Always moves rightward	Can move backwards, depending upon relationship (FF, FS, SF, SS)

Figure 5-7. Activity on arrow vs. activity on node

Figure 5-8 illustrates the four types of dependencies that can occur among project activities, based on a Help screen from Microsoft Project 2013. This screen shows that activity A is the predecessor or "from" activity and B is the successor or "to" activity. After you determine the reason for a dependency between activities (mandatory, discretionary, or external), you must determine the type of dependency. *Note that the terms "activity" and "task" are used interchangeably, as are "relationship" and "dependency."* The four types of dependencies, or relationships, between activities include the finish-to-start (FS) start-to-start (SS), finish-to-finish (FF), and start-to-finish (SF), as described in Figure 5-8.

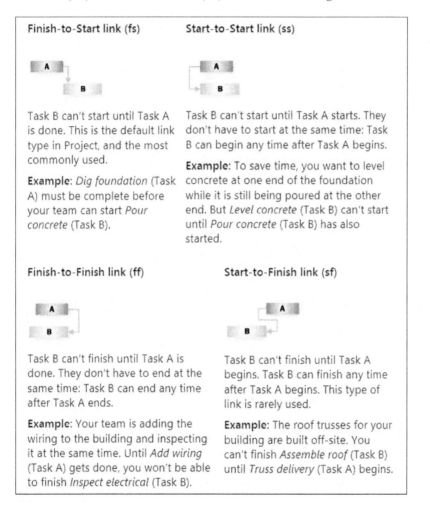

Finish-to-Start link (fs)

Task B can't start until Task A is done. This is the default link type in Project, and the most commonly used.

Example: *Dig foundation* (Task A) must be complete before your team can start *Pour concrete* (Task B).

Start-to-Start link (ss)

Task B can't start until Task A starts. They don't have to start at the same time: Task B can begin any time after Task A begins.

Example: To save time, you want to level concrete at one end of the foundation while it is still being poured at the other end. But *Level concrete* (Task B) can't start until *Pour concrete* (Task B) has also started.

Finish-to-Finish link (ff)

Task B can't finish until Task A is done. They don't have to end at the same time: Task B can end any time after Task A ends.

Example: Your team is adding the wiring to the building and inspecting it at the same time. Until *Add wiring* (Task A) gets done, you won't be able to finish *Inspect electrical* (Task B).

Start-to-Finish link (sf)

Task B can't finish until Task A begins. Task B can finish any time after Task A begins. This type of link is rarely used.

Example: The roof trusses for your building are built off-site. You can't finish *Assemble roof* (Task B) until *Truss delivery* (Task A) begins.

Figure 5-8. Activity dependency types

Figure 5-9 illustrates Project X (shown originally in Figure 5-6) using the precedence diagramming method. Notice the activities are placed inside boxes, which represent the nodes on this diagram. Arrows show the relationships between activities. For example, Activity D has a relationship of dependency with Activity A. This figure was created using Microsoft Project, which automatically places additional information inside each node. Each activity box includes the start and finish date, labeled "Start" and "Finish"; the activity ID number, labeled "ID"; the activity's duration, labeled "Dur"; and the names of resources, if any, assigned to the activity, labeled "Res." The border of the boxes for activities on the critical path (discussed later in this section) appears automatically in red in the Microsoft Project network diagram view. In Figure 5-9, the boxes for critical activities (A, C, E, F, and H) are shown in black. See Appendix A for detailed information on using Project 2013.

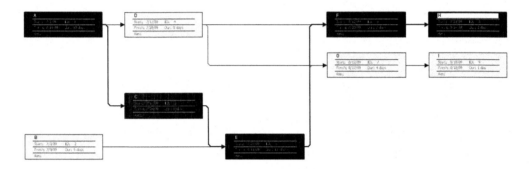

Figure 5-9. Precedence diagramming method network diagram for Project X

Although the AOA diagram might seem easier to understand, the precedence diagramming method is more commonly used than AOA network diagrams. One primary advantage is that PDM allows you to show different types of dependencies among activities, whereas AOA network diagrams use only finish-to-start dependencies. However, because 90% or more of relationships are defined as finish-to-start (FS), you may wonder why everyone does not just use AOA. The answer is simple: The best reason for using PDM is that it is the *only* diagramming method used by the major project management software packages.

Jeff, Pat, and their team reviewed all the project activities and determined which ones had dependencies. They also determined which activities had **lag** time or required a gap in time and which ones had **lead** time or could be overlapped. For example, Jeff and Pat wanted to wait five days after holding the first user training class before holding the second one, because they had agreed to allow the class attendees three days to complete a feedback survey on the class' effectiveness. Once that feedback was obtained, the team would spend two days updating the course materials and then offer the final round of training. Because no work was being done during the three day period that the users were given to complete the survey, it is considered to be lag time. The project schedule network diagram for this small piece of the project would appear as shown in Figure 5-10.

Figure 5-10. Lag example for VAPR training

Note that the size of the box that identifies the activity and the size of the line that connects the activities are not indicators of duration. The three activity boxes are the same size, yet each activity has a different duration. Likewise, the arrows simply indicate the relationship between the activities, and not the duration of any lag (or lead) that exists between the activities. To determine lag and lead, you must look for additional indicators that will be noted adjacent to the connector, such as the "+3d" (3 days lag) on Figure 5-10.

A common question asked when reviewing the above example is, "Why don't you show the users filling in the survey as an activity?" A valid question, but one which may indicate a lack of full understanding of why project schedules are created. The schedule is created as part of defining activities, determining dependencies, and assigning resources. The effectiveness and accuracy of the schedule is based on how well these three processes are managed by the project team. Project activities consume resources (people, facilities, equipment, materials, etc.), and resources cost money. Therefore, every activity costs the project money, whether internal funds (such as internal labor costs) or external funds (contractors, purchases, etc.). However, lag time does not cost the project any money; it is a time when no work is being accomplished.

One could still argue that the surveys are being completed by caregivers who attended the pilot (draft) version of the class, and therefore they cost the organization money. However, because you are giving the attendees three days to fill out a ten minute survey, if you assigned the activity a three day duration it would be misleading. So, in cases like this, a project manager will simply indicate it as lag time. Lag time is also commonly used in projects where equipment must be ordered, as the time between the order and the arrival of the equipment is considered lag time. That is not to say that work does not occur in other parts of the project, but on the equipment thread there should be a lag with a duration set to the expected wait time before the equipment arrives, as shown in Figure 5-11. In this example, the VAPR project team plans to order a new server, wait 13 days before the server arrives, and then install it.

Figure 5-11. Lag example for VAPR server installation

After two examples of lags, what about leads? A lead is simply the inverse of a lag, whereby two activities that have a dependency are allowed to overlap. If you have two activities, A and B, which have a finish-to-start relationship (FS), normally A would have to finish before B may start. However, if you apply a lead, then B can start before A is finished. If it were a two-day lead, then B could start two days before A ends. Leads are indicated in the same way that lags are indicated on the project schedule network diagram, except that the numbers are preceded with a negative sign (i.e. -2d).

Figure 5-12 shows two leads that the VAPR project team introduced into the project. Jeff decided that the first activity required five days to complete, but after two days of identifying the IHI bundle elements they would have enough information to begin figuring out which AHS systems had those required elements. So, they included a -3d (three-day lead) relationship. They also determined that once they identified the AHS systems that contained the required data elements, they could start pulling that data for review and analysis almost immediately. They gave themselves 10 days to identify all the data sources but agreed that after two days of working to identify the systems they would have enough information to start pulling at least some data for review.

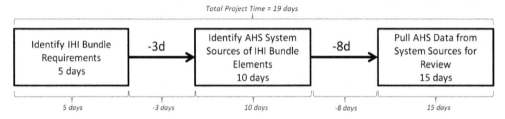

Figure 5-12. Lead examples for VAPR IHI bundle

The activity durations, leads, and lags were entered into Microsoft Project to begin building a detailed Gantt chart for the project, as described later in this section. Remember that the project schedule network diagrams show relationships, but not duration or schedule, with their graphics. In other words, the size of the box and the length of the connecting lines mean nothing!

It is the Gantt chart where the size of the box indicates duration, *and* it can also include connecting lines that indicate relationships. Therefore, the Gantt chart it is often the preferred method of schedule communication. The schedule network diagrams in Figure 5-11 and 5-12 are represented as Gantt charts in Figures 5-13 and 5-14.

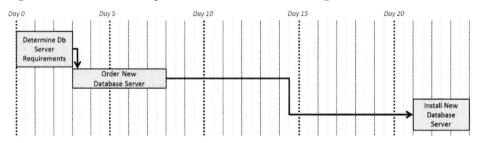

Figure 5-13. Lag example for VAPR server installation (Gantt chart)

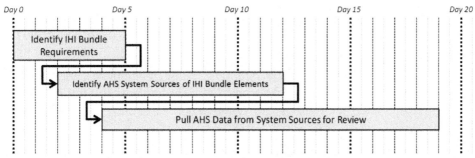

Figure 5-14. Lead example for VAPR IHI bundle (Gantt chart)

Why use schedule network diagrams at all, if Gantt charts can represent both precedence *and* duration with their formatting? There are a few good reasons:

- If your main concern is reviewing and proving activity precedence, having boxes of the same relative size takes away the temptation to focus more on longer activities.

- If your project has many activities or spans a long period of time, the schedule network diagram typically can represent those activities in a smaller physical space.

- If your project is complex, with many dependencies, the Gantt chart has difficulty showing those relationships clearly.

- If your project has dependencies between activities that are in different periods, then the Gantt chart does not show this clearly, as Gantt charts are most often used to show a snapshot of time (such as "this week" or "this month").

Estimating Activity Resources

Before you can estimate the duration for each activity, you must have a good idea of the quantity and type of resources (people, equipment, and materials) that will be assigned to each activity. It is important that the people who help determine what resources are necessary include people who have experience and expertise in similar projects and with the organization performing the project.

Important questions to answer in activity resource estimating include the following:

- How difficult will it be to perform specific activities on this project?

- Is there anything unique in the project's scope statement that will affect resources?

- Are there specific resources better suited to perform the activities?

- What is the organization's history in doing similar activities? Has the organization done similar activities before? What level of personnel did the work?

- Does the organization have appropriate people, equipment, and materials available for performing the work? Are there any organizational policies that might affect the availability of resources?

- Does the organization need to acquire more resources to accomplish the work? Would it make sense to outsource some of the work? Will outsourcing increase or decrease the amount of resources needed and when they will be available?

It is important to thoroughly brainstorm and evaluate alternatives related to resources, especially on projects that involve people from multiple disciplines and companies. Because most projects involve many human resources and the majority of costs are for salaries and benefits, it is most effective to solicit ideas from a variety of people and to address resource-related issues early in a project. The resource estimates, as with most project estimates, should be updated as more detailed information becomes available throughout the project.

Sample Activity Resource Requirements

A key output of the resource estimating process is documentation of activity resource requirements. This list can take various formats. For the VAPR project, Jeff and Pat met with their team, sponsor, and the project steering committee, as needed, to discuss resource requirements for the project. They also discussed which work might be best to outsource, which would be best to perform with internal resources, and which should use both internal and external resources. They entered important resource information for each activity into their project management software.

Figure 5-15 provides an example of two resource requirement entries. The first entry is for an activity described earlier, "Identify IHI Bundle Requirements." Every activity listed within the activity list should have a corresponding resource requirement identified, although in some cases similar activities are grouped and share a common resource requirement entry. In cases where all activity resources for a work package are the same, or very similar, the resource requirements may be determined at the work package level, as shown for item number 1.3.2.

VAPR RESOURCE REQUIREMENTS

Item Number	1.1.1
Item Name	Identify IHI Bundle Requirements
Resources Source	Internal staffing from Enterprise Data Analytics
Resource Requirements	The analyst assigned must be knowledgeable of best-practices, standards, and measures as the IHI bundle will most likely be defined in those terms. They must also be knowledgeable of the current AHS clinical documentation workflows so that they can identify the data elements in AHS terms.
Item Number	1.3.2
Item Name	Database Design
Resources Source	Internal staffing from Enterprise Data Warehouse team
Resource Requirements	This work package will require data architects to review the database requirements and create the resulting database structure to support eventual reporting requirements.

Figure 5-15: Sample activity resource requirements information

Estimating Activity Duration

After working with key stakeholders to define activities, determine their dependencies, and estimate their resources, the next process in project time management is to estimate the duration of activities. It is important to note that **duration** includes the actual amount of time spent working on an activity *plus* elapsed time. For example, even though it might take one workweek or five workdays to do the actual work, the duration estimate might be two weeks to allow extra time needed to obtain outside information or to allow for resource availability. Do not confuse duration with **effort**, which is the number of workdays or work hours required to complete a activity. A duration estimate of one day could be based on eight hours of work or 80. Duration relates to the time estimate, not the effort estimate. Of course, the two are related, so project team members must document their assumptions when creating duration estimates and update them as the project progresses.

The outputs of activity duration estimating include updates to the activity attributes, if needed, and duration estimates for each activity. Duration estimates are provided as a discrete number, such as four weeks; as a range, such as three to five weeks; or as a three-point estimate. Project management software typically requires either a discrete number, required for Critical Path Method (CPM), or a three point estimate, required for Program Evaluation Review Technique (PERT).

A **three-point estimate** is an estimate that includes an optimistic, most likely, and pessimistic estimate, such as three weeks, four weeks, and five weeks, respectively. The optimistic estimate is based on a best-case scenario, whereas the pessimistic estimate is based on a worst-case scenario. The most likely estimate, as it sounds, is an estimate based on a most likely or expected scenario.

Program Evaluation Review Technique (PERT) is a network analysis technique used to estimate project duration when there is a high degree of uncertainty about the individual activity duration estimates. By using the PERT weighted average for each activity duration estimate, the total project duration estimate accounts for the risk or uncertainty in the individual activity estimates. Although CPM only allows single point estimates, and PERT requires 3-point estimates, some of the leading project management software tools allow you to interchange the two techniques by assigning single point estimates to some activities and 3-point estimates to those with more uncertainty.

To use PERT, you calculate a weighted average for the duration estimate of each project activity using the following formula:

$$\text{PERT weighted average} = \frac{optimistic_{time} + 4 * most\_likely_{time} + pessimistic_{time}}{6}$$

Sample Activity Duration Estimates

If Jeff's project team used PERT to determine the schedule for the VAPR project, they would have to collect numbers for the optimistic, most likely, and pessimistic duration estimates for each project activity. For example, suppose the person assigned to identify the IHI bundle requirements estimated that it would take five workdays to complete this activity. Without using PERT, the duration estimate for that activity would be five workdays. Suppose an optimistic time estimate for this activity is four workdays, and a pessimistic time estimate is nine workdays. Applying the PERT formula, you get the following:

$$
\begin{aligned}
\text{PERT weighted average} \quad &= \quad \frac{4d + 4 * 5d + 9d}{6} \\[2ex]
&= \quad \frac{4d + (4)(5d) + 9d}{6} \\[2ex]
&= \quad \frac{4d + 20d + 9d}{6} \\[2ex]
&= \quad \frac{33d}{6} \\[2ex]
&= \quad \textbf{5.5 days}
\end{aligned}
$$

Instead of using the most likely duration estimate of five workdays, the project team would use 5.5 workdays. This may not sound like a great difference, but it is 10% higher than the original single point estimate. For the VAPR project, which is estimated to take one year, if every activity were under-estimated by 10% the project would end up being completed five weeks later than planned.

The main advantage of PERT is that it attempts to address the risk associated with duration estimates. Because many projects exceed schedule estimates, PERT might help in developing schedules that are more realistic. PERT also has disadvantages. It involves more work because it requires several duration estimates, and there are better probabilistic methods for assessing schedule risk, such as Monte Carlo simulations. Monte Carlo takes into account the three-point estimate used by PERT, but it also includes additional probability information. For example, Jeff would ask the person assigned to identify the IHI bundle requirements for an optimistic, pessimistic, and most likely estimate along with the probability of completing that activity between the optimistic and most likely time estimates. Monte Carlo analysis requires special software, or plug-ins to existing software (such as Project 2013), and is fairly complex to set up and manage. Those who use it swear by its accuracy, while those who do not claim that PERT is accurate enough for most project work.

For this project, however, Jeff and his team decided to enter discrete estimates for each activity instead of using PERT or a Monte Carlo simulation. Jeff stressed that people who would do the work should provide the estimate, and they should have at least 75% confidence in meeting each estimate. Theoretically, if everyone had 50% confidence it would wash out as some activities would take more time, some less time, and some would be exactly on target, which would make the project be completed on time. However, because activity owners are usually too optimistic and not all activities are of the same duration, Jeff does not feel comfortable with a 50% probability. His compelling reason is that this project cannot be late due to regulatory constraints, leading Jeff to require a 75% confidence in the activity time estimates.

Figure 5-16 illustrates problems people have in providing good duration estimates!

Figure 5-16: Estimating can be difficult! (www.xkcd.com)

Developing the Project Schedule

Schedule development uses the results of all the preceding project time management processes to determine the start and end dates of project activities and of the entire project. There are often several iterations of all the project time management processes before a project schedule is finalized. The ultimate goal of schedule development is to create a realistic project schedule that provides a basis for monitoring project progress for the time dimension of the project. Project managers must lead their teams in creating realistic schedules and then following them during project execution.

The main output of the schedule development process is the project schedule, which is often displayed in the form of a Gantt chart. **Gantt charts** provide a standard format for displaying project schedule information by listing project activities and their corresponding start and finish dates in a calendar format. Gantt charts are very useful as they show when activities will be started and completed relative not only to dates, but to each other. Remember that the schedule network diagram only shows precedence (which activity depends upon which activities), so the team must refer to the Gantt chart to get that high level view of when work will be performed.

Figure 5-17 shows a simple Gantt chart for Project X, described earlier, created with Microsoft Project (back in 2009; they have been around over 100 years!). Recall that this example only uses finish-to-start dependencies and no lead or lag time. Notice the column heading where the activities are listed reads, "Task Name" instead of "Activity Name." This naming convention is from Microsoft Project and is one of the reasons why PMI has decided to stop using the term task within the PMBOK® Guide. See Appendix A for examples and instructions for using other types of dependencies with Project 2013.

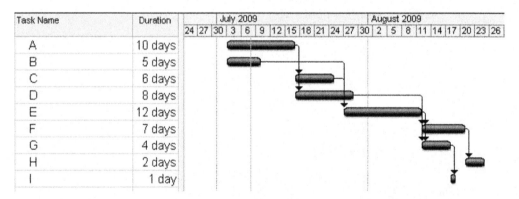

Figure 5-17. Gantt chart for Project X

Recall that the activities on the Gantt chart are those required to build the deliverables at the work package level on the WBS. These activities were previously defined, along with their attributes, and entered into the activity list. Remember also that although only activities have durations and costs, work packages will often appear in the Gantt chart as they serve as summaries for the activities required to build it. Before showing a Gantt chart for the VAPR project, it is important to explain a fundamental concept that assists project teams in developing and meeting project schedules: critical path analysis.

Critical Path Analysis

Many projects fail to meet schedule expectations. **Critical path method (CPM)**—also called **critical path analysis**—is a network diagramming technique used to predict total project duration. This important tool will help you combat project schedule overruns. A **critical path** for a project is the series of activities that determine the *earliest* time by which the project can be completed. It may also be defined as the *longest* path through the network diagram that has the least amount of slack or float. **Slack** or **float** is the amount of time an activity may be delayed without delaying a succeeding activity or the project finish date. There are normally several activities conducted in parallel on projects, and most projects have multiple paths through a network diagram. The longest path in terms of total duration (not the number of activities), is what is driving the completion date for the project. Remember that you are not finished with the project until you have finished *all* activities.

Calculating the Critical Path

To find the critical path for a project, you must first develop a good network diagram as described earlier, which requires a good activity list based on the WBS. To create a network diagram, you must determine the dependencies of activities and also estimate their durations. Calculating the critical path involves adding the durations for all activities on each path through the network diagram. The longest path is the critical path.

Figure 5-18 shows the AOA network diagram for Project X again. Note that you can use either the AOA or the precedence diagramming method to determine the critical path on projects. This figure also shows all the paths—a total of six—through the network diagram. Note that each path starts at the first node (1) and ends at the last node (7) on the AOA network diagram. This figure also shows the total duration of each path, sometimes referred to as its length, through the network diagram. These lengths are computed by adding the durations of each activity on the path. Because path A-C-E-F-H at 37 days has the longest duration, it is the critical path for the project.

What does the critical path really mean? *The critical path shows the shortest time in which a project can be completed.* If one or more of the activities on the critical path takes longer than planned, the whole project schedule will slip *unless* the project manager takes corrective action.

Project teams can be creative in managing the critical path. For example, Joan Knutson, a well-known author and speaker in the project management field, often describes how a gorilla helped Apple computer complete a project on time. Team members worked in an area with cubicles, and whoever was in charge of an activity currently on the critical path had a big, stuffed gorilla on top of his or her cubicle. Everyone knew that this person was under the most time pressure, so they tried not to distract him or her. When a critical activity was completed, the person in charge of the next critical activity received the gorilla.

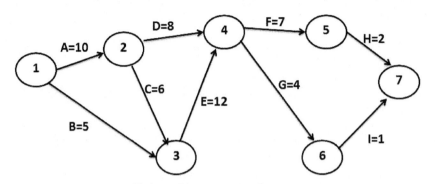

Note: Assume all durations are in days.

Path 1: A-D-F-H   Length = 10+8+7+2 =27
Path 2: A-D-G-I   Length = 10+8+4+1=23
Path 3: A-C-E-F-H   Length = 10+6+12+7+2=37
Path 4: A-C-E-G-I   Length = 10+6+12+4+1 = 33
Path 5: B-E-F-H   Length = 5+12+7+2=26
Path 6: B-E-G-I   Length = 5+12+4+1=22

Figure 5-18. Critical path calculation for Project X

Growing Grass Can Be on the Critical Path

People are often confused about what the critical path is for a project or what it really means. Some people think the critical path includes the most critical activities. However, the critical path focuses on the time dimension of a project. The fact that its name includes the word "critical" does *not* mean that it includes all critical activities in terms of scope, quality, resources, or other areas. For example, Frank Addeman, executive project director at Walt Disney Imagineering, explained in a keynote address at the May 2000 PMI-ISSIG Professional Development Seminar that growing grass was on the critical path for building Disney's Animal Kingdom theme park. This 500-acre park required special grass for its animal inhabitants, and some of the grass took years to grow. The project manager did not assign his top people to watching grass grow! He did use this information, however, to delay the start of other more expensive activities to make effective use of resources. Another misconception is that the critical path is the longest path, in terms of the discrete number of activities, through the network diagram. For a project, however, each activity must be done in order to complete the project, and as such every path, and every activity, is important. The critical path is simply the activity path, or thread, that requires the closest attention in order to not delay the project's completion date.

Other aspects of critical path analysis may cause confusion. Can there be more than one critical path on a project? Does the critical path ever change? In the Project X example, suppose that Activity G has a duration estimate of eight days instead of four days. This new duration estimate would make the length of Path 4 equal to 37 days. Now the project has two paths (paths 3 and 4) with equal, longest durations, so there are two critical paths. Therefore, there *can* be more than one critical path on a project, and for complex projects there may be many critical paths identified. Project managers should closely monitor performance of activities on the critical path to avoid late project completion. If there is more than one critical path, project managers must keep their eyes on all of them.

The critical path on a project can change as the project progresses. For example, suppose Activity B from Figure 5-18 has problems and ends up taking 17 days instead of 5 to finish. Assuming no other activity durations change, path 5, B-E-F-H, becomes the new critical path with a duration of 38 days. Therefore, the critical path can, and often does, change on a project. One of the most common reasons for critical paths changing is that the project manager closely manages those activities on the critical path and in doing so may neglect activities not on the critical path. Once the float is used up on the non-critical activities, they can end up on the critical path as well.

Using Critical Path Analysis to Make Schedule Trade-Offs

It is important to know what the critical path is throughout the life of a project so that the project manager can make trade-offs. If project managers know that one of the activities on the critical path is behind schedule, they need to decide what to do about it. Should the schedule be renegotiated with stakeholders? Should more resources be allocated to other items on the critical path to make up for that time? Is it okay if the project finishes behind schedule? By keeping track of the critical path, project managers and their team take a proactive role in managing the project schedule.

It is common for stakeholders to want to shorten a project schedule estimate. Your team may have done its best to develop a project schedule by defining activities, determining sequencing, and estimating resources and durations for each activity. The results of this work may have shown that your team needs 10 months to complete the project. Your sponsor might ask if the project can be done in eight or nine months. Rarely do people ask you to take longer than you suggested, but it can happen in cases where project work must be slowed to meet available funding, for example. By knowing the critical path, you can use several schedule compression techniques to shorten the project schedule. Each technique focuses on shortening the critical path.

Crashing is a technique for making cost and schedule trade-offs to obtain the greatest amount of schedule compression for the least incremental cost. For example, suppose one of the activities on the critical path for the VAPR project was to develop an online reporting system for mobile phones so physicians could get their VAP bundle compliance data anywhere. If this activity had not yet started and was originally estimated to take four weeks based on one IT person people working full time on the project, Jeff could decide to request one more full-time IT person to this activity to shorten its duration. Since doubling the resources working on an activity rarely cuts the duration in half, the original four week duration may only be reduced to three weeks. In effect Jeff would be doubling the cost of this activity and saving 25% of the duration. This may or may not be considered a reasonable tradeoff, depending on whether the schedule or the budget is more constrained on a given project. Since the VAPR project has a hard compliance deadline, Jeff would probably get leadership approval to spend the extra money in order to meet the required timeline on this project.

Another technique for shortening a project schedule is fast tracking. **Fast tracking** involves doing activities in parallel that you would normally do in sequence. For example, Jeff's project team may have planned not to start any of the work on the training until they finished most of the work on the workflow reengineering. Instead, they could consider starting the training several days earlier, while the reengineering is still being worked on, even though they may have to end up redoing some of the training materials. When fast tracking, the project manager is effectively adding a lead between two activities where one did not exist, or, increasing the lead if one already existed. When you fast track the actual duration of each activity does not change, as it only impacts the overall project duration. The advantage of fast tracking is that it can shorten the time it takes to finish a project without adding substantial cost to the project. The main disadvantage of fast tracking is that it often ends up with some rework for the activities that had the leads applied to them.

Figure 5-19 shows the original (top) and fast-tracked (bottom) timelines for the VAPR activities discussed above. By applying a lead to "Develop Training Materials," Jeff starts that seven-day activity four days earlier, even though he must add one extra day to that activity to allow for rework. Even with that extra rework day added, this total thread was reduced from 22 to 19 days in duration.

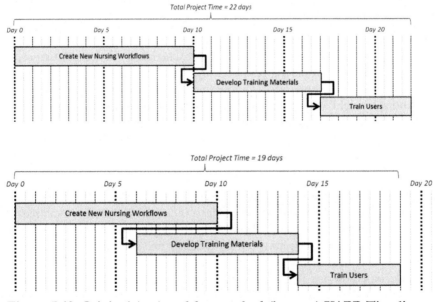

Figure 5-19. Original (top) and fast-tracked (bottom) VAPR Timeline

The third method, **de-scoping**, is commonly used when project stakeholders have included ancillary deliverables to the primary project objectives, and they can be removed to reduce the project timeline. These tag-on deliverables are sometimes added because the project is impacting the same area of this new deliverable, and sometimes because it may help increase the support of key stakeholders. For example, if an academic medical center is considering building an enterprise data warehouse to use within the clinical environment, they may decide to include research capabilities as well in order to gain the support of the physicians, who often serve as faculty and researchers in an academic medical center. If the project timeline is too long, then hospital leadership, who are funding the project, may decide to remove (or delay) the research components of the project.

Importance of Updating Critical Path Data

In addition to finding the critical path at the beginning of a project, it is important to update the schedule with actual activity data so that the project manager will know which activities are most critical to manage going forward. After the project team completes activities, they should document their actual durations. They should also document revised estimates for activities in progress or yet to be started, if needed. These revisions often cause a project's critical path to change, resulting in a new estimated completion date for the project. Again, proactive project managers and their teams stay on top of changes so that they can make informed decisions and keep stakeholders informed of, and involved in, major project decisions.

Critical Chain Scheduling

Another advanced scheduling technique that addresses the challenge of meeting or beating project finish dates is an application of the Theory of Constraints called critical chain scheduling. The **Theory of Constraints (TOC)** is a management philosophy developed by Eliyahu M. Goldratt and discussed in his books *The Goal* and *Critical Chain*.[2] The Theory of Constraints is based on the fact that, like a chain with its weakest link, any complex system at any point in time often has only one aspect or constraint that limits its ability to achieve more of its goal. For the system to attain any significant improvements, that constraint must be identified, and the whole system must be managed with it in mind. **Critical chain scheduling** is a method of scheduling that considers limited resources when creating a project schedule and includes buffers to protect the project completion date.

An important concept in critical chain scheduling is the availability of scarce resources. Some projects cannot be completed unless a particular resource is available to work on one or several activities. For example, if a television station wants to produce a show centered on a particular celebrity, it must first check the availability of that celebrity. As another example, if a particular piece of equipment is needed full time to complete each of two activities that were originally planned to occur simultaneously, critical chain scheduling acknowledges that you must either delay one of those activities until the equipment is available or find another piece of equipment in order to meet the schedule.

Other important concepts related to critical chain scheduling include multitasking and time buffers. **Multitasking** occurs when a resource works on more than one activity at a time. This situation occurs frequently on projects. People are assigned to multiple activities within the same project or different activities on multiple projects. For example, suppose someone is working on three different activities, Activity 1, Activity 2, and Activity 3, for three different projects, and each activity takes 10 days to complete. If the person did not multitask, and instead completed each activity sequentially, starting with Activity 1, then Activity 1 would be completed after day 10, Activity 2 would be completed after day 20, and Activity 3 would be completed after day 30, as shown in Figure 5-20.

However, because many people in this situation try to please all three people who need their activities completed, they often work on the first activities for some time, then the second, then the third, then go back to finish the first activities, then the second, and then the third, as shown in Figure 5-21. In this example, the activities were all half-done one at a time, then completed one at a time. Activity 1 is now completed at the end of day 20 instead of day 10, Activity 2 is completed at the end of day 25 instead of day 20, and Activity 3 is still completed on day 30. This example illustrates how multitasking can delay activity completions. Note that this delay only matters if someone else is depending upon Activity 1 or Activity 2 to be completed before they can begin their work, however, it is rare where a resource is working on an activity that does not serve as a predecessor to someone else's activity.

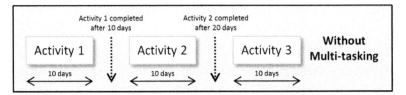

Figure 5-20. Three activities without multitasking (Schwalbe, Information Technology Project Management, Sixth Edition, 2010)

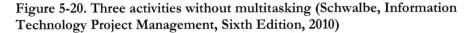
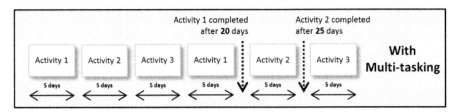

Figure 5-21. Three activities with multitasking (Schwalbe, Information Technology Project Management, Sixth Edition, 2010)

An essential concept to improving project finish dates with critical chain scheduling is to change the way people make activity estimates. Many people add a safety or **buffer**, which is additional time to complete an activity, to an estimate to account for various and sometimes unknown factors. These factors include the negative effects of multitasking, distractions and interruptions, fear that estimates will be reduced, Murphy's

Law, etc. **Murphy's Law** states that if something can go wrong, it will. Critical chain scheduling removes buffers from individual activities and instead creates a **project buffer**, which is additional time added before the project's due date. In a practical sense each major thread of activities usually require their own buffer, managed by the project manager, as it is difficult to manage one large buffer at the end of the project. Critical chain scheduling also protects activities on the critical chain from being delayed by using **feeding buffers**, which are additional time added before critical activities on the critical chain that are preceded by non-critical-path activities.

Figure 5-22 provides an example of a network diagram constructed using critical chain scheduling. Note that the critical chain accounts for a limited resource, X, and the schedule includes use of feeding buffers and a project buffer in the network diagram. The activities marked with an X are part of the critical chain, which can be interpreted as being the critical path using this technique. The activity estimates in critical chain scheduling should be shorter than traditional estimates because they do not include their own buffers. Not having activity buffers should mean less occurrence of **Parkinson's Law**, which states that work expands to fill the time allowed. In other words, if you included a buffer in a activity estimate and you did not need it, you would still use it. The feeding and project buffers protect the date that really needs to be met—the project completion date.

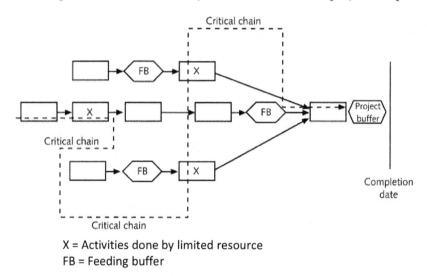

X = Activities done by limited resource
FB = Feeding buffer

Figure 5-22. Example of critical chain scheduling[3]

Feeding buffers are especially important when dealing with external resources that are difficult to schedule. Because the majority of healthcare systems are purchased, configured, and installed by internal staff working with the software vendor's professional services organization, healthcare is often constrained by the vendor's schedule. Typically the vendor will visit the healthcare organization and work with the internal team to get them started on a list of activities due over the following month. The vendor team then leaves the internal project staff to complete their work before returning to review the work and plan out the following month's work. Because the vendor is working on many customer accounts at one time, and they want to keep their staff 100% billable, their staff usually moves from one customer to another over the month, with little to no down time.

If the internal staff at the healthcare organization is late with the work they were supposed to complete since the last vendor visit, the vendor may choose to not return during their scheduled time slot, and their next open slot may be during their already-scheduled visit in two months. This one slip may cause the project to be one month late, even though the internal staff may have only been only one week late. However, because the vendor on-site visit was the constraint (or bottleneck) that drove the project's timeline, the hospital staff should have ensured that the work was done on time. In fact, they should have scheduled to complete it early by applying more resources, if required, even if it meant doing little to nothing the last few days of the month prior to the vendor's visit.

As you can see, critical chain scheduling is a fairly complicated yet powerful tool that involves critical path analysis, resource constraints, and changes in how activity estimates are made in terms of buffers. Several organizations have reported successes with this approach. Some consider critical chain scheduling one of the most important new concepts in the field of project management.

HEALTHCARE PERSPECTIVE

Several healthcare organizations have applied the theory of constraints (TOC) to improve patient flow. Consider a relatively simple system of a physician's office or clinic. The steps in the process could be patients checking in, filling out forms, having vital signs taken by a nurse, seeing the physician, seeing the nurse for a prescribed procedure such as vaccination, and so forth. These steps could take place in a simple linear sequence or chain ...Each link in this chain has the ability to perform its tasks at different average rates. In this example, the first resource can process 13 patients, charts, or blood samples per an hour; the second can process 17, and so forth. One may think that this process can produce 13 per hour, the average of all resources. In fact, this process or chain only can produce an average of eight [patients, charts, or blood samples] per hour. The chain is only as strong as its weakest link and the rate of the slowest resource in this example, the weakest link, is eight. This is true regardless of how fast each of the other resources can process individually, how much work is stuffed into the pipeline, or how complex the process or set of interconnected processes is to complete. Moreover, improving the performance of any link besides the constraint does nothing to improve the system as a whole.[4]

The CEO of a large healthcare organization in England described the success they had in reducing the length of hospital stays by using TOC. "With the help of Theory of Constraint we have been able to move Barnet & Chase Farm Hospitals NHS Trust from one of the worst performing trusts in England to one of the top performing. In Q4 (2007-2008) we were the top performing trust in London for the 4 hour target and 6th across England. Also, by applying the Theory of Constraints to our discharge process we have been able to reduce our length of stay by 27% and we know we can improve further on this."[5]

Sample Project Schedule

Jeff worked with Pat and their team to define project activities, determine activity sequencing, describe activity resources, estimate activity durations, and make schedule trade-offs to perform all of the work required for the project within one year, as desired by the project sponsor. Figure 5-23 provides part of the resulting Gantt chart the team will use to guide their project schedule. This schedule was created in MS Project 2013. Notice that the items in the Activity Name column come from the activity list, which were identified to create the work packages on the WBS. Duration estimates are entered in the "Duration" column, with dependencies between activities indicated in the Predecessor column. When the predecessor column is filled in with the Activity number that precedes it (or multiple numbers, if required), arrows connecting the activities appear on the Gantt chart. The names next to each bar on the Gantt chart indicate the resource assigned to that activity.

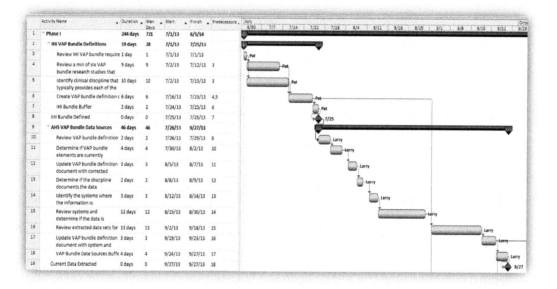

Figure 5-23. Sample project schedule

Note the Duration column indicates the number of working calendar days required to complete the activity, summary activity, or work package (depending upon the line being viewed). However, the "Man Days" column indicates the number of hours/8-hours-per-day for each line. For example, if an activity takes two calendar days, and at the same time another activity is taking place that also takes two days, the elapsed calendar days is two, but the man days is equal to four. Labor cost will be calculated based on man days, not calendar days, as you have to pay labor per day of work

Figure 5-24 shows another view of the Gantt chart for the VAPR project, showing all of the summary activities (represented by thick black lines) and milestones (represented by black diamonds). As noted previously, summary activities do not have durations or resources assigned to them directly. Instead they summarize the durations of the activities that are subordinate to them. Also remember that if you chose to include deliverables from the WBS on the schedule, then they will appear as bold summary lines as well. Including deliverables on the schedule is useful as it helps to identify the time (and later, you will find, the cost) required to complete each work package.

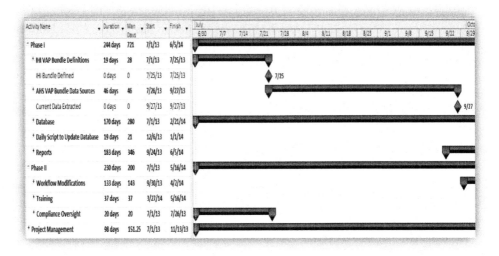

Figure 5-24. Sample Gantt chart showing summary activities and milestones

By using project management software like Project 2013, you can easily see different levels of detail in the schedule information. Also note that Jeff decided to include a few project buffers to account for unexpected factors. One of these buffers (shown in the second last item in Figure 5-23 as the activity "IHI Bundle Buffer") will help ensure that the IT team who will review the bundle will have everything they need when they are scheduled to begin their work. Although Pat is new to project management, Jeff is not, and he has learned that no matter how well you try to schedule everything, it can still be a challenge to finish everything on time without a mad rush at the end. For this reason, he decided to include a total of 20 days in project buffers, spread throughout the riskiest parts of the project, which the project steering committee thought was an excellent idea. Jeff also planned to have a dress rehearsal for the go-live to make sure everything would go smoothly with the actual go-live.

PROJECT COST MANAGEMENT

Project cost management includes the processes required to ensure that a project team completes a project within an approved budget. The main planning processes performed as part of project cost management are planning cost management, estimating costs, and determining the budget. Estimating costs involves developing an approximation or estimate of the costs of the resources needed to complete a project. Cost budgeting involves allocating the overall cost estimate to individual activities over time to establish a baseline for measuring performance. The main documents produced include a cost management plan, cost estimates, and a cost baseline.

Planning Cost Management

The purpose of this process is to determine the policies, procedures, and documentation for planning, managing, executing, and controlling project costs. The project team holds meetings, consults with experts, and analyzes data to help produce a cost management plan, which becomes a component of the project management plan.

Contents of the cost management plan can include the following:
- level of accuracy for cost estimates
- units of measure, such as staff hours or days or a lump sum amount
- variance thresholds for monitoring cost performance, such as a percentage deviation from the baseline plan
- rules of performance measurement, especially if earned value management is used
- formats and frequency for cost reports
- descriptions of each of the other cost management processes
- additional details about cost activities, such as strategic funding choices, procedures for recording costs, and roles and responsibilities for people performing cost activities

---

MEDIA SNAPSHOT

Crowdsourcing provides an interesting approach to funding projects involving new medical products. Instead of obtaining funding from traditional sources, you can solicit funds from a large group of people, especially from an online community. For example, the three co-founders of Inspiration Medical, a Minneapolis-based start-up firm, used crowdsourcing to finance the research and development work they need to develop a product to help people with bleeding problems. Their product is called AllaQuix, a nonprescription pad that quickly stops nuisance bleeding (i.e. bleeding that won't stop from small cuts) for people on blood thinners. The founders estimate that up to one in three adults is incapable, for a variety of reasons, of clotting in the typical two to five minutes. They used social media to introduce their product to potential customers and get feedback before spending hundreds of thousands of dollars on marketing.

Stephen Miller from Inspiration explained, "This is why we haven't put it on a retail shelf yet. Some people first said, "Is this a scam or a joke? So we changed the title from 'Stop nuisance bleeding' to 'Help us launch AllaQuix.' That may have saved us $500,000 in marketing costs."[6]

Estimating Costs

Project teams normally prepare cost estimates at various stages of a project, and these estimates should be fine-tuned as time progresses. Before management approves a project, someone must develop a rough estimate of what it will cost to complete the project. Then, after the project manager and team are assigned to a project, they would prepare a more detailed cost estimate. If this estimate is substantially different from the initial budgeted amount, the project manager should negotiate with the project sponsor to increase or decrease the budget, or to make changes to the scope or time goals to meet cost constraints. As more detailed information becomes available, the project team should update the cost estimates and continue negotiating with the sponsor to meet project goals.

In addition to creating cost estimates, it is also important to provide supporting details for the estimates. The supporting details include any assumptions used in creating the estimate, the acceptable methods and processes that may be used, the description of the project (including references to the scope statement, WBS, and WBS dictionary) that was used as a basis for the estimate, and details on the cost estimation tools and techniques used to create the estimate. These supporting details should make it easier to prepare an updated estimate or similar estimate as needed.

A large percentage of total project costs are often labor costs, whether internal or external. Many organizations estimate the number of people or hours they need for major parts of a project over the life cycle of the project. They also determine the labor rate to apply based on the category of labor. It is important to work with people in the organization's human resources, payroll, or accounting departments to determine these labor rates and apply the appropriate amounts for benefits and overhead so that total labor costs are included in the estimate. For external labor rates, you may refer to current contracts for other external labor, recent vendor bids, or rate information provided by reputable organizations such as Gartner or HIMSS.

Most healthcare projects fall into one of four major categories: construction, technology/systems, research, or clinical workflow. Construction projects involve facilities; technology projects include software development or implementation; research projects involve clinical or bench research; and clinical workflow projects involve changing the way caregivers treat their patients. Each of these project types have a different common ratio of labor to materials cost, as well as different ratios of internal versus external labor costs. Many healthcare projects also include a combination of these four categories, like the VAPR project including both technology and workflow.

Construction, for example, uses very little internal labor costs as most work is subcontracted out and also includes high material costs. Research is most commonly staffed with almost all internal labor and little material costs. Workflow projects may be staffed primarily with internal labor or may make heavy use of consulting services. Technology projects often use a high level of internal labor, but may also use external labor to make up for lack of available skills internally. Technology projects that are implementations of purchased software will frequently require large professional services budgets, as the software vendor (or their associated consulting firm) is usually required to install and configure the system. This situation is especially true for organizations that have limited internal IT staffing, where most of the implementation labor is outsourced.

You have to know your project type, its complexity, your organization's capabilities, and whether or not you have the required skill sets within your organization before you can determine how much it will cost to complete the project activities.

VIDEO HIGHLIGHTS

Michael Porter and Robert S. Kaplan, Harvard Business School professors and authors of the Harvard Business Review article "How to Solve the Cost Crisis in Health Care," discuss this topic in a short (less than ten minute) video. Porter suggests that many efforts to reduce healthcare costs are ineffective because organizations in healthcare don't know how to measure their costs properly. Kaplan says that the definition of costs should be costs within the system and that the patient should be the fundamental costing unit. Costs should focus on particular medical conditions (such as diabetes or knee replacements), and organizations should focus on adding value by comparing costs with patient outcomes.

"The remedy to the cost crisis does not require medical science breakthroughs or new governmental regulation. It simply requires a new way to accurately measure costs and compare them with outcomes… The experiences of several major institutions currently implementing the new approach—the Head and Neck Center at MD Anderson Cancer Center in Houston, the Cleft Lip and Palate Program at Children's Hospital in Boston, and units performing knee replacements at Schön Klinik in Germany and Brigham & Women's Hospital in Boston—confirm our belief that bringing accurate cost and value measurement practices into health care delivery can have a transformative impact."[7]

Cost Estimation Tools and Techniques

As you can imagine, developing a good cost estimate is difficult. Fortunately, several tools and techniques are available to assist in creating them. Three commonly used techniques for creating estimates include the following:

- **Analogous estimates**, also called **top-down estimates**, use the actual cost of a previous, similar project as the basis for estimating the cost of the current project. This technique requires a good deal of expert judgment and is generally less costly than others are, but it can also be less accurate. Analogous estimates are most reliable when the previous projects are similar in fact, not just in appearance. This approach is similar to use analogous estimates for activity durations.

- **Bottom-up estimates** involve estimating individual activities and summing them to get a project total. The size of the individual activities and the experience of the estimators drive the accuracy of the estimates. If a detailed WBS is available for a project, the project manager could have people responsible for work packages develop their own cost estimates for them. The project manager would then add all of the cost estimates to create cost estimates for each higher-level WBS item and finally for the entire project. Like bottom-up estimating used for durations, this approach can increase the accuracy of the cost estimate, but it can also be time intensive and, therefore, expensive to develop.

- **Parametric modeling** uses project characteristics (parameters) in a mathematical model to estimate project costs. A parametric model might provide an estimate of $870 per desktop computer, for example, based on the type of PC required and the location of the installation. Parametric models are most reliable when the historical information used to create the model is accurate, the parameters are readily quantifiable, and the model is flexible in terms of the size of the project. The project manager must be sure that the single-unit estimate, $870 per PC in this case, includes all costs. For example, does this cost include the required cables and wiring? Does it include the monitor, keyboard, and mouse? Does it include any cost allowance for the labor to install the PCs?

Sometimes it makes sense to use more than one approach for creating a cost estimate, and sometimes more than one approach is used on different parts of a project. For example, a project team might develop an analogous estimate for one part of the project, a parametric model for another part, and a bottom-up estimate for the more complex portions (such as software development). Or, they may use parametric or bottom-up estimates for the entire project and then try to identify a similar, analogous project to compare to their new cost estimate. If the estimates were far apart, the team would need to collect more information to develop a better estimate.

Sample Cost Estimate

Every cost estimate is unique, just as every project is unique. This section includes a step-by-step approach for developing the major parts of the cost estimate for the VAPR project. Of course, this example is much shorter and simpler than a real cost estimate would be, but it illustrates an easy-to-follow process and uses several of the tools and techniques described earlier.

It is important to first document any cost-related ground rules and assumptions and to clarify the acceptable methods and processes that may be used for the estimate. For the VAPR project cost estimate, these include the following:

- The WBS will be used as the basis of the cost estimates.

- Each work package owner may choose the most suitable cost estimating method and be able to justify their numbers.

- If a work package exceeds a duration of 160 hours, it should be broken down into two or more smaller work packages. [This number of hours is what AHS uses for projects of one year or less. Other projects may have work packages that are smaller or larger in size.]

- The project manager will report progress on the project using earned value analysis.

- Costs will be provided in U.S. dollars. [Normally only included for multi-national corporations.]

- The project steering committee members' time will not be charged to the project. All other project labor will be charged to the project.

- Internal project labor costs will include a 30 percent benefits charge. For example, if the direct labor rate is $30/hour, the burdened rate, or the rate including benefits and overhead, is $30*1.3=$39 (rounded to the nearest whole-dollar amount).

- Indirect overhead/administration will not be charged to the project.

- Labor costs for employees to cover their salaries while they attend training classes are not included in this estimate.

- Because several risks are related to this project, the estimate includes 10 percent of the total estimate as reserves.

- A computer model of the project estimate will be developed to facilitate the changing of inputs, such as labor rates or the number of labor hours for various activities.

Fortunately, the project team can easily access cost estimates and actual information from similar projects, as both database development and workflow reengineering projects are common at AHS. However, creating near real-time online reporting from the data warehouse is new to AHS, so this piece of the project will have to be estimated more carefully.

Because the estimate must be provided by WBS work package, Jeff and his team reviewed the draft of the project schedule and made further assumptions. They decided that they would assign any costs associated with an activity to the period in which the activity work was taking place, and they needed to create a few more activities in order to do that. For example, the training materials would be ordered weeks before they were going to be used, but there was no activity defined for "Order Materials" since it would only take a few hours. However, in order to assign the training materials costs to the correct period they added an activity for ordering the materials

Figure 5-25 shows a cost model/spreadsheet the team summarizing costs by WBS work package. There are columns for entering the number of labor hours and the costs per hour. Several activities are estimated using this approach. There are also some short comments within the estimate, such as reserves being 10 percent of the subtotal for the estimate. With a computerized model, you can easily change input variables, such as number of hours or cost per hour, to revise the estimate.

It is very important to have several people review the project cost estimate, including the assumptions, methods, and processes utilized. It is also helpful to analyze the total dollar value as well as the percentage of the total amount for each major WBS category. For example, the Chief Nursing Officer may be able to quickly look at the VAPR project cost estimate and decide whether the costs are reasonable, as she has been engaged in many clinical workflow projects in her career. If she feels the cost is out of alignment with her experience, she would discuss her concerns with Jeff and Pat. In the case of VAPR, the costs may be higher as this project is not just about clinical workflow, but it also includes building an entire technology base to support clinical decision-making.

Task Name	Man Days	Internal Labor Rate	Total Internal Labor	External Labor Rate	Total External	Non-Labor Costs	Total Cost
Phase I							
IHI VAP Bundle Definitions	28	$ 55	$ 12,320	$ -	$ -	$ -	$ 12,320
AHS VAP Bundle Data Sources	46	$ 60	$ 22,080	$ -	$ -	$ -	$ 22,080
Database	243	$ 60	$ 116,640	$ -	$ -	$ 170,000	$ 286,640
Daily Update Script	21	$ 60	$ 10,080	$ -	$ -	$ -	$ 10,080
Reports	346	$ 55	$ 152,240	$ -	$ -	$ 240,000	$ 392,240
Phase II		$ -	$ -	$ -	$ -	$ -	$ -
Workflow Modifications	143	$ 55	$ 62,920	$ -	$ -	$ -	62,920
Training	37	$ -	$ -	$ 70	$ 20,720	$ -	20,720
Compliance Oversight	20	$ 120	$ 19,200	$ -	$ -	$ -	19,200
Project Management	151.3	$ 80	$ 96,800	$ -	$ -	$ -	96,800
Contingency			$ 10,000		$ 10,000	$ 35,000	55,000
Totals			**$ 492,280**		**$ 30,720**	**$ 445,000**	**$ 978,000**

Assumptions:
1. Internal labor rates include benefits and overhead. Average hourly rates based on skill levels and departments.
2. External labor rates are based on historical average; may change as contracts are awarded.
3. Non-labor costs include purchasing licenses for using training materials, books, CD/ROMs, travel expenses, etc.; may change as contracts are awarded.
4. Contingency reserves are calculated based on uncertainty/risk of each cost category.

Figure 5-25. Sample cost estimate

After the total cost estimate was approved, Jeff's team would then allocate costs for each month based on the project schedule and when costs would be incurred. Many organizations also require that the estimated costs be allocated into certain budget categories, such as compensation or travel. Using modern project management software tools, this part of the work is straightforward as the cost estimates can be entered into the software as they are developed. Some estimates may have been at the activity level, while others at the work package level. The software will simply aggregate all costs upward, calculating subtotals as it moves up the WBS. Because activities are time based, the work packages also become time based.

Cost Budgeting

Project cost budgeting involves allocating the project cost estimate to activities over time. These activities are based on the work breakdown structure for the project. The WBS, therefore, is a required input to the cost budgeting process. Likewise, the project scope statement, WBS dictionary, activity cost estimates and supporting detail, project schedule, and other plans provide useful information for cost budgeting.

The main goal of the cost budgeting process is to produce a cost baseline. A **cost baseline** is a time-phased budget that project managers use to measure and monitor cost performance. Estimating costs for each major project activity over time provides project managers and top management with a foundation for project cost control using earned value management, as described in Chapter 8. See the *Brief Guide to Microsoft Project 2013* in Appendix A for information on using Project 2013 for cost control.

What Went Wrong?

The United Kingdom's National Health Services (NHS) IT modernization program has been called "the greatest IT disaster in history" by one London columnist. This 10-year program, which started in 2002, was created to provide an electronic patient records system, appointment booking, and a prescription drug system in England and Wales. Britain's Labor government estimated that the program eventually cost more than $55 billion, a $26 billion overrun. Problems included incompatible system features, arguments among contractors about who's responsible for what, and lack of inputs by physicians, to name a few.

On September 22, 2012, government officials announced that they were scrapping the program. Health Secretary Andre Lansley said that the program "let down the NHS and wasted taxpayer's money."[8] Poor planning, poor execution, and poor monitoring and controlling were all evident in this project disaster.

Sample Cost Baseline

The VAPR project team used their cost estimate along with the project schedule and other information to allocate costs for each month. Figure 5-26 provides an example of a cost baseline for this project. Again, it is important for the team to document the assumptions they made when developing the cost baseline and have several experts review it. The cost baseline should also be updated as more information becomes available. Figure 5-27 provides a sample cash flow report by quarter, generated from their same project management software tool.

VAPR Project Phase I	1	2	3	4	5	6	7	8	9	10	11	12	Total
IHI VAP Bundle Definitions	12,320												$ 12,320
AHS VAP Bundle Data Sources	1,920	10,560	9,600										$ 22,080
Database	13,440		5,280	193,520	19,200	18,720	22,080	14,400					$ 286,640
Daily Script to Update Database						9,600	480						$ 10,080
Reports			4,400	20,240	18,480	10,560	20,240	17,600	18,480	201,760	76,960	3,520	$ 392,240
Phase II													
Workflow Modifications			480	11,040	9,920	11,440	10,560	11,000	7,600	880			$ 62,920
Training									2,130	11,840	6,750		$ 20,720
Compliance Oversight	1,600	1,600	1,600	1,600	1,600	1,600	1,600	1,600	1,600	1,600	1,600	1,600	$ 19,200
Project Management	9,680	8,873	9,680	8,873	8,873	8,067	8,873	6,453	6,453	6,453	6,453	8,067	$ 96,800
Contingency	5,500	5,042	5,500	5,042	5,042	4,583	5,042	3,667	3,667	3,667	3,667	4,583	$ 55,000
Totals	$ 44,460	$ 26,075	$ 36,540	$ 240,315	$ 63,115	$ 64,570	$ 68,875	$ 54,720	$ 39,930	$ 226,200	$ 95,430	$ 13,187	$ 978,000

Figure 5-26. Sample cost baseline by month

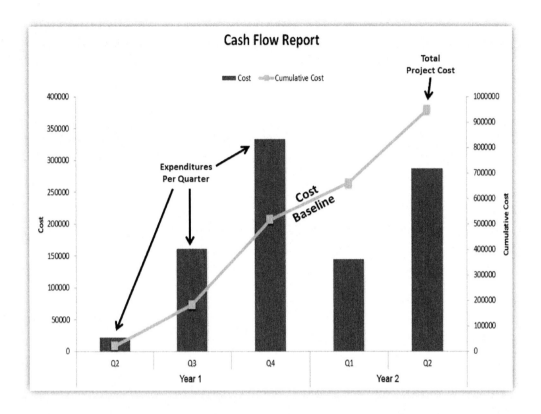

Figure 5-27. Sample cash flow report

CASE WRAP-UP

Pat learned a lot by working with Jeff, an experience project manager, while planning the VAPR project. While planning time and cost aspects of the project they required input from a variety of stakeholders. As a clinician, Pat was more effective than Jeff at getting other clinicians involved, but Jeff was more successful working with the IT staff. It was a good partnership.

Pat was surprised that even in the IT group, who work with projects all the time, that some of the staff wanted to plan to the bottom-most detail, while others were adamant that they were wasting time planning and wanted to jump in and start the work. She thought Jeff did a good job getting both groups to come to the middle.

Both Jeff and Pat appreciated the ongoing support provided by members of the project steering committee. They were happy that the committee insisted on a formal process to analyze, develop, and document both time and cost projections for the project. These baselines would provide a solid basis for measuring progress. Jeff reminded everyone that good cost and time planning doesn't shorten the project's timeline or save money, but it does result in a more accurate timeline and less budget surprises later.

CHAPTER SUMMARY

Successful project managers know how important it is to develop, refine, and follow plans to meet project goals. This chapter summarizes the planning processes and outputs for project time and cost management.

Planning processes for time management include planning schedule management, defining activities, sequencing activities, estimating activity resources, estimating activity durations, and developing a project schedule. A project network diagram shows the sequencing of project activities, and a Gantt chart is a standard format for displaying project schedule information by listing activities and their corresponding start and finish dates in a calendar format.

It is also important to understand critical path analysis to make schedule trade-off decisions. Critical chain scheduling can also help in scheduling when there are scarce resources involved in a project.

Planning processes for cost management include planning cost management, estimating costs, and determining the project budget. There are several methods for creating cost estimates, such as analogous, bottom-up, and parametric. A cost baseline is a time-phased budget that project managers use to measure and monitor cost performance.

Samples of several planning documents for time and cost management are provided for the VAPR project.

QUICK QUIZ

1.   What is the first step in planning a project schedule?

   A. creating a schedule management plan

   B. developing an activity list

   C. assigning resources to the project

   D. determining activity sequencing

2.   The _____ rule is that all work required for a deliverable is included in its sub-deliverables when defining activities.

   A. golden

   B. hierarchy

   C. roll-up

   D. WBS 100%

3.   A(n) _____ normally does not have any cost or duration.

   A. activity

   B. milestone

   C. critical task

   D. baseline

4.   What is the most common type of dependency between activities?

   A. finish-to-start

   B. start-to-finish

   C. start-to-start

   D. finish-to-finish

5.   The _____ method is a network diagramming technique used to predict total project duration.

   A. PERT

   B. Gantt chart

   C. critical path

   D. crashing

6.   _____ is a technique for making cost and schedule trade-offs to obtain the greatest amount of schedule compression for the least incremental cost.

A. Crashing

B. Fast tracking

C. De-scoping

D. Parametric modeling

7.   Critical chain scheduling considers limited resources when creating a project schedule and includes _____ to protect the project completion date.

A. reserves

B. multitasking

C. buffers

D. outsourcing

8.   Using a(n) _____ approach to developing cost estimates requires a good deal of expert judgment and is generally less costly than others are, but it can also be less accurate.

A. bottom-up

B. parametric

C. expert judgment

D. analogous

9.   The _____ must be the basis for a project cost estimate if you plan to create a cost baseline and use earned value management as part of monitoring and controlling costs.

A. project schedule

B. cost model

C. Gantt chart

D. WBS

10.   A _____ is a time-phased budget that project managers use to measure and monitor cost performance.

A. cost baseline

B. cost estimate

C. life-cycle budget

D. cash flow analysis

Quick Quiz Answers

1. A; 2. D; 3. B; 4. A; 5. C; 6. A; 7. C; 8. D; 9. D; 10. A

DISCUSSION QUESTIONS

1. Why does having good plans for the project schedule and costs help project teams during project execution? Why is it difficult to develop good plans in these areas?

2. What are the main planning processes performed as part of project time management? What are some of the most common outputs created, and how are they used?

3. What is critical path analysis? Should you know the critical path for all projects? Why or why not?

4. What is critical chain scheduling, and how is it different from critical path analysis? Give an example of its use in healthcare.

5. What are the main planning processes performed as part of project cost management? What are some of the most common outputs created, and how are they used?

6. What are some approaches for creating a cost estimate? Why is it important to develop a good cost estimate? What do you think about the cost estimating approach used on the VAPR project?

7. What is a cost baseline? How is it prepared, and how is it used?

EXERCISES

Note: These exercises can be done individually or in teams, in-class, as homework, or in a virtual environment. Learners can either write their results in a paper or prepare a short presentation or video to show their results.

1. Find an example of a large healthcare project that took more than a year to complete. Describe some of the planning work completed for the project as part of project time and cost management. Summarize your findings.

2. Review the features boxes in this chapter with examples of What Went Right, What Went Wrong, Healthcare Perspectives, and the Media Snapshot. Discuss some of the information presented, and find additional references related to topics discussed in two of these examples. Summarize your findings.

3. Consider Figure 5-28. All duration estimates are in days, and the network proceeds from Node 1 to Node 9.

Activity	Initial node	Final node	Duration estimate
A	1	2	2
B	2	3	2
C	2	4	3
D	2	5	4
E	3	6	2
F	4	6	3
G	5	7	6
H	6	8	2
I	6	7	5
J	7	8	1
K	8	9	2

Figure 5-28. Network diagram data for a small project

a. Draw an AOA network diagram representing the project. Put the node numbers in circles and draw arrows from node to node, labeling each arrow with the activity letter and estimated duration.

b. Identify all the paths on the network diagram and note how long they are.

c. What is the critical path for this project, and how long is it?

d. What is the shortest possible time it will take to complete this project?

e. Enter the information into Project 2013. See the *Brief Guide to Microsoft Project 2013* in Appendix A for detailed instructions on using this software. View the network diagram and activity schedule table to see the critical path and float or slack for each activity. Provide screen shots of the Gantt chart and network diagram views and the activity schedule table. Interpret this information for someone unfamiliar with project time management.

4. Create a cost estimate/model for redecorating a room using spreadsheet software. Assume you have one month and $5,000 to spend. Develop a WBS for the project and create a cost model based on your WBS. Document the assumptions you made in preparing the estimate and provide explanations for key numbers. (Note: Feel free to pick a different scenario you are familiar with for this exercise.)

5. Watch the Video Highlight in this chapter where Michael Porter and Robert S. Kaplan discuss the cost crisis in health care. Find at least two other references related to this topic and discuss how it relates to project cost management. Summarize your findings and opinions.

TEAM PROJECTS

Note: These team projects can be done in-class, as homework, or in a virtual environment. Learners can either write their results in a paper or prepare a short presentation or video to show their results.

1. Your organization initiated a project to raise money for an important charity. Assume that there are 1,000 people in your organization. Also assume that you have six months to raise as much money as possible, with a goal of $100,000. Using the scope statement and WBS you created in the previous chapter, create a Gantt chart and cost estimate for the project.

2. You are part of a team in charge of a project to help people in your company (500 people) lose weight. This project is part of a competition, and the top "losers" will be featured in a popular television show. Assume that you have six months to complete the project and a budget of $10,000. Using the scope statement and WBS you created in the previous chapter, create a Gantt chart and cost estimate for the project.

3. Using the information you developed in Project 1 or 2 role-play a meeting to review one of these planning documents with key stakeholders. Determine who will play what role (project manager, team member from a certain department, senior managers, and so on). Be creative in displaying different personalities (a senior manager who questions the importance of the project to the organization, a team member who is very shy or obnoxious).

4. Perform the planning tasks (only for the knowledge areas covered in this chapter) for one of the case studies provided in Appendix B. Remember to be thorough in your planning so that your execution goes smoothly.

5. As a team, find at least six examples of Gantt charts for various types of projects. Discuss the similarities and differences between how the activities are defined, how durations and dependencies are entered, etc. Also discuss the quality of these examples. Include screen shots of the files and citations. Remember that many software products, like MindView Microsoft Project, include sample or template files.

KEY TERMS

activity – A distinct, scheduled portion of work performed during the course of a project

activity attributes — Information that provides schedule-related information about each activity, such as predecessors, successors, logical relationships, leads and lags, resource requirements, constraints, imposed dates, and assumptions related to the activity.

activity list — A tabulation of activities to be included on a project schedule.

activity-on-arrow (AOA) approach, or the **arrow diagramming method (ADM)** — A network diagramming technique in which activities are represented by arrows and connected at points called nodes to illustrate the sequence of activities.

analogous estimates, or **top-down estimates** — The estimates that use the actual cost of a previous, similar project as the basis for estimating the cost of the current project.

bottom-up estimates — Cost estimates created by estimating individual activities and summing them to get a project total.

buffer — Additional time to complete a activity, added to an estimate to account for various factors.

burst — An occurrence when two or more activities follow a single node on a network diagram.

cost baseline — A time-phased budget that project managers use to measure and monitor cost performance.

crashing — A technique for making cost and schedule trade-offs to obtain the greatest amount of schedule compression for the least incremental cost.

critical chain scheduling — A method of scheduling that takes limited resources into account when creating a project schedule and includes buffers to protect the project completion date.

critical path — The series of activities that determine the *earliest* time by which the project can be completed; it is the *longest* path through the network diagram and has the least amount of slack or float.

critical path method (CPM), or **critical path analysis** — A network diagramming technique used to predict total project duration.

dependency, or **relationship** — The sequencing of project activities.

de-scoping, — A schedule compression technique where you remove deliverables that are ancillary to the primary project objectives in order to reduce the project timeline

discretionary dependencies — The dependencies that are defined by the project team.

duration — The actual amount of time spent working on an activity *plus* elapsed time.

effort — The number of workdays or work hours required to complete a activity.

external dependencies — The dependencies that involve relationships between project and non-project activities.

fast tracking — A schedule compression technique where you do activities in parallel that you would normally do in sequence.

feeding buffers — Additional time added before activities on the critical path that are preceded by non-critical-path activities.

Gantt charts — A standard format for displaying project schedule information by listing project activities and their corresponding start and finish dates in a calendar format.

lag — when an activity requires a gap in time before it can start

lead — when an activity can overlap a preceding one

mandatory dependencies — The dependencies that are inherent in the nature of the work being performed on a project.

merge — A situation when two or more nodes precede a single node on a network diagram.

milestone — A significant event on a project.

multitasking — When a resource works on more than one activity at a time.

Murphy's Law — If something can go wrong, it will.

network diagram — A schematic display of the logical relationships among, or sequencing of, project activities.

node — The starting and ending point of an activity on an activity-on-arrow network diagram.

parametric modeling — A technique that uses project characteristics (parameters) in a mathematical model to estimate project costs.

Parkinson's Law — Work expands to fill the time allowed.

precedence diagramming method (PDM) — A network diagramming technique in which boxes represent activities.

Program Evaluation and Review Technique (PERT) — A network analysis technique used to estimate project duration when there is a high degree of uncertainty about the individual activity duration estimates.

project buffer — The additional time added before a project's due date to account for unexpected factors.

slack or **float** — The amount of time an activity may be delayed without delaying a succeeding activity or the project finish date.

task – Work that is done in support of operational, functional, or project performance. Tasks are not part of the schedule (activities are shown on the schedule). Tasks include many management functions such as things done to manage the team, run a production line, or build relationships.

Theory of Constraints (TOC) — A management philosophy that states that any complex system at any point in time often has only one aspect or constraint that is limiting its ability to achieve more of its goal.

three-point estimate — An estimate that includes an optimistic, most likely, and pessimistic estimate.

END NOTES

[1] Luc K. Richard, "Reducing Schedule Risk, Parts 1 and 2," (www.Gantthead.com) (November 10, 2003 and January 31, 2005).

[2] Goldratt, Eliyahu, *Critical Chain and The Goal*. Great Barrington, MA: The North River Press (1997 and 2004).

[3] Goldratt, Eliyahu, *Critical Chain*. p. 218.

[4] Anne M. Breen, Tracey Burton-Houle, and David C. Aron, "Applying the Theory of Constraints in Health Care: Part 1 - The Philosophy," Quality Management in Health Care, Volume 10, Number 3 (Spring 2002).

[5] R. Stratton and A. Knight, "Managing Patient Flow Using Time Buffers," Journal of Manufacturing Technology Management, Volume: 21 Issue: 4 (2010).

[6] Neal St. Anthony, "Crowdsourcing gets valuable R&D cash," Minneapolis Star Tribune (May 6, 2013).

[7] Michael Porter and Robert Kaplan, "How to Solve the Cost Crisis in Health Care," Harvard Business Review, (September 2011).

[8] Press Association, "U.K. Health Service To Dismantle National Health IT Program," iHealthBeat (September 23, 2011).

Chapter 6

Planning Projects, Part 3
(Project Quality, Human Resource, Communications, Stakeholder, Risk, and Procurement Management)

LEARNING OBJECTIVES

After reading this chapter, you will be able to:

- Create plans incorporating the components for project quality, human resource, communications, stakeholder, risk, and procurement management
- Demonstrate the understanding of the project quality management planning, and explain the purpose and contents of a quality management plan, project dashboard, quality metrics, and quality checklists
- Explain the project human resource management planning process, and create a human resource plan
- Describe the importance of using a project communications management plan, a project Web site, and other collaboration tools
- Demonstrate the importance of creating a stakeholder management plan
- Discuss the five project risk management planning processes, and explain how a risk management plan, a probability/impact matrix, a risk register, and risk-related contractual agreements are used in risk management planning
- Explain a make-or-buy analysis, procurement management plans, requests for proposal/quote, contract statements of work, and supplier evaluation matrices

---

OPENING CASE

Jeff and his team continued to plan various aspects of the Ventilator Associated Pneumonia Reduction (VAPR) project. They anticipated a need for additional server capacity for the databases and more licenses for their report writer. These technology costs composed a large percentage of the Phase I part of the project. Phase II was different as Pat did not foresee technology costs, but she did plan to outsource the production of the computer-based training (CBT) curriculum. The Academic Health Systems (AHS) technology department outsourced most of this type of work because it tended to come in spurts, but Pat knew she might have to find another source because their preferred supplier had already committed to another AHS project. Pat knew that developing and providing quality training courses was very important to this project and would be the difference between it being accepted or rejected by the clinicians.

Both Jeff and Pat knew that successfully planning the human resource, communications, risk, and procurement management dimensions were also important, especially because the project involved so many different stakeholders—nurses, physicians, therapists, infection control, and the patient quality group. Some of the other projects going on in these areas might affect the resources available to the VAPR project, which concerned Jeff. He told Pat that they really had to focus on project integration management to make sure they considered resource availability along with the project's scope, schedule, and budget when considering project risk.

Jeff knew a great deal about project management, but it was Pat who really understood the clinical care side of the project. She reminded Jeff that regardless of the schedule or budget, project quality was the most important aspect to consider. Pat recognized that the only thing worse than getting no data was getting the wrong data, as clinicians were making life and death decisions based on the data being presented to them.

Jeff knew Pat well enough to know that she would pull the plug on the project, even if it meant risking her own job, in order to stop the wrong data from getting to caregivers. He respected Pat for standing up for the patient's well-being, but he hoped that through solid planning and intense testing their VAPR project would roll out as planned.

Fortunately, AHS had well-defined processes for planning all aspects of projects that Jeff had used many times. Pat and Jeff decided to work together in developing the plans for the two project phases, both to help Pat learn more about managing projects and to ensure the two phases were aligned and integrated.

INTRODUCTION

Everyone knows that it is important to effectively plan the scope, time, and cost dimensions of a project and to develop the overall project management plan as part of integration management. However, some project managers neglect planning in the other knowledge areas—quality, human resource, communications, risk, procurement, and stakeholder management. It is important to skillfully plan *all* of these areas because they are all crucial to project success. This chapter summarizes key information on planning in these knowledge areas and specific actions that Jeff, Pat, and their team took. The next chapter shows how these plans provide the basis for project execution.

SUMMARY OF PLANNING PROCESSES AND OUTPUTS

Figure 6-1 shows the project planning processes and outputs for quality, human resource, communications, risk, procurement, and stakeholder management based on the *PMBOK® Guide, Fifth Edition*. As mentioned earlier, these planning documents, as well as other project-related information, would be available to all team members for the VAPR project. This chapter provides samples of some of these outputs, as well as a few additional ones, such as a project dashboard and a project Web site.

The following sections describe planning processes in these knowledge areas and then provide examples of applying them to the VAPR project at AHS. Although stakeholder management is listed as the last or tenth knowledge area in the *PMBOK® Guide, Fifth Edition*, it is presented in this text after communications management because the two are closely related. Templates for creating several of these planning documents are available on the companion Web site for this text.

Knowledge area	Planning process	Outputs
Project quality management	Plan quality management	Quality management plan
		Process improvement plan
		Quality metrics
		Quality checklists
		Project documents updates
Project human resource management	Plan human resource management	Human resource plan
Project communications management	Plan communications management	Communications management plan
		Project documents updates
Project stakeholder management	Plan stakeholder management	Stakeholder management plan
		Project documents updates
Project risk management	Plan risk management	Risk management plan
	Identify risks	Risk register
	Perform qualitative risk analysis	Project documents updates
	Perform quantitative risk analysis	Project documents updates
	Plan risk responses	Project management plan updates
		Project documents updates
Project procurement management	Plan procurement management	Procurement management plan
		Procurement statement of work
		Procurement documents
		Source selection criteria
		Make or buy decisions
		Change requests
		Project documents updates

Figure 6-1. Planning processes and outputs for project quality, human resource, communications, risk, procurement, and stakeholder management

PROJECT QUALITY MANAGEMENT

Project quality management ensures that the project will satisfy the stated or implied needs for which it was undertaken. There is a significant difference between *stated* and *implied* needs. Stated needs are those that the stakeholders specify that they need. In the case of the VAPR project, the project team needs to know whether or not the IHI Ventilator Bundle best practices are being followed for each patient currently on a ventilator, and they need to know this while there is sufficient time to correct the deficiency.

Perhaps more important in many projects, and certainly in clinical care projects, are the implied stakeholder requirements. In some industries and certainly in many projects, data accuracy and precision may not be as critical as data availability. For example, in a sales-oriented organization, leadership may be satisfied with sales figures presented year-to-date (or month-to-date) in the thousands, tens of thousands, or even millions. The data is accurate for the purposes intended.

When dealing with clinical care, however, it is often the digits after the decimal place that matter (precision), and in all cases it must be accurate if clinical care decisions will be made based on this data. There is an implied need for all clinical care projects that the data is accurate, and there is a second implied need that it is precise for the intended purpose. For example, a *yes*, *no*, or *suspect* listed in a lab result may be all that is needed to make some clinical decisions, whereas in others the caregiver may want the exact (precise) lab result that drove that *yes*, *no*, or *suspect* result.

Key outputs produced as part of project quality management planning include a quality management plan, quality metrics, and quality checklists. Before describing these outputs, it is important to understand what quality is and why it is an important part of project management.

The International Organization for Standardization (ISO) defines **quality** as "the degree to which a set of inherent characteristics fulfill requirements" (ISO9000:2000). Other experts define quality based on conformance to requirements and fitness for use. **Conformance to requirements** means that the project's processes and products meet written specifications. For example, Jeff's project team might write specifications stating that the database must be available twenty-four hours a day, seven days a week. As part of quality management, Jeff's team would verify that this type of availability was possible given their equipment budget and that there was software available that could upload the daily updates while still being available for reporting.

Fitness for use, on the other hand, means that a product can be used as it was intended. For example, AHS may identify low-cost desktop computers that are powerful enough to serve as the database servers, but that are not designed to be run 24x7 with a constant load on them. These machines, though powerful, were designed to be used as desktops by casual users so they do not have the server-quality capacitors, memory, and disk drives in them that are designed to handle continuously high usage. These desktop computers would be fit to be used as desktop PCs for one user, but they will be prone to failure in other uses.

Recall that project management involves meeting or exceeding stakeholder needs and expectations. To understand what quality means to the stakeholders, the project team must develop good relationships with them—especially the main customer for the project. *After all, the customer ultimately decides that the quality level is acceptable.* Many projects fail because the project team focuses only on meeting the written requirements for the main products being produced and ignores other stakeholder needs and expectations for the project. If a project's stakeholders are not satisfied with the quality of the project management or the resulting products or services, the project team will need to adjust scope, time, and cost to satisfy stakeholder needs and expectations. Meeting only written requirements for scope, time, and cost is not sufficient.

Quality, therefore, and customer satisfaction, in particular, must be considered on an equal level of importance with project scope, time, and cost. In years past project constraints were focused on scope, time, and cost--the triple constraint--as described in Chapter 1, but the number of tightly-coupled constraints recognized by PMI has increased. This means that if the project scope, schedule, budget, risk, resources, or quality needs to change, it will most likely impact the other project constraints.

Some people have asked how customer satisfaction can be a constraint, but it is no less of a constraint than time or cost. Why? Because the need for customer satisfaction will often drive the project team to do, or not do, certain things as part of the project. In order to guarantee customer satisfaction, the team may find they have limited options for completing some or all parts of project work.

Planning Quality Management

Quality planning includes identifying which quality standards are relevant to the project and how best to satisfy those standards. It also involves designing quality into the products and services of the project as well as the processes involved in managing the project. It is important to describe important factors that directly contribute to meeting customer requirements. The project management plan, stakeholder register, risk register, requirements documentation, enterprise environmental factors, and organizational process assets (i.e. policies related to quality and related standards and regulations) are all important inputs to the quality planning process.

The quality management plan describes how the project management team will implement quality policies. Like other project plans, its format and contents vary based on the particular project and organizational needs. It can be a long, formal document or short and informal. Some project teams also create a process improvement plan as an output of planning quality management. As the name implies, a process improvement plan describes how to analyze processes in order to identify specific activities that can enhance their value. For example, the plan might describe the current process for selecting suppliers and suggest how to improve that process to make it more efficient.

Sample Quality Management Plan

Jeff, Pat, and their team worked together to create a quality management plan for the VAPR project, as shown in Figure 6-2. The primary purpose of the plan was to ensure that all the products and services produced as part of the project are of known quality and sufficient quantity to meet customer expectations.

VAPR Quality Management Plan
May 29

Introduction

The main goal of this project is to develop new clinical workflows, and supporting systems, that will align with the IHI Ventilator Associated Pneumonia best practices bundle in order to reduce the AHS VAP incidence rate. The project includes the identification, collection, and testing of clinical data from one or more existing AHS clinical systems into a new data mart that will be used to deliver reports to caregivers. The reports must be accurate, timely, and readily accessible in order to provide the caregivers time to correct any shortcomings in compliance with the IHI bundle. Key stakeholders from technology, data analytics, nursing, respiratory therapy, and resident physicians must be engaged in the design, testing, training, and rollout of the VAPR system.

Quality Standards

The standards that apply to this project are summarized as follows:

Standard	Metric
The Institutes of Medicine has identified six quality categories that must be addressed when dealing with patient care. All AHS clinical care projects must address on more of these categories.	VAPR will improve patient safety by reducing the VAPR incidence rate by 25% in the first 90 days after implementation. It will also improve equity of care as all ventilated patients will receive the same best-practices ventilator protocol. It will also improve effectiveness as the IHI bundle has been proven to reduce VAP.
All direct patient care staff will complete computer-based or in-class training relevant to their workflows when any of the following occurs • the staff member is hired or transitions into a new role , • before a workflow is modified, or • on their hire date anniversary.	Computer based training for the VAPR workflow changes are available 30 days prior to go live and be incorporated into the annual clinician online training curriculum.
All patient care systems will be HIPAA compliant.	VAPR reports (mobile and desktop PC) to be encrypted and require network logins. PHI on mobile platforms to include room number and patient initials only. Any vendors working on the project must have a signed Business Associate Agreement (BAA) on file before working onsite or given access to systems.
All patient care systems will support or align with HITECH and Meaningful Use requirements.	VAPR does not decrease MU compliance.
All new bedside patient care systems will be	VAPR reports to be available both on unit PCs

mobile-device ready.	and iPads (mobile optimized) before training begins.
Any system used for direct patient care will include fully documented testing use cases and documented testing results that include testers from each respective discipline that is expected to eventually use the system.	Use cases developed for the new VAP protocols (based on the IHI bundle). Testing team to include at least one nurse, one physician, and one respiratory therapist.

Problem Reporting and Corrective Action Processes

Project plans will include clear roles and responsibilities for all key stakeholders. All stakeholders are expected to watch for and document any suspected issues in the VAPR issue log (www.ahs.com/projects/vapr/issues_log). An issue is anything that will prevent the project from achieving its goals if it is not resolved.

There is no approval required to document and submit an issue, and all issues must be documented even if they have already been resolved (for improving the AHS knowledge base). All new issues will be reviewed by the project managers within four hours of documentation and assigned to the appropriate staff member for resolution. Unresolved issues will be escalated to the two project champions, and if still unresolved, to the project sponsor.

Urgent issues should be documented (as above) and Jeff Birdwell, the senior project manager, should be contacted directly (in person or phone call) to discuss the issue and its potential impact on the project. Urgent issues include those where a patient is at immediate risk of harm or injury, or, where an immediate action is required to keep the project on schedule, on budget, or within scope. If Jeff Birdwell cannot be contacted in a timely manner then escalate the urgent issue directly to the project sponsor. It is crucial to address issues as early as possible and to develop several alternative solutions.

Supplier Quality and Control

The project manager will closely monitor work performed by any outside contractors, suppliers, or vendors, with assistance from our supplier management department. All contracts must clearly state quality standards and metrics that are in alignment with those of this project.

Figure 6-2. Sample quality management plan

Quality Metrics

A **metric** is a standard of measurement. Metrics allow organizations to measure their performance in certain areas and to compare them over time or with other organizations. Examples of common metrics used by organizations include failure rates of products produced, availability of goods and services, and customer satisfaction ratings.

Individual projects also have metrics. Before deciding on the metrics to use for a particular project, it is important to clarify the project goals, business case for the project, and success criteria. Knowing this information, you can then decide what data will give you the information you need, and how to collect it. For example, the VAPR project's success criteria, as documented in the project charter, included metrics based on:

- *Time*: Completing the project within one year
- *Cost*: Spending $980,000 or less

- *VAP incidence reduction*: Reducing incidences by at least 50% within six months of implementation based on the number of VAP events per 1000 ventilator days.

AHS' senior management, therefore, should collect and analyze data to ensure these metrics, as well as other metrics related to the project, are being met. If AHS is unwilling or unable to collect these metrics, then they should not be used as success criteria, as there would be no objective way to determine if they have been met or not. Jeff believed that the above metrics would be easy to collect because AHS always collects project cost and schedule performance information. The infection control department also tracks the VAP incidence rate as part of the ongoing patient quality program, so they will not need to implement new tracking measures for any of these criteria.

Sometimes a project sponsor chooses to use metrics that are not already measured, such as improving employee satisfaction or patient referral rates, or perhaps identifying patient transportation choices. These metrics may require new processes to be put into place to gather this information, and as such they can be costly to measure. In these cases the project sponsor should consider either changing the acceptance criteria or budgeting for those expenses required to collect the required metrics both before and after the project is implemented. Regardless of the metric utilized, project teams should consider using charts, graphs, and icons to keep track of metrics in a summarized, easy to understand format, such as in a **project dashboard** – a graphical screen summarizing key project metrics.

BEST PRACTICE

Dragan Milosevic, author of the *Project Management Toolbox*, has done several studies to investigate what companies that excel in project delivery capability do differently from others. After analyzing data from hundreds of companies, he found four key practices these best-performing companies follow:

1. They build an integrated project management toolbox. In other words, they use several standard and advanced project management tools. They tailor these tools to their organizations and provide employees with lots of templates.
2. They grow competent project leaders, emphasizing business and soft skills. These organizations identify good project leaders and provide training, mentoring, and a career path for them.
3. They develop streamlined, consistent project delivery processes. Project management methodologies are well defined and followed.
4. And probably the hardest of all, they install a sound but comprehensive set of project performance metrics. It is difficult defining, measuring, and tracking metrics across an organization, but in order to improve project delivery capability, these metrics are crucial.[1]

Sample Project Dashboard and Quality Metrics Description

Figure 6-3a provides a sample project dashboard that could be used on the VAPR project. Figure 6-3b shows other examples of project dashboards from www.projectmanager.com. Most dashboards use red, yellow, and green to indicate the status of each metric, where green indicates the metric is on target, yellow means it is slightly off target/caution, and red indicates the metric is off target/problem area. (These examples use different shades of gray because color is not available.) The VAPR project dashboard also describes how each metric is measured and explains the reason for the status rating. You will learn more about earned value charts, a tool for measuring overall scope, time, and cost goals, in Chapter 8. In order to use a project dashboard to help monitor and control a project, you must plan what information you will collect, how you will track it, and how you will create the project dashboard.

Ventilator Associated Pneumonia Reduction (VAPR)
Project Dashboard As of April 10

Metric	Description	Status	How Measured	Explanation
Scope	Meeting project goals	◕	Earned value chart	On target
Time	Staying on schedule	●	Earned value chart	Slightly behind schedule
Cost	Staying on budget	◕	Earned value chart	Under budget
VAP Bundle	Identify AHS systems with required elements	◕	Percent of elements identified in AHS systems	All elements identified and available
VAP reduction	Reduce by 50% within six months	↔	Infection Control data	Cannot collect until after implementation
Percent of ICU staff trained	Train all ICU staff prior to go live	○	Training Management System test results	Learning management system down for four days causing a delay in training. We expect to catch up quickly.

◕ On Target   ● Off Target / problem area
○ Slightly off target / caution area   ↔ Not able to collect data yet

Figure 6-3a. Sample VAPR project dashboard

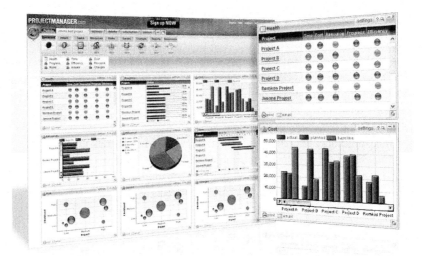

Figure 6-3b. Sample project dashboards from www.projectmanager.com

As mentioned in the sample quality management plan, two important metrics related to the VAPR project include training on clinical workflow changes and mobile-ready clinical applications. Figure 6-4 provides more information on these metrics.

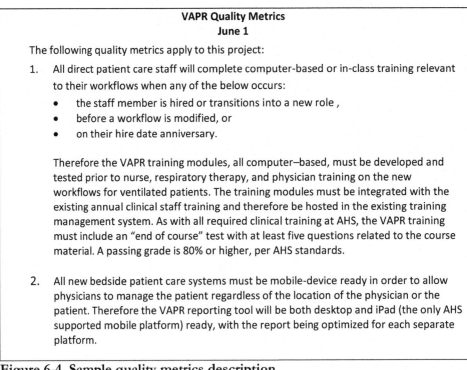

VAPR Quality Metrics
June 1

The following quality metrics apply to this project:

1. All direct patient care staff will complete computer-based or in-class training relevant to their workflows when any of the below occurs:
    - the staff member is hired or transitions into a new role ,
    - before a workflow is modified, or
    - on their hire date anniversary.

    Therefore the VAPR training modules, all computer–based, must be developed and tested prior to nurse, respiratory therapy, and physician training on the new workflows for ventilated patients. The training modules must be integrated with the existing annual clinical staff training and therefore be hosted in the existing training management system. As with all required clinical training at AHS, the VAPR training must include an "end of course" test with at least five questions related to the course material. A passing grade is 80% or higher, per AHS standards.

2. All new bedside patient care systems must be mobile-device ready in order to allow physicians to manage the patient regardless of the location of the physician or the patient. Therefore the VAPR reporting tool will be both desktop and iPad (the only AHS supported mobile platform) ready, with the report being optimized for each separate platform.

Figure 6-4. Sample quality metrics description

Quality Checklists

A **checklist** is a list of items to be noted or consulted. Checklists help project teams verify that a set of required topics or steps has been covered or performed. A single project can have many different checklists. For example, there can be checklists related to interviewing project team members, selecting suppliers, reviewing important documents, ensuring a room is ready for training, and so on.

Sample Quality Checklist

Because Pat is developing the training curriculum due to her clinical background, but Jeff is more familiar with the AHS training requirements, Jeff suggested that he create a checklist for Pat to use to verify that she has followed all of the AHS standards for training programs. Figure 6-5 is a sample checklist that Jeff provided to Pat for ensuring that the program she develops adheres to the standard.

Quality Checklist
June 20

Project Name: VAPR Project

Checklist Purpose: VAPR Online Training Program Standards

- ☐ Program includes at least 10 slides.
- ☐ Program slides use the AHS training template for background graphics, logos, etc.
- ☐ Program describes the workflow from start to finish.
- ☐ Program describes the impact (patient, financial, safety, etc.) of not following the prescribed workflow.
- ☐ Program includes an "end of course" test that includes at least five questions.
- ☐ Passing score for the test is an 80% or higher.

Figure 6-5. Sample quality checklist

PROJECT HUMAN RESOURCE MANAGEMENT

Many corporate executives have said, "People are our most important asset." People determine the success and failure of organizations and projects. Project human resource management is concerned with making effective use of the people involved with a project. The main output produced as part of project human resource management planning is a human resource plan, which includes a project organizational chart, a responsibility assignment matrix, a resource histogram, and a staffing management plan. Chapter 7, which covers project execution, includes much more information on project human resource management, as Pat encounters some problems related to this topic. Planning human resources effectively will help her face these challenges.

Project Organizational Charts

After identifying the important skills and types of people needed to staff a project, the project manager should work with top management and project team members to create an organizational chart for the project. Similar to a company's organizational chart, a **project organizational chart** is a graphical representation of how authority and responsibility is distributed within the project. The size and complexity of the project determines how simple or complex the organizational chart is.

Healthcare Perspective

Planning for human resource management is a challenge on many projects, but recent research has found that it is even more important to pay attention to this area on healthcare projects to avoid increasing stress on already high-stressed workers. PMI funded a study to consider factors that would improve the health care sector's project success rate.

The researchers suggest that a major problem is that healthcare workers do not understand the differences between service work and project work. Most healthcare professionals have always been engaged in continuous improvement activities to provide better service to patients, but they have not been trained to make more radical, disruptive changes that challenge the status quo. In other words, they prefer the logic of their ongoing service work and continuous improvement, not the logic required to work on a project, which by its nature is a temporary endeavor that produces a unique product, service, or result that is often radically different from the status quo. Healthcare projects are done to create something that is delivered to the organization, unlike operational work which produces outcomes aimed at patients. "In other words, it is only once the project's outcome is implemented and becomes 'the new way we work now' that it starts exerting its impact on patients."[2]

The authors of the study suggest that academic and corporate training programs need to train healthcare workers in project management, emphasizing the "soft" as well as "hard" skills. People on project teams need to learn to collaborate on achieving project goals and understand their roles on the project team, which may differ from their roles in their day-to-day work. Management also needs to structure project teams to be successful by properly planning workers time and payment to allow them to successfully engage in project work.

Sample Project Organizational Chart

Figure 6-6 shows a project organizational chart that Jeff and Pat put together. Notice that both Jeff and Pat have a direct reporting line to the project sponsor, Dr. Shoemaker, and the project team leaders (or staff) report to either Jeff or Pat, depending on the project phase in which they will be engaged. Also note that the project steering committee, project sponsor, and project champions have a strong role on the project. Dotted lines are used to represent indirect reporting relationships, such as that between Pat and Dr. Scheerer.

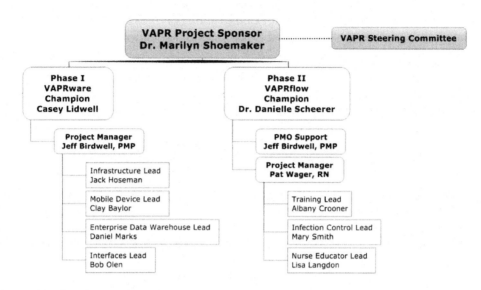

Figure 6-6. Sample project organizational chart

Responsibility Assignment Matrices

A **responsibility assignment matrix (RAM)** is a matrix that maps the work of the project as described in the work breakdown structure (WBS) to the people responsible for performing the work. A RAM allocates work to responsible and performing organizations, teams, or individuals, depending on the desired level of detail. For smaller projects, it is best to assign work packages, or even project activities, to individuals. For larger projects, it is more effective to assign the work to organizational units or teams. In addition to using a RAM to assign detailed activities or work packages, you can use a RAM to define general project management related roles and responsibilities on projects, sometimes referred to as tasks.

Project managers may create multiple RAMs if it meets their need. For example, they may have one WBS that only includes the project management related tasks, such as schedule maintenance, issue log oversight, risk register responsibilities, etc. They may create a second RAM that is based on specific work packages or activities. RAMs, like all project management tools, should be tailored to meet the needs of the project and the organization. Because a RAM may include project management tasks, activities, or work packages, we will refer to these items as "elements."

Sample Responsibility Assignment Matrix

Some organizations, including AHS, use **RACI charts**—a type of responsibility assignment matrix that indicates **R**esponsibility (who does the element), **A**ccountability (who signs off on the element or has authority for it), **C**onsultation (who has information necessary to complete the element), and **I**nformed (who needs to be notified of element status/results) roles for project stakeholders.

     Figure 6-7a shows a RACI chart for Phase I work packages. Notice that it lists tasks vertically and individuals or groups horizontally, and each intersecting cell contains at least one of the letters R, A, C, or I. If a person (or group) has no interaction with the element listed, be sure to put a hyphen or other special character in the intersecting cell for clarity. For the first element, IHI Bundle Definition, Jeff is listed as being accountable for getting it done and Pat is responsible for doing the work. No other team members will be involved, indicated by the hyphen in the remaining columns. Note that each task may have multiple R, C, or I entries, but there can only be one A entry to clarify which particular individual or group has accountability for each element (e.g., only one A in a matrix row). One person can also have multiple roles for each element, such as being both responsible and accountable for a specific element. Figure 6-7b shows a task based RACI chart.

VAPR Project RACI Chart
Work Packages

Work Package	Jeff	Pat	Bob	Mark	Clay
IHI Bundle Definition	A	R	I	I	-
AHS VAP Bundle Data Sources	A	R	C	R	-
Database	A	I	C	R	C
Daily Script to Update Database	A	I	R	C	R
Reports	A	C	I	R	R

R: Responsible   A: Accountable   C: Consulted   I: Informed

Figure 6-7a. Sample RACI chart, work package based

VAPR Project RACI Chart
Work Packages

Work Package	Jeff	Pat	Bob	Mark	Clay
IHI Bundle Definition	A	R	I	I	-
AHS VAP Bundle Data Sources	A	R	C	R	-
Database	A	I	C	R	C
Daily Script to Update Database	A	I	R	C	R
Reports	A	C	I	R	R

R: Responsible   A: Accountable   C: Consulted   I: Informed

Figure 6-7b. Sample RACI chart, project task based

Resource Histograms

A **resource histogram** is a column chart that shows the number of resources required for or assigned to a project over time. In planning project staffing needs, senior managers often create a resource histogram in which columns represent the number of people (or person hours, if preferred) needed in each skill category, such as managers, IT specialists, and HR specialists. By stacking the columns, you can see the total number of people needed each month. After resources are assigned to a project, you can view a resource histogram for each person to see how his or her time has been allocated. You can create resource histograms using spreadsheets or project management software.

Sample Resource Histogram

Jeff worked with other managers to estimate how many internal resources they would need for the VAPR project over time. They decided that in addition to the project leadership, they would require resources from analytics (AN), nurse educators (NU), respiratory therapy (RT), physicians (MD), and information technology (IT). Figure 6-8 shows the resulting resource histogram for internal resources, showing the total number of people, or head count, by month. For example, it shows the need for a project manager (PM) from the PMO for .75 of an FTE (full time equivalent), or ¾ of one person's time for the first phase and then dropping to .25 FTE once Phase I is completed. Jeff would fill this role, of course. In addition they would require analytics resources (Pat), IT resources (Bob, Clay, Mark), nursing resources as needed for testing and piloting of the workflow, and physician resources during workflow reengineering and piloting. Remember that they will also need someone to develop the computer based training, and although this resource may be contract labor, they still list them in the matrix because this resource will be working directly with the project team. Note that months six and seven have the highest resource usage as this is where the two phases overlap.

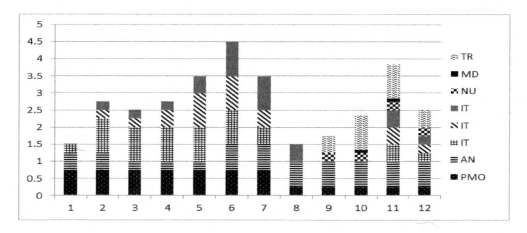

Figure 6-8. Sample resource histogram

Staffing Management Plans

A **staffing management plan** describes when and how people will be added to and removed from a project. The level of detail can vary based on the type of project. The staffing management plan describes the number of and types of people needed to work on the project. It also describes how these resources will be acquired, trained, rewarded, and reassigned after their work on the project is completed. All these considerations are important to meeting the needs of the project, the employees, and the organization.

Sample Staffing Management Plan

Figure 6-9 provides part of a staffing management plan for the VAPR project.

VAPR Project Staffing Management Plan
June 1

Introduction
The primary goal of this project is to revise the clinical workflows for ventilated patients within the intensive care units so that they align with the IHI Ventilator Bundle, an evidenced-based set of practices that prevent ventilator associated pneumonia.

Staffing Requirements
This project will require the following internal staff:
- Project manager (PM) for Phase I
- Project manager (PM) for Phase II
- PMO Support for Phase II (PMO)
- SME from clinical analytics
- Nursing educator
- Physician
- IT department staffing (database developer, script developer, interface developer, report developer)

Staff Assignments
The project manager will work through functional managers to assign individuals to the project. Other than for physicians, all roles will be allocated in .25 FTE increments (staff will all be assigned as .25, .5, .75, or 1 FTE). To minimize communication issues and handoff problems, no roles can be filled by a combination of staff. To ensure consistency, all staff assigned to a role will remain in that role for the life of the project.

Training, Rewards, and Reassignment
Due to the short timeline and compliance requirements for this project, staff assigned to this project will have appropriate experience. The project manager will do his or her best to provide a challenging and enjoyable work environment. Assignment to the project will not affect an individual's salary, but the project manager will write a performance evaluation and recommend appropriate rewards. If an individual is not performing as expected, the project manager will work with him or her and the appropriate functional manager to determine whether corrections can be made or if reassignment is necessary.

Attachment A: Resource histogram

Figure 6-9. Sample staffing management plan

PROJECT COMMUNICATIONS MANAGEMENT

Many experts agree that the greatest threat to the success of any project is a failure to communicate. It is often said that project managers spend 90% of time communicating. Yet many project managers fail to take the time to plan for it. Even though having a communications management plan does not guarantee that all project communications will flow smoothly, it certainly helps.

Figure 6-10 provides a humorous example of miscommunication based on selfishness and bad timing. (It's a take-off from the story about the woman who cuts her long hair to buy her husband a chain for his watch while he sells his watch to buy a comb for her hair.) A Roomba is an automatic vacuum cleaner, and Left 4 dead is an Xbox video game, in case you didn't know. Another example of miscommunications follows.

Figure 6-10. Poor communications (www.xkcd.com)

What Went Wrong?

I was asked to prepare a memo reviewing our company's training programs and materials. In the body of the memo in one of the sentences, I mentioned the "*pedagogical approach*" used by one of the training manuals. The day after I routed the memo to the executive committee, I was called into the HR director's office, and told that the executive vice president wanted me out of the building by lunch. When I asked why, I was told that she wouldn't stand for perverts (pedophiles?) working in her company. Finally, he showed me her copy of the memo, with her demand that I be fired—and the word "*pedagogical*"—circled in red. The HR manager was fairly reasonable, and once he looked the word up in his dictionary and made a copy of the definition to send back to her, he told me not to worry. He would take care of it. Two days later, a memo to the entire staff came out directing us that no words that could not be found in the local Sunday newspaper could be used in company memos. A month later, I resigned. In accordance with company policy, I created my resignation memo by pasting words together from the Sunday paper.[3]

Project communications management involves generating, collecting, disseminating, and storing project information. Key outputs produced for the VAPR project include a communications management plan and a project Web site.

Communications Management Plans

Because project communication is so important, every project should include a **communications management plan**—a document that guides project communications. The communications management plan will vary with the needs of the project, but some type of written plan should always be prepared and updated as needed. The communications management plan should address the following items:

- Stakeholder communications requirements
- Information to be communicated, format, content, and level of detail
- Identification of who will receive the information and who will produce it
- Suggested methods or guidelines for conveying the information
- Description of the frequency of communication
- Escalation procedures for resolving issues
- Revision procedures for updating the communications management plan
- A glossary of common terminology used on the project

VIDEO HIGHLIGHTS

People who design new healthcare products know how important it is to communicate with both healthcare professionals and consumers when planning new products. For example, Worrell recognized that there was an information imbalance between the patient and the physician relationship. They decided to include thought-leading physicians and patients in their design process to help them develop breakthrough products. They created a short film that describes a novel approach to stakeholder communications.

In "Design we can all live with," you can hear the perspectives of patients, product developers, and physicians. For example, a patient with an implanted device said that he wants to make sense of his medical information. He understands that doctors often do not have time to educate them, and there are more cost-effective ways to get information. Doctors admit that they do not really understand their patients, and they told product designers the information that they really needed to make informed decisions. A good Web site, for example, can provide the information both patients and doctors need.

- Patient: "I want to be treated as an educated consumer of healthcare…I called and I said I want all my records… They said to me, 'Sure. Can you please go to our Web site, download the form, sign it, and fax it to us.' What is this, 1995?"
- Product developer: "In the future, though, we're going to have to do a much better job of considering the needs of different stakeholders – hospital administrators, payers – and to be sure, we're going to have to incorporate the voice of patients."
- Physician: "I think this dialog is the beginning of the creation of something that's going to change healthcare. That's going to give everybody access. And, this is just the beginning of something that may fix our failed healthcare system."[6]

Sample Communications Management Plan

Jeff and the project management team drafted a communications management plan for the VAPR project as shown in Figure 6-11. The project steering committee reviewed it and provided suggestions on how to keep communication lines open. They advised Jeff to stress the importance of communications with *all* project stakeholders. They also mentioned the fact that people communicate in different ways and recommended that her team not be afraid of over-communicating by providing the same information in multiple formats. The steering committee noted that it is not enough to provide formal documents; Jeff and the team should use face-to-face communications, e-mails, phone calls, collaboration tools, and other communications media to ensure optimal communications.

VAPR Communication Management Plan Version 1.0
June 3

1. Stakeholder Communications Requirements

Because this project involves a variety of clinical disciplines, the project team will use interviews, checklists, and lessons learned from past clinical workflow projects to determine the communications requirements for the project stakeholders. Each of the three clinical disciplines will have specific communications needs, in addition to those of organizational leadership that must be determined, analyzed and fulfilled.

2. Communications Summary

The following table summarizes various stakeholders, communications required, the delivery method or format of the communications, who will produce the communications, and when it will be distributed or the frequency of distribution. All communications produced will be archived and available on the project Web site. The project team will use various templates and checklists to enhance communications. The team will also be careful to use the appropriate medium (that is, face-to-face meeting, phone, e-mail, Web site, and so on) and follow corporate guidelines for effective communications. Note the comments/guidelines as well.

Stakeholders	Communications Name	Delivery Method/Format	Owner	Due Date/ Frequency
Project steering committee	Weekly status report	Email	Jeff Birdwell	Tuesday, 10am
Project steering committee	Bi-weekly committee meeting	Meeting	Marilyn Shoemaker, Chair	1st & 3rd Wednesdays, 5pm
Sponsor and champions	Monthly summary status report	Email	Jeff Birdwell	First Monday of each month
ICU Directors	Monthly summary status report	E-mail, intranet site, and announcement at department meetings	Pat Wager	First Wednesday of each month
Project team	Weekly status meetings	Meeting (30 mins)	All team	Tuesday, 2pm
Project team	Daily report to PM	Stand-up meeting (15 mins)	All team	Daily, 8am

---

3. Guidelines

- Make sure people understand your communications. Use common sense techniques to check comprehension, such as having them explain what you mean in their own words.
- Avoid acronyms. Not every reader or listener understands them, and many will not bother to ask you to explain them resulting in poor communication.
- Be adaptable. Physicians see patients from 8am to 5pm. If you need their input, plan meetings outside of this timeframe.
- Start meetings on time, and end meetings early if you can. When a nurse or respiratory therapist is at your meeting, some other caregiver is covering his/her patients.
- If you only need to communicate information outward, and not make decisions, consider other communication tools and cancel a standing meeting.
- Email meeting agendas at least 24 hours in advance of the meeting so participants come prepared.
- When canceling meetings due to lack of agenda items, do so at least 24 hours in advance.
- Hold everyone accountable for completing action items.
- Use templates as much as possible for written project communications. The project Web site includes a link to all project-related templates.
- Use the titles and dates of documents in e-mail headings and have recipients acknowledge receipt.
- Prepare and post meeting minutes within 24 hours of a meeting.
- Use checklists where appropriate, such as reviewing product requirements and conducting interviews.
- Use corporate facilitators for important meetings, such as kickoff meetings and supplier negotiations.

4. Escalation Procedures for Resolving Issues

Issues should be resolved at the lowest level possible. When they cannot be resolved, affected parties should alert their immediate supervisors of the issues. If it is critical to the project or extremely time-sensitive, the issue should be brought directly to the project manager. If the project manager cannot resolve an issue, he or she should bring it to the project steering committee or appropriate senior management, as required.

5. Revision Procedures for this Document

Revisions to this plan will be approved by the project manager. The revision number and date will be clearly marked at the top of the document.

Figure 6-11. Sample communications management plan

Project Web Sites and Other Collaboration Tools

More and more project teams now post all or part of their project information to project Web sites and use various other tools to collaborate. Project Web sites provide a centralized way of delivering project documents and other communications as well as accessing collaboration tools. Some teams also create blogs to post various entries or use wikis to collaboratively write meeting minutes or other project documentation. Project teams can develop project Web sites, blogs, or wikis using various tools, or their enterprise project management software might provide all of the communication tools they require. There are hundreds of tools available to communicate and collaborate (from Microsoft, Google, Atlassian, etc.), which can be overwhelming. It is important to select and use tools properly to help meet project communications requirements, and to limit the number of different tools where possible in order to avoid confusion.

Sample Project Web site

Jeff, Pat, and the project team entered detailed project information into the company's enterprise project management software. From within that system, Jeff could control who could and could not see various types of information. In addition, he used the organization's content management system (CMS) to create a project-specific Web site. This site would be available on the corporate intranet. Dr. Shoemaker, the sponsor, felt it was important to provide all employees basic information about the project, and she knew that it would reduce the number of questions, and rumors, about the project. The home page for the VAPR project included summary information, such as objectives and key milestones. It also included links to information on team members, the project schedule, project archives, a search feature, a discussions feature, and contact information.

A quick and free way to create a team project Web site is to use Google sites. Figure 6-12 shows a sample created by students at Augsburg College in Minneapolis. The purpose of their project was to raise awareness and funds for the StepUP program. StepUP is an innovative residential college recovery program where students live in dedicated alcohol/drug-free residence halls and participate fully in the student community. You can see one of their deliverables, a poster/flyer advertising the event (a big yard sale on campus) in the figure. The team collaborated on project documents using Google docs, logged estimated and actual hours using a Google spreadsheet, received comments from their project sponsor and instructor, and presented all progress information via the site. They received a sponsor rating of 10/10 and made almost $1,000! See the companion Web site for instructions on creating a Google site and links to this and other sample sites.

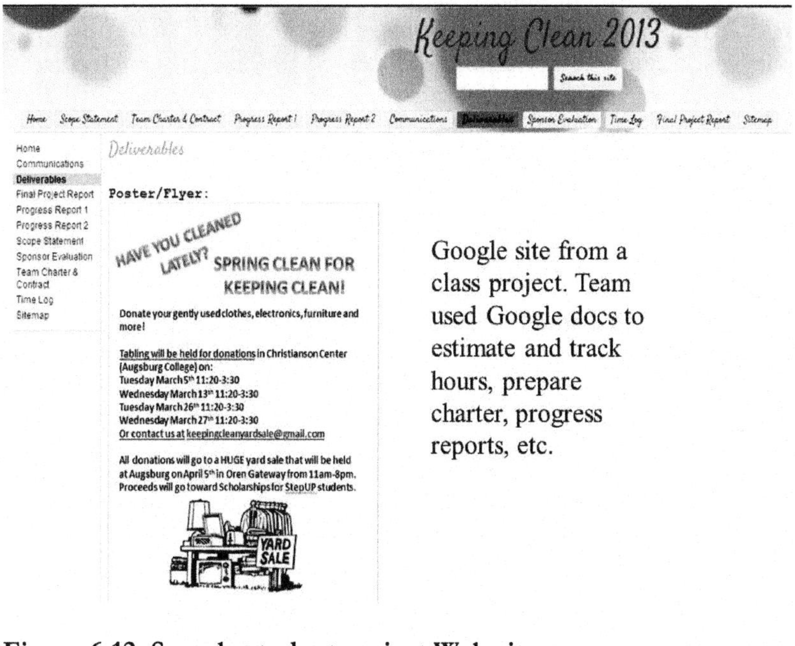

Figure 6-12. Sample student project Web site

PROJECT STAKEHOLDER MANAGEMENT

Project stakeholder management planning involves determining strategies to effectively engage stakeholders in project decisions and activities based on their needs, interests, and potential impact. Outputs of this process are a stakeholder management plan and project documents updates.

What Went Right?

Many healthcare projects are successful because teams of interdisciplinary professionals collaborate to create something that's best for very special stakeholders—patients. For example, The National Intrepid Center of Excellence (NICOE), located at The Walter Reed National Military Medical Center in Bethesda, Maryland, won the 2012 American Institute of Architects national healthcare design award for their patient-centered design. The mission of NICOE is to provide imaging, assessment, diagnosis and treatment for mild to moderate traumatic brain injury and other psychological health issues suffered by wounded U.S. soldiers returning from the wars in Iraq and Afghanistan. The $65 million center, designed by SmithGroup JJR architects, was completed in 2010, and it is a prototype for similar centers worldwide.

Brenna Costello, the lead medical planner and architect at SmithGroup JJR, said that everything at NICOE is patient centered. "'They first go through a patient-intake clinic where they meet with all their clinical-care coordinators from various disciplines (diagnostic, physical rehabilitation, behavioral health) in a comfortable lounge setting,' says Costello. The building's layout is derived from brain analysis: left represents organization and uniformity; right creativity and flexibility. So the L-shaped wing was designed to contain clinical, research and administrative functions, while the central "drum" was planned for the public, educational and rehabilitation centers. 'All the different clinical disciplines are co-located in a clinical hub so that the patient can more easily move between treatment appointments, and caregivers can collaborate on treatment plans much more effectively,' says Costello, who is the Detroit-based firm's national expert on rehabilitation design."[4]

Stakeholder Management Plans

After identifying and analyzing stakeholders, the project manager and team should develop a stakeholder management plan to guide them in effectively engaging stakeholders to make sure good decision are made throughout the life of the project. This plan may be formal or informal, based on the needs of the project.

In addition to information found in the stakeholder register (i.e. stakeholder identification information, assessment information, and classification) a stakeholder management plan can include the following:

- Current and desired engagement levels

- Interrelationships between stakeholders

- Communication requirements

- Potential management strategies for each stakeholder

- Methods for updating the stakeholder management plan

Because a stakeholder management plan often includes sensitive information, it should *not* be part of the official project documents, which are normally available for all stakeholders to review. Often only project managers and a few other team members prepare the stakeholder management plan. In many cases, parts of the stakeholder management plan are not even written down, and if they are, distribution is strictly limited. Regardless of how restricted access is to this plan, Jeff reminded Pat that anything that is written down or stored on a computer can (and probably will) find its way into the wrong hands. He suggested that they use positive terms, to the extent possible, when describing stakeholder management strategies.

Figure 6-13 provides an example of part of a stakeholder management plan that the team could use on the VAPR project. It is important for project managers to take the time to develop this plan to help them meet stakeholder needs and expectations. In addition, as new stakeholders are added to the project and more information is provided, the plan should be updated. Early in this project, for example, all of the stakeholders are internal to the company; later on, however, there may be external stakeholders as well.

Name	Title	Power/ Interest	Project Engagement	Potential Management Strategies
David Waters, MD	Executive Medical Director	High / Medium	Supportive	Dr. Waters is always interested in projects that improve patient care. He is the chief physician and can help us gain their buy-in.
Danielle Scheerer, MD, PhD	Chief Quality Officer	High / High	Leading	Dr. Scheerer is charged with improving patient care, but she rarely serves as project champion. She believes this project will improve patient outcomes and reduce costs to AHS significantly. We need to keep her close to the work and bring her in when we meet clinical resistance. She is a result-oriented person who will make things happen.
Casey Lidwell, MHA	Chief Analytics Officer	Medium / Low	Supportive	Casey is supportive, but his commitment is to provide the data required by those on the clinical phase of the project. His interest is to meet their needs, but he has no personal commitment to the project and has several other high priority projects on his plate. He was chosen as the Phase I champion by the sponsor in order to improve his project commitment, but we need to work to keep him engaged.

Figure 6-13. Sample stakeholder management plan

PROJECT RISK MANAGEMENT

Although it is a frequently overlooked aspect of project management, good risk management can often result in significant improvements in the chance of a project succeeding. What is risk as it relates to a project? PMI defines a project **risk** as an uncertainty that can have a *negative or positive* effect on meeting project objectives. Note that some people only view risks as negative and call positive risks opportunities. The main planning processes performed as part of project risk management are planning risk management, identifying risks, performing qualitative risk analysis, performing quantitative risk analysis, and planning risk responses. Key documents produced include a risk management plan, a probability/impact matrix, risk response strategies, a risk register, and risk-related contractual agreements.

Planning Risk Management

The first process of six processes in planning for risk management is called planning risk management, and its main output is a risk management plan. A risk management plan documents the procedures for managing risk *throughout the life of a project*. Project teams should hold several planning meetings early in the project's life cycle to help develop the risk management plan. The project team should review project documents as well as corporate risk management policies, risk categories, lessons learned from past projects, and templates for creating a risk management plan. It is also important to review the risk tolerances of various stakeholders. For example, if the project sponsor is risk-averse, the project might require a different approach to risk management than if the project sponsor were a risk seeker. Generally speaking any project that impacts direct patient care can be considered risk adverse, as the impact of project issues can directly impact the patient's health. Although there may be some exceptions, when it comes to patient care there is little room for error.

A risk management plan outlines how risk management will be performed on a particular project. Like other specific knowledge area plans, it becomes a subset of the project management plan. The general topics that a risk management plan should address include the methodology for risk management, roles and responsibilities, budget and schedule estimates for risk-related activities, risk categories, probability and impact definitions, and risk documentation. The level of detail included in the risk management plan will vary with the needs of the project.

Media Snapshot

Many projects related to health care are undertaken even though planners know there is a risk of public controversy. For example, the city of New York spent two years and over $400,000 producing a public education campaign targeting teenage pregnancy, which included hiring a marketing firm to conduct focus groups with teenagers, parents of teenagers, and parents who had children when they were teenagers. The Bloomberg administration had implemented several projects in the past to reduce teenage pregnancy, such as mandating sex education in public schools and empowering high school nurses to provide birth control, including the morning-after pill. The city's teenage pregnancy rate declined by 27 percent in the past ten years, about the same as the national rate of decline. The Bloomberg administration said that nearly 90% of teenage pregnancies in New York City were unplanned.

Several groups were offended by the new campaign, which included posters with a photo of a curly-haired boy with a sad, tearful face, saying, "I'm twice as likely not to graduate high school because you had me as a teen." Another poster showed a dark-skinned girl looking up at the sky and saying, "Honestly Mom ... chances are he won't stay with you. What happens to me?" Opponents say the ads reinforce negative stereotypes about teenage mothers and do not offer any information to help girls prevent unplanned pregnancies. The criticism escalated into a sharp exchange between the mayor's office and Planned Parenthood of New York City, who said the poster campaign stigmatized teenage parents and their children.

The mayor's office said that it was "'past time' to be 'value neutral' about teenage pregnancy and that it was important to 'send a strong message that teen pregnancy has consequences—and those consequences are extremely negative, life-altering and most often disproportionately borne by young women.' Haydee Morales, vice president for education and training at Planned Parenthood of New York City, said the organization was "shocked and taken aback" by the tone of the new campaign."[5]

In addition to a risk management plan, many projects also include contingency plans, fallback plans, and reserves.

- **Contingency plans** are predefined actions that the project team will take if an identified risk event occurs. For example, if the project team knows that the new version of a product they need might not be available in time, they might have a contingency plan to use the existing, older version of the product.

- **Fallback plans** are developed for risks that have a high impact on meeting project objectives, and are put into effect if attempts to reduce the risk are not effective. For example, a new college graduate might have a main plan and several contingency plans on where to live after graduation, but if none of those plans work out, a fallback plan might be to live at home for a while. Sometimes the terms *contingency plan* and *fallback plan* are used interchangeably, and some people view fallback plans as contingency plans of last resort.

- **Contingency reserves** or **contingency allowances** are funds held by the project sponsor that can be used to mitigate cost or schedule overruns if known risks occur. For example, if a project appears to be off course because the staff is not experienced with a new technology and the team had identified that as a risk, the project sponsor might provide additional funds from contingency reserves to hire an outside consultant to train and advise the project staff in using the new technology. **Management reserves** are funds held for unknown risks. Contingency plans, fallback plans, and reserves show the importance of taking a proactive approach to managing project risks.

Sample Risk Management Plan

Jeff knew that it was important to use a formal risk management strategy. He had some experience working with clinicians, but Pat had worked decades in the clinical environment, and she was worried about this project not being accepted by physicians or nurses. On the other hand, there were some positive risks that could help them be successful if they came to fruition. Pat and Jeff sat down to determine how they should manage project risk, and by using risk management plans from other projects, with their added knowledge about this project, they were able to put a plan together quickly. Figure 6-14 shows the initial risk management plan.

Identifying Risks

You cannot manage risks until you identify them. Identifying risks involves determining which risks are likely to affect a project and documenting the characteristics of each. The main output of this process is the start of a risk register, as described in more detail later in this chapter. Teams often hold several brainstorming sessions with various stakeholders and experts to help identify project risks. They also review documents, gather information, analyze assumptions, and use other tools and techniques to identify risks. Interviewing is a common tool used to identify risks in a clinical setting. As discussed previously, physicians (and some other caregivers) are only paid if they are treating patients. Further, if they are not treating their patients, there is generally not a pool of other caregivers who can treat their patients. Patients go to see a specific doctor, to be seen by their doctor, and not to be seen by just whoever is available. When interviewing clinicians, plan to conduct interviews that are ten minutes or less in duration and you will gain higher participation rates.

Risk events refer to specific, uncertain events that may occur to the detriment or enhancement of the project. For example, negative risk events might include the performance failure of a product produced as part of a project, delays in completing work as scheduled, increases in estimated costs, supply shortages, litigation against the company, and labor strikes. Examples of positive risk events include completing work sooner than planned or at an unexpectedly reduced cost, collaborating with suppliers to produce better products, and obtaining good publicity from the project.

VAPR Risk Management Plan
June 8

1. Methodology

The project team will review information related to clinical projects that either changed clinical workflows based off of best practices, or that directly impacted the intensive care units. The team will use a variety of risk identification techniques, including brainstorming, interviews of project and clinical leadership, and risk-related checklists.

2. Roles and Responsibilities

Jeff Birdwell, the project manager for Phase I, will be responsible for leading the team and other stakeholders in performing risk-related activities for both phases. As detailed tasks and deliverables are determined, the project manager will delegate those tasks as appropriate.

3. Budget and Schedule

As specific risk-related tasks and deliverables are determined, budget and schedule information will be provided.

4. Risk Categories

Risks will be categorized based on risk source and risk impact. Risk sources will be technical, clinical, leadership, resources, funding, project management, and environment. Risk impact categories will be scope, budget, quality, and schedule.

5. Risk Probability and Impact

Risk probability will use five probability scales: 0-20%, 21-40%, 41-60%, 61-80%, and 81-100%. Each of those probability ranges will be assigned a value of 1, 2, 3, 4, and 5, respectively. The project impact choices are defined as follows, and will also be defined values of 1 through 5.

Impact	Score	Definition
Failure	5	If this risk occurs, the project will fail to meet one or more project objectives.
Severe	4	If this risk occurs, the customer will know that the risk occurred and the project will require that the project budget, timeline, or resources be adjusted.
Moderate	3	If this risk occurs, the project team will know that the risk occurred but the customer will most likely not. The project's budget or timeline reserves will need to be utilized.
Minimal	2	If this risk occurs, the project team will know the risk occurred but they will handle the risk event without additional funding or time.
None	1	If this risk occurs, it will most likely not impact the project.

Each risk will be assigned a score, based on the Probability * Impact scores, with the resulting scores ranging from 1 to 25. All risks with a score of 12 or higher will be further analyzed with a detailed response plan created. Any score of 25 will be managed as an urgent risk and managed as an issue. All scores lower than 12 will be put on a watch list and monitored.

6. Risk Documentation

All risk-related information will be summarized in a risk register on the Web site.

Figure 6-14. Sample risk management plan

Performing Qualitative Risk Analysis

After identifying risks, it is important to evaluate the risks to determine which ones need the most attention. Qualitative risk analysis often results in stratifying risks into groups, such as high, medium, and low. A probability/impact matrix, as described in the following section, is a good tool to help decide which risks are most important on a project.

There are two important dimensions of risk events: *probability* of the risk event occurring and the *impact* or consequence if the risk does occur. People often describe a risk event probability or impact as being high, medium, or low, but for most projects that does not provide enough granularity. How would you feel if your doctor simply stated there was a high chance of successful surgery What is high? 100%? 90%? 50%? Likewise, what is the impact if the surgery does not go well? Even though project teams are dealing with many uncertainties, they need as much information about risk as that they can get.

Sample Probability/Impact Matrix

Pat decided to start working with clinical project stakeholders early in the project to begin identifying several negative and positive risk events. She did this primarily through interviews and small focus groups that she held during slow parts of nursing shifts. Jeff, meanwhile, held his own risk sessions where he invited the interface, data analytics, reporting, data warehousing, and compliance staff to participate. He held a brainstorming session in which over 100 risk events were identified. To differentiate between the two, he asked participants to first identify negative risk events and to then identify positive ones. After people identified a risk event and wrote it down on a sticky note, they added their name in the corner and handed it to Jeff for posting on the wall. Jeff did not participate – he simply facilitated.

Once the team felt they had identified most of the risks, Jeff had them come up in pairs and put their risk on the matrix. In order to do this, each person had to also determine the probability of each particular risk event occurring and its impact on the project. After everyone put their sticky notes in the appropriate sections of the matrix they combined and reworded risk events to improve collaboration and avoid duplicates. Jeff then had them go to the risk matrix again in pairs to identify any risk that they believed was scored incorrectly. Jeff facilitated a process where they discussed those risks that were in question. Because only about 15% were questioned, this process went quickly.

Figure 6-15 shows part of the resulting probability/impact matrix. Note that based on the risk management plan, each box in the matrix is assigned a score that is the product of the probability and impact scores (remember that each column and each row is assigned a 1 to 5 score). For example, risks 1 and 2 are listed in the top right of the matrix, each with a risk score of 25. Risk 3 is also in the top right corner, but assigned a score of 20. Risk 4 is assigned a score of 16, risk 5 a score of 12, and so forth. Based on the risk management plan, the team then determined that they needed to create risk response plans for risks 1, 2, 3, 4, and 5, as they were the only ones with a score higher than a twelve. However, the risk management plan also instructed that any risk with a score of 25 be treated as an issue, since they have such a high probability and a high impact, so risks 1 and 2 will be moved to the issue log immediately and managed as such.

The team then discussed in detail how they planned to respond to these risks and documented the results in the risk register, as described in the following section. Any risk below a score of 12 would be put on the watch list, which simply means they will be watched but no plans will be put into place today for them. This risk matrix also has a "none" impact row because during brainstorming *all* ideas should be accepted. However, during the further analysis many risks, once reviewed carefully, are determined that even if they did occur they would not impact the project. It is preferred that these risks still be captured and watched, as over time their probability and impact to the project may change.

	0-20%	21-40%	41-60%	61-80%	<80%	
Failure				Risk 3	Risk 1 Risk 2	
	5	10	15	20	25	
Severe			Risk 5	Risk 4		
	4	8	12	16	20	
Moderate	Risk 7		Risk 6			**Impact**
	3	6	9	12	15	
Minimal	Risk 8					
	2	4	6	8	10	
None	Risk 9					
	1	2	3	4	5	

Probability

Figure 6-15. Sample probability/impact matrix

Performing Quantitative Risk Analysis

Qualitative risk analysis is based on individual and group opinions, being derived from the experience, education, and knowledge of the stakeholders. However, quantitative risk analysis attempts to take the top risks identified during qualitative analysis and perform a more rigorous numerical analysis on them. Quantitative analysis takes more time, and often the data required is difficult to acquire with any degree of accuracy. Therefore, many project teams only perform qualitative risk analysis. The nature of the project and availability of time and money often drive the type of risk analysis techniques used. For example, large, complex, and expensive projects involving leading-edge technologies often undergo extensive quantitative risk analysis due to the high degree of uncertainty. Data gathering often involves interviewing experts and collecting probability distribution information. Quantitative risk analysis and modeling techniques include expected monetary value, decision tree analysis, simulation, and sensitivity analysis, with expected monetary value being the easiest to perform.

Planning Risk Responses

There are several strategies that teams can plan for responding to risks. These responses vary depending on whether or not the risk will have a negative or positive potential impact on meeting project objectives. The four basic response strategies for negative risks, or threats, are:

1. Risk avoidance or eliminating a specific threat, usually by eliminating its causes. Of course, not all risks can be eliminated, but specific risk events can be. For example, Pat's Phase II training team leader might decide in their plans that they would not to use a new learning management system and instead use the one already use at ASHS – even if they aren't delighted with their current tool.

2. Risk acceptance or accepting the consequences should a risk occur. For example, Pat may decide that they will use the current training registration system, and if it has problems they will deal with them at that time (passive acceptance). Or, Pat may decide that they will use the current training registration system, but in case it has problems she will develop a contingency plan now that she will implement if there are eventual problems (active acceptance).

3. Risk transference or shifting the consequence of a risk and responsibility for its management to a *third party*. For example, if the mobile device reporting technology is new to AHS, Jeff may decide to hire an outside contractor at a fixed price to develop this piece of the project. Jeff would be transferring the uncertainty to the vendor. To be transference, you must transfer the risk outside the organization!

4. Risk mitigation, or reducing the impact of a risk event by reducing the probability of its occurrence. You can also mitigate a risk by mitigating the impact if it does occur, or you may attempt to mitigate (reduce) both the probability *and* the impact. For example, if there were a risk concerning a hurricane, the team could reduce the probability of a hurricane striking by moving the work to outside the hurricane season, or move the project work to outside the hurricane zone. They could also, or instead, reduce the impact by still doing the work in the hurricane zone, and still do it during hurricane season, but be sure the work is being performed within a hardened IT data center that is designed to withstand a hurricane.

    Positive risks, or opportunities, also have four basic response strategies:

1. Risk exploitation, or doing whatever you can to make sure that the risk (opportunity) is fully realized. They key here is that the project manager "will do what it takes" to be sure the opportunity is realized. For example, suppose AHS decided to work on a fundraising project for their children's hospital, and the project included running a golf tournament to raise funds. Instead of using their own internal public relations department, they may decide to hire the area's top public relations firm to organize news coverage of the event, write a press release, or hold some other public event to ensure the tournament raises the most money for the children.

2. Risk sharing or sharing ownership of the risk to another party. Using the same example of the golf tournament to raise money for the children's hospital, the project manager could form a partnership with a local golf course that has experience in managing fund raising tournaments. This will improve the tournament's chances of success. When risk sharing, all parties involved bring something to the table, and each shares in the project's success.

3. Risk enhancement or changing the size of the opportunity by identifying and maximizing key drivers of the positive risk. For example, an important driver of getting good public relations for the golf tournament might be to get everyone at AHS excited about the tournament so that they can get others interested in playing and sponsoring the event. AHS may decide to use their own internal public relations department for getting the staff excited about the tournament. Risk enhancement is very similar to risk exploitation, but exploitation is generally considered more aggressively applied. In this example, it is the difference between hiring the best available (exploitation) versus using staff currently available (enhancement) to handle public relations work.

4. Risk acceptance also applies to positive risks when the project team cannot or chooses not to take any actions toward a risk. For example, suppose the golf tournament project manager has heard that a celebrity may sign up to play in the tournament. Although it may be wise to try to enhance this risk (#3, above), it is likely that the project manager has no influence over this celebrity. Therefore, they may decide to accept the risk (opportunity), and if the celebrity does sign up, then they will decide how to best utilize this information to the benefit of the children.

Risk Registers

A **risk register** is a document that contains results of various risk management processes, often displayed in a table or spreadsheet format. It is a tool for documenting potential risk events and related information. The risk register often includes the following headings:

- *An identification number for each risk event:* The project team might want to sort or quickly search for specific risk events, so they need to identify each risk with some type of unique descriptor, such as an identification number.

- *A rank for each risk event:* The ranking system is defined in the risk management plan. In the case of the VAPR project, the rank is defined by the risk score, calculated by multiplying the probability (1-5 scale) multiplied by the impact (1-5 scale). A score of 25 would be the highest ranked risk, and 1 the lowest.

- *The name of the risk event:* For example, defective product, poor survey results, reduced consulting costs, or good publicity.

- *A description of the risk event:* Because the name of a risk event is often abbreviated, it helps to provide a detailed description in the risk register. For example, *reduced consulting costs* might be expanded in the description to say that the organization might be able to negotiate lower-than-average costs for a particular consultant because the consultant enjoys working for the company.

- *The category of the source of the risk event:* For example, a lack of clinician acceptance of VAPR may be due to lack of clinical leadership support.

- *The root cause of the risk event:* It is important to find the **root cause** of a problem—the real or underlying reason a problem occurs. By finding the root cause, you can deal with it directly rather than dealing with the symptoms of the problem. You can help identify the root cause of problems by creating a cause-and-effect or fishbone diagram (see Chapters 7 and 8), or continually asking why until you find a root cause. For example, the root cause of lack of clinical support for VAPR may be lack of clinical leadership support. If you ask why this is, you may find that leadership does not understand the research that supports the VAPR project. If you ask why this is, you may find that the research supporting the VAPR project has not been communicated. If you ask why, …. Generally asking *why?* five times will get to the root cause (thus the term, "The Five Whys" to define this technique).

- *Triggers for each risk event:* **Triggers** are indicators or symptoms of actual risk events. For example, the city being put into a hurricane watch would be a good trigger for the hurricane risk. When the trigger occurs, it is time to look at the risk more closely and determine if the response plan needs to be implemented.

- *Potential responses to each risk event:* There can be one or more potential responses to each risk event, as described earlier.

- *The risk owner, or person who will own or take responsibility for the risk event:* One person should be responsible for monitoring each risk event.

- *The probability of the risk event occurring:* The chance of the risk event becoming a reality, rated according to the scale defined within the risk management plan.

- *The impact to the project if the risk event occurs:* The impact to project success if the risk event actually occurs, rated according to the scale defined within the risk management plan. Remember, the impact is defined as what will happen to the project if the risk really does occur – not the trigger – but the risk itself.

- *The status of the risk event:* Did the risk event occur? Was the response strategy completed? Is the risk event no longer relevant to the project? For example, a clause may have been written into a contract to address the risk event of a defective product so that the supplier would have to replace the item at no additional cost. In this example since the risk was already responded to by changing the contract, the risk would be closed.

- *Watch dates:* Some risks have specific dates that need to be monitored. For example, for the risk of a hurricane, it would only have to be monitored during hurricane season.

Sample Risk Register

Jeff began developing a risk register after he and the other stakeholders had prepared the probability/impact matrix. Figure 6-16 shows the format of the risk register and one of the entries. Note that the risk event identification (ID) number is shown in the first column, followed by the rank of the risk event. The risk events are sorted by rank order. As information is added, deleted, or changed, the risk register will be updated on the Web site.

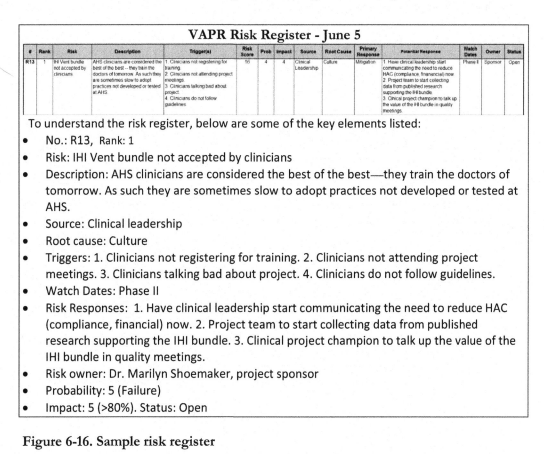

Figure 6-16. Sample risk register

Risk-Related Contract Decisions

Many projects, including the VAPR project, involve outside suppliers. Work done by outside suppliers or sellers should be well documented in **contracts**, which are mutually binding agreements that obligate the seller to provide the specified products or services, and obligate the buyer to pay for them. Project managers should include clauses in contracts to help manage project risks. For example, sellers can agree to be responsible for certain negative risks and incur the costs themselves if they occur. Or there can be incentive or penalty clauses in contracts based on seller performance to encourage positive risks and discourage negative risks. You can also use certain types of contracts, such as fixed-price contracts, to reduce the risk of incurring higher costs. Competition for supplying goods and services can also help reduce negative risks and enhance positive risks.

Sample Risk-Related Contract Decisions

Jeff did not have any risk-related contract decisions for Phase I, but Pat did. As described earlier, Pat had to use a new supplier for their online training program, and she asked Jeff for help in preparing a contract. As with most hospitals and large practice plans, AHS had an in-house legal department. Pat could count on them to develop the legal components of the contract, but it would be up to her and Jeff to develop the statement of work and acceptance criteria for the work. The statement of work, deliverables schedule, and acceptance criteria would be required before procurement could advertise the work. The procurement department also told Pat that they had a set of guidelines that she should follow when considering using outside resources, with a few of them shown in Figure 6-17.

AHS Guidelines for Contracting for Outside Services or Resources

- Contract signing: All contracts must be reviewed by the AHS legal department before being signed by the seller. Once reviewed and approved by AHS legal, the seller must sign the contract and deliver to AHS via mail or fax. Once received AHS legal will then sign the contract and return to the seller via mail or fax. Only the AHS legal department has the right to sign contracts on behalf of AHS.
- Contract termination clauses: These clauses list circumstances under which the buyer and/or seller can terminate a contract and how final payment will be settled. All the contracts must include a termination clause.
- Incentive clauses: These clauses provide incentives for the seller to provide goods or services at certain times, of certain quality, and so on. Incentive clauses can include extra payments or profit sharing, if appropriate.
- Penalty clauses: These clauses specify penalties that will be applied when the seller does not provide goods or services as specified in the contract. For example, if a product is delivered late, the seller might be required to pay a certain dollar amount for each day the product is late.
- Fixed price contracts: To minimize the negative risk of paying more than planned for specific goods or services, AHS issues fixed priced contracts, which specify that the seller agrees to a fixed price and bears the risk if it costs more to provide the goods or services than originally assumed. [This is a type of risk transfer, as AHS is paying more for fixed price contracts but the seller assumes the risk.]

Figure 6-17. Sample guidelines for contract decisions

As you can see, risk management planning addresses procurement-related topics, such as preparing risk-related contractual agreements. The following section addresses planning tasks directly related to project procurement management.

PROJECT PROCUREMENT MANAGEMENT

Project procurement management includes acquiring or procuring goods and services for a project from outside the organization. As the business world continues to become more competitive and global, more and more projects include procurement. Many project managers realize the advantages of buying goods and services required for their projects, especially as sellers with better goods and services continue to become increasingly available. They also realize that they can find qualified sellers throughout the world. Remember that project managers strive to do what is best for the project and the organization, and that often means acquiring goods and services from the outside. Good procurement management often provides a win-win situation for both buyers and sellers.

Key outputs produced by planning procurements include make-or-buy decisions, procurement management plans, procurement statements of work, procurement documents, source selection criteria, and change requests.

Make-or-Buy Decisions

With a make-or-buy decision, an organization decides if it would benefit more by making a product or performing a service itself, or by buying the product or service from a supplier. If there is no need to buy products or services from outside the organization, the organization can avoid the costs involved in managing procurement management processes. **Make-or-buy analysis** requires that the organization analyze several things before making a decision:

- Analyze whether the skills required to provide the product or service will be required long term by the organization. If they will, should you keep the work internal?

- If you have no one with the skills required internally, how long will it take to train someone to have the skills? Or, how long will it take to hire the resource with the required skills? What work will not get done by this resource if they are committed to this new work?

- Analyze how long it will take an internal resource to complete the work, compared to the time required by a seller. Sellers typically have faster turnaround, but is quick turnaround required?

- Estimate the internal costs of providing a product or service, and comparing that estimate to the cost of outsourcing. It may be less costly to do the work internally, but will quality be the same?

Many organizations also use a lease-or-buy analysis to decide if they should purchase or lease items for a particular project. For example, suppose you need a piece of equipment for a project that has a purchase price of $12,000. Assume it also has a daily operational cost of $400. Suppose you can lease the same piece of equipment for $800 per day, including the operational costs. You can set up an equation that shows the amount of time it will take for the purchase cost to equal the lease cost. In this way, you can determine when it makes sense financially to buy rather than lease the equipment. In the equation that follows, d = the number of days you need the piece of equipment.

$$\$12,000 + \$400(d) = \$800(d)$$

Subtracting $400(d) from both sides, you get:

$$\$12,000 = \$400(d)$$

Dividing both sides by $400, you get:

$$d = 30$$

which means that the purchase cost equals the lease cost in 30 days. Therefore, if you need the equipment for less than 30 days, it would be more economical to lease it. If you need the equipment for more than 30 days, you should purchase it. Note that this simple example assumes there is no disposal value for the purchased item and does not include any tax considerations.

Sample Make-or-Buy Decision

Pat had a significant make-or-buy decision for the computer-based training (CBT) part of the VAPR Project for Phase II. Pat had to decide if they wanted to try to use the internal training staff, find a new CBT provider, or try to train someone on their team to develop the required CBTs. Internal resources would normally be less expensive than external contractors, and Pat estimated they would save at least $10 per hour because AHS training staff, on average, only make $40 per hour, fully burdened with fringe benefits, while their preferred CPT provider (TechTalk, not available for this project), charged $50 per hour.

Pat contacted the internal training department and asked for a list of recommended CBT providers. They suggested that Pat contact TechTalk to ask for names of other solid CBT providers, and they provided three potential sources as well as an estimate of the work if they could have done it. Pat also searched online and found a new company in the area. She asked each company to provide a short proposal, references, samples of similar CBT they developed, and pricing for the work, including a firm range of hours. Figure 6-18 summarizes the make-or-buy data and analysis for developing the CBT.

VAPR Make-Or-Buy Analysis
July 6

Background: AHS needs to train 1200 nurses, 128 respiratory therapists, and 92 physicians in the use of the IHI Ventilator Bundle and new AHS workflows required to support the bundle. All training will be conducted online.

Decision Being Analyzed: Development of Computer Based Training (CBT) program.

Option 1: (Make): Use in-house training team to develop the CBTs. Resources may not be available. Training developer cost per hour: $40. Estimated hours required (+/- 20%): 280.

Total: $11,200 (280 hours X $40 per hour)

Option 2: (Vendor: TechTalk): Outsource development to AHS' normal CBT provider. Note: Work can't be started for at least 14 months. Not a realistic option. Training developer cost per hour: $50. Estimated hours required (+/- 10%): 190

Total: $9,500 (190 hours X $50 per hour)

Option 3: (Vendor: All About Training): Outsource development to a CBT provider found online. In business for 1 year. Training developer cost per hour: $60. Estimated hours required (+/- 10%): 260.

Total: $15,260 (260 hours X $60 per hour)

Option 4: (Vendor: Greek Geeks): Outsource development to a CBT provider recommended by TechTalk. In business for 9 years. Training developer cost per hour: $70. Estimated hours required (+/- 5%): 160.

Total: $11,200 (160 hours X $70 per hour)

Recommendation: We believe that Option 4, Greek Geeks, is the best option. They will commit to not going 5% over their estimated hours, and they received great reviews for a similar CBT.

Figure 6-18. Sample make-or-buy analysis

Procurement Management Plans

A procurement management plan is a document that describes how the procurement processes will be managed, from developing documentation for making outside purchases or acquisitions to contract closure. Like other project plans, the contents of procurement management plans vary with project needs. Some projects must follow government directives, such as the **Federal Acquisition Regulation (FAR),** which provides uniform policies for acquisition of supplies and services by executive agencies in the U.S. Other projects may follow state or local directives if they are part of state or local government, which includes a large number of healthcare institutions.

Topics that can be included in a procurement management plan are as follows:

- Guidelines on types of contracts to be used in different situations

- Standard procurement documents or templates to be used, if applicable

- Guidelines for creating contract work breakdown structures, statements of work, and other procurement documents

- Roles and responsibilities of the project team and related departments, such as the purchasing or legal department

- Guidelines on using independent estimates for evaluating sellers' cost proposals

- Suggestions on managing multiple providers

- Processes for coordinating procurement decisions, such as make-or-buy decisions, with other project areas

- Constraints and assumptions related to purchases and acquisitions

- Lead times for purchases and acquisitions

- Risk-mitigation strategies for purchases and acquisitions, such as insurance contracts and bonds

- Guidelines for identifying prequalified sellers and organizational lists of preferred sellers

- Procurement metrics to assist in evaluating sellers and managing contracts

Types of Contracts

Contract type is a key consideration in a procurement management plan. Different types of contracts can be used in different situations. Three broad categories of contracts are fixed price, or lump sum; cost reimbursable; and time and material. A single contract can actually include all three of these categories, if it makes sense for that particular procurement. For example, you could have a contract with a seller that includes purchasing specific products for a fixed price or lump sum, some services that are provided on a cost-reimbursable basis, and other services that are provided on a time-and-material basis. It is important to understand and decide which approaches to use to meet particular project needs.

- **Fixed-price contracts** or **lump-sum contracts** involve a fixed total price for a well-defined product or service. The buyer incurs little risk or uncertainty in this situation because the price is predetermined. Because the seller accepts all risk, these contracts are often more expensive as the seller must include risk in his estimate. They face a challenging task, as they must weigh the risk they face against the competition they may face on bidding for this work. This sometimes results in sellers bidding too low on this type of contract, which is fine when things go well but may cause them to lose money if they encounter problems on the project. Although the buyer does not have to pay more when a seller starts to lose money, they do need to be concerned as the seller may try to cut quality or leave out minor deliverables when they find themselves in this situation. Fixed-price contracts generally have well-defined deliverables and deadlines, and may include incentives for meeting or exceeding selected project objectives. For example, the contract could include an incentive fee that would be paid for early delivery of the CBT training program, or perhaps for surpassing specified performance requirements. This is referred to as a fixed-price incentive (FPI) contract. Standard thinking says a firm-fixed price (FFP) contract has the least amount of risk for the buyer, followed by a fixed-price incentive (FPI) contract. However, some argue that FPI has less risk as it incentivizes the seller to perform at a higher standard.

- **Cost-reimbursable contracts** involve payment to the seller for direct and indirect actual costs. For example, the salaries for people working directly on a project and materials purchased for a specific project are direct costs, whereas the cost of providing a work space for those workers, office furniture, electricity, a cafeteria, and so on, are indirect costs. Indirect costs are often calculated as a percentage of direct costs. Cost-reimbursable contracts often include fees such as a profit percentage, and they can also include incentives for meeting or exceeding selected project objectives. For example, many contracts to build homes are cost-reimbursable contracts. The buyer might expect the home to cost a certain amount, but the total cost could vary if any of the costs of individual goods or services increase or decrease. The buyer reimburses the contractor for costs incurred, and pays a fee or profit percentage as well. Buyers absorb more of the risk with cost-reimbursable contracts than they do with fixed-price contracts. For example, if the cost of wood doubles, the buyer would have to absorb the additional cost.

- **Time-and-material (T&M) contracts** are a hybrid of both fixed-price and cost-reimbursable contracts. For example, Pat could decide to hire an independent consultant who can develop the CBT. AHS might agree to pay the contractor $45 per hour plus $1500 to cover required equipment. The equipment fee might also be based on approved receipts for purchasing items, with a ceiling of $1,500. The consultant would send an invoice to AHS on an agreed upon schedule, listing the materials purchased, the number of hours worked, and a description of the work produced. This type of contract is often used for services that are needed when the work cannot be clearly specified and total costs cannot be estimated in a contract. When using T&M contracts, the buyer typically has control over the contractor's work, and the contractor is often seen as an extension of the project manager's staff.

Unit pricing can also be used to require the buyer to pay the supplier a predetermined amount per unit of service. The total value of the contract is a function of the quantities needed to complete the work. For example, many companies use unit price contracts for purchasing computer hardware. If the company purchases only one unit, the cost is $1,000, but if the company purchases between 5 and 50 units, the contracted cost drops to $940 per unit. If it purchases over 50 units, the cost reduces to $900 per unit. This flexible pricing strategy is often advantageous to both the buyer and seller.

Sample Procurement Management Plan

Figure 6-19 displays a section of a procurement management plan for the VAPR project.

VAPR Procurement Management Plan
July 1

Guidelines on Types of Contracts: To reduce AHS' risk, contracts for the VAPR project should be fixed price as often as possible. When goods or services cannot be well defined, time and material contracts should be considered. The representative from the contracting department will work with the project manager to determine the appropriate contract type for each contract developed.

Standard procurement documents or templates: AHS' procurement department has all required templates, forms, documents, and processes (instructions) posted on the AHS Procurement intranet site. The project team will review these documents and templates and use them as often as possible. Any exceptions will be discussed with and approved by Procurement.

Guidelines for creating procurement documents: AHS' intranet site provides guidelines for creating many procurement documents. The VAPR project team should review their current work breakdown structure and scope statement to provide the basis for contract work breakdown structures and statements of work.

Roles and responsibilities: Jeff Birdwell, project manager and PMO representative, is the main contact for all procurement matters directly related to the VAPR project. Procurement and legal will coordinate all activities with and through him.

Figure 6-19. Sample procurement management plan

Procurements Documents: Requests for Proposals or Quotes

When organizations decide to procure goods or services, they often create documents to describe what they plan to procure and how potential sellers should respond. Two common examples of procurement documents include a Request for Proposal (RFP) and a Request for Quote (RFQ).

- A **Request for Proposal (RFP)** is a document used to solicit proposals from prospective suppliers. A **proposal** is a document in which sellers describe what they will do to meet the requirements of a buyer. It can be expensive and time-consuming to prepare a good RFP or proposal for a large contract, such as building a new hospital or designing a complex information system. RFPs are for complex problems where the solution is not clear. For example, there may be several different ways to meet the CBT needs of the AHS VAPR project. Pat and Jeff wrote and issued an RFP that outlines training requirements so that suppliers could respond with their unique proposals describing how they would meet those needs. The VAPR team assumed that they would use the

AHS learning management system to host the training, but a vendor may respond with an option for them to house the training system on the vendor's equipment to improve performance and reliability—something the team may not have considered before.

- A **Request for Quote (RFQ)** is a document used to solicit quotes from prospective suppliers. An RFQ is very similar to an RFP, except that the RFQ is more often used to procure work with known specifications or small quantities, or for contracts whose value are below the organization's RFP threshold. Note that some companies define an RFQ to be the same as an IFB, defined next.

- An **Invitation For Bid (IFB)** is a document used to solicit bids on items that are considered standard items or commodities. For example, AHS may publish an IFB if they want to purchase one millions sheets of 20 pound, white, 98 brightness, coated, laser printer paper. The lowest priced seller is normally picked and there is no negotiation expected with an IFB.

- A **Request for Information (RFI)** is a document used to identify potential sellers that may respond to a subsequent RFP. The RFI is an instrument used to prequalify sellers so that the actual RFP responses will be fewer in number. The RFI may ask questions about the potential sellers' financial situation, existing customer base, resource breadth and depth, technology utilized, and so on that may be important to the buyer but not part of the RFP itself. RFIs typically cannot be protested as they are only used to develop a qualified sellers list for the RFP. Once a qualified sellers list is developed for an RFP, the RFP is distributed only to those on the list, and only those on the list may respond.

RFPs and RFQs can be issued in several ways. The organization might contact one or several preferred sellers directly and send the RFP or RFQ only to them. To reach more sellers, the organization might post the information on its Web site, or advertise on other sites or in newspapers. Project managers must carefully consider which approaches are most appropriate in various situations. IFBs and RFIs are most often advertised broadly.

Topics addressed in an RFP usually include the following:

- Purpose of the RFP

- Background information, describing the organization issuing the RFP and the project itself

- Basic requirements for the products and/or services being proposed

- Hardware and software environment (for technology-related proposals)

- RFP process, describing how sellers should prepare and submit their proposals

- Statement of work and schedule information

- Appendices providing more detailed information, as appropriate

A simple RFP might be three- to five-pages long, whereas an RFP for a larger, more complicated procurement might be hundreds of pages long. Remember, RFPs are used for complex problems and often allow the seller to propose their own solution.

Sample Request for Proposal

Pat issued a brief RFP to obtain proposals for the CBT. The RFP would be for a fixed-price contract for developing three CBT courses. One course would be for nurses, one for respiratory therapists, and one for physicians. The CBTs would each be one hour or less in duration, with the nursing and therapy modules broken down into multiple modules of 10 minutes or less so that users could watch the modules during short downtimes on the floor. The physician module, however, would only be thirty minutes or less, and it would be broken down into a series of three- to five-minute mini-modules. This would allow physicians to watch snippets of the CBT between patients while rounding. All CBT would be accessible via computers or smartphones after users set up accounts and downloaded the appropriate software.

Figure 6-20 shows a synopsis of the RFP. AHS's training manager suggested that they send the RFP to specific vendors but to also post it on the state's business site and AHS's procurement page. Based on their initial estimates, they believed that they could procure this work for less than $15,000, and probably closer to $11,000. They budgeted $15,000 to be safe.

Request for Proposal
August 1
Project Name: Ventilator Associated Pneumonia Reduction (VAPR) Project
RFP Name: Computer Based Training Module Development

Purpose of RFP
Academic Health Systems (AHS) is modifying clinical workflows to better align with Institute for Healthcare Improvement (IHI) identified best practices. Because all clinical care changes require that all staff who are involved in direct patient care undergo training on the changes, AHS utilizes computer-based training (CBT) in order to more efficiently deliver the training. This RFP is for the development and production of the CBTs required for this clinical workflow change.

Background Information
AHS employs approximately 10,000 full time employees and is the third largest employer in the state and the largest in the county. Being an academic medical center, their goal is to provide leading-edge healthcare technology to their patients, ensuring they get the best care in the state. As healthcare is ever evolving, AHS must also be ready to modify their practices based on proven techniques, protocols, or processes adopted by other organizations. One of these best practices is a series of five patient care elements that have been proven to reduce the incidence of Ventilator Associated Pneumonia. The bundle, referred to as the IHI Ventilator Bundle, requires a shift in patient care protocols and as such these changes must be documented and staff must be trained before the protocols may be implemented on the patient care floors.

Basic Requirements
The basic requirements for this work include developing three computer based training modules for Nursing (RN) workflow changes, Respiratory Therapist (RT) workflow changes, and Physician (MD) workflow changes. The workflow changes are based on a new best practices workflow being adopted for patients on ventilators. See the statement of work for more details.

RFP Process
Prospective sellers will send written proposals to AHS no later than August 10. To prepare your proposal, use the outline in Appendix B, and examine Appendix C for our evaluation criteria. We expect to award the contract no later than August 20.

Statement of Work and Schedule Information
See Appendix D for a statement of work. The work must be completed no later than February 28.

Appendices

Figure 6-20. Sample RFP

Contract Statements of Work

Another important procurement document is a **contract statement of work (SOW)**, a document that describes the goods or services to be purchased. The SOW should be included with the RFP to clarify the work that needs to be performed. The contract SOW is a type of scope statement that describes the work in sufficient detail to allow prospective suppliers to both determine if they are capable of providing the goods and services required and to determine an appropriate price for the work. A contract SOW should be clear, concise, and as complete as possible. It should describe all services required and include performance information, such as the location and timing of the work. It is important to use appropriate words in a contract SOW—for example, *must* instead of *may*. *Must* implies that something has to be done; *may* implies that there is a choice involved. The contract SOW should specify the products and services required for the project, use industry terms, and refer to industry standards.

Sample Contract Statement of Work

Figure 6-21 shows the contract SOW for the CBT training module development.

Contract Statement of Work
August 1

Project Name: Ventilator Associated Pneumonia Reduction (VAPR) Project
Contract Name: Computer Based Training Module Development

Scope of Work:
1. The seller must produce three computer-based training modules for Nursing (RN) workflow changes, Respiratory therapist (RT) workflow changes, and Physician (MD) workflow changes.
2. The RN and RT modules must be no more than one hour in duration each, and each module must be broken down into multiple sub-modules, each no more than ten minutes in duration. This is to allow the staff to complete their respective module in small time bites.
3. The MD module must be no more than 30 minutes in duration, and must be broken down into multiple sub-modules, each no more than 5 minutes in duration.
4. Each major module must have a test at the end of no more than 20 questions. These questions may be broken down by sub-module as long as each sub-module has at least 5 questions at its end, with a total of at least 20 for all sub-modules for each group (RN, RT, MD).
5. General content to be provided by the seller based on interviews conducted by the seller.
6. Design, layout, and flow of all training programs to coordinate with existing AHS CBTs.
7. Each module may include animations and videos, based on requirements provided by the seller. Animations and videos to be produced by the seller. Standard medical video content to be provided by the buyer.
8. The modules must be able to be run from the CeleTone Learning Management System in use by AHS. Supplier may use their own system as long as it connects with this one.
9. The exam scores must be integrated back into the CeleTone Learning Management System in use by AHS.
10. The buyer will own the copyright to all work, including drafts, graphics, videos, flows, and all content.
11. Complete the above work no later than May 1.

Location of Work:
The seller can perform the work at any location. The seller must physically meet with representatives from AHS in our facility at least twice during the term of the contract, with weekly written status updates provided by the seller.

Period of Performance:
Work is expected to start on or around April 1 and end no later than May 1.

Deliverables Schedule:
The seller will prepare a detailed schedule for all of the work required, including dates for all deliverables and meetings. After meeting with representatives from AHS to review and update the schedule, the seller will agree to the schedule for this work.

Applicable Standards:
The seller will use readily available CBT development software to produce the required training modules for this project. Draft and final CBT modules will be delivered via a secure upload/download site, such as Dropbox.

Acceptance Criteria:
The seller will work closely with the project manager, Pat Wager, to clarify expectations and to ensure the delivery of acceptable work. All expectations to be specified by AHS before work begins by the seller. Pat will provide written acceptance/non-acceptance of all deliverables.

Special Requirements:
The seller's staff assigned to work on this contract must have clinical knowledge or experience developing clinical based CBTs. This experience or knowledge is subject to verification by the buyer. The seller will coordinate travel arrangements with AHS to minimize travel costs. The seller must have an existing Business Associate Agreement (BAA) with AHS, or be willing and able to execute one according to HIPAA regulations and guidelines within thirty days of contract execution.

Figure 6-21. Sample contract statement of work

Source Selection Criteria and the Supplier Evaluation Matrices

It is highly recommended that buyers use formal supplier evaluation procedures to help select sellers. If a formal evaluation method is used, the criteria must be developed before the procurement documents, such as the RFP, are distributed to potential sellers. You cannot create the criteria once the RFP responses are received, as it would lead toward bias and would open the process up to protests by the non-winning vendors. In addition to reviewing their proposals or quotes, buyers should also review sellers' past performance, talk to recent customers, interview their management team, and request sample products or demos, if applicable. After doing a thorough evaluation, many organizations summarize criteria and evaluations using a **supplier evaluation matrix**—a type of weighted scoring model. Recall from Chapter 2 that a weighted scoring model provides a systematic process for selection based on numerous criteria. For example, suppliers are often evaluated on criteria related to cost, quality, technology, past performance, and management. The weights for all of the criteria must add up to 100%.

Sample Supplier Evaluation Matrix

Pat knew her team would have to evaluate the CBT vendors who responded to the RFP they were about to publish, but she was not that familiar with the process of creating the evaluation criteria. She turned again to Jeff for guidance, and he provided old RFPs from similar projects. Pat and Jeff then prepared a simple matrix to evaluate the suppliers, as shown in Figure 6-22. In this example, Supplier 1 has the highest weighted score, so that supplier would be selected. Note that the criteria were created concurrently with the RFP.

VAPR Project CBT Production Evaluation Matrix
August 1

Criteria	Weight	Raw Scores			Weighted Scores		
		Vendor 1	Vendor 2	Vendor 3	Vendor 1	Vendor 2	Vendor 3
Past performance	15%	70	95	100	10.5	14.25	15
Cost	20%	80	70	70	16	14	14
Technological Approach	40%	100	75	70	40	30	28
Management Approach	15%	90	100	60	13.5	15	9
Financial Stability	10%	85	100	100	8.5	10	10
Weighted Scores		425	440	400	88.5	83.25	76

Figure 6-22. Sample supplier evaluation matrix

CASE WRAP-UP

Both Jeff and Pat were pleased with their progress on planning all aspects of the VAPR project. Several members of their project team and the project steering committee had complimented Pat on her ability to get key clinical stakeholders involved. They also liked the way she admitted her own areas of weakness and sought out advice from Jeff and the two project champions. Pat, being humble, was quick to point out that the project's success thus far was due more to Jeff and their excellent leadership support. Everyone felt confident that they were ready to tackle the challenges they would face during project execution.

CHAPTER SUMMARY

Successful project managers know how important it is to develop, refine, and follow plans to meet project goals. This chapter summarizes the planning processes and outputs for quality, human resource, communications, stakeholder, risk, and procurement management.

Planning outputs related to quality management include a quality management plan, a project dashboard, quality metrics descriptions, and a quality checklist.

Planning outputs related to human resource management include creating a human resource plan, which includes a project organizational chart, responsibility assignment matrix, resource histogram, and staffing management plan.

Planning outputs related to communications management include developing a communications management plan and project Web site.

Planning outputs related to stakeholder management include developing a stakeholder management plan.

Risk management includes five planning processes: plan risk management, identify risks, perform qualitative risk analysis, perform quantitative risk analysis, and plan risk responses. Planning outputs related to risk management include developing a risk management plan, a probability/impact matrix, risk response strategies, a risk register, and risk-related contract decisions.

Planning outputs related to procurement management include make-or-buy decisions and preparing a procurement management plan, requests for proposal/quote, a contract statement of work, and source selection criteria (such as a supplier evaluation matrix).

Samples of several planning documents are provided for the VAPR project.

QUICK QUIZ

1. _____ is defined as the degree to which a set of inherent characteristics fulfill requirements.

    A. Fitness for use

    B. Conformance to requirements

    C. Metrics

    D. Quality

2. _____ allow organizations to measure their performance in certain areas—such as failure rates, availability, and reliability—and compare them over time or with other organizations.

    A. Ratings

    B. Metrics

    C. Quality-control charts

    D. Checklists

3. A RACI chart is a type of _____.

    A. project organizational chart

    B. resource histogram

    C. responsibility assignment matrix

    D. project dashboard

4. A _____ describes when and how people will be added to and taken off of a project.

    A. project organizational chart

    B. resource histogram

    C. responsibility assignment matrix

    D. staffing management plan

5.   Topics such as who will receive project information and who will produce it, suggested methods or guidelines for conveying the information, frequency of communication, and escalation procedures for resolving issues should be described in a _____.

A.   communications management plan

B.   staffing management plan

C.   team contract

D.   scope statement

6.   Suppose you are a member of Pat's Phase II team and you are having difficulties communicating with one of the CBT providers providing important information about the training program. What strategy might you use to help improve communications?

A.   put all communications in writing

B.   put all communications on your project Web site

C.   use several different methods to communicate with this person

D.   ask Pat to find a better person to provide the technical content

7.   What two dimensions should you use when evaluating project risks?

A.   probability and impact

B.   cost and schedule

C.   negative and positive

D.   source and responsibility

8.   A _____ is a document that contains results of various risk management processes, often displayed in a table or spreadsheet format.

A.   risk event

B.   trigger

C.   risk register

D.   risk management plan

9.   You can purchase an item you need for a project for $10,000 and it has daily operating costs of $500, or you can lease the item for $700 per day. On which day will the purchase cost be the same as the lease cost?

     A.   day 5

     B.   day 10

     C.   day 50

     D.   day 100

10.   You want to have the least risk possible in setting up a contract to purchase goods and services from an outside firm. As the buyer, what type of contract should you use?

     A.   fixed price

     B.   unit price

     C.   cost reimbursable

     D.   time and materials

Quick Quiz Answers

1. D; 2. B; 3. C; 4. D; 5. A; 6. C; 7. A; 8. C; 9. C; 10. A

DISCUSSION QUESTIONS

1.   What is the main purpose of a project quality management plan? What are two metrics besides those provided in this chapter that Pat and her team could use on the VAPR project? Besides ensuring that CBTs are ready for training, where else might they use a checklist on the project?

2.   What is the main purpose of a staffing management plan? What tool should you use to graphically show total staffing needs for a project? What tool should you use to clarify roles and responsibilities for tasks?

3.   Why is it so difficult to ensure good communication on projects? What strategies can any project team use to improve communications?

4.   What is it important to plan for stakeholder engagement? Why is some of the information sensitive when planning how to work with stakeholders? Give examples of how you have planned in advance how to work with difficult stakeholders.

5.   Why is risk management often neglected on projects? Why is it important to take the time to identify and rank risks throughout the project's life?

6. What is the difference between an RFP and an RFQ? Give an example of the appropriate use of each. How does procurement planning differ for government projects versus those in private industry?

EXERCISES

Note: These exercises can be done individually or in teams, in-class, as homework, or in a virtual environment. Learners can either write their results in a paper or prepare a short presentation or video to show their results.

1. Find an example of a large healthcare project that took more than a year to complete. Describe some of the tasks performed in planning the quality, human resource, communications, stakeholders, risk, and procurement aspects of the project. Summarize your findings.

2. Search the Internet for "project dashboard." Find at least three different charts or examples that can be used on a project dashboard. Summarize your findings and your assessment of their value.

3. Your company is planning to launch an important project starting January 1, which will last one year. You estimate that you will need one half-time project manager; two full-time business analysts for the first six months; two full-time marketing analysts for the whole year; four full-time business interns for the months of June, July, and August; and one full-time salesperson for the last three months. Use spreadsheet software to create a stacked-column chart showing a resource histogram for this project, similar to the one shown in this chapter. Be sure to include a legend to label the types of resources needed, and use appropriate titles and axis labels. You can use the resource histogram template on the companion Web site to make this exercise easier.

4. List three negative risk events and three positive risk events for the VAPR project. Briefly describe each risk, and then rate each one as high, medium, or low in terms of probability and impact. Plot the results on a probability/impact matrix. Also, prepare an entry for one of the risks for the risk register.

5. Assume the source selection criteria for evaluating proposals for a project is as follows:

    •   Management approach 15%

    •   Technical approach 15%

    •   Past performance 20%

    •   Price 20%

    •   Interview results and samples 30%

    Use the sample in this chapter as a guide along with the supplier evaluation template from the companion Web site to calculate the total weighted scores for three proposals. Enter scores for Proposal 1 as 80, 90, 70, 90, and 80, respectively. Enter scores for Proposal 2 as 90, 50, 95, 80, and 95. Enter scores for Proposal 3 as 60, 90, 90, 80, and 65. Summarize the results and your recommendation.

6.   Watch the Video Highlight for this chapter, and find at least one other video created in the past year about planning a healthcare project, focusing on the knowledge areas in this chapter. Summarize the videos and your opinions of them.

7.   Review the features boxes in this chapter with examples of What Went Right, What Went Wrong, Healthcare Perspective, Best Practice, and the Media Snapshot. Discuss some of the information presented, and find additional references related to topics discussed in two of these examples. Summarize your findings.

TEAM PROJECTS

Note: These team projects can be done in-class, as homework, or in a virtual environment. Learners can either write their results in a paper or prepare a short presentation or video to show their results.

1.   Your organization initiated a project to raise money for an important charity. Assume that there are 1,000 people in your organization. Also, assume that you have six months to raise as much money as possible, with a goal of $100,000. Create a checklist to use in soliciting sponsors for the fundraiser, a responsibility assignment matrix for various stakeholders, a project Web site (just the home page), a probability/impact matrix with six potential negative risks, and a request for quote for obtaining items your team will need. Be creative in your responses. Remember that this project is entirely run by volunteers.

2.   You are part of a team in charge of a project to help people in your company (500 people) lose weight. This project is part of a competition, and the top "losers" will be featured in a popular television show. Assume that you have six months to complete the project and a budget of $10,000. Develop metrics for the project, a project organizational chart, a communications management plan, and a risk register with at least three entries for the project.

3.   Using the information you developed in Team Project 1 or 2, role-play a meeting to review one of these planning documents with key stakeholders. Determine who will play what role (project manager, team member from a certain department, senior managers, and so on). Be creative in displaying different personalities (a senior manager who questions the importance of the project to the organization, a team member who is very shy or obnoxious).

4.   Develop a project dashboard for your team project. Be sure to include at least eight different metrics. Discuss how you created it, show the actual dashboard you created, and describe how it can be used throughout the project.

5.   Perform the planning tasks (only for the knowledge areas covered in this chapter) for one of the case studies provided in Appendix B. Remember to be thorough in

your planning so that your execution goes smoothly. Be sure to have your sponsor and other stakeholders provide inputs on your plans.

KEY TERMS

bid — A document prepared by sellers providing pricing for standard items that have been clearly defined by the buyer.

blogs — Easy-to-use journals on the Web that allow users to write entries, create links, and upload pictures, while allowing readers to post comments to particular journal entries.

checklist — A list of items to be noted or consulted.

communications management plan — A document that guides project communications.

conformance to requirements — The process of ensuring that the project's processes and products meet written specifications.

contingency plans — The predefined actions that the project team will take if an identified risk event occurs.

contingency reserves or **contingency allowances** — The funds held by the project sponsor that can be used to mitigate cost or schedule overruns if known risks occur.

contracts — The mutually binding agreements that obligate the seller to provide the specified products or services, and obligate the buyer to pay for them.

contract statement of work (SOW) — A document that describes the goods or services to be purchased.

cost-reimbursable contract — A contract that involves payment to the seller for direct and indirect actual costs.

fallback plans — The plans that are developed for risks that have a high impact on meeting project objectives, and are put into effect if attempts to reduce the risk are not effective.

Federal Acquisition Regulation (FAR) — Regulation that provides uniform policies for acquisition of supplies and services by executive agencies in the U.S.

fitness for use — The ability of a product to be used as it was intended.

fixed-price or **lump-sum contract** — A type of contract that involves a fixed price for a well-defined product or service.

Invitation For Bid (IFB) – A procurement document used to solicit quotes from potential sellers when the specifications are clearly identified by the buyer and the seller is selected based primarily on price. Unlike an RFP, potential sellers have little or no input regarding solutions or approaches to solutions with an IFB. Sometimes used interchangebly with RFQ.

make-or-buy analysis — The process of estimating the internal costs of providing a product or service and comparing that estimate to the cost of outsourcing.

management reserves — Funds held for unknown risks.

metric — A standard of measurement.

project dashboard — A graphic screen summarizing key project metrics.

project organizational chart — A graphical representation of how authority and responsibility is distributed within the project.

proposal — A document in which sellers describe what they will do to meet the requirements of a buyer.

quality — The degree to which a set of inherent characteristics fulfill requirements.

RACI charts — A type of responsibility assignment matrix that shows **R**esponsibility, **A**ccountability, **C**onsultation, and **I**nformed roles for project stakeholders.

Request for Proposal (RFP) — A document used to solicit proposals from prospective suppliers for products or services that are complex in nature, high in value, or which may be met with a variety of solutions or approaches by the seller. Price is typically not the primary determining factor with an RFP.

Request for Quote (RFQ) — A document used to solicit quotes or bids from prospective suppliers for the purchase of limited quantities of goods, commodity goods, or products/services with known specifications. Sometimes used interchangeably with an IFB.

resource histogram — A column chart that shows the number of resources required for or assigned to a project over time.

responsibility assignment matrix (RAM) — A matrix that maps the work of the project as described in the WBS to the people responsible for performing the work.

risk — An uncertainty that can have a negative or positive effect on meeting project objectives.

risk events — The specific, uncertain events that may occur to the detriment or enhancement of the project.

risk register — A document that contains results of various risk management processes, often displayed in a table or spreadsheet format.

root cause — The real or underlying reason a problem occurs.

staffing management plan — A plan that describes when and how people will be added to and taken off of a project.

time-and-material contract — A type of contract that is a hybrid of both a fixed-price and cost-reimbursable contract.

triggers — The indicators or symptoms of actual risk events.

END NOTES

[1] Dragan Milosevic, Portland State University, "Delivering Projects: What the Winners Do," PMI Conference Proceedings (November 2001).

[2] Francois Chiocchio et al, "Stress and Performance in Health Care Project Teams," Project Management Institute (2012)

[3] Jokes Unlimited, "Quotes from Companies," (Accessed online June 2009).

[4] Sara Pepitone, "Project: NICOE in Bethesda, Maryland", Interior Design (November 1, 2012).

[5] Kate Taylor, "Posters on Teenage Pregnancy Draw Fire," The New York Times (March 6, 2013)

[6] Worrell, "Design we can all live with," YouTube, (September 24, 2010)

Chapter 7
Executing Projects

LEARNING OBJECTIVES
After reading this chapter, you will be able to:

- List several processes and outputs of project execution
- Discuss what is involved in directing and managing project work as part of project integration management, including the importance of producing promised deliverables, implementing solutions to problems, evaluating work performance data, and requesting changes to a project
- Explain the importance of recommending corrective actions and updating project–related information as part of quality assurance
- Describe the executing processes performed as part of human resource management, summarize important concepts related to managing people, and explain what is involved in leveling resources, assigning staff, reviewing resource calendars, and assessing team performance
- Discuss important communications concepts, and describe the process of managing communications
- Describe the process of managing stakeholder engagement and how to create and use an issue log
- Explain the executing processes performed as part of procurement management, and describe what is involved in selecting sellers and preparing agreements or contracts

> ## OPENING CASE
>
> Jeff and Pat reviewed initial project plans with the steering committee for the VAPR project. Committee members felt that everything was going well so far and that it was time to commit more resources to the project. At later steering committee meetings, Jeff brought up several challenges he was facing in executing the project plans for Phase I. One of the most significant problems, and one which was difficult to articulate in steering committee meetings, was the lack of commitment from the Phase I champion, Casey. He was just too busy. In addition, there were several conflicts between various stakeholders on how to perform certain tasks, and several people complained about a lack of communication about the project. The IT people supporting the project were over allocated as they were also working on other projects, yet some of their tasks were on the critical path for the project.
>
> Things were just not going as smoothly as Jeff had hoped, although he never expected things to run perfectly. Jeff would need to use his experience—especially his soft (interpersonal) skills—as well as advice from the project steering committee, Pat, and other people he could trust, to deal with these and other challenges.

INTRODUCTION

Whereas project planning is considered the most unappreciated project management process group, project execution is usually the most noticed. Although good plans are important, it is even more important to execute them well. In fact, the June 21, 1999, issue of *Fortune* summarized research showing that without a doubt, the main reason Chief Executive Officers (CEOs) failed was poor execution. Failed CEOs simply did not get things done, were indecisive, and did not deliver on commitments. The same is true for today's project managers and all leaders. Stakeholders expect to see results from their projects through effective execution—it is not enough that you had a good plan.

Recall that, in general, the majority of a project's time and budget is spent on project execution. Many of the deliverables and outputs created in the other process groups are fairly similar from project to project, but no two projects are ever executed in the exact same way. Why? Because by definition projects create new products or services that have a defined scope, and therefore no two projects are exactly alike. This means that projects inherently include uncertainty. Although project teams attempt to identify risks so that they can be managed, no one can ever predict all of the challenges that project teams will face in trying to meet project goals. This chapter summarizes the main processes involved in executing projects and discusses some challenges that Jeff and Pat faced in managing the execution of the VAPR project. It should not be a surprise that some of the challenges they faced included working together, even though they shared a mutual respect for the skills and experience that each brought to the project.

What Went Wrong?

There is no shortage of examples to illustrate the poor state of executing good healthcare in the U.S. Below are just a few examples:

• The Doctors television show on January 23, 2013, was called, "Could your hospital be killing you?" Dr. Marty Makary, author of *Unaccountable: What Hospitals Won't Tell You and How Transparency Can Revolutionize Health Care*, described how you could fill a jumbo jet every day with dead people from patients dying from medical errors. He also discussed the problems in how medical professionals are paid, often based on quotas, and that health insurance seems more concerned with giving providers access to patients instead of the reverse.

• Joe Flower, author of *Healthcare Beyond Reform: Doing it Right for Half the Cost*, states that the U.S. ranks below other countries in healthcare, even though we pay much more for it. "If we look mostly at markers that are better proxies for how well a particular national healthcare system serves its citizens—maternal and infant mortality, rates of diabetes treatment—and include especially surveys of how much its citizens and its doctors just plain like the system, the United States consistently ranks behind almost every other first-tier economy in almost every category."[1]

SUMMARY OF EXECUTING PROCESSES AND OUTPUTS

Figure 7-1 summarizes processes and outputs of project execution by knowledge area, based on the *PMBOK® Guide, Fifth Edition*. Notice that not every knowledge area is included, and change requests and updates to the project management plan, project documents, and organizational process assets are outputs of several knowledge areas. Although there are many planning processes related to scope, time, cost, and risk management, these knowledge areas do not have tasks directly related to project execution. Changes to common project constraints are addressed in the next chapter on project monitoring and control. This chapter focuses on processes and outputs that project teams perform to execute projects and provides specific examples for AHS' VAPR project.

Knowledge area	Executing process	Outputs
Project integration management	Direct and manage project work	Deliverables Work performance data Change requests Project management plan updates Project documents updates
Project quality management	Perform quality assurance	Change requests Project management plan updates Project documents updates Organizational process assets updates
Project human resource management	Acquire project team	Project staff assignments Resource calendars Project management plan updates
	Develop project team	Team performance assessment Enterprise environmental factors updates
	Manage project team	Change requests Project management plan updates Project documents updates Enterprise environmental factors updates Organizational process assets updates
Project communications management	Manage communications	Project communications Project documents updates Project management plan updates Organizational process assets updates
Project stakeholder management	Manage stakeholder engagement	Issue log Change requests Project management plan updates Project documents updates Organizational process assets updates
Project procurement management	Conduct procurements	Selected sellers Agreements Resource calendars Change requests Project management plan updates Project documents updates

Figure 7-1. Executing processes and outputs

PROJECT INTEGRATION MANAGEMENT

During project execution, the project manager must direct and manage stakeholders to complete the project. Project managers can follow several important practices to help accomplish this challenging job:

- *Coordinate planning and execution:* Recall that the main purpose of project planning is to guide execution. If the project manager and team did a good job planning, the plans will be easier to execute. As things change, team members need to update the plans to keep everyone working on the same page.

- *Develop and use soft skills:* Several studies suggest that soft skills (for example, strong leadership, effective team building, strong communication, motivation, negotiation, conflict management, and problem solving) are crucial to the success of project managers, especially during project execution. Project managers must lead by example in demonstrating the importance of creating good project plans and then following them in project execution. Project managers often create plans for things they need to do themselves, such as meeting with key stakeholders, reviewing important information, and so on. If project managers follow through on their own plans, their team members are more likely to do the same.

- *Provide a supportive organizational culture:* Good project execution requires a supportive organizational culture. For example, organizational procedures can help or hinder project execution. If an organization has useful guidelines and templates for project management that everyone in the organization follows, it will be easier for project managers and their teams to plan and do their work. If the organization uses the project plans as the basis for performing and monitoring progress during execution, the culture will promote the relationship between good planning and execution. Even if the organizational culture is not supportive, project managers can create a supportive culture within their own project and work on improving the culture in other parts of the organization.

- *Step beyond your defined boundaries:* Even with a supportive organizational culture, project managers might sometimes find it necessary to exert authority that may not have been clearly assigned to them. It has been said that any decent project manager should have been told, "You went beyond your authority," at least once a year or they are not being as effective as they should be. Why? Because if you have not tested your boundaries, then you do not know exactly what they are. In the end, project managers are responsible for their projects, and sometimes they must make decisions or take actions and ask for permission (or forgiveness) later. Note that it is not the job of the project manager to skirt policies and procedures, regardless of the motives. In the healthcare industry, policies and procedures are in place to protect the patient, ensure compliance, and maintain good relationships with third-party payers. Project managers are leaders, and they must adhere to the same policies that staff members are expected to follow. If they do not, then they undermine the very structure they are working to support. However, they do need to make decisions and take actions to keep the project moving.

- *Capitalize on product, business, and application area knowledge:* The application area of the project directly affects project execution because the products of the project are produced during project execution. For example, if a project involves constructing a new building, the project manager and other stakeholders would need to use their expertise in architecture, engineering, and construction to produce the product successfully. Project managers should use their expertise to guide their team and make important decisions.

- *Use project execution tools and techniques:* For example, following a project management methodology and using a project management information system can help project execution go more smoothly. The project management methodology should include guidelines on how to communicate project status, handle conflicts, work with suppliers and other stakeholders, and perform other important tasks.

As listed in Figure 7-1, the main outputs produced during execution as part of project integration management are deliverables, work performance data, change requests, project management plan updates, and project documents updates. Updating the project management plan and other project documents is self-explanatory. These other outputs will be described in more detail, along with a discussion of how to solve problems that often occur during execution.

Deliverables

Most project sponsors would say that the most important output of any project is its deliverables. Recall that deliverables are products or services produced or provided as part of a project. They include product and process-related items. For the VAPR project at AHS, key product-related deliverables include the new data warehouse tables, the data in those tables, the scripts to build the tables, the procedures around supporting those tables and scripts, the new clinical workflows, and the training program. Process-related deliverables include research of the existing data warehouse tables, analysis of the IHI VAP bundle elements, and the review of the sources of the IHI elements within the AHS systems.

Sample Deliverables

The VAPR project is fictitious, so it is impossible to show the actual deliverables produced during execution. You may be familiar with similar projects that produced new clinical workflows or training programs. Because VAPR includes a wide variety of deliverables and will affect patient care, it is especially important to ensure that quality expectations are clear for each of the deliverables. The section on quality later in this chapter describes the importance, and role, of quality assurance during project execution.

Work Performance Data

One of Jeff's main jobs during project execution was collecting, assessing, and communicating work performance data during Phase I, and he assisted Pat during Phase II. They agreed to use the "management by wandering around" (MBWA) approach, meaning they informally observed and talked to the project team members and other stakeholders as much as possible. They both wanted to know firsthand how project activities were progressing to know enough about what was going on to be able to offer suggestions when needed. This is one reason why Jeff would manage Phase I and Pat would manage Phase II. Each of them was considered a subject matter expert for the work being executed in each of their respective phases. If they were not, then they would have to rely on subject matter experts to assist the team with project-specific questions. Of course, Jeff and Pat also used more formal communications, such as status reports, the project Web site and project dashboard (as described in Chapter 6), survey results, and stakeholder feedback to address work performance on the project.

Sample Work Performance Data

A common way to summarize work performance data is by using a milestone report. Recall that a milestone is a significant event on a project, such as completing a major deliverable or awarding a major contract. Figure 7-2 provides part of a milestone report for the VAPR project. Notice that in addition to listing the milestones, the report lists the planned date for completion (in month/day format), the status, the person responsible for the milestone, and issues/comments. The dates are listed in chronological order. Most project management software tools include a standard milestone report, and you can often create customized reports to tailor the content and format of reports. It is also a good idea to list recently completed and upcoming milestones on the project's Web site.

Change Requests

Often, a number of change requests emerge during project execution. Recall that a process for handling changes should be defined during project planning as part of the project management plan. Chapter 8, which covers monitoring and controlling projects, provides detailed information on handling changes. It is important during project execution to request appropriate changes. Project managers, team members, suppliers, champions, users, and project sponsors can make change requests, so it is important to have a good process in place for handling them.

Ventilator Associated Pneumonia Reduction (VAPR)

Project Milestone Report

Feb 14

Milestone	Date	Status	Responsible	Issues/Comments
IHI Bundle Defined	7/25	Complete	Pat	IHI Bundle defined as of 7/25 but IHI is considering changing the bundle based on new research on sedation vacation efficacy.
Current Data Extracted	9/27	Complete	Larry	Some source data is questionable for IHI bundle purposes.
Database Designed	11/25	Complete	Mark	
Data Initial Load	2/21	Complete	Larry	Completed early on 2/11.
Data Tested	3/13	Behind Schedule	Crystal	Running behind where we expected to be due to problems in data integrity in source system. May hit due date if we can get more time from source system teams to investigate data problems.
Workflows Developed	4/2	In progress	Pat	Expect to meet schedule.
Training Program Developed	5/1	Not started	Nick	Outsourced.
Reports Developed	6/5	Not started yet	Peter	Peter may be taking leave (FMLA) during this period. We have started looking for alternative resources.

Figure 7-2. Sample milestone report for reporting work performance data

Sample Change Request

Successful project teams use well-defined processes and standard forms for requesting project changes. Some changes are requested using other established change processes. For example, when Jeff requested that the data in the source systems be reviewed for integrity, he had to submit a work order through the AHS Help Desk, as the functional teams that managed these systems were not part of the project. For other change requests—especially those that may impact achieving scope, time, or cost goals of the project, or those impacting the configuration of a deliverable—a formal change request form should be submitted through the appropriate channels.

Figure 7-3 provides a sample of a completed change request form for the VAPR project. It is important to clearly identify the benefits of the change along with the impact to the budget, schedule, quality, scope, and other project constraints. Likewise, there is often a cost (to those same constraints) of *not* making the change, and that should also be addressed.

Project Change Request

Project Name: VAPR
Date Request Submitted: September 22
Title of Change Request: Use the vendor's online training system instead of the AHS internal online training system for go live training.
Change Order Number: A200-17
Submitted by: Nick Whatley, Training Manager

Change Category: _X_Scope __Schedule **X** Cost __Technology __Other

Description of change requested:
We do not have the resources to migrate the vendor's training program into the AHS online training system prior to go live. We request that we use the vendor's online training program system for go live and then migrate to our system for annual renewal training.

Events that made this change necessary or desirable:
The IT person assigned to our project has several other important projects on-hand and is not a full-time project resource. The IT department does not expect to be able to migrate the vendor's training program to the AHS system prior to go live based on the schedule.

Justification for the change/why it is needed/desired to continue/complete the project:
We can use the vendor's online training system for the initial training cycle and then migrate the package to the AHS system after go live to handle the annual renewal training. If we do not we may delay the VAPR project by 10 days or more.

Impact of the proposed change on:
Scope: None   **Schedule:** None   **Cost:** $2500 (for 60 days usage)   **Staffing:** None

Risk: Low. The vendor's system is robust and has been in use for over 10 years. The migration to our system will be the same migration that we planned before go live, but instead will be after go live. The only risk is related to problems with our users having trouble logging in, but the vendor's system supports Shibboleth single-sign on, so we expect no problems.

Other: None

Suggested implementation if the change request is approved: Include the overtime pay in the normal paycheck.

Required approvals:

Name/Title	Date	Approve/Reject
Marilyn Shoemaker, RN, Ph.D., Sponsor		
Danielle Scheerer, MD, Clinical Champion		
Julia Portman, VP of IT		

Figure 7-3. Sample change request

Implemented Solutions to Problems

All project teams face obstacles, experience setbacks, and have to spend precious time managing issues. Some surface early during project initiation or planning, but many do not occur until project execution, when many things are happening at once. Many problems can be avoided by doing a good job of initiating, planning, or monitoring and controlling the project, but other problems cannot be avoided. Any time a team of people set out to create something new there will be inherent uncertainty in the new work. Some common problems encountered during project execution include the following:

1. The project sponsor, champion, and/or other senior managers are not very supportive of the project.

2. Project stakeholders, such as people who would use the products and services the project is attempting to create, are not sufficiently involved in project decision-making.

3. The project manager is inexperienced in managing people, working in a particular organization, or understanding the application area of the project.

4. The project objectives or scope are unclear.

5. Estimates for time and cost goals are unreliable or unrealistic.

6. Project stakeholders most impacted by the project are covertly or overtly working to undermine the project as it will change their workflows, or perhaps cut jobs, in their areas.

7. Organizational leadership across the required disciplines is not engaged or supportive of the project. For example, a project that is being driven by nursing is not supported by physicians.

8. Business needs or technology changes have impacted the project.

9. People working on the project are incompetent or unmotivated.

10. There are poor conflict-management procedures.

11. Communications are poor.

12. Suppliers are not delivering as promised.

The first five problems should have been addressed during project initiation or planning (and were addressed in previous chapters), but they can also cause difficulties during execution as frequently leaders and other stakeholders only appear to be supportive but are not committed to the project. Stakeholders or leadership not being engaged and addressing business and technology changes are discussed in the next chapter on monitoring and controlling. The last four problems are discussed in this chapter and presented in the context of the VAPR project.

Sample Implemented Solutions to Problems

Jeff and Pat had been working hard to direct and manage project execution, but they encountered several problems in their respective project phases. The following sections discuss the problems of incompetent or unmotivated people working on the project and poor conflict-management procedures. Later sections discuss strategies for improving communications and supplier delivery.

Issues with Competence and Motivation

Nick, the project team member assigned to coordinate the training material vendor, was supposed to devote twenty-five percent of his time to the project during Phase II. As was common at AHS, however, Nick was also working on several other high priority projects and running the day-to-day enterprise training for AHS. He saw the value in the VAPR project but was not motivated to focus on it as he recognized his other project work as even more valuable to AHS.

Nick was the most skilled and experienced trainer and was Pat's first choice for this project role. In fact, he was her only choice as she had worked with him several times over the years at AHS, and she had no experience with other members of the training team. She was disappointed because when she approached Nick about filling this role, he did not tell her that he was too busy. In hindsight, Pat realized that he really was not excited about working on the project and was probably just being too nice to decline her request.

Pat met with Jeff to ask for advice. Jeff, always preferring the direct approach, suggested that Pat talk with Nick and confront the problem directly. Jeff liked Nick and had positive experiences working with him, and he believed that Nick had already recognized the problem and was trying to figure out a solution himself.

Pat met with Nick and asked him if he had the time or desire to work on this project. Although surprised that she would ask him directly, Nick confided that he was swamped and that he should never have accepted this work. Pat asked Nick if he could recommend someone else who could be more committed to the project. To Pat's surprise, Nick offered a name immediately—Bill. Apparently, Nick had already spent some time thinking about this situation and was trying to figure out a solution, but he was afraid to talk to Pat about the problem. Pat requested that she be given Bill's qualifications and that she be allowed to interview him, which Nick agreed to enthusiastically. After the interview, Pat was satisfied that Bill would be a good addition to the team, and she presented the recommendation to the steering committee and project leadership before offering him the position. Bill accepted, and the team agreed it was a win-win situation.

Poor Conflict Management

Most large projects are high-stake endeavors that are highly visible within organizations. They require tremendous effort from team members, are expensive, require significant resources, and can have an extensive impact on the way work is done in an organization. When the stakes are high, conflict is never far away, and even small projects with low budgets have conflicts—it is a natural part of work and life in general. Project managers should lead their teams in developing norms for dealing with various types of conflicts that might arise. For example, team members should know that disrespectful behavior toward any project stakeholder (including each other) is inappropriate, and that team members are expected to try to work out small conflicts themselves before elevating them to higher levels. The team contract, created during project planning, should address team conduct and conflict management.

Blake and Mouton (1964) delineated five basic modes for handling conflicts. Each strategy can be considered as being high, medium, or low on two dimensions: importance of the task or goal, and importance of the relationship between the people having the conflict.

1. *Confrontation*: When using the **confrontation mode**, project managers directly face a conflict using a problem-solving approach that allows affected parties to work through their disagreements. This approach is also called the problem-solving mode. It is best used when *both the task and the relationship are of high importance*. For example, Pat confronted Nick when she recognized that he was not able to fulfill his commitments on the project. They discussed the problem and decided it was best for both parties for Nick to leave the project team and for Bill to join it. This mode reflects a win/win approach.

2. *Compromise*: With the **compromise mode**, project managers use a give-and-take approach to resolve conflicts, bargaining and searching for solutions that will bring some degree of satisfaction to all the parties in a dispute. This give-and-take approach works best when both the task and the relationship are of medium importance. For example, suppose one of Pat's stakeholders wanted to add a new topic to one of the online courses for no extra cost, and the supplier wanted payment for it, as agreed to in their contract. They could compromise and add the new topic at a discounted cost. This mode reflects a lose/lose approach, since both parties are giving up something, and they will frequently continue to find ways to gain back what they lost in the compromise.

3. *Smoothing*: When using the **smoothing mode**, the project manager de-emphasizes or avoids areas of differences and emphasizes areas of agreement. This method, sometimes called the accommodating mode, is best used when the *relationship is of high importance and the task is of low importance*. For example, two members of the project steering committee might totally disagree on whether they should provide incentive bonuses to suppliers for achieving outstanding ratings on the training. Pat could use the smoothing mode to ensure that the relationship between the steering committee members remains harmonious by discussing with these team members the areas in which they agree and by downplaying the topic of bonuses during meetings.

4. *Forcing*: The **forcing mode** can be viewed as the win-lose approach to conflict resolution. People exert their viewpoints even though they contradict the

viewpoints of others. This approach is appropriate when *the task is of high importance and the relationship is of low importance.* For example, assume Pat must get the training vendor to deliver the work earlier than agreed in the contract in order to meet a new compliance deadline. If they decline her request, she can threaten the loss of future work with AHS. Pat would use the forcing mode because she cares more about the task getting done than how the vendor feels about her or AHS.

5. *Withdrawal:* When using the **withdrawal mode**, project managers retreat or withdraw from an actual or potential disagreement. Sometimes they withdraw from the conflict in order to let the staff in conflict work it out on their own, and sometimes because the conflict or its resolution are not critical to the project or to the project manager. This approach, sometimes called the avoidance mode, is the least desirable conflict-handling mode as the problem most often continues to fester. It may be appropriate when *both the task and the relationship are of low importance.*

More recent studies recognize a sixth conflict-handling mode:

6. *Collaborating:* Using the **collaborating mode**, decision makers incorporate different viewpoints and insights to develop consensus and commitment. *It can also be effective when both the task and relationship are of high importance.*

Figure 7-4 summarizes information about these conflict-handling modes.

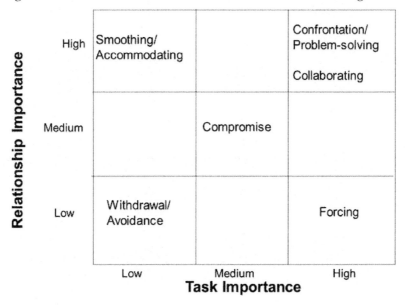

Figure 7-4. Conflict-handling modes

Effective project managers often use confrontation or collaborating for conflict resolution instead of the other modes. The term *confrontation* may be misleading. This mode focuses on a win-win, problem-solving approach, in which all parties work together to find the best way to solve the conflict.

Project managers must also realize that not all conflict is bad. In fact, conflict can often be good. Conflict often produces important results, such as new ideas, better alternatives, and motivation to work harder and more collaboratively. Project team members might become stagnant or develop **groupthink**—conformance to the values or ethical standards of a group—if there are no conflicting viewpoints on various aspects of a project. Research suggests that task-related conflict, which is derived from differences over team objectives and how to achieve them, often improves team performance. Emotional conflict, however, which stems from personality clashes and misunderstandings, often depresses team performance. Project managers should create an environment that encourages and maintains the positive and productive aspects of conflict.

Healthcare Perspective

Managing conflict can be especially complex within a healthcare organization where there are multiple disciplines, and each discipline has an assumed rank in relation to the others. Then within each discipline there are further ranks, resulting in multiple hierarchies that can influence, control, or impact a project team.

Project managers may find themselves considering falling on their swords to keep the peace, but this is a short-term solution that encourages unprofessional behavior between the disciplines. A better approach is to quickly recognize unproductive conflict and confront it, respectively and professionally, when it occurs.

To do this successfully, it is critical that project managers build trusting relationships and form alliances with high-ranking physicians, nurses, therapists, administrators, and other leaders within the organization. This takes time and a history of proven successes by project managers, so new project managers must rely on the relationships built by their sponsors and champions while they work to build their own.

PROJECT QUALITY MANAGEMENT

It is one thing to develop a plan for ensuring quality on a project; it is another to ensure delivery of quality products and services. The main quality management process required during execution is performing quality assurance. **Quality assurance** includes all the activities related to satisfying the relevant quality standards for a project. For example, it was important for the VAPR project that the reports would be available to nurses on their carted laptops as well as on the physicians' iPads. These two platforms are very different in how they transfer, analyze, and present their data to the user, and the needs of the two different user types were very different. It was critical that the needs of the different disciplines, and the technologies available, were well understood before designing the solution. To this end, Jeff made sure that the database designed and developed during

Phase I would handle both platforms equally well. In Phase II, Pat made sure that she had both a technology expert and a reporting expert when she met with users to determine their specific reporting requirements.

Another goal of quality assurance is continual quality improvement. Many companies understand the importance of quality assurance and have entire departments dedicated to this discipline. These companies have detailed processes in place to make sure that their products and services conform to various quality requirements. It is no different within healthcare, where the Chief Quality Officer (CQO), typically a physician, is frequently responsible for the quality of patient care within the organization. The CQO also knows they must deliver healthcare to its patients at increasingly lower reimbursement rates, and so they must also be business-savvy.

To be successful in the increasingly regulated healthcare environment, successful organizations evaluate other organizations' best practices and adopt and adapt them in order to continuously improve the way they deliver healthcare. Gone are the days when healthcare organizations only looked inward for good ideas. They must now compare themselves to other healthcare organizations as part of a growing trend in transparency, resulting in a continuously higher quality bar being set for everyone. See Chapter 10 for more information on, and examples of, best practices in project management.

Top management and project managers can impact the quality of projects most significantly by implementing quality assurance. Key outputs of quality assurance include change requests, project management plan updates, and project documents updates. Another output is updates to organizational process assets. Recall that organizational process assets include formal and informal plans, policies, procedures, guidelines, information systems, financial systems, management systems, lessons learned, and historical information that can be used to influence a project's success.

Quality Assurance Techniques

It is important for organizations to use common techniques to identify areas in which they would benefit from taking actions to improve quality. Several quality improvement techniques include benchmarking, quality audits, and process analysis.

- **Benchmarking** generates ideas for quality improvements by comparing specific project practices or product characteristics to those of other projects or products within or outside of the organization itself. For example, one reason that AHS initiated the VAPR project was because it discovered that their Ventilator Associated Pneumonia incidence rates were higher than the CMS reported averages for their region. There are many benchmarks in healthcare, some formal and some not. The Joint Commission (JC), Centers for Medicare and Medicaid Systems (CMS), Institutes for Healthcare Improvement (IHI), and many other oversight organizations create regulations or standards with which healthcare organizations are expected to comply.

- A **quality audit** is a structured review of specific quality management activities that helps identify lessons learned, which could improve performance on current or future projects. In-house auditors or third parties with expertise in specific areas can perform quality audits, which can be either scheduled or random. Recall that the primary goal of the VAPR project was to reduce the VAP incidence rate at AHS, which will be accomplished by providing caregivers with IHI bundle compliance information in a timely manner. However, the delivery of the compliance data will not matter if the data is late or inaccurate. A quality audit would be used to ensure that the quality expectations of the project are being met by analyzing the results of the quality control (testing) processes early in the project. Therefore, if there are problems with the data, corrective actions can be taken during Phase I so that the data would be correct in time for reporting in Phase II.

- Process analysis involves analyzing how a process operates and determining improvements. Many organizations use **lean**, a system based on the Toyota Production System to help improve results and efficiency by eliminating waste and reducing idle time and non-value added activities. Root cause analysis is often part of process analysis. **Cause-and-effect diagrams**—also called fishbone diagrams (because their structure resembles a fishbone) or Ishikawa diagrams (named after their creator)—can assist in ensuring and improving quality by finding the root causes of quality problems. Recall from Chapter 6 that a root cause is the real or underlying reason a problem occurs. Jeff and his team created several of these diagrams to find the root causes of data quality problems, as described in the next section.

Sample Quality Assurance Technique: Cause and Effect Diagram

After the initial data load during Phase I, Jeff's team reported that one of the IHI Ventilator Bundle elements, the head of bed elevation (HOB), did not appear to be accurate. The IHI recommends that ventilated patients maintain a head elevation of 30 degrees or more in an effort to retard liquids from accumulating in the lungs. AHS added this information to clinical documentation several years earlier, and they included two checkboxes that indicated "head up" and "head down." It was a simple matter for the nurse to choose the state of the bed's head, up or down, when they documented the patient's condition during rounding.

When analyzing the data, however, Jeff's team noticed that the majority of vented patients were documented as having their head of bed in the down position for most of the day. Only at shift changes did the HOB show as being in the elevated position. All intra-shift recordings were documented as being in the down position. Jeff was baffled, and he and his team assumed it was a technology problem, such as a bad interface, incorrect translation tables, or perhaps a database problem. However, he was experienced enough to know he did not want to limit his perspective, so he decided to sit with his team to create a cause-and-effect diagram to attempt to identify why the data was so inconsistent. Although not foolproof, it can help a team think outside the box. Their work is shown in Figure 7-5.

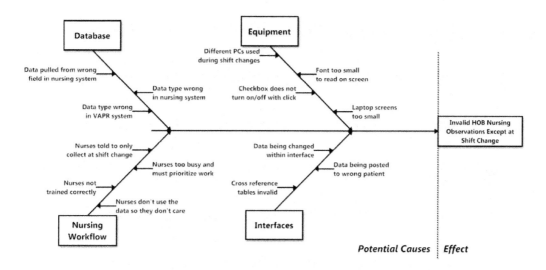

Figure 7-5. Sample cause-and-effect diagram

After following through on all the technology causes (equipment, interface, and database) to no avail, all that was left to consider were the nursing workflow causes, and this was out of area of expertise. He turned to Pat to review the problem they discovered, fully expecting her to be as perplexed as he and his team were. However, she was not.

Pat just shook her head as her eyes moved to the floor. "Sloppiness, followed by laziness," she replied. Jeff asked her to explain. Pat told the group that often the IT department creates sloppy solutions that allow nurses to be lazy in their documentation. She guessed that the data element on the nursing documentation was a required field, and IT received complaints that it was slowing down documentation. So, in a half-considered response, IT made the field's value default to "down" because at least eighty percent of AHS patients were not on a ventilator, and the value for them did not matter. She added that because the value defaults, the nurses do not change it during routine rounding during the day. However, at shift change, nurses thoroughly document the patient's condition for the nurse who is coming on in the next shift, so the data is corrected at shift change.

The correct solution, she continued, other than having it never default, would be for the system to default to "not applicable" if the patient was not ventilated, and to not default if the patient was ventilated. In an effort to prove her point, Pat then moved to the conference room's computer and opened up the nursing documentation system. In two minutes, she showed the team how the system allowed the nurse to indicate HOB as up or down with the check of one box. However, as she predicted, the default was set to down. This default led to the majority of vented patients appearing to be in the "head down" status for most of the day, with the head only being recorded in the up positions during shift changes. This meant that it would fail the IHI best practice for head of bed elevation. Pat agreed to take this problem to Dr. Scheerer, the CQO and Phase II champion, to have the nursing documentation system corrected. They also agreed that Jeff would update the issue in the issue log based on this meeting and assign it to Pat for final resolution.

PROJECT HUMAN RESOURCE MANAGEMENT

Effective project human resource management is crucial to project execution. The main processes project managers perform include acquiring, developing, and managing the project team. Key outputs include project staff assignments, resource calendars, team performance assessment, change requests, and updates to the project management plan, enterprise environmental factors, and organizational process assets.

Resource calendars are simply calendars for each resource showing when the resources are available to work on the project activities. Before discussing project staff assignments and team performance assessment, it is important to understand basic concepts related to dealing with people in a work setting. Key concepts include motivation, influence, and effectiveness.

Motivation

Psychologists, managers, coworkers, teachers, parents, and most people in general still struggle to understand what motivates people, or why they do what they do. **Intrinsic motivation** causes people to participate in an activity for their own enjoyment. For example, some people love to read, write, or play a musical instrument because it makes them feel good. **Extrinsic motivation** causes people to do something for a reward or to avoid a penalty. For example, some young children would prefer *not* to play an instrument, but do so to receive a reward or avoid a punishment. Why do some people require no external motivation whatsoever to produce high-quality work while others require significant external motivation to perform routine tasks? Why can't you get someone who is extremely productive at work to do simple tasks at home? Mankind will continue to try to answer these overarching questions, but a basic understanding of motivational theory will help anyone who has to work or live with other people. For project managers, the better they understand and can apply these theories, the more effective they will be at motivating teams toward project objectives.

Maslow's Hierarchy of Needs

Abraham Maslow, a highly respected psychologist who rejected the dehumanizing negativism of psychology in the 1950s, is best known for developing a hierarchy of needs. In the 1950s, proponents of Sigmund Freud's psychoanalytic theory were promoting the idea that human beings were not the masters of their destiny and that their actions were governed by unconscious processes dominated by primitive sexual urges. During the same period, behavioral psychologists saw human beings as controlled by the environment. Maslow argued that both schools of thought failed to recognize unique qualities of human behavior: love, self-esteem, belonging, self-expression, and creativity. He argued that these unique qualities enable people to make independent choices, which give them full control over their destiny.

Figure 7-6 shows the basic pyramid structure of **Maslow's hierarchy of needs**, which states that people's behaviors are guided or motivated by a sequence of needs. At the bottom of the hierarchy are physiological needs, such as air, water, and food. After physiological needs are satisfied, safety needs—such as shelter from bad weather, lack of physical or mental abuse, and a low-crime environment—guide behavior. After safety needs are satisfied, social needs—such as having friends, belonging to groups, and having a sense of community—come to the forefront, and so on up the hierarchy. Examples of esteem needs include personal achievement, recognition, and respect, whereas self-actualization needs include a sense of fulfillment and belief that one is working to his or her potential. The order of these needs in the pyramid is significant. Maslow suggests that each level of the hierarchy is a prerequisite for the level above. For example, it is not possible for people to consider self-actualization if they have not addressed basic needs concerning security and safety. People in an emergency situation, such as a flood or hurricane, cannot be concerned with personal growth but will be motivated solely by the requirements of personal survival. After a particular need is satisfied, however, it no longer serves as a potent motivator of behavior.

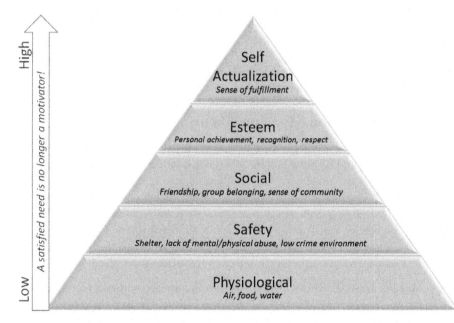

Figure 7-6. Maslow's hierarchy of needs

The bottom four needs in Maslow's hierarchy—physiological, safety, social, and esteem needs—are referred to as deficiency needs, and the highest level, self-actualization, is considered a growth need. Only after meeting deficiency needs can individuals act on growth needs. Self-actualized people are problem-focused, have an appreciation for life, are concerned about personal growth, and can have peak experiences.

Most people working on corporate projects probably have their basic physiological and safety needs met. If someone has a sudden medical emergency or is laid off from work, however, physiological and safety needs move to the forefront. It may not be your staff member that has the medical emergency or that has been laid off—it could be a member of their family, although by extension it becomes a physiological and safety need for your staff member. It is crucial that project managers understand that life goes on outside of work, and being adaptive to those needs creates a loyal project team.

To motivate project team members, the project manager needs to understand each person's motivation, especially with regard to social, esteem, and self-actualization needs. For example, team members new to a company and city might be motivated by social needs. To address social needs, a project manager could organize gatherings and social events for new workers. If a project manager knew a team member was interested in pursuing an advanced degree, he or she could offer suggestions on graduate programs, provide information on tuition reimbursement policies, and allow the team member some scheduling flexibility to balance work and school.

Maslow's hierarchy conveys a message of hope and growth. People can work to control their own destinies and naturally strive to achieve higher and higher needs. Some cultures disagree with Maslow's philosophy and have other beliefs on motivation. Recent brain research also suggests that there are physiological reasons for certain behaviors. In any case, successful project managers know that to provide appropriate motivation and maximize team performance. They must understand team members' personal goals and needs, and by fulfilling them, they can best meet project objectives.

Herzberg's Motivation-Hygiene Theory

Frederick Herzberg, a psychologist and professor, is best known for distinguishing between motivational factors and hygiene factors when considering motivation in work settings. He called factors that cause job satisfaction motivators, and factors that cause dissatisfaction hygiene factors. A hygiene factor is a basic necessity, such as air-conditioning during hot weather. Air-conditioning does not in itself provide team satisfaction, but without it, you would have disgruntled staff on hot workdays. Note that hygiene factors vary based on culture. For example, in some cultures air conditioning in offices is unheard of, whereby in the U.S. it is considered a minimum standard in the office workplace.

Head of Case Western University's psychology department, Herzberg wrote the book *Work and the Nature of Man* in 1966 and the famous *Harvard Business Review* article "One More Time: How Do You Motivate Employees?" in 1968. Herzberg analyzed the factors that affected productivity among a sample of 1,685 employees. Popular beliefs at that time were that work output was most improved through larger salaries, job security, larger fringe benefit packages, or a more attractive work environment. According to Herzberg, these hygiene factors would cause dissatisfaction if *not* present but would *not* motivate workers to put in more effort if present. Herzberg found that people were motivated to work mainly by feelings of personal achievement and recognition. Motivators, Herzberg concluded, included achievement, recognition, the work itself, responsibility, advancement, and growth. Herzberg's theory is also known as the Herzberg Two Factor Theory, as shown in Figure 7-7.

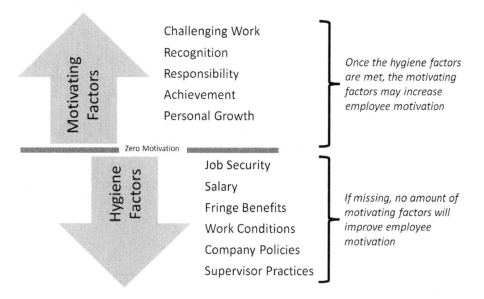

Figure 7-7: Herzberg's two factor theory

Motivating and hygiene factors are important concepts for project managers to understand, because their work environment and culture may make it difficult for them to motivate their teams (i.e. if job security, good fringe benefits, etc. are missing). Conversely, if the organization treats their employees fairly and provides an adequate working environment, project managers will understand that and offer team members challenging work, recognize them for their successes, and provide opportunities to allow staff to grow in their careers. These things, according to Herzberg, will motivate their staff.

McClelland's Acquired-Needs Theory

David McClelland proposed that an individual's specific needs are acquired or learned over time and shaped by life experiences. The main categories of acquired needs include achievement, affiliation, and power. Normally, one or two of these needs is dominant in individuals.

- *Achievement*: People with a high need for achievement (nAch) seek to excel and tend to avoid both low-risk and high-risk situations to improve their chances of achieving something worthwhile. Achievers need regular feedback and often prefer to work alone or with other high achievers. Managers should give high achievers challenging projects with achievable goals. Achievers should receive frequent performance feedback, and although money is not an important motivator to them, it is an effective form of feedback.

- *Affiliation*: People with a high need for affiliation (nAff) desire harmonious relationships with other people and need to feel accepted by others. They tend to conform to the norms of their work group and prefer work that involves

significant personal interaction. Managers should try to create a cooperative
work environment to meet the needs of people with a high need for affiliation.

- *Power.* People with a need for power (nPow) desire either personal power or
institutional power. People who need personal power want to direct others and
can be seen as bossy. People who need institutional, or social, power want to
organize others to further the goals of the organization. Management should
provide those seeking institutional power with the opportunity to manage
others, emphasizing the importance of meeting organizational goals.

The Thematic Apperception Test (TAT) is a tool to measure the individual needs
of different people using McClelland's categories. The TAT presents subjects with a series
of ambiguous pictures and asks them to develop a spontaneous story for each picture,
assuming they will project their own needs into the story.

McGregor's Theory X and Theory Y

Douglas McGregor was one of the great popularizers of a human relations approach to
management, and he is best known for developing Theory X and Theory Y. In his
research, documented in his 1960 book *The Human Side of Enterprise,* McGregor found that
although many managers spouted the right ideas, they actually followed a set of
assumptions about worker motivation that he called Theory X (sometimes referred to as
classical systems theory). People who believe in Theory X assume that workers dislike and
avoid work if possible, so managers must use coercion, threats, and various control
schemes to get workers to make adequate efforts to meet objectives. Theory X managers
assume that the average worker wants to be directed and prefers to avoid responsibility, has
little ambition, and wants security above all else.

When research seemed to demonstrate that these assumptions were not valid,
McGregor suggested a different series of assumptions about human behavior that he called
Theory Y (sometimes referred to as human relations theory). Managers who believe in
Theory Y assume that individuals do not inherently dislike work but consider it as natural
as play or rest. The most significant rewards are the satisfaction of esteem and self-
actualization needs, as described by Maslow. McGregor urged managers to motivate people
based on these more valid Theory Y notions.

It is important for project managers to understand the leadership culture of their
organization, as they tend to lean toward X or toward Y, even though there may be outliers
within the organization. It is also critical that project managers understand their own
inclinations, as an X project manager would find it difficult to work within an organization
led by Y leadership. Of course the inverse is also true. Likewise, if the project manager's
leadership beliefs do not mesh with those of the organization, the project team will be
much less effective as they attempt to adjust to, and resist, the different leadership style.

Thamhain and Wilemon's Influence Bases

Many people working on a project do not report directly to project managers, and project managers often do not have control over project staff that report to them. For example, people are free to change jobs. If they are given work assignments they do not like, many workers will simply quit or transfer to other departments or projects. H. J. Thamhain and D. L. Wilemon investigated the approaches project managers use to deal with workers and how those approaches relate to project success. They identified nine influence bases available to project managers:

1. *Authority:* The legitimate hierarchical right to issue orders

2. *Assignment:* The project manager's perceived ability to influence a worker's assignment to future projects

3. *Budget:* The project manager's perceived ability to authorize the use of discretionary funds

4. *Promotion:* The ability to improve a worker's position

5. *Money:* The ability to increase a worker's pay and benefits

6. *Penalty:* The project manager's perceived ability to dispense or cause punishment

7. *Work challenge:* The ability to assign work that capitalizes on a worker's enjoyment of doing a particular task, which taps an intrinsic motivational factor

8. *Expertise:* The project manager's perceived specialized knowledge that others deem important

9. *Friendship:* The ability to establish friendly personal relationships between the project manager and others

Top management grants authority to the project manager, but not necessarily the power to control personnel assignments, budgets, promotions, and penalties. Team members, however, may misperceive their project manager's sphere of influence and expect him to have the power, for example, to grant promotions and transfers. If project managers' power is limited, they can still influence workers by providing challenging work, and they can increase the power of their influence by using expertise and friendship.

Thamhain and Wilemon found that projects were more likely to fail when project managers relied too heavily on using *authority, money, or penalty* to influence people. When project managers used *work challenge and expertise* to influence people, projects were more likely to succeed. The effectiveness of work challenge in influencing people is consistent with Maslow's and Herzberg's research on motivation. The importance of expertise as a means of influencing people makes sense on projects that involve special knowledge. For example, people working on a project to build a spaceship would expect the project manager to have appropriate education and experience in that area. They would also be impressed if he or she had actually worked on other space projects or traveled into space.

Video Highlights

Books and articles are written every year on the topic of human motivation. Many videos are also available on this subject. One humorous example is Jimmy Kimmel's popular video on the Handsome Men's Club, illustrating Jimmy's Theory X approach to management.

Another popular, more educational video is by Daniel Pink. RSA Animate used its whiteboard drawing technique to summarize key points from Pink's book in a YouTube video called "Drive: The surprising truth about what motivates us." Pink narrates the video, summarizing several studies about how money often causes people to perform worse on tasks that involve cognitive skills. He suggests that organizations pay people enough to take money off the table and stop using the carrot and stick approach to motivation.

Pink suggests that managers focus on the following three motivators:

- *Autonomy:* People like to be self-directed and have freedom in their work. Maslow, Herzberg, and other researchers also found that people are motivated by autonomy. Pink gives an example of how a software company in Australia, Atlassian, lets people decide what they want to work on and with whom for one day every quarter. Workers show the results of their work that day in a fun meeting. This one day of total autonomy has produced a large number of new products and fixes to problems.

- *Mastery:* People like to get better at things, such as playing an instrument, participating in a sport, writing software, and other work-related activities. Pink states that several products like Unix, Apache, and Wikipedia were created because people enjoyed the challenge and mastery involved.

- *Purpose:* People want to work for a good purpose. When the profit motive is separated from the purpose motive, people notice and do not perform as well. Many great products were created for a purpose. For example, the founder of Skype wanted to make the world a better place, and Steve Jobs wanted to put a ding in the universe.

Covey's Effectiveness Research

Stephen Covey, author of *The 7 Habits of Highly Effective People* and several other books, expanded on the work done by Maslow, Herzberg, and others to develop an approach for helping people and teams become more effective. Covey's first three habits of effective people—be proactive, begin with the end in mind, and put first things first—help people achieve a private victory by becoming independent. After achieving independence, people can then strive for interdependence by developing the next three habits—think win/win; seek first to understand, then to be understood; and synergize. (**Synergy** is the concept that the whole is equal to more than the sum of its parts.) Finally, everyone can work on Covey's seventh habit—sharpen the saw—to develop and renew their physical, spiritual, mental, and social/emotional selves.

Project managers can apply Covey's seven habits to improve effectiveness on projects, as follows:

1. *Be proactive:* Covey, like Maslow, believes that people have the ability to be proactive and choose their responses to different situations. Project managers must be proactive, anticipate, and plan for problems and inevitable changes on projects. They can also encourage team members to be proactive in their work.

2. *Begin with the end in mind:* Covey suggests that people focus on their values, what they really want to accomplish, and how they really want to be remembered in their lives. He suggests writing a mission statement to help achieve this habit. Many organizations and projects have mission statements that help them focus on their main purpose. Project managers must help their teams stay focused on project objectives, regardless of what may be going on around them in the workplace.

3. *Put first things first:* Covey developed a time-management system and matrix to help people prioritize their time. He suggests that most people need to spend more time doing things that are important but not urgent. Important but not urgent activities include planning, reading, and exercising. Project managers should focus on important and not urgent activities, such as developing various project plans, building relationships with major project stakeholders, and mentoring project team members. They also need to avoid focusing only on important and urgent activities—that is, putting out fires. This habit can often be achieved through more thorough planning.

4. *Think win/win:* Covey presents several paradigms of interdependence, with "think win/win" being the best choice in most situations. When you use a win/win paradigm, parties in potential conflict work together to develop new solutions that make them all winners. Project managers should strive to use a win/win approach in making decisions, but sometimes, especially in competitive situations, they must use a win/lose paradigm.

5. *Seek first to understand, then to be understood:* **Empathic listening** is listening with the intent to understand by putting yourself in the shoes of the other person. You forget your personal interests and focus on truly understanding the other person and feeling what he or she is feeling. To really understand other people, you must learn to focus on others first. When you practice empathic listening, you can begin two-way communication. Making empathic listening a habit enables project managers to fully understand their stakeholders' needs and expectations.

6. *Synergize:* In projects, a project team can synergize by creating collaborative products that are much better than a collection of individual efforts. For example, engineers helped the crew of the *Apollo 13* return to Earth safely by working together to develop a solution to their potentially deadly technical problems. One person came up with an idea, which prompted another person to have an idea, and so on. The team devised a solution that no one person

could have discovered. Covey also emphasizes the importance of valuing differences in others to achieve synergy. Synergy is essential to many complex projects; in fact, several major breakthroughs in technology, such as manned flight, drug development, and various computer technologies, occurred because of synergy. Synergy is not possible without the project team feeling free to express disagreement with established paradigms.

7. *Sharpen the saw:* When you practice sharpening the saw, you take time to renew yourself physically, spiritually, mentally, and socially. The practice of self-renewal helps people avoid burnout. Project managers must make sure that they themselves and their project team have time to retrain, reenergize, and occasionally even relax to avoid burnout. Everyone on the project team should leave better trained, more skilled, and more marketable than they were when they joined the team.

Several experts suggest that empathic listening is a powerful skill for project managers and their teams to possess. Understanding what motivates key stakeholders and customers can mean the difference between project success and project failure. After project managers and team members begin to practice empathic listening, they can communicate and work together to tackle problems more effectively.

Before you can practice empathic listening, you first have to get people to talk to you. In many cases, you must work on developing a rapport with other people before they will really open up to you. **Rapport** is a relationship of harmony, conformity, accord, or affinity. Without rapport, people cannot begin to communicate, or the strong person might dominate the weaker one. For example, if you meet someone for the first time and find that you cannot communicate, you need to focus on developing rapport. Rapport can be difficult to establish when you aren't given the opportunity to spend time together or when dealing with busy clinicians. However, techniques such as cross-discipline team-building activities, leadership or project team retreats, and leadership summits are often used in healthcare to help staff build rapport more quickly.

One technique for establishing rapport is using a process called mirroring. **Mirroring** is the matching of certain behaviors of the other person. Although establishing rapport involves a number of complex human interactions, the simple technique of mirroring can sometimes help. You can mirror someone's voice tone and/or tempo, breathing, movements, or body postures. This technique must be applied carefully as you must be comfortable with the mirror image you are attempting to portray. You must also understand your authority and position in regards to those you are interacting with, as it would not be appropriate to match the tone of a supervisor who is reprimanding you for a poorly thought out decision that cost the organization money or caused patient injury.

You can see from the material covered in this chapter so far that many important topics related to motivation, influence, and effectiveness are relevant to project management. Projects are done by and for people, so it is important for project managers and team members to understand and practice key concepts related to these topics. Jeff and Pat kept these topics in mind to successfully execute the project.

What Went Right?

Most medical schools and other healthcare programs include courses related to communications, especially when it comes to understanding and building rapport with patients. For example, NBC's Nightly News on June 12, 2012 aired a story called "Teaching Doctors to Listen." In the story, Dr. Nancy Snyderman interviewed Dr. Rachel Remen, creator of a course for medical students called "The Healer's Art." Remen said the course enables service-oriented medical students to bring their full humanity to their work by using experiential learning and reflection.

Remen explained that several years ago she noticed that several journal articles documented the problem of many young medical students and doctors becoming cynical, depressed, and burned out. She decided to create a course to help students learn to connect better with their patients. First created over twenty years ago at the University of California San Francisco, the course is now in place in half of U.S. medical schools. Several students who took the course believed it helped them tremendously, especially in finding the balance between high tech and high touch in their work and personal lives.

Acquiring the Project Team and Making Project Staff Assignments

There's a saying that the project manager who is the smartest person on the team has done a poor job of recruiting. After developing a staffing management plan during project planning, project managers must work with other managers in their organizations to assign personnel to their project or to acquire additional human resources needed to staff their project. Project managers with strong influencing and negotiating skills are often good at getting internal people to work on their project. However, the organization must ensure that people assigned to the project best fit the project's requirements, and that these people are motivated to remain on the project.

Several organizations, publications, and Web sites address the need for good staff acquisition and retention. William C. Taylor, cofounder of *Fast Company* magazine and a renowned speaker, also believes that people today are more demanding and have higher expectations of their jobs than just earning a paycheck. His company's research has found that the top three reasons people leave their jobs (by choice) are because:

1. They feel they do not make a difference.

2. They do not get proper recognition.

3. They are not learning anything new or growing as a person.

Best Practice

Best practices can also be applied to include the best places for people to work. For example, Fortune Magazine lists the "100 Best Companies to Work For" in the United States every year, with Google taking the honors in 2007, 2008, 2012, and 2013. Google built a large, outdoor sports complex in 2011 to help keep its employees in shape. They also provide indoor recreation with their bowling alleys and dance studio. The company also offers a generous amount of leave for new parents—18 weeks for mothers and 12 weeks for fathers – as well as $500 worth of "baby bonding bucks." [2] Of course, employees are top-notch workers, and Google has been known to hire less than one percent of applicants.

The top-ranked healthcare company in 2013 was CHG Healthcare Services in Salt Lake City, Utah, ranked #3 behind Google and SAS. "What makes it so great? Employees of this medical staffing firm compete in talent shows, trivia contests, and activities like a Dress as Your Favorite President competition. Extra paid time off is given to sales teams that meet their goals. New this year: two on-site health centers." [3]

In fact, employee wellness programs have become an important trend of best companies in the past few years. "The reasons for this are obvious; rising insurance rates and cost of care, colluding with increased incident of chronic disease and an aging workforce, necessitate measures for preserving employee well-being and containing expenses…the number of companies offering employees financial rewards or other incentives for participating in wellness programs…we saw 55 of the 100 Best Companies offering health incentives. Currently the largest cash reward offer is $2,600, with the average award coming in at $460." [4]

Figure 7-8 shows a cartoon describing how many people feel about Google.

Figure 7-8. Best place to work if you can get hired (www.xkcd.com)

Resource Loading and Leveling

Once people are assigned to projects, there are two techniques available to project managers that help them use project staff most effectively: resource loading and resource leveling. **Resource loading** refers to the amount of individual resources an existing schedule requires during specific time periods. Resource loading helps project managers develop a general understanding of the demands a project will make on the organization's resources, as well as on individual people's schedules. Project managers often use resource histograms, as described in Chapter 6, to depict period-by-period variations in resource loading. A histogram can be very helpful in determining staffing needs or in identifying staffing problems.

A resource histogram can also show when work is being over allocated to a certain person or group. **Over allocation** means more resources than are available are assigned to perform work at a given time. For example, Figure 7-9 provides a sample resource histogram created in Microsoft Project. The data was actually from one of the template files Microsoft used to provide with the software. This histogram illustrates how much one individual, Joe Franklin, is assigned to work on the project each week. The percentage numbers on the vertical axis represent the percentage of Joe's available time that is allocated for him to work on the project. The top horizontal axis represents time in weeks. Note that Joe Franklin is over allocated most of the time. For example, for most of March and April and part of May, Joe's work allocation is 300 percent of his available time. If Joe is normally available eight hours per day, this means he would have to work 24 hours a day to meet this staffing projection! Many people don't use the resource assignment features of project management software properly.

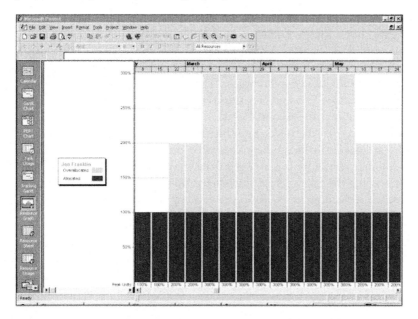

Figure 7-9. Sample resource histogram showing an overallocated individual

Resource leveling is a technique for resolving resource conflicts by delaying tasks. It is a form of network analysis in which resource management concerns drive scheduling decisions (start and finish dates). The main purpose of resource leveling is to create a smoother distribution of resource usage. Project managers examine the network diagram for areas of slack or float, and to identify resource conflicts. For example, you can sometimes remove over allocations by delaying noncritical tasks, which does not result in an overall schedule delay. Other times you will need to delay the project completion date to reduce or remove over allocations. Over allocation is one type of resource conflict. If a certain resource is over allocated, the project manager can change the schedule to remove resource over allocation. If a certain resource is under allocated, the project manager can change the schedule to try to improve the use of the resource. Resource leveling, therefore, aims to minimize period-by-period variations in resource loading by shifting tasks within their slack allowances.

Under allocation can also be a problem on many healthcare projects. One reason is because staff tends to add time buffers to their work estimates, and when they finish the work early they are not prone to report their activity completion until the due date. This is why critical chain scheduling can shorten project schedules; the reserve time is controlled by the project manager. A second reason is that project managers try to manage uncertainty by not allocating staff for their full work day. Once that expectation is set by project managers, the staff finds other ways to fill their day, ways that are not related to direct project work. The third reason is that staff are often waiting on other project work to be completed before they can begin their activities. Even if they only wait a half day per week, that can add up to a great deal of lost resources throughout the life of a project.

Figure 7-10 illustrates a simple example of resource leveling. The network diagram at the top of this figure shows that Activities A, B, and C can all start at the same time. Activity A has a duration of two days and will take two people to complete; Activity B has a duration of five days and will take four people to complete; and Activity C has a duration of three days and will take two people to complete. The histogram on the lower-left of this figure shows the resource usage if all activities start on day one. The histogram on the lower right of Figure 7-10 shows the resource usage if Activity C is delayed two days, its total slack allowance. Notice that the lower-right histogram is flat or leveled; that is, its pieces (activities) are arranged to take up the least space (lowering the highest number of workers needed). You may recognize this strategy from the computer game Tetris, in which you earn points for keeping the falling shapes as level as possible. The player with the most points (most level shape allocation) wins. Resource leveling has several benefits:

- When resources are used on a more constant basis, they require less management. For example, it is much easier to manage a part-time project member who is scheduled to work 20 hours per week on a project for the next three months than it is to manage the same person who is scheduled to work 10 hours one week, 40 the next, 5 the next, and so on.

- Resource leveling may enable project managers to use a just-in-time inventory type of policy for using subcontractors or other expensive resources. For example, a project manager might want to level resources related to work that must be done by particular subcontractors such as testing consultants. This leveling might allow the project to use four outside consultants full-time to do testing for four months instead of spreading the work out over more time or needing to use more than four people. The latter approach is usually more expensive.

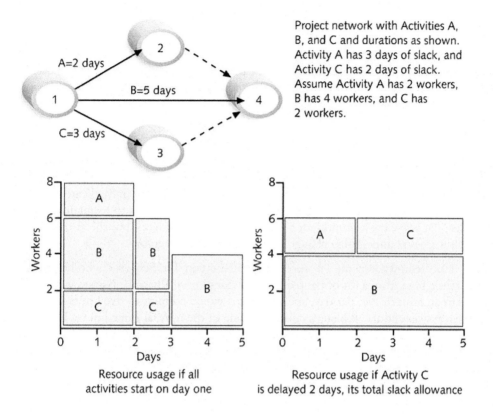

Project network with Activities A, B, and C and durations as shown. Activity A has 3 days of slack, and Activity C has 2 days of slack. Assume Activity A has 2 workers, B has 4 workers, and C has 2 workers.

Resource usage if all activities start on day one

Resource usage if Activity C is delayed 2 days, its total slack allowance

Figure 7-10. Resource leveling example (Schwalbe, Information Technology Project Management, Sixth Edition, 2010)

- Resource leveling results in fewer problems for project personnel and accounting departments. Increasing and decreasing labor levels and particular human resources often produce additional work and confusion. For example, if a person with expertise in a particular area is only assigned to a project two days a week and another person they need to work with is not assigned to the project those same days, they cannot work well together. The Accounting department might complain when subcontractors charge a higher rate for billing less than 20 hours a week on a project. The accountants will remind project managers to strive for getting the lowest rates possible.

- Resource leveling often improves morale. People like to have some stability in their jobs. It is very stressful for people not to know from week to week or even day to day what projects they will be working on and with whom they will be working.

Sample Project Staff Assignments

Jeff worked with the functional managers in IT to staff Phase I for the VAPR project. As usual he could not get commitments from the managers for some of his first choices, but he had a very good relationship with all of the functional teams and knew that they would try to provide him the staffing he needed.

Pat had a bit more difficulty staffing for Phase II, as she primarily needed time from clinicians whose primary jobs were caring for patients, not working on projects. Following Jeff's advice Pat was asking for clinical resources to be committed at least half time on the project for a few weeks each. However, nursing units were thinly staffed due to cost-cutting measures implemented in response to federal cutbacks in Medicare and Medicaid reimbursement rates, and physicians were being pressured to maintain full schedules. Pat knew it was important to AHS to reduce VAP rates, but she also understood that healthcare was undergoing change, and it was hard on everyone.

Uncertain what to do, Pat engaged her champion, Dr. Scheerer, who helped her obtain a little time from a lot of people over the duration of Phase II. Nurses would commit to an hour or two per day, and physicians would commit to five hours per week, with the physician hours all being available outside of the normal clinic hours. This made Pat's job more difficult as she now had to manage a larger team, and she had to coordinate the physician activities after hours, but she knew she was fortunate to get any time from nurses and physicians. To make matters worse, Pat was not able to get a commitment of who would be assigned to the project. She simply received a promise that the nurse managers would make staff available for a few hours a day to review workflows.

Because Jeff had put Pat's name into the resource bucket in the project schedule for all of the workflow activities in Phase II, he suggested that Pat replace her name with the names of the staff who will be engaged in the various activities. Pat explained to Jeff that she was not given the resources that she requested, but instead given a large number of people for very short periods of time. They decided it would be best to create a resource called "Nursing Pool" and another called "Physician Pool" to include in the schedule.

Although he was glad Pat got some commitment, Jeff expressed his concern that it would be more difficult to manage such a large number of staff members who are only committed for short periods of time. Jeff told Pat that the biggest problem would be communications, as having a larger team increases the chances of miscommunications because it provides additional paths for the wrong message to get out, and it creates more channels of communication required for the proper communications. As the project team grows, the communication paths grow even faster, as discussed later in this chapter.

To keep everyone up to date on current project staffing assignments, Jeff provided a current team roster on the project Web site, including team member names, roles, and contact information. For the part time resources assigned to work with Pat in Phase II, they too were listed, but they were included as resource pools. As suppliers were added to the project, he included supplier staff information as well. Figure 7-11 provides a sample of part of the team roster for the VAPR project.

VAPR Team Roster

Name	Role on Project	Position	Email	Office
Dr. Marilyn Shoemaker	Project Sponsor	Chief Nursing Officer	shoemaker_m	MH205
Casey Lidwell	Phase I Project Champion	Chief Analytics Officer	Lidwell_c	MH237
Dr. Danielle Scheerer	Phase II Project Champion	Chief Quality Officer	scheeerer_d	MH239
Jeff Birdwell	Project Manager, Phase 1	Sr. Project Manager	birdewell_j	BB209
Pat Wager	Project Manager, Phase 2	Sr. Clinical Analyst	wagstaff_p	CD223
Larry Storm	Team Member, Ph I	Database Administrator	storm_l	BB103
Stan Budding	Team Member, Ph I	Sr. Analyst	Budding_s	BB201
Jack Hotman	Team Member, Ph I	Systems Administrator	Hotman_j	PH301
Crystal Droyd	Team Member, Ph I	Sr. Data Analyst	Droyd_c	BB104
Mark Danner	Team Member, Ph I	Manager, Data Analytics	Danner_m	BB201
Peter Land	Team Member, Ph I	Data Developer	Land_p	CD201
Nursing Pool	Team Member, Ph II	Nursing	TBD	TBD
Physician Pool	Team Member, Ph II	Physician	TBD	TBD
Training Vendor	Training Supplier	Training Development	TBD	TBD

Figure 7-11. Sample team roster

Developing the Project Team and Assessing Team Performance

Even if a project manager has successfully recruited enough skilled people to work on a project, he or she must ensure that people can work together as a team to achieve project goals. Many failed projects have been staffed by highly talented individuals; however, it takes teamwork to complete projects successfully. The main goal of team development is to help people work together more effectively to improve project performance.

Dr. Bruce Tuckman published his four-stage model of team development in 1965 and modified it to include an additional stage in the 1970s. The **Tuckman model** describes five stages of team development:

1. *Forming* involves the introduction of team members, either at the initiation of the team or as new members are introduced. This stage is necessary, but little work is actually achieved. The project manager should strive to move through this state quickly, and using team-building activities is one way to do that. When the project manager is out, the team has no direction.

2. *Storming* occurs as team members have different opinions as to how the team should operate. People test each other, and there is often conflict within the team. The conflicts are often of a personal nature and frequently without basis. The project manager needs to be sure the team focuses on the critical issues and coaches them to be more accepting of each other's differences. When the project manager is out, conflict increases.

3. *Norming* is achieved when team members have developed a common working method, and cooperation and collaboration replace the conflict and mistrust

of the previous phase. Differences now are typically focused on how to get the work done or the type of technology to use to solve problems, but overall the team works well together. The project manager allows the team to make more decisions and leads them through a more participative style. When the project manager is out, work continues.

4. *Performing* occurs when the emphasis shifts to reaching the team goals rather than working on team process. Relationships are settled, and team members are likely to build loyalty toward each other. At this stage, the team is able to manage tasks that are more complex and cope with greater change. Note that not all teams are able to progress through the team development stages to reach the performance level. When at this stage, the project manager tends to rely more on delegation as the team makes many of the necessary day-to-day decisions. When the project manager is out, no one notices.

5. *Adjourning* involves the breakup of the team after they successfully reach their goals and complete the work. Teams might also adjourn due to poor performance or project cancellation.

There is an extensive body of literature on team development. This section highlights a few important tools and techniques, including training, team-building activities, and reward and recognition systems. Keep in mind that having teams focus on completing specific tasks is often the most effective way to help teams be productive.

Training

Project managers often recommend that people take specific training courses to improve individual and team development. For example, Jeff recommended that Stan, one the IT members of his project team, take training courses in designing data structures for mobile devices so that he could contribute even more to this project. Early in the project, Jeff and Pat also organized a special team-building session for their combined project team where the team was given an opportunity to learn more about each other and the expectations of project leadership. In addition to traditional, instructor-led training, many organizations provide e-learning opportunities for their employees so that they can learn specific skills at any time and any place, similar to the courses being developed for the VAPR project.

Online e-learning, or computer-based training (CBT), is very common within healthcare due to the large number of training courses workers are required to take every year. A nurse may be required to take fifty or more refresher courses per year, and it would be difficult and expensive to take traditional courses. In all cases, it is important to make sure that the timing and delivery method for the training is appropriate for the specific situation and the individuals involved. For example, if an eight-hour course was required for physicians, it would most likely be scheduled on a Saturday because they book clinic time out between six weeks to six months in advance. It would not be ethical, or professional, for them to have to cancel all patients for a day just to attend training.

Team-Building Activities

Many organizations provide in-house team-building training activities, and many also use specialized services provided by external companies that specialize in this area. Two common approaches to team-building activities include using physical challenges and psychological preference indicator tools.

Sometimes, organizations have teams of people go through certain physically challenging activities to help them develop as a team. Military basic training or boot camps provide one example. Men and women who want to join the military must first make it through basic training, which often involves several strenuous physical activities such as rappelling off towers, running and marching in full military gear, going through obstacle courses, passing marksmanship training, and mastering survival training. Many non-military organizations use a similar approach by sending teams of people to special locations, where they work as a team to navigate white-water rapids, climb mountains or rocks, participate in ropes courses, and so on.

More often, organizations have teams participate in mental team-building activities in which they learn about themselves, about each other, and how to work as a group most effectively. It is important for people to understand and value each other's differences to work effectively as a team. Two common tools used in mental team building include the Myers-Briggs Type Indicator and the Wilson Learning Social Styles Profile, and there are several others (i.e. StrengthsFinder, Belbin Team Roles, etc.). Effective teams include a variety of personalities. The main purpose of these tools is to help people understand each other and learn to adjust their personal communication styles to work well as a team.

The **Myers-Briggs Type Indicator (MBTI)** is a popular tool for determining personality preferences. During World War II, Isabel B. Myers and Katherine C. Briggs developed the first version of the MBTI based on psychologist Carl Jung's theory of psychological type. The four dimensions of psychological type in the MBTI are as follows:

1. *Extrovert/Introvert (E/I):* This first dimension determines if you are generally extroverted or introverted. The dimension also signifies whether people draw their energy from other people (extroverts) or from inside themselves (introverts). About 75 percent of people in the general population are extroverts.

2. *Sensation/Intuition (S/N):* This second dimension relates to the manner in which you gather information. Sensation (or Sensing) type people take in facts, details, and reality and describe themselves as practical. Intuitive type people are imaginative, ingenious, and attentive to hunches or intuition. They describe themselves as innovative and conceptual. About 75 percent of people in the general population have a preference for sensation.

3. *Thinking/Feeling (T/F):* This third dimension represents thinking judgment and feeling judgment. Thinking judgment is objective and logical, and feeling judgment is subjective and personal. The general population is generally split evenly between these two preferences.

4. *Judgment/Perception (J/P):* This fourth dimension concerns people's attitude toward structure. Judgment type people like closure and task completion. They tend to establish deadlines and take them seriously, expecting others to do the same. Perceiving types prefer to keep things open and flexible. They regard deadlines more as a signal to start rather than complete a project and do not feel that work must be done before play or rest begins. People are generally split evenly between these two preferences.

There are 16 MBTI categories based on combinations of the four dimensions. For example, one MBTI category is ESTJ, another is INFP, and another is ENTP. Project managers can often benefit from knowing their team members' MBTI profiles by adjusting their management styles for each individual. For example, if the project manager is a strong N and one of the team members is a strong S, the project manager should take the time to provide more concrete, detailed explanations when discussing that person's task assignments. Project managers might also want to make sure that they have a variety of personality types on their team. For example, if all team members are strong introverts, it might be difficult for them to work well with other stakeholders who are often extroverts.

Many organizations use Wilson Learning's Social Styles Profile in team-building activities. Psychologist David Merril, who helped develop the Social Skills Profile, categorizes four approximate behavioral profiles, or zones. People are perceived as behaving primarily in one of four zones, based on their assertiveness and responsiveness:

- "Drivers" are proactive and task oriented. They are firmly rooted in the present, and they strive for action. Adjectives to describe drivers include pushy, severe, tough, dominating, harsh, strong-willed, independent, practical, decisive, and efficient.

- "Expressives" are proactive and people oriented. They are future oriented and use their intuition to look for fresh perspectives on the world around them. Adjectives to describe expressives include manipulating, excitable, undisciplined, reacting, egotistical, ambitious, stimulating, wacky, enthusiastic, dramatic, and friendly.

- "Analyticals" are reactive and task oriented. They are past oriented and strong thinkers. Adjectives to describe analyticals include critical, indecisive, stuffy, picky, moralistic, industrious, persistent, serious, expecting, and orderly.

- "Amiables" are reactive and people oriented. Their time orientation varies depending on whom they are with at the time, and they strongly value relationships. Adjectives to describe amiables include conforming, unsure, ingratiating, dependent, awkward, supportive, respectful, willing, dependable, and agreeable.

Figure 7-12 shows these four social styles and how they relate to assertiveness and responsiveness. Note that the main determinants of the social style are levels of assertiveness—if you are more likely to tell people what to do or ask what should be done—and how you respond to tasks—by focusing on the task itself or on the people involved in performing the task. For example, a driver is assertive in telling other people what to do and focuses on completing tasks. An amiable prefers to ask others what to do and focuses on pleasing people versus completing tasks.

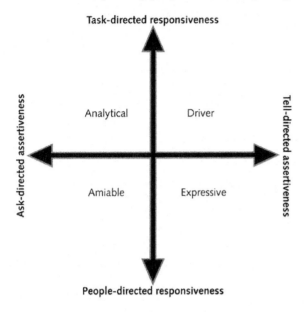

Figure 7-12. Social styles of Wilson Learning (Schwalbe, Information Technology Project Management, Sixth Edition, 2010)

Knowing the social styles of project stakeholders can help project managers understand why certain people may have problems working together. For example, drivers are often very impatient working with amiables, and analyticals often have difficulties understanding expressives. Project managers can use their facilitation skills to help all types of people communicate better with each other and focus on meeting project goals.

Reward and Recognition Systems

Another important tool for promoting team development is the use of team-based reward and recognition systems. If management rewards teamwork, it promotes or reinforces people to work more effectively in teams. Some organizations offer bonuses, trips, or other rewards to workers who meet or exceed company or project goals. Project managers can recognize and reward people who willingly work overtime to meet an aggressive schedule objective or go out of their way to help a teammate. If teamwork is the essential goal, project managers should be sure to reward examples of teamwork. They should, however, recognize individuals who volunteer to put in additional time to meet a deadline or show other exemplary behaviors above and beyond those of the rest of the team.

It is important to understand the culture of your company and of the people on the project before you attempt to reward them. For example, in many Asian countries the culture is focused more on teamwork, as opposed to Western countries where the focus is more on individual effort. If you reward an individual in some Asian countries it would embarrass them. In some Western countries, including the United States, rewarding a team would demotivate staff if, in fact, only two or three of the members were strong contributors. Once you understand the culture, you must also understand your staff, as some staff members would prefer a private "thank you" and a pat on the back while others would prefer public recognition and a nice certificate to hang to hang on their wall.

Project managers must continually assess their team's performance. When they identify weaknesses in individuals or in the entire team, it's their job to find the best way to develop their people and improve performance.

Sample Team Performance Assessment

Project managers assess team performance in several different ways. As mentioned earlier, Jeff believed in management by wandering around, and he liked to have many short, informal discussions with various stakeholders, especially his project team members. He also made an effort to observe them working alone and as a team and assessed the quality of deliverables they produced. Jeff and other project managers at AHS filled out performance appraisals for each team member once a year or when a project was completed. These appraisals could then be used by the functional managers as part of their annual performance evaluations, although this was optional at AHS. These performance appraisals, and what they will be used for, should be addressed in the human resources management plan that was developed during planning. It should also be reviewed with each prospective project team member to ensure understanding.

Jeff also felt that it was important for people to assess their own performance as well as the performance of their teammates. He talked to each team member individually and the team as a group about this assessment because he knew that some people felt uncomfortable evaluating themselves or other people. Jeff stressed that he had successfully used this approach in the past, and he would keep the information confidential. His main goal was to help everyone work well together on the project. Figure 7-13 is a sample of an informal questionnaire that Jeff periodically asked his project team members to fill out to assist in performance assessment. Jeff would then review each person's assessment, and if necessary, talk with the team member "off the record." He would take corrective actions as needed to ensure that the team is performing well.

Managing the Project Team

Another human resource management process performed as part of executing a project is managing the project team, which, of course, is no small task. After assessing team performance and related information, the project manager must decide if changes to the project should be requested or if updates need to be made to enterprise environmental factors, organizational process assets, or the project management plan. Project managers also must use their soft skills to find the best way to motivate and manage each team member, as described earlier in this chapter. The following sections describe tools and techniques to help manage project teams and offer general advice on managing teams.

Team Performance Assessment
August 1

Project Name: VAPR Project

Individual's Name: _____ **Project Manager**: <u>Jeff Birdwell</u>

Date: _____

1. Using a scale of 0-100, assess how you think **the project team** is performing: ___
2. Briefly explain your rationale behind the score in #1.
3. Using a scale of 0-100, assess how **you** are performing on this project: _____
4. Briefly explain the rationale behind your score in #3.
5. Of the current project work underway, what do you feel is most critical to complete?
6. What can **you** do to improve your performance?
7. What can **project leadership** do to **help you** meet your goals on this project?
8. Is there anything you see that can prevent the project team from meeting project objectives? If so, explain.
9. What suggestions do you have for improving team performance?

Figure 7-13. Sample team performance assessment

Tools and Techniques for Managing Project Teams

Several tools and techniques are available to assist in managing project teams:

- *Observation and conversation:* It is hard to assess how your team members are performing or how they are feeling about their work if you seldom watch and evaluate their performance or discuss these issues with them. Many project managers, like Jeff, like to physically see and hear their team members at work. Informal or formal conversations about how a project is going can provide crucial information. For virtual workers, project managers can still observe and discuss work and personal issues via e-mail, telephone, or other communications media. However, these tasks are more difficult when working virtually as all communication has to planned, which is similar to holding a formal status meeting for non-virtual teams. Team and individual dynamics are very different during planned meetings, so the project manager loses the ability to make spontaneous observations when working with virtual teams.

- *Project performance appraisals:* Just as general managers provide performance appraisals for their workers, so can project managers. The need for and type of project performance appraisals varies depending on the length of the project, the complexity of the project, organizational policies, contract requirements, and related communications. Even if a project manager does not provide official project performance appraisals for team members, it is still important to provide timely performance feedback. If a team member hands in sloppy or late work, the project manager should determine the reason for this behavior and take appropriate action. Perhaps the team member had a death in the family and could not concentrate. Perhaps the team member was planning to leave the project. The reasons for the behavior would have a strong impact on the action the project manager would take.

- *Conflict management:* Few projects are completed without any conflict. Some types of conflict are actually desirable on projects, but many are not. As described previously in this chapter, there are several ways to handle conflicts. It is important for project managers to understand strategies for handling conflicts and to proactively manage them.

- *Interpersonal skills:* As described in previous chapters, interpersonal skills are crucial for successful project managers, especially during project execution. These soft skills, sometimes also referred to as emotional intelligence, are particularly important in team development. Examples of important interpersonal skills include leadership, influence, effective decision making, empathy, creativity, and group facilitation.

General Advice on Managing Teams

Effective project managers must be good team leaders. Suggestions for ensuring that teams are productive include the following:

- Be patient with your team and treat everyone with respect. Assume the best about people; do not assume that your team members are lazy and careless.

- Fix the problem instead of blaming people. Help people work out problems by focusing on behaviors.

- Establish regular, effective meetings. Focus on meeting project objectives and producing positive results.

- Allow time for teams to go through the basic team-building stages of forming, storming, norming, performing, and adjourning. Do not expect teams to work at the highest performance level from the start; not all teams will even reach that level. However, help them move along the stages as quickly as possible.

- If a user is not supportive of the project, team members may be severely criticized, either professionally or personally, during formal or informal meetings. Depending on how powerful the user is, these abusive situations can negatively impact the project, resulting in poor morale or turnover. Project managers must report abusive incidents like these to their project sponsors.

- Clinical projects may bring the team members face-to-face with physicians, nurses, therapists, and administrators who may have limited interest in the project. Further, the clinicians' focus is on patient care, and often projects take them away from their patients. Help the team understand that the behavior of clinicians and others is not personal.

- Limit the size of work teams to three to seven members to enhance communications. Break down the work further, if required.

- Plan some social activities to help team members and other stakeholders become acquainted. Make the social events fun and not mandatory.

- Be sure the team knows who the customer is. All projects are undertaken for a business and/or clinical reason, and the project team members are simply the resources assigned to complete the project work. Customers are to be treated with respect, at all times, even when conflict arises.

- Stress team identity. Create traditions that team members enjoy. For long projects, create a team name, define a mascot, and design a logo. Use signage, t-shirts, hats, or other logo products to sell your team's identity.

- Nurture team members and encourage them to help each other. Identify and provide training that will help individuals and the team as a whole become more effective.

- For projects of a long duration, or on projects that have key resources without backup, be sure to cross-train team members. This approach reduces project risk and improves team morale as people improve their skill sets.

- Acknowledge individual and group accomplishments.

- Take the additional actions necessary to work with virtual team members. If possible, have a face-to-face or phone meeting at the start of a virtual project or when introducing a virtual team member. Screen people carefully to make sure they can work effectively in a virtual environment. Clarify how virtual team members will communicate.

- Do not allow low performers to remain on the team. The quickest way to lower team morale and increase team turnover is to allow poor performance, or unprofessional behavior, to go unresolved.

Project Communications Management

Good communications management is also crucial to project execution. The process of managing communications involves gathering information to create, distribute, store, retrieve, and dispose of communications in accordance with the communications management plan. The main outputs are project communications and updates to project documents, the project management plan, and organizational process assets.

Important Project Communications Concepts

It is important to address key concepts related to improving project communications, including formal and informal communications, nonverbal communications, using the appropriate communications medium, understanding individual and group communication needs, and the impact of team size on project communications.

Formal and Informal Communications

It is not enough for project team members to submit formal status reports to their project managers and other stakeholders and assume that everyone who needs to know that information will read the reports. In fact, many people may prefer to have a two-way conversation about project information rather than reading detailed reports, e-mails, or Web pages to try to find pertinent information. These people may want to know the people working on their projects and develop a trusting relationship with them, and so they use informal discussions about the project to develop these relationships. Therefore, project managers must be good at nurturing relationships through good communication. Many experts believe that the difference between good project managers and excellent project managers is their ability to nurture relationships and use empathic listening skills, as described earlier.

Nonverbal Communications

People make or break projects, and people like to interact with each other to get a true feeling for how a project is going. Research poses the theory that in a face-to-face interaction, 58 percent of communication is through body language, 35 percent through how the words are said, and a mere 7 percent through the content or words that are spoken. The author of this information (see *Silent Messages* by Albert Mehrabian, 1980) was careful to note that these percentages were specific findings for a specific set of variables. Even if the actual percentages are different in verbal project communications today, it is safe to say that it is important to pay attention to more than just the actual words someone is saying. Nonverbal communications, such as a person's tone of voice and body language, are often more important than the words being used.

Using the Appropriate Communications Medium

Several references provide guidelines about how well different types of media—such as hard copy, phone calls, voice mail, e-mail, face-to-face meetings, Web sites, instant messaging, text messaging, tweeting, videos, etc.—are suited to different communication needs. For example, if you were trying to assess commitment of project stakeholders, a face-to-face meeting would be the most appropriate medium to use. A phone call would be adequate, but the other media would probably not be appropriate. Project managers must assess the needs of the organization, the project, and individuals in determining which communication medium to use, and when.

Media Snapshot

Some companies encourage workers to use social media tools to get to know their colleagues better, especially for global work teams. A 2011 survey, however, shows that companies have changed their tune after realizing that worker productivity often suffers due to social media and other distractions. According to harmon.ie, a company specializing in social and collaborative tools, nearly 60% of work interruptions involved either using tools like social networks, text messaging, and IM. The survey found that 45% of employees work only 15 minutes or less without getting interrupted, and 53% waste at least one hour a day due to distractions. Based on an average salary of $30 per hour, that wasted hour a day translates into $10,375 of lost productivity per work each year. 68% of survey respondents said their employers use corporate policies and/or technologies to minimize distractions at work, with the most popular policy of blocking access to Facebook and other websites unrelated to work.[5]

Psychologists have even created a term—Internet addiction disorder (IAD)—for the increasingly common addiction to web-based activity. Many children suffer from this disorder, especially in Asian countries like China, Taiwan, and South Korea. "Earlier research has found some changes in the brain of people who are hooked on the Web, and a new study shows reductions in volume of certain areas of the brain and in its white matter – the highways of connection between brain cells – of young people who are addicted to the Internet. What's interesting is that these brain changes mirror the ones in people who are addicted to other kinds of things, like heroin, for example."[6]

Understanding Individual and Group Communication Needs

Many top managers think they can remediate project delays simply by adding people to a project. Unfortunately, this approach often causes setbacks because of the increased complexity of communications. In his popular book *The Mythical Man-Month,* Frederick Brooks illustrates this concept very clearly. People are not interchangeable parts. You cannot assume that a task originally scheduled to take two months of one person's time can be done in one month by two people. A popular analogy is that you cannot take nine women and produce a baby in one month![7]

In addition to understanding that people are not interchangeable, it is also important to understand individuals' personal preferences for communications. People have different personality traits, which often affect their communication preferences. For example, if you want to praise a project team member for doing a good job, an introvert might be more comfortable receiving that praise in private, whereas an extrovert might like everyone to hear about his or her good work. An intuitive person might want to understand how something fits into the big picture, whereas a sensing person might prefer to have more focused, step-by-step details. A strong thinker might want to know the logic behind information, whereas a feeling person might want to know how the information affects him or her personally, as well as other people. Someone who is a judging person might be very driven to meet deadlines with few reminders, whereas a perceiving person might need more assistance in developing and following plans.

Geographic location and cultural backgrounds also add to the complexity of project communications. For example, if project stakeholders are in different countries, it is often difficult or impossible to schedule times for two-way communication during normal working hours. Language barriers can also cause communication problems—for example, the same word may have very different meanings in different languages. Times, dates, and other units of measure are also interpreted differently. People from some cultures also prefer to communicate in ways that may be uncomfortable to others. For example, managers in some countries still do not allow workers of lower ranks or women to give formal presentations.

The Impact of Team Size on Project Communications

Another important aspect of information distribution is the number of people involved in a project. As the number of people involved increases, the complexity of communications increases because there are more communications channels, or pathways, through which people can communicate. This is why Jeff was so concerned when Pat told him that instead of getting a few half-time clinical staff to work in Phase II she would get a large number of clinical staff, each committed to work just a few hours each.

To clarify this concept to Pat, Jeff went to the white board to draw out how channels of communications are driven by staff size, shown in Figure 7-14. He started with a project that has only two people on it, and showed that there is only one path where the two may communicate. If he adds 50% more people, going from two to three members, there are now three communications paths, raising the paths available by 300%. If he then doubles the three-person team to a six-person team, the number of paths increase by 500% as they grow to fifteen channels. Jeff said it is always easier to manage a smaller team of people, but sometimes project managers are not given a choice, and this was one of those times. They agreed that it would take more work to keep all resources aligned, but they could work together to coordinate the staff and still be successful.

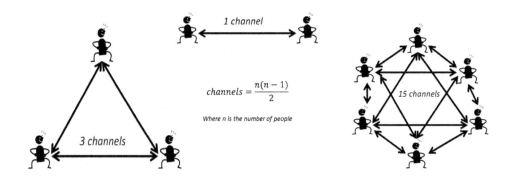

$$channels = \frac{n(n-1)}{2}$$

Where n is the number of people

Figure 7-14. Channels of communications

As Jeff described, the number of communication channels in relation to the number of people involved can be calculated as follows:

$$\text{number of communication channels} = \frac{n(n-1)}{2}$$

where n is the number of people involved.

The lesson is a simple one: If you want to enhance communications, you must consider the interactions among different project team members and stakeholders. It is often more effective to form several smaller teams within a large team and to then create an integrated work team that has representations from each of the smaller teams. The integrated work team would meet regularly to discuss how the work of each smaller team impacts the other teams as well as clarifying (and perhaps adjusting) the work boundaries between the teams. In essence the project is run as many smaller sub-projects, with the integrated work team serving to coordinate activities between the smaller sub-projects.

As you can see, information distribution involves more than creating and sending status reports or holding periodic meetings. Many good project managers know their personal strengths and weaknesses in this area and surround themselves with people who complement their skills. It is good practice to share the responsibility for project communications management with the entire project team.

Project Communications and Updating Business Processes

Getting project information to the right people at the right time and in a useful format is just as important as developing the information in the first place. The communications management plan prepared during project planning serves as a good starting point for project communications. During execution, project teams must address important considerations for creating and distributing project communication, as described previously. One of the outputs of managing communications is organizational process assets updates, such as improving business processes. The next chapter provides examples of work performance information, such as progress and status reports.

Sample Updates to Business Processes

Organizations have many different assets to help them improve business processes. Examples of these assets include various policies and procedures, guidelines, information systems, financial systems, management systems, lessons learned, and historical documents that help people understand, follow, and improve business processes.

As part of the VAPR project, Pat's Phase II team followed several existing business processes and provided new information to update some of them. For example, they used several communications media already well established at AHS, such as e-mail and project Web sites. Pat's team also used several new technologies to enhance communications and processes. Examples of these updated business processes include the following:

- Pat and her team used instant messaging and texting on a regular basis both within their team and with suppliers. One of the people working on the project was on the other side of the world, so they found it very useful to use instant messaging and texting. Their project management information system also included a team-messaging feature that they used extensively.

- AHS provided Webcast-type tools to allow the project team to meet virtually with suppliers and anyone not on site that day. In fact, because they had such a large campus (four hospitals, a remote data center, and over one hundred other buildings) they often used these tools to conduct meetings with their own internal staff. The Webcasts included visuals, such as PowerPoint slides, along with audio and animation to point to and write in key information. There were several other interactive features available in the Webcasts, such as polling the audience and letting other people add their audio input.

- The Web-based courses that suppliers were developing for the project included discussion threads and an "Ask the Expert" feature, in which learners could ask specific questions of the instructor or experts within the company on various topics related to the course. The questions and their answers were automatically added to a database that future learners could access. They also created several short videos to include in the system to address the most frequently asked questions.

- Pat and Jeff each maintained their own, personal, project blogs to document important events and lessons they were learning while managing the project. Pat had used blogs for communicating with her family in the past, such as documenting her last trip to Europe, but she had never used one in a work setting before, and Jeff had never used one at all. Pat found it very helpful for personal reflection and knew it would help her write her final lessons-learned document for the project, and Jeff thought that it was a good concept. They both agreed that no patient-identifying information, personnel-related information, project finance information, or other sensitive information would be posted to the blog. Although the blog was set up to be personal and only viewable by them, AHS' data security and privacy rules still prevailed.

The project steering committee—pleased and fascinated with the success of these new communications media—asked Jeff and Pat to prepare guidelines on how to effectively use these tools for other projects. They gladly agreed to do so, once the project was completed.

PROJECT STAKEHOLDER MANAGEMENT

As mentioned earlier, stakeholder management is now a separate knowledge area according to PMI. After identifying stakeholders and planning stakeholder management, project managers must manage stakeholder engagement during project execution. This process involves working with various project stakeholders to meet their needs and expectations, addressing stakeholder issues as they occur, and fostering engagement in project decisions and activities. The key benefit of managing stakeholder engagement, if done well, is that it allows the project manager to increase support and minimize resistance from stakeholders, significantly increasing the chances to achieve project success.

Managing Stakeholder Engagement

Many teachers are familiar with the term *engagement* as schools have emphasized the importance of engaging students to help them learn. Most teachers, especially in elementary and high schools, have their students in a room for most of the day, so they can easily see if students are engaged or not. If students are not coming to class, sleeping during class, chatting with classmates about unrelated subjects, texting or using technology for unrelated activities, or just looking bored or confused, teachers know the students are not engaged. Teacher training includes many ideas and hands-on experiences in engagement. Most classes start with some kind of ice-breaker so students and teachers can get to know each other. Several activities and exercises are built-into lesson plans to engage students.

Likewise, it is important for project managers to engage their stakeholders to help their projects succeed. Although project managers do not have project stakeholders in a room in front of them for a large portion of the day like teachers often do, they can take actions to manage stakeholder engagement. The stakeholder management plan should identify key stakeholders and describe strategies for managing relationships with them. It is easy to say that all project managers have to do is follow their plans, but managing stakeholder engagement, like managing student engagement, can be extremely difficult.

It is important to set the stage early that stakeholder engagement is expected and welcomed. A project manager's leadership and interpersonal skills are crucial in making that happen. It is also important to set expectations as to what level of engagement is required during different parts of the project. For example, stakeholders must be very engaged during planning, as that is when requirements and acceptance criteria are defined, schedules and budgets developed, etc. However, once the project execution begins, stakeholder engagement shifts based on the stakeholder's role. Stakeholders at the leadership level may serve on project oversight committees, while stakeholders at the user level may participate in user testing.

Key inputs to managing stakeholder engagement include the stakeholder management plan, communications management plan, change log, and organizational process assets. Important tools and techniques include communication methods, interpersonal skills, and management skills. Many of the outputs are similar to other knowledge areas, such as change requests and updates to the project management plan, project documents, and organizational process assets. A unique output of managing stakeholder engagement is an issue log.

Sample Issue Log

Many project managers keep an **issue log** to document, monitor, and track issues that need to be resolved for effective work to take place. An **issue** is a matter under question or dispute that could impede project success. Issues could include situations in which people disagree, situations that need more clarification or investigation, or general concerns that need to be addressed. It is important to acknowledge issues that can hurt team performance and take action to resolve them. There should be only one issue log, and it should always be kept up-to-date to avoid miscommunications.

Figure 7-15 shows part of an issue log that Jeff and Pat used to document and manage issues on their project. It includes columns for the issue number, the issue description, the impact of the issue on the project, the date the issue was reported, who reported the issue, who the issue resolution was assigned to, the priority of the issue (High, Medium, or Low), the due date to report back on the issue, the status of the issue, and comments related to the issue. Their project management software included an online issue log that could be sorted and filtered various ways. For example, Jeff always sorted issues by priority so that he could focus on high priorities. He also sorted them by who reported the issue and who was assigned to each issue to make sure that the appropriate people were making progress.

Issue Log as of August 5

Issue #	Issue Description	Impact on Project	Date Reported	Reported By	Assigned To	Priority (H/M/L)	Due Date	Status	Comments
1	HOB data from nursing documentation not valid except at shift change	IHI bundle requires this data. Can't deliver reports, or improve VAP rates if data is missing or wrong	Aug 2	Larry	Stan	H	Sep 2	Open	Stan working with Pat to resolve. Appears to be a problem with the way the nursing documentation input form was designed
2	Not all ICU doctors have iPads	May have to purchase 30-40 iPads to cover the remaining doctors. Max cost of $200k	Aug 5	Crystal	Danielle	M	Apr 15	Open	Do not need until just prior to training. Can push purchase into next fiscal year. Management wants iPad report delivery

Figure 7-15. Sample issue log

PROJECT PROCUREMENT MANAGEMENT

Many projects include work performed by outside sources. The main executing task performed as part of project procurement is conducting procurements. Key outputs include selected sellers, agreements or contract awards, resource calendars, change requests, and updates to the project management plan and project documents.

Conducting Procurements

After planning for procurements, the next procurement management process involves conducting procurements, which involves obtaining seller responses to proposals or bids, selecting sellers, and making agreements, often by awarding contracts. Prospective sellers do most of the work in this process by preparing their proposals and bids, normally at no cost to the buyer. The buying organization is responsible for deciding how to approach sellers and providing required procurement documents. These documents generally include a summary letter, a request for proposal or quote, and a contract statement of work, as described in Chapter 6. Documents created as part of conducting procurements include a qualified sellers list and contracts.

Organizations can use several different methods to approach and select qualified sellers or suppliers, depending on their type of organization, organizational policies, and complexity of the work being procured. Before choosing a method, project managers need to understand their own organization's procurement policies. The methods include:

- *Approaching a preferred supplier:* Sometimes, a specific supplier might be the number-one choice for the buyer. In this case, the buyer gives procurement information to just that company. If the preferred supplier responds favorably, the organizations proceed to work together. Many organizations have formed good working relationships with certain suppliers, so they want to continue working with them.

- *Approaching several qualified suppliers:* In many cases, several suppliers could meet an organization's procurement needs. The buying organization can send procurement information to those potential sellers and then evaluate the results. If it does not get the desired response, the buyer can either expand its list of potential sellers until it gets the desired response or revise its procurement plans.

- *Advertising to many potential suppliers:* In many cases, several suppliers may be qualified to provide the goods and services, and the buyer may not know who they are in advance. Advertising the procurement and receiving proposals and bids from multiple sources often takes advantage of the competitive business environment. Increased globalization and virtual project teams have increased tremendously as organizations find suitable sellers around the globe. As a result of pursuing a competitive bidding strategy, the buyer can receive better goods and services than expected at a lower price.

Sample Qualified Seller List

The VAPR project required goods and services for only one part of the project—creating the CBT that describes the new ventilator protocols for clinicians. Recall that AHS had a preferred vendor (TechTalk) for online training services, but that supplier was not available during the timeframe required for the project. They developed a short qualified sellers list, as provided in Figure 7-16.

Ventilator Associated Pneumonia Reduction Project
Qualified Sellers List
September 9

Seller Name/ Web Site	Areas of Expertise	Staff (FTE)	Reputation
Greek Geeks greek-geeks.com	E-learning, custom course development, higher education course development (curriculum, video, exams, grading, forums).	18	Very good reputation, but mainly within the higher education market where they do 70% of their work. Higher price per hour than all others.
All About Training (AAT) aat.com	E-learning, custom course development, department of defense focus.	35	Has many partnerships with other companies, prices higher than TechTalk, but AAT has more flexibility due to larger staff size.
TechTalk techtalk.com	E-learning, custom course development	9	Very small firm but well respected by customers. Long time vendor of choice by AHS.

Figure 7-16. Sample qualified sellers list

After buyers receive proposals or bids, organizations can select a supplier or decide to cancel the procurement. Selecting suppliers or sellers, often called source selection, involves evaluating proposals or bids from sellers, choosing the best one, negotiating the contract, and awarding the contract. Several stakeholders in the procurement process should be involved in selecting the best suppliers for the project. Often, teams of people are responsible for evaluating various sections of the proposals. There might be a technical team, a management team, and a cost team to focus on each of those major areas. Frequently buyers will develop a **short list** of the top three to five suppliers to reduce the work involved in selecting a source. Reviewers often follow a more detailed proposal evaluation process for sellers who make the short list, often checking their references, requesting special presentations, or having them provide sample products. Recall that a weighted scoring model is often used to help select sellers.

It is customary to conduct contract negotiations during the source selection process. Sellers on the short list are often asked to prepare a best and final offer (BAFO). Expert negotiators often conduct these negotiations, especially for contracts involving large amounts of money. In addition, senior managers from both buying and selling organizations often meet before making final decisions. The final output of the seller selection process is a contract. It is also appropriate on some projects to prepare a contract management plan to describe details about how the contract will be managed.

Sample Agreement or Contract

As mentioned in Chapter 6, a contract is a mutually binding agreement that obligates the seller to provide the specified products or services, and obligates the buyer to pay for them. The VAPR project would include contracts with just one supplier based on their plans. Projects may have many contracts, and each contract may vary greatly from the others.

Some contracts might be short, fixed-price contracts, while others might be much longer and involve fixed-price, cost-reimbursable, and unit-pricing aspects. The VAPR project is only using a short, fixed-price contract, but they could have also contracted out the entire project, which would have resulted in a more complex procurement.

Figure 7-17 provides a sample of part of a contract or service agreement, as some contracts are called. Note the reference to exhibit A, the statement of work. (A sample was provided in Chapter 6 and sent out to prospective sellers as part of the procurement package.) This document should be modified based on the selected seller's proposal. There is also a reference to a schedule for the work, which the seller also prepared as part of the proposal. It is good practice to include a detailed statement of work and schedule as part of the contract to clarify exactly what work the seller will perform and when.

Academic Health Systems
Service Agreement
August 10

Title of Work: Online Training Program for VAP Clinical Workflows

This is an Agreement made as of _____ by Greek Geeks, 2255 River Road, Boston, MA (the "Seller"), and Academic Health Systems, 4300 Medical Parkway, Providence, RI (the "Buyer").

THE SELLER AND THE BUYER AGREE THAT:

1. The Work: The Seller will create the Work as set forth in Exhibit A hereto. The Buyer will provide the Seller with the format and specifications in which each element of the Work is to be submitted. The Seller agrees to conform to such format and specifications.

2. Delivery of the Work: The Seller agrees to deliver to the Buyer the Work in form and content acceptable to the Buyer on or before the dates outlined in Exhibit B of this Agreement, time being of the essence to the Buyer.

3. Right to Terminate: If the Seller materially departs from the agreed-upon schedule or if the Work is not satisfactory to the Buyer (based on reviews of drafts, market conditions, and/or other criteria as determined by the Buyer), the Buyer may at its option:

    A. Allow the Seller to finish, correct, or improve the Work by a date specified by the Buyer;

    B. Terminate this Agreement by giving written notice to the Seller.

4. Payments: The Buyer will pay the Seller a fixed price of $11,200 upon accepted completion of the Work.

5. Exhibit: The following Exhibit is hereby incorporated by reference into this Agreement:

    Exhibit A: Statement of Work

    Exhibit B: Schedule

IN WITNESS WHEREOF, THE PARTIES HERETO HAVE EXECUTED THIS Agreement as a sealed instrument as of the date first above written.

	Academic Health Systems	Greek Geeks
By:	_____	_____
Date	_____	_____

Figure 7-17. Sample agreement or contract

CASE WRAP-UP

Jeff and Pat collaborated while leading their two project teams, one for each phase, as they executed the work to complete the VAPR project. Like most project managers, however, they faced several challenges. For example, it was hard for Pat to confront Nick about getting the training work done on time. However, after she took Jeff's advice about confronting him directly, the problem was quickly resolved. Jeff and his team also had to determine how to address the incorrect data coming out of the nursing documentation system for head of bed (HOB) settings. Jeff consulted with Pat in on this problem once he had exhausted all technology causes, and she quickly found the root cause of the problem.

Both Pat and Jeff were happy with the way they, and their teams, were working together on the project objectives and how they used the skills and experiences of each other when needed. The team was motivated to deliver a high quality product that would improve patient care, and everyone understood the importance of the data, the reports, the workflow, and even the training program being both accurate and complete.

There was no one playing the hero. Everyone was working as a well-oiled team.

CHAPTER SUMMARY

Good execution is crucial to project success. Without it, the products, services, and results planned from the project cannot materialize. This chapter summarizes the executing processes and key outputs for project integration, quality, human resource, communications, and procurement management.

Executing outputs related to integration management include deliverables, implemented solutions to problems, work performance data, change requests, project management plan updates, and project document updates.

Executing outputs related to quality management change requests, project management plan updates, project document updates, and organizational process assets updates. Quality assurance techniques include benchmarking, quality audits, and cause and effect diagrams.

The human resource management processes project managers perform during execution include acquiring, developing, and managing the project team. Key outputs include project staff assignments, resource calendars, team performance assessments, change requests, and updates to the project management plan, enterprise environmental factors, project documents, and organizational process assets. Project managers must also apply concepts related to motivation, influence, effectiveness, resource loading, and resource leveling to lead people during project execution.

Executing outputs related to communications management include project communications and updates to project documents, the project management plan, and organizational process assets. Project managers must apply important communications concepts, such as formal and informal communications, nonverbal communications, the appropriate communications medium, individual and group communication needs, and the impact of team size on project communications.

Executing outputs related to procurement management include selected sellers, agreements, resource calendars, change requests, and updates to the project management plan and project documents.

Samples of several executing outputs are provided for the VAPR project.

QUICK QUIZ

1. *Fortune* magazine summarized research showing that the main reason CEOs failed was due to _____.

   A. poor planning

   B. poor execution

   C. global competition

   D. low stock prices

2. Which of the following is not an example of a soft skill?

   A. leadership

   B. motivation

   C. team building

   D. financial analysis

3. Most project sponsors would say that the most important output of any project is _____.

   A. a satisfied customer/sponsor

   B. good financial results

   C. its deliverables

   D. good plans

4. Which of the following conflict handling modes do successful project managers use most often?

   A. confrontation

   B. compromise

   C. smoothing

   D. forcing

5. _____ includes all of the activities related to satisfying the relevant quality standards for a project.

   A. Quality assurance

   B. Quality control

   C. Customer satisfaction

   D. ISO certification

6. _____ diagrams can assist in ensuring and improving quality by finding the root causes of quality problems.

    A. Pareto, or Ishikawa

    B. Mind map

    C. Fishbone, or Ishikawa

    D. Social styles

7. Which of the following statements is false?

    A. The highest need in Maslow's pyramid is called self-actualization.

    B. Most people today prefer managers who follow Theory X versus Theory Y.

    C. Herzberg distinguished between motivating and hygiene factors.

    D. Projects are more likely to succeed when project managers influence team members by using work challenge and expertise.

8. Some project managers like to assess team performance by using a technique known as MBWA, which stands for _____.

    A. management by wondering aloud

    B. management by wandering around

    C. measuring by work areas

    D. measuring by watching alertly

9. If a project team goes from three people to six, how many more communications channels are there?

    A. 3

    B. 6

    C. 9

    D. 12

10. Buyers often develop a _____ of the top three to five suppliers to reduce the work involved in selecting a source.

    A. short list

    B. weighted decision matrix

    C. qualified sellers list

    D. BAFO

Quick Quiz Answers

1. B; 2. D; 3. C; 4. A; 5. A; 6. C; 7. B; 8. B; 9. D; 10. A

DISCUSSION QUESTIONS

1.   Describe practices that should be followed in directing and managing project execution. Why are deliverables such an important output of project execution? What are some of the typical problems that project teams face during project execution?

2.   What is quality assurance, and how does it affect project execution? What are tools and techniques used in performing quality assurance? How did Kristin's team use one of these tools to help improve quality?

3.   Why is human resource management so important during project execution? How does Maslow's hierarchy of needs affect motivation? What are some examples of motivators and hygiene factors, according to Herzberg? What are the three main categories in McClelland's acquired-needs theory? What is the difference between Theory X and Theory Y? What are the five steps in Tuckman's team-building model?

4.   What are the advantages of resource leveling?

5.   Why is communications management so important during project execution? What is the difference between formal and informal communications? Why are nonverbal communications so important?

6.   Why do communications become more complicated when team size increases?

7.   What is stakeholder engagement? What can project managers do to engage stakeholders? Can they use any techniques that your teachers have used to engage students in classes? Why or why not?

8.   What is involved in conducting procurements? How do project teams develop a list of qualified sellers? What are some of the main topics addressed in a contract or agreement?

EXERCISES

Note: These exercises can be done individually or in teams, in-class, as homework, or in a virtual environment. Learners can either write their results in a paper or prepare a short presentation or video to show their results.

1.   Find an example of a large healthcare project that took more than a year to complete. Describe some of the tasks performed to execute the integration, quality, human resource, communications, and procurement aspects of the project. Summarize your findings.

2.   Assume that you are working on a one-year project that involves about 20 team members and many different stakeholders working across the globe. Even though your team created a communications management plan and you have all types of communication technologies available, everyone knows that communications is a problem. Create a cause and effect diagram to identify potential root causes of the communications problems. You can use the cause and effect diagram template or create the diagram by hand or using other software. Be creative in your response.

3.   Take the Myers-Briggs Type Indicator (MBTI) test and research information on this tool. There are several Web sites that have different versions of the test available free, such as *www.humanmetrics.com*, *www.personalitytype.com*, and *www.keirsey.com*. Document your results and your opinion of using this test as a team-building tool. Be sure to summarize and cite at least two references related to using it in team-building on projects, highlighting pros and cons.

4.   Review the following scenarios, and then describe what communications media you think would be most appropriate to use, and why.

    a.   Many of the technical workers on the project come in between 9:30 and 10:00 a.m., while the business users always come in before 9:00 a.m. The business users have been making comments. The project manager wants the technical staff to come in by 9:00 a.m., although many of them leave late.

    b.   Your company is bidding on a project for the entertainment industry. You know that you need new ideas on how to put together the proposal and communicate your approach in a way that will impress the customer.

    c.   Your business has been growing successfully, but you are becoming inundated with phone calls and e-mails asking similar types of questions.

    d.   You need to make a general announcement to a large group of people and want to make sure they get the information.

5.   Develop your own scenarios for when it would be appropriate to use each of the six conflict-handling modes discussed in this chapter (confrontation, compromise, smoothing, forcing, withdrawal, and collaborating). Be creating in presenting your ideas.

6.   Watch the YouTube video by RSA Animate about Daniel Pink's views on motivation. (See the link on healthcarepm.com or search for it on youtube.com.) Discuss the video with at least two of your classmates and then summarize your observations and opinions.

7.   Find at least three videos and/or articles related to engaging people in a work setting, preferably in healthcare. What are some of the common challenges managers face in engaging workers and other stakeholders? What techniques can be useful in improving stakeholder engagement on projects? Summarize your findings.

TEAM PROJECTS

Note: These team projects can be in-class, as homework, or in a virtual environment. Learners can either write their results in a paper or prepare a short presentation or video to show their results.

1.   Your organization initiated a project to raise money for an important charity. Assume that there are 1,000 people in your organization. Also, assume that you have six months to raise as much money as possible, with a goal of $100,000. List three problems that could arise while executing the project. Describe each problem in detail, and then develop realistic approaches to solving them. Be creative in your responses, and reference ideas discussed in this chapter. Remember that this project is run solely by volunteers.

2.   You are part of a team in charge of a project to help people in your company (500 people) lose weight. This project is part of a competition, and the top "losers" will be featured in a popular television show. Assume that you have six months to complete the project and a budget of $10,000. You are halfway through the project, and morale is very low. People are also complaining about a lack of communication and support on the project. Although many people have been participating and have lost weight, many have plateaued or started gaining weight back. Identify four strategies you can implement to improve morale and communications, referencing some of the theories discussed in this chapter.

3.   Using the information you developed in Team Project 1 or 2, role-play a meeting to brainstorm and develop strategies for solving problems with key stakeholders. Determine who will play what role (project manager, team member from a certain department, senior managers, and so on). Be creative in displaying different personalities (a senior manager who questions the importance of the project to the organization, a team member who is very shy or obnoxious).

4.   Perform the executing tasks for one of the case studies provided in Appendix B. (Note: Your instructor might select just a few of these tasks as they can be very time-consuming.) If you are working on a real team project, perform the applicable executing tasks for that project. Remember to address common problems, focus on deliverables, and practice good soft skills.

5.   As you are executing your team project, document the top three problems you have experienced and how you are dealing with them.

KEY TERMS

benchmarking — The process of generating ideas for quality improvements by comparing specific project practices or product characteristics to those of other projects or products within or outside of the performing organization.

cause-and-effect diagrams — Also called fishbone or Ishikawa diagrams, these diagrams can assist in ensuring and improving quality by finding the root causes of quality problems.

collaborating mode — The conflict-handling mode where decision makers incorporate different viewpoints and insights to develop consensus and commitment.

compromise mode — The conflict-handling mode that uses a give-and-take approach to resolve conflicts.

confrontation mode — The conflict-handling mode that involves directly facing a conflict using a problem-solving approach that allows affected parties to work through their disagreements.

empathic listening — The process of listening with the intent to understand by putting yourself in the shoes of the other person.

extrinsic motivation — A motivation that causes people to do something for a reward or to avoid a penalty.

forcing mode — The conflict-handling mode that involves exerting one's viewpoint at the potential expense of another viewpoint.

groupthink — The conformance to the values or ethical standards of a group.

intrinsic motivation — A motivation that causes people to participate in an activity for their own enjoyment.

issue — a matter under question or dispute that could impede project success.

issue log — a tool used to document, monitor, and track issues that need to be resolved for effective work to take place.

Maslow's hierarchy of needs — A hierarchy that states that people's behaviors are guided or motivated by a sequence of needs (physiological, safety, social, esteem, and self-actualization).

mirroring — The matching of certain behaviors of the other person.

Myers-Briggs Type Indicator (MBTI) — A popular tool for determining personality preferences.

overallocation — When more resources than are available are assigned to perform work at a given time.

quality assurance — The activities related to satisfying the relevant quality standards for a project.

quality audit — A structured review of specific quality management activities that helps identify lessons learned, which could improve performance on current or future projects.

rapport — A relationship of harmony, conformity, accord, or affinity.

resource leveling — A technique for resolving resource conflicts by delaying tasks.

resource loading — The amount of individual resources an existing schedule requires during specific time periods.

short list — A list of the top three to five suppliers created to reduce the work involved in selecting a source.

smoothing mode — The conflict-handling mode that de-emphasizes or avoids areas of differences and emphasizes areas of agreement.

synergy — The concept that the whole is equal to more than the sum of its parts.

Tuckman model — A model that describes five stages of team development (forming, storming, norming, performing, and adjourning).

withdrawal mode — The conflict-handling mode that involves retreating or withdrawing from an actual or potential disagreement.

END NOTES

[1]Joe Flower, *Healthcare Beyond Reform: Doing It Right for Half the Cost*, Productivity Press, p. 3 (2013).

[2]Parrack, Dave, "Google receives record number of applications – 75,000 people for 6,000 jobs," Tech.blorge (February 7, 2011).

[3]Fortune, 100 Best Companies to Work For (2013).

[4]Leslie Caccamese, "Trends from the 2013 Fortune 100 Best Companies to Work For: Focus on the Future" (2013).

[5]Nerny, Chris, "Survey: Facebook and Twitter hurt work productivity," IT World (May 20, 2011).

[6]Walton, Alice G. "Internet Addiction Shows Up in the Brain," Forbes (January 17, 2012).

[7]Frederick Brooks, *The Mythical Man-Month,* Addison-Wesley Professional (1995).

Chapter 8
Monitoring and Controlling Projects

LEARNING OBJECTIVES
After reading this chapter, you will be able to:
• List several processes and outputs of project monitoring and controlling, and describe outputs common to all knowledge areas
• Discuss monitoring and controlling project work and performing integration change control as part of project integration management and how to use earned value management
• Explain the importance of validating and controlling scope
• Describe the schedule control process and schedule performance measurement tools, such as tracking Gantt charts
• Discuss tools and techniques to assist in cost control
• List the Seven Basic Tools of Quality, and provide examples of how they assist in performing quality control
• Summarize methods for controlling communications
• Discuss different approaches to controlling stakeholder engagement
• Describe the process of controlling risks
• Explain how to control procurements

OPENING CASE

Jeff and Pat worked closely with the project steering committee to monitor and control the Ventilator Associated Pneumonia Reduction (VAPR) project. They knew that the steering committee was keeping a watchful eye on this project to ensure that it met its objectives and also addressed changing business needs, especially since the project required two phases that would have to be tightly integrated. They were also excited, but somewhat concerned, about having a nurse run Phase II as in the past someone from IT ran most internal system projects.

There were also rumors surfacing that the Institute for Healthcare Improvement (IHI), the publisher of the Ventilator Bundle AHS was adopting, was getting pressure from the healthcare community to modify the bundle based on new research.

At their weekly meetings, Jeff, Pat, and their teams provided performance information and discussed changes that were required. Jeff and Pat would then attend the steering committee meetings to provide a face-to-face opportunity for committee members to ask more details about the published status reports. The steering committee asked Pat to have the online training provider send a representative to the status meetings during the part of the project when they were doing work. The vendor would not serve as a member of the committee, but would be present to provide details on their work.

INTRODUCTION

Monitoring and controlling involves regularly measuring progress to ensure that the project is meeting its objectives and addressing current business needs. The project manager and other staff monitor progress against plans and take corrective action when necessary. This chapter summarizes the main tasks involved in monitoring and controlling projects and provides examples of key outputs from this process group for the VAPR project.

SUMMARY OF MONITORING AND CONTROLLING PROCESSES AND OUTPUTS

Figure 8-1 summarizes processes and outputs of project monitoring and controlling by knowledge area, based on the *PMBOK® Guide, Fifth Edition.* Notice that every knowledge area except project human resource management is included. Also note that several knowledge areas include similar outputs that have been discussed in earlier chapters, such as change requests and updates to the project management plan, project documents, and organizational process assets.

Knowledge area	Monitoring and controlling process	Outputs
Project integration management	Monitor and control project work	Change requests Work performance reports Project management plan updates Project document updates
	Perform integrated change control	Approved change requests Change log Project management plan updates Project documents updates
Project scope management	Validate scope	Accepted deliverables Change requests Work performance information Project document updates
	Control scope	Work performance information Change requests Project management plan updates Project documents updates Organizational process assets updates
Project time management	Control schedule	Work performance information Schedule forecasts Change requests Project management plan updates Project documents updates Organizational process assets updates
Project cost management	Control cost	Work performance information Cost forecasts Change requests Project management plan updates Project documents updates Organizational process assets updates
Project quality management	Control quality	Quality control measurements Validated changes Verified deliverables Work performance information Change requests Project management plan updates Project documents updates Organizational process assets updates

Knowledge area	Monitoring and controlling process	Outputs
Project communications management	Control communications	Work performance information Change requests Project documents updates Organizational process assets updates
Project stakeholder management	Control stakeholder engagement	Work performance information Change requests Project documents updates Organizational process assets updates
Project risk management	Control risks	Work performance information Change requests Project management plan updates Project documents updates Organizational process assets updates
Project procurement management	Control procurements	Work performance information Change requests Project management plan updates Project documents updates Organizational process assets updates

Figure 8-1. Monitoring and controlling processes and outputs

PROJECT INTEGRATION MANAGEMENT

The main monitoring and controlling tasks performed as part of project integration management include monitoring and controlling project work and performing integrated change control. These are crucial tasks that must be done well to ensure project success.

Monitoring and Controlling Project Work

Project changes are inevitable, so it is important to develop and follow a process to monitor and control them. Monitoring and controlling project work includes collecting, measuring, and disseminating performance information. It also involves assessing measurements and analyzing trends to determine what process improvements can be made. The project team should continuously monitor project performance to assess the overall health of the project and identify areas that require special attention.

The project management plan, performance reports, enterprise environmental factors, and organizational process assets are all important inputs for monitoring and controlling project work. The main tools and techniques include expert judgment, project management information systems, meetings, and analytical techniques, such as earned value management. Work performance reports are a key output, and they often include earned value information, described in the next section. More information on performance reports is provided later in this chapter under project communications.

Forecasting with Earned Value Management

Earned value management (EVM) is a project performance measurement technique that integrates scope, time, and cost data. Given a baseline, project managers and their teams can determine how well the project is meeting scope, time, and cost goals by entering actual information and then comparing it to the baseline. As defined in Chapter 4, a baseline is a starting point, a measurement, or an observation that is documented so that it can be used for future comparison.

In earned value management, a baseline includes the following:

- Scope (WBS tasks)

- Time (start and finish estimates for each task)

- Cost information (cost estimates for each task)

Actual information includes whether or not a WBS deliverable was completed or approximately how much of the work was completed; when the work actually started and ended; and how much it actually cost to do the completed work. Some project teams do not define work using a WBS or have cost estimates for each task. Some project teams do not periodically enter actuals for scope, time, and cost information. If you do not have a good baseline or actual information, you cannot use earned value management.

In the past, earned value management was primarily used on large government projects. Today, however, more and more companies are realizing the value of using this tool to help control projects. Most project management software products, including Microsoft Project 2013, provide tables and reports for entering and viewing earned value information. See Appendix A for detailed instructions on using this software for earned value management.

Earned value management involves calculating three values for each activity, summary activity, or work package from a project's WBS.

1. The **planned value (PV)** is that portion of the approved total cost estimate planned to be spent on an activity during a given period. The cost baseline for the VAPR project included $22,080 to be spent on identifying the systems that would contain the clinical data required to identify whether or not the IHI Ventilator Bundle was being followed. The work package, identified as *AHS VAP Bundle Data Sources*, included forty-six days (about two months) of work by Larry for a total cost of $22,080. Therefore the planned value (PV) for that activity for those two months would be $22,080.

2. The **actual cost (AC)** is the total direct and indirect costs incurred in accomplishing work on an activity during a given period. For example, suppose it actually took forty-six days, but cost only $21,000, to identify the data

sources because the fringe benefit rate dropped, or because we used a slightly less expensive resource to complete the work. The actual cost (AC) for the work package would therefore be $21,000.

3.   The **earned value (EV)** is an estimate of the value of the physical work actually completed. It is based on the original planned costs for the activity and the rate at which the team is completing work on the activity to date. The **rate of performance (RP)** is the percentage of actual work completed divided by the percentage of work planned to have been completed at any given time. For example, for the identify data sources work package discussed above, suppose it is only half completed by the end of the two month period, when it should have been totally completed. The rate of performance for that activity would be 50%. However, in our example, the work package was totally completed at the end of the period, as planned, so the RP is 100%. Because the PV was $22,080, the EV would also be $22,080. Note that you cannot earn more work (EV) for a given *activity* (or *work package, or project*) than was planned (PV), although you may earn more work for a given *period* than was planned by doing work planned for future periods early.

In the above three examples of PV, AC, and EV the work package was planned to take eight weeks to complete. Generally speaking *activities* should take between eight and eighty hours (known as the *8/80 Rule*), primarily to assist the project manager with more closely managing the work. For work packages, which consist of multiple activities such as our example above, there is no such restriction. For tracking purposes, however, work packages are generally less than sixty days in duration.

Figure 8-2 summarizes the general formulas used in earned value management. Note that all of the formulas for variances and indexes start with EV, the earned value. Variances are calculated by subtracting the actual cost or planned value from EV, and indexes are calculated by dividing EV by the actual cost or planned value. You can use the indexes to help forecast what the project will cost when completed (the Estimate At Completion, or EAC) and when the project will finish, the Estimated Time to Complete.

You can use earned value management at either a detailed or a summary level. In other words, you can use a detailed WBS and its associated time and cost data (using level four, five, or whatever is the most detailed), or you can apply earned value at a higher WBS level, such as level two or three. Indeed, you may even use EVM all the way down to the activity level or all the way up to a phase or project level.

Term	Formula
Rate of Performance (RP)	RP $= percentage\ of\ work\ actually\ completed$ $/percentage\ of\ work\ planned\ to\ have\ been\ completed$
Earned Value (EV)	EV = PV × RP (or the summation of all work completed)
Cost Variance (CV)	$CV = EV - AC$
Schedule Variance (SV)	$SV = EV - PV$
Cost Performance Index (CPI)	$CPI = \dfrac{EV}{AC}$
Schedule Performance Index (SPI)	$SPI = \dfrac{EV}{PV}$
Estimate At Completion (EAC)	$EAC = \dfrac{BAC}{CPI}$
Estimated Time to Complete	$\dfrac{Original\ Time\ Estimate}{SPI}$

Figure 8-2. Earned value formulas

Figure 8-3 summarizes the earned value information and also computes the cost and schedule variance and the cost and schedule performance indexes for the VAPR project task for course development for the *AHS VAP Bundle Date Sources* work package.

Term	Formula	Calculation	Value
Earned Value (EV)	n/a	n/a	$22,080
Planned Value (PV)	n/a	n/a	$22,080
Actual Cost (AC)	n/a	n/a	$21,000
Cost Variance	EV–AC	$22,080 − $21,000	+$1,080
Schedule Variance (SV)	EV–PV	$22,080 − $22,080	$0
Cost Performance Index (CPI)	$\dfrac{EV}{AC}$	$\dfrac{\$22,080}{\$21,000}$	1.05
Schedule Performance Index (SPI)	$\dfrac{EV}{PV}$	$\dfrac{\$22,080}{\$22,080}$	1.00

Figure 8-3. Earned value calculations for one work package

Earned value calculations for all project activities that are planned to date are required to estimate the earned value for the entire project. Some activities may be over budget or behind schedule, whereas others may be under budget and ahead of schedule. By adding all of the earned values for all project activities, you can determine how the project as a whole is performing and forecast both when it will be completed and how much it will cost at completion.

> **Note:** In general, negative numbers (i.e. -$1,000) for cost and schedule variance indicate problems in those areas. Negative numbers mean the activity/project is costing more than planned (over budget) or taking longer than planned (behind schedule). Positive numbers (i.e. $1,000) mean it is under budget or ahead of schedule, and $0 means it is right on target. Likewise, CPI and SPI less than one indicate problems. The indices (CPI and SPI) are normally very close to 1, such as .84, .93, 1.02, 1.14, etc., as an index indicates a ratio.

The **budget at completion (BAC)**, or the approved total budget for the project, can be divided by the cost performance index to calculate a new **estimate at completion (EAC)**, which is a forecast of how much the project will cost upon completion based on current conditions. Likewise, the approved time estimate for the project can be divided by the schedule performance index to calculate when the project will be completed. Earned value, therefore, provides an excellent way to monitor project performance and provide forecasts based on performance to date.

Sample Forecast Using an Earned Value Chart

You can graph earned value information to track project performance and to forecast when it will be completed and for how much. Figure 8-4a shows an earned value chart for a project that has larger and simpler variances than VAPR's to make the chart easier to read. Figure 8-4b includes the calculations use to plot the various points on the chart.

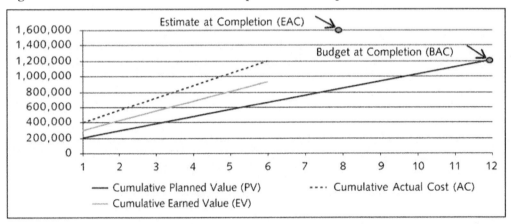

Figure 8-4a. Sample earned value chart

Term	Formula	Calculation	Value
Earned Value (EV)	n/a	n/a	$900,000
Planned Value (PV)	n/a	n/a	$600,000
Actual Cost (AC)	n/a	n/a	$1,200,000
Cost Variance (CV)	EV – AC	$900k-$1200k	-$300,000
Schedule Variance (SV)	EV – PV	$900k-$600k	$300,000
Cost Performance Index (CPI)	$\dfrac{EV}{AC}$	$\dfrac{\$900k}{\$1200k}$	0.75
Schedule Performance Index (SPI)	$\dfrac{EV}{PV}$	$\dfrac{\$900k}{\$600k}$	1.50
New Estimate at Completion (EAC)	$\dfrac{BAC}{CPI}$	$\dfrac{\$1200k}{0.75}$	$1,600,000
New Time Estimate	$\dfrac{OrigTimeEstimate}{SPI}$	$\dfrac{12\ months}{1.50}$	8 months

Figure 8-4b. Sample earned value chart calculations

The budget at completion is $1.2 million for this one-year project. The BAC point on the chart, therefore, is at 12 months and $1.2 million. Based on data for months one through six, an earned value chart was created. In this example, the planned value is $100,000 for each month, so the cumulative planned value at month six is $600,000. The earned value is $150,000 each month, with the cumulative earned value at month six of $900,000. (The project has completed 50% more work than expected at this point in the project). The actual cost is $200,000 each month, with the cumulative actual cost at month six of $1,200,000. (The project has spent 200% more than expected at this point in the project). You can also forecast when the project will be completed and what its final cost will be based on this information.

Notice that the new EAC point is provided on the chart in Figure 8-4a at eight months and at the cost of $1,600,000. Viewing earned value information in chart form helps you visualize how the project has been performing and forecasts both the end date and the total cost. You can see the planned performance for the life of the project by looking at the planned value line. If the project goes exactly as planned, it will finish in twelve months and cost $1,200,000, as represented by the original BAC point. Notice in the example that the actual cost line is always above the earned value line, which indicates that the project is spending more than planned for the work being completed. For example, it may have spent $100 to complete only $80 worth of work. Furthermore, the planned value line in this example is always below the earned value line, which indicates that the project has been ahead of schedule the first six months. The forecasted completion date, therefore, is earlier than planned while the forecasted total cost is higher than planned. By reviewing all three lines, it is evident the project is ahead of schedule but spending much more money than required for the work being completed.

If there are serious cost and schedule performance variations, management may decide to terminate projects or take other corrective action. In the above example, management might decide to continue spending more to finish the project early, or they might decide to slow down and use less expensive resources to save money. The estimate at completion (EAC) is an important input to budget decisions, especially if total funds are limited. Earned value management is an important technique because when used effectively, it helps in evaluating progress and making sound management decisions.

Best Practice

The Centers for Medicare & Medicaid Services (CMS) believe that earned value management an important tool for project managers. CMS manages approximately twenty percent of the entire Federal budget, so it is important that they use the taxpayers' dollars as efficiently and effectively as possible. CMS suggests the following best practices for using earned value management:

- Define strong work packages
- Choose measures of earned value wisely
- Conduct integrated baseline reviews
- Control changes to the performance measurement baseline (PMB) and document them
- Provide both graphic and numeric depictions of earned value management metrics
- Analyze, report on, and act on variances monthly

"Once an investment—with its individual projects—is approved for funding, it falls to the investment manager and the project managers to insure that the projects are implemented successfully. Earned value monitoring and management provides early warning when a project is straying from its baseline plan, and shows whether actions taken to correct the situation are effective. Health and Human Services (HHS) requires that certain investments track and report on cost and schedule status monthly."[1]

Integrated Change Control

Integrated change control involves identifying, evaluating, and managing changes throughout the project's life cycle. The three main objectives of integrated change control are as follows:

1. *Influencing the factors that cause changes to ensure that changes are beneficial*: Changes can often be good for a project, so it is important to let everyone know that and focus on promoting changes that are beneficial. For example, changes that improve quality, reduce costs, save time, or improve stakeholder relationships are beneficial.

2. *Determining that a change has occurred*: To determine that a change has occurred, project managers must know the status of key project areas at all times. In addition, they must communicate significant changes to senior management and key stakeholders, who normally do not like surprises—especially

unpleasant ones. The types of changes that might occur could be an alteration or variation to the scope of work, a deviation or departure in a work product or deliverable from established requirements, or a trend or non-random variance of actual project performance from the plan. All project changes should be documented in a **change log**, including a brief description of the change, its effect on project constraints, and if the change is approved or not.

3. *Managing actual changes as they occur.* Managing change is a key role of project managers and their teams. It is important that project managers exercise discipline in managing the project to help control the number of changes that occur. Managers should focus on achieving project goals rather than putting out fires.

The project management plan provides the baseline for identifying and controlling project changes as follows:

- A section of the plan describes the work to be performed on a project, including key deliverables for the project and quality requirements.

- The schedule section of the plan lists the planned dates for completing key deliverables.

- The budget section provides the planned cost for these deliverables.

The project team must focus on delivering the work as planned. If the project team or someone else causes significant changes during project execution, project managers must formally revise the project management plan and have it approved by the project sponsor.

PROJECT SCOPE MANAGEMENT

The main monitoring and controlling tasks performed as part of project scope management are validating scope and controlling scope. Key outputs are deliverables that are accepted by the customer and work performance information. It is difficult to create a good project scope statement and WBS. It is often even more difficult to validate the project scope and minimize scope changes. Some project teams know from the start that the scope is very unclear and that they must work closely with the project customer to design and produce various deliverables. Some project teams use an agile approach in this type of environment, as described in Chapter 3. For all types of projects and approaches to managing them, it is important to develop and follow a process for scope validation that meets unique project needs. Careful procedures must be developed to ensure that customers are getting what they want and that the project team has enough time and money to produce the desired products and services.

Even when the project scope is well defined, many projects suffer from scope creep. Even for fairly simple projects, people have a tendency to want more. How many people do you know, for example, who said they wanted a simple wedding or a basic new house constructed, only to end up with many more extras than they initially planned? In contrast, some projects also suffer from *not* delivering the minimum scope due to time or cost issues. A couple may have planned to go on a luxurious honeymoon until they saw how much the wedding cost, or a new homeowner may have settled for an unfinished basement in order to move in on time. These scenarios are similar to those faced by a project manager who must deal with balancing the constraints of scope, time, cost, resources, and risk, among others, for much larger and more complex projects than a wedding or a new home.

Validating Scope

Scope validation involves formal acceptance of the completed project deliverables by the project customer or designated stakeholders. This acceptance is often achieved through customer inspection and then documented by a sign-off on key deliverables. To receive formal acceptance of the project scope, the project team must develop clear documentation of the project's products and procedures, which the appropriate stakeholders can then evaluate for completeness as well as determine their satisfaction with the results. For example, part of the scope of Pat's project phase was to develop the new workflows based on the IHI Ventilator Bundle. As part of scope validation, the project steering committee asked that the Medical Executive Committee, Quality Council, and Clinical Workflow Council all review and approve the workflow changes prior to creating the training program. Once these three groups review the workflows and approve them, they are considered to be accepted deliverables. Scope planning documents, such as the WBS dictionary for that work package, would define the scope validation procedure required.

The scope management plan, scope baseline, requirements documentation, requirements traceability matrix, verified deliverables, and work performance data are the main inputs for scope validation. A **verified deliverable** has been checked for correctness as part of quality control. The main tools for performing scope validation are inspection and group decision-making. The customer inspects the work after it is delivered to decide if it is acceptable. If the user agrees that it meets their needs, then it is considered to be an **accepted deliverable** and becomes an output of this process. If it is not accepted, there will most likely be change requests as outputs. Note that the customer is often more than one person, so group decision-making is often required for the inspection and acceptance.

Sample of Accepted and Unaccepted Deliverables

The VAPR project included many deliverables. Jeff and Pat, the project sponsor, the project steering committee, and other stakeholders—including nurses and physicians who must use the new reports and workflows—were all involved in validating deliverables. Jeff and the technical team, with Pat's assistance, verified that the databases and reports were correct for Phase I. However, for Phase II Pat required that the actual end users be more engaged in both testing and acceptance of the deliverables.

Pat worked closely with her project team and the training provider to make sure that deliverables were being developed correctly along the way. She knew that working closely with key stakeholders and reviewing progress was often the best way to ensure that final deliverables would be acceptable. Jeff knew from experience that foregoing draft reviews and delaying consultation with stakeholders until the final deliverable was ready often resulted in disaster. Therefore he recommended that she engage these stakeholders early and often throughout Phase II.

Figure 8-5 provides a sample deliverable acceptance form used by AHS for validating deliverables produced by suppliers. The project manager was responsible for signing off on the acceptance, but because these deliverables included a technology component Pat decided to also include Nick, the training manager, in the review and acceptance process as his team were familiar with online training programs.

Deliverable Acceptance Form

Project Name: Ventilator Associated Pneumonia Reduction (VAPR) Project

Deliverable Name: Online training program for VAP workflow changes

Project Manager: Pat Wager, RN

Project Sponsor: Marilyn Shoemaker, Ph.D.   **Date:** March 12

The undersigned acknowledge that AHS has reviewed the deliverable noted above. Signature(s) and date(s) adjacent to the titles below indicate acceptance of the delivery of the work completed for this deliverable on behalf of our organization, and attest to agreement that this deliverable has been completed. No further work should be done on this deliverable.

If the deliverable is not acceptable, indicated by "n/a" in the signature block, reasons are stated and corrective actions are described.

Name	Title	Signature	Date
Pat Wager	Project Manager	n/a	
Nick Orchard	Training Manager	n/a	

1. **Was this deliverable completed to your satisfaction?   Yes_____No X**

2. **Please provide the main reasons for your satisfaction or dissatisfaction with this deliverable.**

As stated in the contract statement of work, AHS requires original source documents for all software, documents, or training programs created by our suppliers. The final materials delivered did not include the source code or discuss why it was not added. We believe it was an oversight that can be corrected with a minimal amount of additional work.

3. **If the deliverable is not acceptable, describe in detail what additional work must be done to complete it.**

The supplier will provide all original documents, code, or programs utilized to create the VAP Workflow Training Program for AHS. We request that these deliverables be provided in CD, DVD, or USB key fob format. A minimum of two copies must be provided, on two different mediums, with fourteen days of this notice as provided for in the abovementioned contract.

Contact's signature for resubmission of deliverable if found unacceptable:

Pat Wager

Figure 8-5. Sample deliverable acceptance form

In this example, Pat and Nick documented the fact that they did *not* accept the initial training deliverable and provided feedback on what had to be done to make it acceptable. Pat did talk to the supplier about the changes required before accepting this particular deliverable—the source code for the training program, which AHS always requires for vendor-provided software—but the supplier still did not deliver what was expected. The deliverable acceptance form provides formal documentation to ensure that deliverables meet project needs. In this case, because the particular deliverable was part of a contract, the supplier would not be paid until the deliverable was accepted.

Controlling Scope

You cannot control the scope of a project unless you have first clearly defined the scope and set a scope validation process in place. You also need to develop a process for soliciting and monitoring changes to project scope. Stakeholders should be encouraged to suggest beneficial changes and discouraged from suggesting unnecessary changes.

PROJECT TIME MANAGEMENT

The main monitoring and controlling task performed as part of project time management is controlling the schedule or schedule control. Project managers often cite delivering projects on time (schedule control) as one of their biggest challenges, because schedule problems often cause more conflict than other issues. During project initiation, priorities and procedures are often most important, but as the project proceeds, especially during the middle and latter stages of a project, schedule issues become the predominant source of conflict.

Perhaps part of the reason schedule problems are so common is that time is easily and simply measured. After a project schedule is set, anyone can quickly estimate schedule performance by subtracting the original time estimate from the time actually expended. People often compare planned and actual project-completion times without taking into account the approved project changes. Time is also the variable with the least amount of flexibility. Time passes no matter what happens on a project.

Individual work styles and cultural differences may also cause schedule conflicts. For example, one dimension of the Myers-Briggs team-building tool that was described in Chapter 6 (Judgment/Perception, or J/P) deals with peoples' attitudes toward structure and deadlines. Some people (J's) prefer detailed schedules and focus on task completion. Others (P's) prefer to keep things open and flexible. Different cultures and even entire countries have different attitudes about schedules. For example, some countries close businesses for several hours every afternoon so workers can take naps. Others observe religious or secular holidays during which little work is accomplished. Cultures may also have different perceptions of work ethic—some may value hard work and strict schedules, whereas others may value the ability to remain relaxed and flexible.

Media Snapshot

Many people of all cultures and ages enjoy using smart phone apps, and they can be very useful in monitoring and controlling medical conditions such as diabetes. According to the Diabetes Report Card 2012, over eight percent of Americans have diabetes, and about 33% of U.S. adults have pre-diabetes. Many apps are available to help people manage their diabetes, and Healthline lists their top ten favorites, which of course are only supplements to physician-supervised care. Below are their descriptions of the top three, all available for free:

- dLife Diabetes Companion is the gold standard of diabetes apps. Backed by the popular dLife diabetes website, it offers users access to over 400 videos—cooking demos, inspiring testimonials, and useful information—from the award-winning dLife TV show. You can also get expert answers to 4,000 questions, look up nutritional information for 25,000 foods, and discover 9,000 diabetic recipes organized by ease, cooking times, ratings, and complete nutritional info. Finally, you can also track and manage your carbohydrate, insulin, and blood glucose data easily and conveniently and get a complete view of your diabetes management with easy-to-read reports.
- Fooducate - Healthy Food Diet & Nutrition Scanner: You might be a foodie, but you're not a detective. So let this multiple award-winning app, with a clean, simple interface, that grades your groceries, uncover what's really inside your favorite food products, and provide healthier alternatives. With over 200,000 products represented, including those from private labels Whole Foods and Trader Joe's, it holds the largest database of UPCs. Just scan the product barcode or search by category, and let Fooducate automatically tell you a product's nutrition grade.
- Glooko Logbook includes but also goes beyond expected tagging, note taking, nutritional tracking, trend viewing, and sharing summaries. This wondrous app saves time and ensures accuracy by actually syncing to your meter. Just connect your iPhone to your meter with the Glooko MeterSync Cable and you can download your full meter of blood glucose readings (from 11 popular meters) directly to your phone to quickly and most accurately create an error-free logbook. You can even sync readings from multiple meters into one logbook. That way you can spend less time imputing data and more time learning from it.[2]

The goal of schedule control is to know the status of the schedule, influence the factors that cause schedule changes, determine whether the schedule has changed, and manage changes when they occur. A key output of schedule control is work performance information.

Sample Work Performance Information

Earned value management, as described earlier, is a tool for measuring scope, time, and cost performance. Given the earned value and planned value, you can see how well the project team is meeting schedule goals and forecast when it will be completed based on past schedule performance. Additional ways to measure schedule performance include:

- *Indicators:* Many senior managers like to focus on high-level color indicators of performance, such as green (on target), yellow (fair), and red (poor). They will oversee projects or tasks with red or yellow indicators much more closely than those with green indicators. When using color indicators, it is also useful to include trend indicators, such as ↔ (neutral), ↓ (downward), and ↑ (improving) For example, the schedule may be green now, but trending downward, which serves as a warning to leadership to watch the schedule more closely. Project management software offers color indicators as well as other reports to show schedule performance information. For example, Microsoft Project 2013 includes activity reports to show "should have started tasks" and "slipping tasks" to quickly identify problem areas.

- *Milestone completion:* Experienced managers and buyers know that it is not enough to merely review indicators; they like to see the planned and actual completion dates of project milestones *and* the physical evidence that the work was actually completed. For example, people having a house built often check on the physical progress to make sure work is completed on schedule. Even though the contractor reports that key milestones are being completed, the buyer wants to see and review the work in person.

- *Worker morale and discipline:* Reviewing morale and work behavior is also a good way to measure schedule performance. If project team members are always working extra hours, the schedule might not be realistic. The project manager might need to negotiate a new schedule or request more resources. On the other hand, if workers are coming in late and leaving early while still producing quality work on time, the schedule might not be challenging enough. Project managers must empower team members to be responsible for completing work on time, yet they often have to use discipline to keep things on track and do what is in the best interest of the organization.

- *Performance review meetings and tracking Gantt charts:* Another way to control project schedules is by holding periodic performance review meetings with the project sponsor or appropriate stakeholders. The project steering committee for the VAPR project held bi-weekly meetings to make sure the project was meeting schedule and other goals. Project managers often illustrate schedule progress at these meetings with a **tracking Gantt chart**—a Gantt chart that compares planned and actual project schedule information. Many project managers believe that tracking Gantt charts are an excellent tool for tracking project schedule performance and reporting that information to stakeholders. Figure 8-6 provides a sample tracking Gantt chart created in Appendix A. The tracking Gantt chart shows bars for both planned and actual start and finish dates for each task as well as the percent of work completed. In this example, things are going well until Subtask 1 under Main task 2 (the last checked item in row 6) takes much longer than planned.

		Task Name	Duration	Start	Finish	Predecessors	Resource Names	Dec 23, 12 S	M	Jan 13, 13 T	W	T	Feb 3, 13 F	S	Feb 24, 13 S	M	T
0		⁴ tracking	36 days	Mon 1/7/13	Mon 2/25/13											57%		
1	✓	⁴ Main task 1	15 days	Mon 1/7/13	Fri 1/25/13						100%							
2	✓	Subtask 1	1 wk	Mon 1/7/13	Fri 1/11/13		Resource 1,Resource 2,Resource 3	100%										
3	✓	Subtask 2	1 wk	Mon 1/14/13	Fri 1/18/13 2		Resource 1,Resource 2,Resource 3		100%									
4	✓	Subtask 3	1 wk	Mon 1/21/13	Fri 1/25/13 3		Resource 1,Resource 2		100%									
5		⁴ Main task 2	21 days	Mon 1/28/13	Mon 2/25/13								35%					
6	✓	Subtask 1	2.2 wks	Mon 1/28/13	Mon 2/11/13 4		Resource 2,Resource 3				100%							
7		Subtask 2	1 wk	Tue 2/12/13	Mon 2/18/13 6		Resource 2,Resource 3				0%							
8		Subtask 3	1 wk	Tue 2/19/13	Mon 2/25/13 7		Resource 1					0%						
9		Subtask 4	2 wks	Mon 1/28/13	Fri 2/8/13 4		Resource 1				0%							

Figure 8-6. Sample schedule performance measurement with a tracking Gantt chart

To serve as a schedule performance measurement tool, a tracking Gantt chart uses a few additional symbols not found on a normal Gantt chart:

- Notice that the tracking Gantt chart in Figure 8-6 often shows two horizontal bars for tasks. The top horizontal bar represents the planned or baseline duration for each task. The bar below it represents the actual duration. If the top and bottom bars are the same length and start and end on the same date, the actual schedule was the same as the planned schedule for that task. If the bars do not start and end on the same date, the actual schedule differed from the planned or baseline schedule. If the top horizontal bar is shorter than the bottom one, the task took longer than planned. If the top horizontal bar is longer than the bottom one, the task took less time than planned. A striped horizontal bar represents the planned duration for summary tasks. Recall that summary tasks are tasks that are decomposed into smaller tasks. The black bar adjoining the striped horizontal bar shows the progress for summary tasks.

- A white diamond on the tracking Gantt chart represents a slipped milestone. A **slipped milestone** refers to a milestone activity that was actually completed later than originally planned.

- Percentages to the right of the horizontal bars display the percentage of work completed for each task. For example, 100% indicates that the task is finished, whereas 50% indicates that the task is still in progress and is 50% completed.

- In the columns to the left of the tracking Gantt chart, you can display baseline and actual start and finish dates. See Appendix A for more information on tracking Gantt charts.

Project sponsors hate surprises, so the project manager must be clear and honest in communicating project status. By no means should project managers create the illusion that the project is going fine when, in fact, serious problems have emerged. When conflicts arise that could affect the project schedule, the project manager must alert the project sponsor and other stakeholders and work with them to resolve the conflicts. The communications management plan should describe escalation procedures for resolving issues.

PROJECT COST MANAGEMENT

Cost control includes monitoring cost performance, ensuring that only appropriate project changes are included in a revised cost baseline, and informing project stakeholders of authorized changes to the project that will affect costs. The project management plan, project funding requirements, work performance data, and organizational process assets are inputs to the cost-control process. Outputs of cost control include work performance information, cost forecasts, change requests, project management plan updates, project documents updates, and updates to organizational process assets, such as lessons-learned documents.

Several tools and techniques assist in project cost control:

- *Earned value:* An important tool for cost control is earned value management, as described earlier under integration management.

- *Forecasting:* It is very useful to predict or forecast future costs based on past performance.

- ***To Complete Performance Index (TCPI):*** This index is the cost performance that must be achieved on the remaining work in order to meet a specified goal, such as the BAC or EAC. The formula for the TCPI based on the BAC is (BAC-EV)/(BAC-AC), and based on the EAC the formula is (BAC-EV)/(EAC-AC). Only use the latter formula if the project is running over budget, and use the former formula (based on BAC) if the project is at or under budget. If the TCPI is >1.00, then the project team must more efficiently manage their costs, and if it is <1.00, then they can more freely make use of their budget.

- *Performance reviews:* These reviews, often done as part of review meetings, can be a powerful aid for controlling project costs, just as they are for controlling schedules. People often perform better when they know they must report on their progress and are held accountable for their performance.

- *Variance analysis:* Cost performance measurements like the CV and CPI show the degree of cost variance. It is important to analyze cost variance and determine if corrective action is needed.

- *Project management software:* Software packages, such as Microsoft Project 2013, have many cost-management features to help you enter budgeted costs, set a baseline, enter actuals, calculate variances, and run various cost reports.

- *Reserve analysis:* This technique is used to monitor the status of contingency and management reserves for the project to determine if they are still needed or if additional reserves need to be requested.

PROJECT QUALITY MANAGEMENT

The main project quality management task for monitoring and controlling is performing quality control. Key outputs include quality-control measurements, validated changes, verified deliverables, work performance information, change requests, and updates to the project management plan, project documents, and organizational process assets. Although one of the main goals of quality control is to ensure and improve quality, the main outcomes of this process are verified deliverables, rework, and process adjustments.

- Verified deliverables are deliverables that have demonstrated that they will meet the requirements defined by the key stakeholders. This process ensures that the deliverables are correct. Later they will be reviewed by the stakeholders as part of validating scope, where they will be reviewed for completeness and acceptance.

- Rework is action taken to bring rejected items into compliance with product requirements or specifications or other stakeholder expectations. Rework can be very expensive, so the project manager who excels at quality planning and quality assurance can reduce the need for rework.

- Process adjustments correct or prevent further quality problems. Based on the implementation of quality-control measurements, process adjustments often result in updates to the quality baseline, organizational process assets, and the project management plan.

Note that healthcare organizations can improve quality while also reducing costs, as shown in the Video Highlights example.

Video Highlights

Virginia Mason Medical Center announced in early 2013 that it received the Distinguished Hospital Award for Clinical Excellence™ for the third year in a row from Healthgrades, a leading provider of comprehensive information about physicians and hospitals. This distinction places them among the top 5 percent of more than 4,500 hospitals nationwide for clinical performance.

The situation was quite different several years ago. When the Virginia Mason Medical Center in Seattle was losing money for the first time in its history, CEO Dr. Gary Kaplan, MD, turned to an unlikely place for help: giant automaker Toyota. In this video, health correspondent Betty Ann Bowser reports on the hospital's success in lowering costs and improving health outcomes. For example, they are trying to totally eliminate waiting rooms. If there are a lot of people in a waiting room, you know that the workflow is inefficient. Virginia Mason Medical Center now has workflow managers who help minimize waste, including the waste of patients' time. Some of the tangible benefits of reducing waste include a reduction in liability costs by 60% since 2004 and improved patient care. Also, the amount of time nurses spend in direct contact with patients has increased from only 35% to 90%.[3]

Sample Quality-Control Tools

Many different tools and techniques for performing quality control and developing control measurements are available. Some of these tools and techniques are also used for quality planning and assurance. The following seven tools are known as the Seven Basic Tools of Quality:

1. *Cause-and-effect diagram*: As described in Chapter 7, cause-and-effect diagrams (also called fishbone or Ishikawa diagrams) help you find the root cause of quality problems. Figure 8-7, shown in the Healthcare Perspective feature, provides a sample diagram that can be used to find the root cause of slow turnaround times for lab results.

Healthcare Perspective

The Institute for Healthcare Improvement (IHI) is an independent not-for-profit organization based in Cambridge, Massachusetts. They provide free information on their Web site to help improve healthcare worldwide. For example, they describe how you can use several tools, including cause and effect diagrams, Pareto diagrams, and flowcharts to help analyze and solve various quality problems.

For example, a common problem in healthcare is the long turnaround time for lab results. You can use a cause and effect or fishbone diagram to help figure out what is the root cause of the problem. Potential categories of causes might include the environment, people, materials, methods, and equipment. You could list several more specific problems under each of those categories, such as specimen vials and lab supplies under the materials. You could then break down potential causes related to both even further, to include unavailable and spoiled, as shown in the following figure.[4]

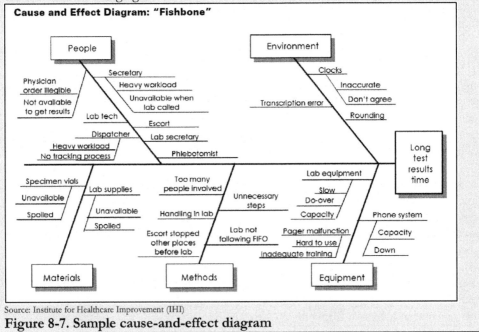

Source: Institute for Healthcare Improvement (IHI)

Figure 8-7. Sample cause-and-effect diagram

2. *Control chart:* A **control chart** is a graphical display of data that illustrates the results of a process over time. Control charts allow you to determine whether a process is in control or out of control. When a process is in control, any variations in the results of the process are created by random events. Processes that are in control do not need to be adjusted. When a process is out of control, variations in the results of the process are caused by nonrandom events. When a process is out of control, you need to identify the causes of those nonrandom events and adjust the process to correct or eliminate them. Figure 8-8 provides an example of a control chart for a process that manufactures 12-inch rulers. Assume that these are wooden rulers created by machines on an assembly line. Each point on the chart represents a length measurement for a ruler that comes off the assembly line. The scale on the vertical axis goes from 11.90 to 12.10. These numbers represent the lower and upper specification limits for the ruler. The lower and upper control limits on the control chart are 11.91 and 12.09 inches, respectively. This means the manufacturing process is designed to produce rulers between 11.91 and 12.09 inches long. Looking for and analyzing patterns in process data is an important part of quality control. You can use control charts and the seven run rule to look for patterns in data. The seven run rule states that if seven data points in a row are all below the mean, above the mean, increasing, or decreasing, then the process needs to be examined for nonrandom problems. In Figure 8-8, data points that violate the seven run rule are starred. The first starred point has seven data points in a row that are all below the mean. The second one has seven data points in a row that are all decreasing. (Note that you include the first point in a series.) In the ruler-manufacturing process, these data points may indicate that a calibration device may need adjustment. For example, the machine that cuts the wood for the rulers might need to be adjusted, or the blade on the machine might need to be replaced. In healthcare, control charts may be used to analyze medication administration timeliness, number of patients seen per shift, or patient wait times.

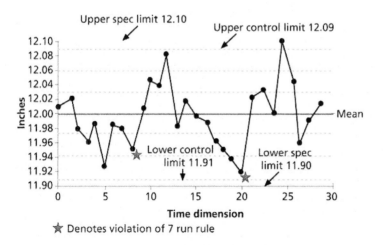

Figure 8-8. Sample control chart (Schwalbe, Information Technology Project Management, Sixth Edition, 2010)

3.   *Run charts:* A **run chart** displays the history and pattern of variation of a process over time. It is a line chart that shows data points plotted in the order in which they occur. You can use run charts to perform trend analysis to forecast future outcomes based on historical results. For example, trend analysis can help you analyze how many defects have been identified over time to determine if there are trends. Figure 8-9 shows a sample run chart, charting the number of defects each day for three different types of defects. Notice that you can easily see the patterns of Defect 1 continuing to decrease over time, Defect 2 increasing over time, and Defect 3 fluctuating each month. In healthcare, run charts may be used to track patient falls, medication errors, or incidence rates of hospital acquired conditions, such as VAP. In run charts downward movement is typically desired performance, while upward trends are considered poor performance. Note: The *PMBOK Guide, Fifth Edition*, lists check sheets or tally sheets as one of the seven basic tools of quality, while many other sources list run charts instead. Both are often used to count the number of specific types of defects or other processes over a period of time.

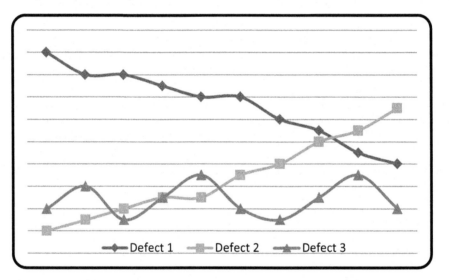

Figure 8-9. Sample run chart

4.   *Scatter diagram:* A **scatter diagram** helps show if there is a relationship between two variables. The closer data points are to a diagonal line, the more closely the two variables are related. Figures 8-10a and 8-10b provide samples of scatter diagrams that Pat's project team might create to compare nursing compliance with the IHI ventilator best practices with their ages to see if there is a relationship between those two variables. In the first example, Figure 8-10a, there appears to be a possible relationship between age and compliance. In the second example, Figure 8-10b, there does not appear to be a relationship. Note how in the first example the data points more closely resemble a solid diagonal line compared to the widely scattered data points in the second example. You can use statistical techniques to see if there is a statistically significant relationship.

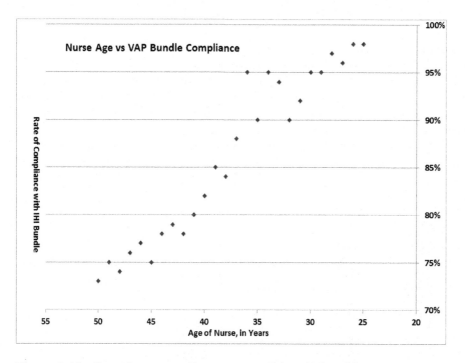

Figure 8-10a. Sample scatter diagram, possible relationship

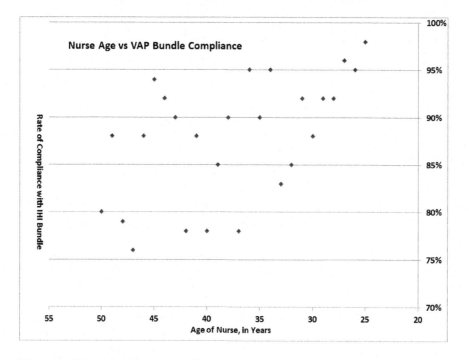

Figure 8-10b. Sample scatter diagram, no apparent relationship

5. *Histograms:* A **histogram** is a bar graph of a distribution of variables. Each bar represents an attribute or a characteristic of a problem or situation, and the height of the bar represents its frequency. Chapter 6 provides a sample resource histogram, showing the number of people required for a project over time. The VAPR project team created a histogram to show how many data collection issues they experienced each month related to the project. Note that the team worked to develop solutions to reduce the number of data problems they experience each month, evidenced by a downward trend in data issues. Figure 8-11 shows the sample histogram.

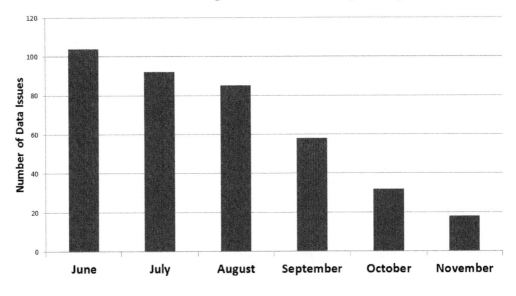
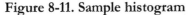

Figure 8-11. Sample histogram

6. *Pareto charts:* A **Pareto chart** is a special type of histogram that can help you identify and prioritize problem areas. The variables described by the histogram are ordered by frequency of occurrence in a column chart, and a line chart is added to show cumulative percentage on the right of the chart. Pareto charts help you identify the vital few contributors that account for most quality problems in a system. Pareto analysis is sometimes referred to as the 80/20 rule, meaning that 80% of problems are often due to 20% of the causes. Figure 8-12 is a sample Pareto chart that the VAPR project team developed that represents the breakdown of data problems for the month of June, the first month on the histogram shown in Figure 8-11. It shows the number of data problems they discovered that month, grouped by the reason for the invalid data. Notice that the first two reasons, incorrect data entry by clinicians and interface failures, account for over 80% of the problems. This chart directed the project team to focus on improving those two areas as they would have the most impact on data problems. Note that Pareto charts work best when the problem areas are of equal importance. For example, if a life-threatening problem were reported, it should be addressed prior to addressing lesser problems, regardless of the occurrence frequency.

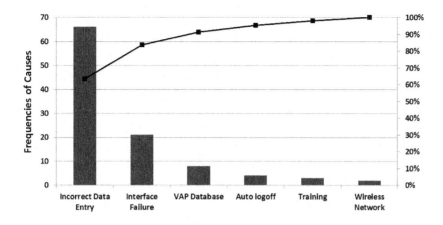

Figure 8-12. Sample Pareto chart

7. *Flowcharts:* **Flowcharts** are graphical displays of the logic and flow of processes that help you analyze how problems occur and how processes can be improved. They show activities (using the square symbol), decision points (using the diamond symbol), and the order of how information is processed (using arrow symbols). Figure 8-13 provides a simple example of a flowchart that shows the process used to determine what kind of email to send to the nursing unit managers each day. Jeff's team used this flowchart to create an automated system that imports the data, analyzes it, and creates and sends the reports and emails automatically. Flowcharts are also very useful when developing test plans, as they represent how the system or process *should* work.

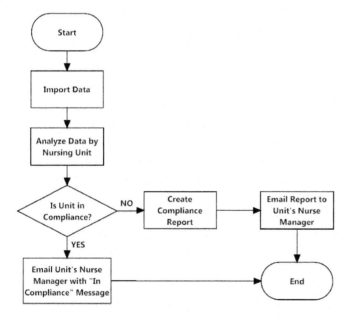

Figure 8-13. Sample flowchart for VAPR project

Figure 8-14 provides a humorous example of using math and statistics to demonstrate quality in a personal relationship.

Figure 8-14. A statistically significant relationship (www.xkcd.com)

PROJECT COMMUNICATIONS MANAGEMENT

Controlling communications involves monitoring and controlling communications throughout the project life cycle to ensure that stakeholder information needs are met. Key outputs include work performance information, change requests, project documents updates, and organizational process assets updates. Work performance information may take many forms, based on the needs of the stakeholders. Project document updates may include a variety of documents, and in many cases will include revisions to work performance reports that were created during monitoring and controlling project work, discussed earlier.

Work Performance Reports

Work performance reports keep stakeholders informed about how resources are being used to achieve project objectives. The project management plan, work performance data and measurements, and organizational process assets are all taken into account when creating work performance reports during monitoring and controlling. Performance reports are normally provided as status reports, progress reports, forecasts, and recommendations. They may be represented in document format or through online dashboards or other electronic mediums. Sometimes status and progress reports are considered the same thing, but many suggest they serve different purposes. Below are common performance report formats:

- **Status reports** describe where the project stands at a specific point in time. Recall the importance of project constraints. Status reports address where the project stands in terms of meeting scope, time, and cost goals. Is work being accomplished as planned? How long did it take to do certain tasks? How much money has been spent to date? Status reports can take various formats depending on the stakeholders' needs.

- **Progress reports** describe what the project team has accomplished during a certain period. In many projects, each team member prepares a weekly or monthly progress report. Team leaders often create consolidated progress reports based on the information received from team members.

- **Forecasts** predict future project status and progress based on past information and trends. How long will it take to finish the project based on how things are going? How much more money will be needed to complete the project? Project managers can also use earned value management, as described earlier in this chapter, to answer these questions by estimating the budget at completion and the projected completion date based on how the project is progressing.

- Project dashboards, as described in Chapter 6, summarize key project metrics in a way that decisions can be made from them. They often contain a variety of information pulled from status, progress, and forecast reports.

Stakeholders often review project performance information at status review meetings, such as the ones Jeff and Pat had with their project steering committee. Status review meetings are a good way to highlight important information, empower people to be accountable for their work, and have face-to-face discussions about key project issues. Many project managers also hold periodic status review meetings with their own team members to exchange important project information and motivate people to make progress on their parts of the project. Likewise, many senior managers, who are often part of a review board or oversight committee, hold status review meetings. At these meetings, several program and project managers must report overall status information to keep everyone abreast of important events and to learn from each other as well.

What Went Right?

Communicating information about improving a large system like healthcare can be very challenging, especially in trying to measure improvements. Many people are becoming familiar with the term "the Triple Aim," which refers to simultaneously improving population health, improving the patient experience of care, and reducing per capita cost. The Institute for Healthcare Improvement (IHI) developed the Triple Aim as a statement of purpose, and it has also become the organizing framework for the U.S. National Quality Strategy and for many of the sites around the world that have been involved in IHI's Triple Aim prototyping initiative.

Monitoring and controlling is an important part of this initiative. "A useful system of measurement for the Triple Aim is essential to this work. Although no single organization or region has yet achieved an ideal, comprehensive measurement system for the Triple Aim, good examples and data sources are now available to illustrate how measurement can fuel a learning system to enable simultaneous improvement of population health, experience of care, and per capita cost of health care." [5]

Sample Performance Report

Figure 8-15 provides a sample progress report that Pat gave at a performance review meeting with the VAPR project steering committee during Phase II. Notice that the report references an earned value chart, similar to the one shown earlier in this chapter. Also notice the use of metrics that are of key interest to senior managers, such as the number of people trained to date and registered for courses. Issues, suggestions, and project changes are also important sections of the report. Performance review meetings should focus on addressing these items to ensure that projects succeed.

Progress Report

Project Name: Ventilator Associated Pneumonia Reduction (VAPR) Project
Project Manager Name: Pat Wager
Date: March 3
        Reporting Period: February 1 – February 28

Work completed this reporting period:
- Identified and gained approval from a high VAP-incidence critical care unit to participate in the VAPR pilot program.
- Recommended and gained approval for the rollout order for remaining ICUs.
- Developed a formal workflow transition plan.
- Transition plan approved by Med Exec Committee and Quality Council.
- Awaiting transition plan approval by Clinical Workflow Council. Expected March 5.

Work to complete next reporting period:
- Review transition plan with each discipline.
- Determine training requirements for clinicians.

What's going well and why:
- Nurses and physical therapists have been engaged from the start due to the ongoing support by the CNO and CNIO.
- ICUs have been very cooperative regarding the pilot program.

Suggestions/Issues:

    Engage the Executive Medical Director and Chief Medical Information Officer in order to help get the appropriate message to physicians about the benefits of VAPR. Our Phase II sponsor, Dr. Scheerer, is in the ideal position to work with these two physician leaders.

Project changes:

    No major changes to report. The earned value chart in Attachment 1 shows planned value, actual cost, and earned value information to date. We are very close to our plans, running slightly ahead of schedule and a bit over budget. We expect to complete the project on budget and on time.

Figure 8-15. Sample performance report

PROJECT STAKEHOLDER MANAGEMENT

You cannot control stakeholders, but you can control their level of engagement. In reality you cannot even control their engagement, but you can, and should, attempt to influence engagement so that their input is available when required. Controlling stakeholder engagement involves monitoring overall project stakeholder relationships and adjusting strategies and plans for engaging stakeholders as needed. If project managers perform this process well, they can maintain or increase the efficiency of stakeholder engagement activities as the project evolves and the environment changes. Controlling (or even influencing) stakeholder engagement is particularly difficult in healthcare. This is due to the multiple organizational hierarchies (physician, nursing, therapy, administration, etc.) as well as the fact that when some stakeholders are engaged, they are not earning revenue for the organization. An IT staff member, therapist, nurse, hospitalist, family practitioner, and surgeon may all be important to a project's success, but keeping them all engaged at the same level is difficult due to their varying availability.

The project management plan, issue log, work performance data, and project documents are important inputs to this process. The project team uses reporting systems, expert judgment, and meetings as the main tools and techniques. The outputs of controlling stakeholder engagement are work performance information, change requests, project documents updates, and organizational process assets updates.

On some projects, stakeholder engagement is controlled by making them key members of the project team. For example, Northwest Airlines (now part of Delta) used innovative ideas to control project scope on a large software development project called ResNet. The project manager controlled stakeholder engagement by interviewing reservation agents for positions as programmers on the project team. There were many people excited about the opportunity, so the project manager had great candidates to choose from. Northwest Airlines made sure that user needs were understood by having them actually develop the user interface for the new reservation system. See the companion Web site for a detailed case study on ResNet.

In healthcare IT projects involving new systems such as an Electronic Medical Record, nurses, therapists, medical students, and even physicians are often recruited to be members of the project team. Nurses and therapists will often assume the roles of system configurator, builder, or analyst—roles typically filled by IT staff. This marriage between clinician role and IT role has led to the growth of clinical informatics.

If you cannot have key stakeholders on the project team, you can control their engagement by planning for it and then following and adjusting those plans as needed. For example, if you plan for several senior managers to attend a kick-off meeting, meet with them in advance to develop a good relationship with them. Put them on the agenda and give them a specific role in the meeting. Encourage open dialog and participation of key stakeholders in review meetings. For example, the ResNet project manager required all progress reports to include issues, primarily as a means to engage stakeholders in discussing and resolving issues.

What Went Wrong?

As well as monitoring and controlling project work, it is important to monitor and control critical stakeholders in healthcare, like physicians. A 2012 article published by the American Medical Association revealed results about physician burnout. Over 7,000 physicians completed surveys (27% response rate), and almost 46% of physicians reported at least one symptom of burnout using the Maslach Burnout Inventory. They study also found that there were differences in burnout by specialty, with physicians in family medicine, general internal medicine, and emergency medicine reporting the highest burnout rates.

The study also compared burnout rates and work-life balance between physicians with other working adults. A summary of the findings include the following:

- Physicians were more likely to have symptoms of burnout (37.9% vs. 27.8%)
- Physicians were more likely to be dissatisfied with work-life balance (40.2% vs. 23.2%)
- Individuals with a bachelor's degree, master's degree, or professional or doctoral degree other than an MD or DO degree were at lower risk for burnout.[6]

PROJECT RISK MANAGEMENT

Controlling risks involves executing the risk management processes to respond to risk events. Recall from Chapter 6 that a risk event is a specific, uncertain event that may occur to the detriment or enhancement of the project. Executing the risk management processes means ensuring that risk awareness is an ongoing activity performed by the entire project team throughout the project. Project risk management does not stop with the initial risk analysis. Identified risk events may not materialize, or their probabilities of occurrence or impact may diminish or increase. Similarly, new risk events are normally identified as the project progresses. Newly identified risk events need to go through the same process of analysis and control as those identified during the initial risk assessment. A redistribution of resources devoted to risk management may be necessary because of relative changes in risk exposure.

Carrying out individual risk management plans involves monitoring risks based on defined milestones and making decisions regarding risks and their response strategies. It might be necessary to alter a strategy if it becomes ineffective, implement planned contingency activities, or eliminate a risk event from the list of potential risks. Project teams sometimes use **workarounds**—unplanned responses to risk events—when they do not have contingency plans in place.

Risk reassessment, risk audits, variance and trend analysis, technical performance measurement, reserve analysis, reserve analysis, and status meetings are all tools and techniques for performing risk control. Outputs of this process include work performance information, change requests, project management plan updates, project documents updates (especially updating the risk register), and organizational process asset updates.

Sample Risk Register Updates

The number one risk event in the initial risk register for the VAPR project was lack of physician support for the IHI Ventilator Bundle. Because the project was now halfway completed, the risk register had changed significantly as new risks were identified while others were deemed irrelevant, and most of the risks had their probability or impact changed. Jeff and Pat knew that they had to regularly review the risk register and ensure that their response plans were still adequate.

For example, halfway through the project, the Phase II project champion and AHS Chief Quality Officer, Dr. Danielle Scheerer, informed Pat that the IHI was considering changing their bundle based on some new research. The new bundle, although not yet approved, would eliminate the vacation sedation part of the bundle. Sedation vacation occurs when heavily sedated patients have their sedation lightened for a period of time each day to see if they are ready to have the ventilator removed. Dr. Scheerer did not know if the bundle would change, but she did note that recent research was suggesting that sedation vacation was not helpful, and she suspected that the IHI may have to respond to that research soon.

This information resulted in the identification of several new risks related to what, if anything, would replace that bundle element. It also raised concerns with both Pat and Jeff because they had personally conducted their own research, based on other healthcare institutions who had implemented the IHI bundle, and from all accounts the sedation vacation was a critical part of the bundle. They worried that if removed from the bundle, then the entire VAPR project would not show the improved VAP rates that they expected.

Because nothing was changing at this point, Jeff and Pat simply identified the risks and decided to accept them, noting there was nothing they could do now and that if the bundle did indeed get changed, then it was because the IHI reached the conclusion, using evidence-based medicine, that the sedation vacation was not critical. However, it would require them to change their data loads, data analysis scripts, reports, and training program, so if changed it could increase project costs significantly. The later in the project the bundle was modified, the more the changes would cost to implement.

As you can see, the risk register must be constantly updated as part of project monitoring and control.

PROJECT PROCUREMENT MANAGEMENT

Controlling procurements ensures that the seller's performance meets agreements or contractual requirements. The contractual relationship is a legal relationship and, as such, is subject to state and federal contract laws. It is very important that appropriate legal and contracting professionals be involved in writing and administering contracts.

Several tools and techniques can help in contract administration:

- Contract change-control system

- Procurement performance reviews

- Inspections and audits

- Performance reporting

- Payment systems

- Claims administration

- Records management system

In addition to work performance information, change requests, project management plan updates, and organizational process asset updates, a key output of controlling procurement are updates to project documents, especially procurement documents. Procurement documentation includes the contract itself along with requested unapproved contract changes and approved change requests, typically using formal change orders. It is very important to document all changes to the contract and communicate those changes to all affected stakeholders. For example, if the supplier developing the online training program for the VAPR project agreed to add a topic to the course at no extra cost, that agreement must be added to the contract to make it legally enforceable. Likewise, if AHS decided to change the due date of the online training program, they would need to update that information in the contract as well. Significant, or material, contract changes are made by having both parties—the buyer and the seller—sign an addendum to the contract. Immaterial changes, often called administrative changes, such as changes to where payments should be sent, are generally managed with simple correspondence between the two parties.

Project team members must be aware of the potential legal problems of not understanding a contract. Changes must be handled properly for items under contract. Without understanding the provisions of contracts, project managers might not realize that they are authorizing the contractor to do additional work at additional cost. This can put the project managers at risk within their own organizations, as they are spending resources without appropriate authority. Therefore, change control is an important part of the contract administration process.

Suggestions for Controlling Procurements

The following suggestions help ensure adequate change control and good contract administration:

- Changes to any part of the project need to be reviewed, approved, and documented by the same people in the same way that the original part of the plan was approved.

- Evaluation of any change should include an impact analysis. How will the change affect the scope, time, cost, and quality of the goods or services being provided? There must also be a baseline against which to compare and analyze changes.

- Changes must be documented in writing. Project team members should document all important meetings and telephone calls.

- Project managers and their teams must stay closely involved with suppliers to make sure that their deliverables meet business needs and work in the organization's environment. Do not assume that work will run smoothly because you hired a reputable supplier. The buying organization needs to provide expertise as well.

- Have backup plans in case the procurement does not produce the desired results.

As you can see, proper monitoring and controlling of projects is essential to their success.

CASE WRAP-UP

The project steering committee kept a watchful eye on the VAPR project. They were impressed with Jeff's proven leadership abilities and the way he handled inevitable changes on the project. They were also very happy with Pat's performance as a project manager, and they were excited that they were going to have a nurse who could manage clinical projects going forward. They especially liked the detailed, honest progress reports Pat provided to them and felt that because she had a clinical background she really understood the clinical workflows. They enjoyed brainstorming ideas to solve some of the issues presented to them at review meetings, and Pat was always very open to their suggestions. Everyone was confident the project would be completed successfully.

CHAPTER SUMMARY

Monitoring and controlling involves regularly measuring progress to ensure that the project is meeting its objectives and addressing current business needs. The project manager and other staff monitor progress against plans and take corrective action when necessary.

Every knowledge area except project human resource management includes processes and outputs to help monitor and control projects. Outputs common to several knowledge areas include change requests, work performance information, organizational process assets updates, project management plan updates, and project document updates.

As part of integration management, project managers must monitor and control project work and perform integrated change control. Earned value management is a project performance measurement technique that integrates scope, time, and cost data. You can use it to forecast when a project will be completed and how much it will cost given past performance data.

Monitoring and controlling processes related to scope management include validating scope and controlling scope, and its unique output includes accepted deliverables.

Controlling costs and schedules are common challenges for project managers. Earned value management can aid in creating cost and schedule forecasts.

Unique outputs of controlling quality include quality control measurements and verified deliverables. There are seven basic tools of quality to assist in performing quality control.

Performance reports include progress reports, status reports, forecasts, dashboards, and other methods of presenting information for the purpose of providing updates, raising awareness, or making decisions.

You cannot control stakeholders, but you can control their engagement. Soft skills are very important in this process because you are really influencing stakeholders, not controlling them.

It is important to reassess risks, and an important output of controlling risks is updating the risk register.

Project managers must also control procurements and update information related to agreements and contracts.

Samples of several monitoring and controlling outputs are provided for the VAPR project.

QUICK QUIZ

1.   Which knowledge areas include tasks related to controlling?

   A. project scope, time, cost, and quality management

   B. project integration, scope, time, cost, and quality management

   C. project human resource, communications, risk, and procurement management

   D. all ten knowledge areas except project human resource management

2.   _____ is a project performance measurement technique that integrates scope, time, and cost data.

   A. Integrated change control

   B. Flowcharting

   C. Earned value management

   D. Forecasting

3.   _____ involves formal acceptance of the completed project scope by the stakeholders.

   A. Scope creep

   B. Scope validation

   C. Deliverable acceptance

   D. Customer sign-off

4.   _____ issues cause the most conflict over the life of projects.

   A. Change control

   B. Scope creep

   C. Cost

   D. Schedule

5.   A _____ chart is a histogram that can help you identify and prioritize problem areas.

   A. Pareto

   B. control

   C. run

   D. scatter

6. When a process is out of control, variations in the results of the process are caused by _____ events.

    A. random

    B. nonrandom

    C. planned

    D. unplanned

7. Which of the following is false concerning controlling stakeholder engagement?

    A. You cannot control stakeholders, but you can control their level of engagement.

    B. Reporting systems, expert judgment, and meetings are all tools and techniques for controlling stakeholder engagement.

    C. Northwest Airlines (now Delta) assigned users to a project team to develop a new reservation system in order to increase stakeholder engagement.

    D. It is not a good idea to include issues during progress review meetings so you do not upset key stakeholders.

8. _____ predict future project status and progress based on past information and trends.

    A. Forecasts

    B. Status reports

    C. Progress reports

    D. Histograms

9. _____ are unplanned responses to risk events.

    A. Contingencies

    B. Reserves

    C. Workarounds

    D. Over allocations

10.   Which of the following is not a suggestion for controlling procurements?

   A.   Do not spend too much time documenting changes in writing; verbal agreements are fine.

   B.   Have backup plans in case the procurement does not produce the desired results.

   C.   Evaluation of any change should include an impact analysis.

   D.   Do not assume that work will run smoothly because you hired a reputable supplier.

Quick Quiz Answers

1. D; 2. C; 3. B; 4. D; 5. A; 6. B; 7. D; 8. A; 9. C; 10. A

DISCUSSION QUESTIONS

1.   What is involved in monitoring and controlling projects? What outputs of monitoring and controlling are common to all knowledge areas?

2.   Explain how earned value management helps you monitor project performance and forecast future cost and schedule information. What do you need to do to use earned value management?

3.   What are the three main objectives of integrated change control?

4.   What is the difference between scope validation and scope control? Why are both important to project success?

5.   What are some of the tools and techniques for performing time, cost, and quality control? What are the Seven Basic Tools of Quality?

6.   Why is it important to keep the risk register up to date?

7.   Why is it important to document contract changes? Why should project teams be watchful for constructive change orders?

EXERCISES

Note: These exercises can be done individually or in teams, in-class, as homework, or in a virtual environment. Learners can either write their results in a paper or prepare a short presentation or video to show their results.

1.   Find an example of a large project that took more than one year to complete, preferably in the healthcare industry. Describe some of the tasks performed to monitor and control the project. Summarize your findings.

2.   Given the following information for a one-year project, answer the following questions. Assume you have actual and earned value data at the end of the second

month. Recall that PV is the planned value, EV is the earned value, AC is the actual cost, and BAC is the budget at completion.

$$PV = \$23,000$$

$$EV = \$20,000$$

$$AC = \$25,000$$

$$BAC = \$120,000$$

a. What is the cost variance, schedule variance, cost performance index (CPI), and schedule performance index (SPI) for the project?

b. How is the project progressing? Is it ahead of schedule or behind schedule? Is it under budget or over budget?

c. Use the CPI to calculate the estimate at completion (EAC) for this project.

d. Use the SPI to estimate how long it will take to finish this project.

e. Sketch the earned value chart for this project, using Figure 8-4 as a guide. Assume the data for month 1 is half of the values given for PV, EV, and AC at the end of month 2.

3. Follow the steps for using Microsoft Project 2013 provided in the *Brief Guide to Microsoft Project 2013* in Appendix A through the section on earned value management. Open the data files as directed and then establish a baseline plan, create a tracking Gantt chart, and implement earned value management using this software.

4. Assume you are working on a project to improve customer service. Create a Pareto chart based on the information in the following table. Use the Pareto chart template from the companion Web site or sketch the chart by hand so that your resulting chart looks similar to the example in this chapter.

Customer complaints	Frequency/week
Customer is on hold too long	90
Customer gets transferred to wrong area or cut off	20
Service rep cannot answer customer's questions	120
Service rep does not follow through as promised	40

5. Watch the YouTube video mentioned in the Video Highlights feature of this chapter called "Rooting Out Waste in Health Care by Taking Cue From Toyota." Describe the major changes Virginia Mason Medical Center implemented and the challenges they faced. Summarize your findings and opinions.

TEAM PROJECTS

Note: These team projects can be done in-class, as homework, or in a virtual environment. Learners can either write their results in a paper or prepare a short presentation or video to show their results

1. Your organization initiated a project to raise money for an important charity. Assume that there are 1,000 people in your organization. Also, assume that you have six months to raise as much money as possible, with a goal of $100,000. List three problems that could arise while monitoring and controlling the project. Describe each problem in detail, and then develop realistic approaches to solving them. Be creative in your responses, and use at least one quality-control tool in your analysis. Remember that this project is run solely by volunteers.

2. You are part of a team in charge of a project to help people in your company (500 people) lose weight. This project is part of a competition, and the top "losers" will be featured in a popular television show. Assume that you have six months to complete the project and a budget of $10,000. You are halfway through the project, and morale is very low. People are also complaining about a lack of communication and support on the project. Although many people have been participating and have lost weight, many have plateaued or started gaining weight back. Create an issue log to document these and related issues. Also create a new entry for the risk register for this project.

3. Using the information you developed in Team Project 1 or 2, role-play a meeting to brainstorm and develop strategies for solving problems with key stakeholders. Determine who will play what role (project manager, team member from a certain department, senior managers, and so on). Be creative in displaying different personalities (a senior manager who questions the importance of the project to the organization, a team member who is very shy or obnoxious).

4. Brainstorm two different quality related problems that you are aware of at your college or organization. Then review the charts found in the section of this chapter on the seven basic tools of quality and create two charts to help analyze the quality problems. Summarize the problems and how the charts help to visualize them.

5. Perform the monitoring and controlling tasks for one of the case studies provided in Appendix B. If you are working on a real team project, create relevant monitoring and controlling documents, such as performance reports or quality assurance-related charts using the templates and samples in this chapter as guides.

KEY TERMS

accepted deliverable – a verified deliverable that has been reviewed by the stakeholders during the validate scope process and accepted as meeting their needs.

actual cost (AC) — The total direct and indirect costs incurred in accomplishing work on an activity during a given period.

budget at completion (BAC) — The approved total budget for the project.

change log — A document that lists each project change, its effect on project constraints, and if the change is approved or not.

control chart — A graphical display of data that illustrates the results of a process over time.

earned value (EV) — An estimate of the value of the physical work actually completed.

earned value management (EVM) — A project performance measurement technique that integrates scope, time, and cost data.

estimate at completion (EAC) — A forecast of how much the project will cost upon completion.

flowcharts — The graphic displays of the logic and flow of processes that help you analyze how problems occur and how processes can be improved.

forecasts —Reports that predict future project status and progress based on past information and trends.

histogram — A bar graph of a distribution of variables.

integrated change control — The process of identifying, evaluating, and managing changes throughout the project's life cycle.

Pareto chart — A histogram that can help you identify and prioritize problem areas.

planned value (PV) — That portion of the approved total cost estimate planned to be spent on an activity during a given period.

progress reports — Reports that describe what the project team has accomplished during a certain period.

rate of performance (RP) — The percentage of actual work completed divided by the percentage of work planned to have been completed at any given time.

run chart — A chart that displays the history and pattern of variation of a process over time.

scatter diagram — A diagram that helps show if there is a relationship between two variables.

scope validation — The formal acceptance of the completed project deliverables by the customer or designated stakeholders.

slipped milestone — A milestone activity that was actually completed later than originally planned.

status reports — Reports that describe where the project stands at a specific point in time.

*to-*complete performance index (TCPI) — The cost performance that must be achieved on the remaining work in order to meet a specified goal, such as the BAC or EAC.

tracking Gantt chart — A Gantt chart that compares planned and actual project schedule information.

verified deliverable — A deliverable that has been completed and checked for correctness as part of quality control.

workarounds — The unplanned responses to risk events.

END NOTES

[1]CMS Centers for Medicare & Medicaid Services, Division of Information Technology Investment Management Enterprise Architecture & Strategy Group Office of Information Services, "Earned Value Management Best Practices" (Nov 19, 2009).

[2]Tracy Rosecrans, Best Apps for Diabetics, Healthline (August 28, 2012).

[3]PBS News Hour, "Rooting Out Waste in Health Care by Taking Cue From Toyota," YouTube (Oct. 24, 2012).

[4]Institute for Healthcare Improvement, "Cause and Effect Diagram," Cambridge, Massachusetts (www.ihi.org) (2004).

[5]Matthew Stiefel, and Kevin Nolan, "A Guide to Measuring the Triple Aim: Population Health, Experience of Care, and Per Capita Cost." Institute for Healthcare Improvement (2012).

[6]Tait D. Shanafelt, MD; Sonja Boone, MD; Litjen Tan, PhD; Lotte N. Dyrbye, MD, MHPE; Wayne Sotile, PhD; Daniel Satele, BS; Colin P. West, MD, PhD; Jeff Sloan, PhD; Michael R. Oreskovich, MD, "Burnout and Satisfaction With Work-Life Balance Among US Physicians Relative to the General US Population," Archives of Internal Medicine 2012;172(18):1377-1385 (2012).

Chapter 9
Closing Projects

LEARNING OBJECTIVES
After reading this chapter, you will be able to:
- Describe common ways to close or terminate projects
- List several processes and outputs of project closing
- Discuss the process of closing a project or phase performed as part of project integration management, explain the importance of a project close-out meeting and knowledge transfer, and describe the contents of a customer acceptance/project completion form, final project report, transition documents, and lessons-learned report
- Explain the process of closing procurements performed as part of project procurement management, and describe the contents of a written notice of a closed contract
- Provide advice on closing projects

OPENING CASE

The Ventilator Associated Pneumonia Reduction (VAPR) project was almost finished. Jeff's team had created a new database to house the Institute for Healthcare Improvement (IHI) bundle data collected from the Academic Health Systems (AHS) nursing documentation system. They developed inbound interfaces and import scripts to pull that data, back loaded data for the past three years to use for testing, and successfully completed unit testing. The training vendor completed the online training program, and Pat's team reviewed and approved their work. The pilot nursing unit staff went through training and used the new workflows and reports as part of end user acceptance testing, with the staff being very accepting of the new process. The pilot users offered a few suggestions to improve the report and the overall process, and the team implemented those before rolling the new VAPR reports and workflows out to the entire organization. Eighty-eight percent of critical care units completed their training on time, prior to the rollout, with the actual rollout being what AHS would call a "non-event." In other words, it went very smoothly. The project steering committee was looking forward to Jeff's and Pat's final report and presentation on the project.

INTRODUCTION

Closing activities for phases and projects involves gaining stakeholder and customer acceptance of the final products and services, and bringing the phase or project to an orderly end. It includes verifying that all of the deliverables are complete, and often includes a final presentation and report. For both projects that are completed and those that are canceled before completion, it is important to formally close the project and reflect on what can be learned to improve future projects. As philosopher George Santayana said, "Those who cannot remember the past are condemned to repeat it."

There are four common ways to close or terminate a project:

1. *Integration:* A project is completed, and products and services created are integrated into operations, as was done in the VAPR project. This is the most common approach and may include new systems, processes, or workflows. Project staff and other resources are released and distributed back into their original functional teams.

2. *Addition:* A project creates a new product or service that results in a new unit in the organization, such as a department, division, or company. This often occurs when a project involves creating a new service line, procedural area, nursing unit, or clinic. Generally project managers returns to their original roles but the remaining project staff (often the clinical subject matter experts), along with additional resources, shift to staff the new function.

3.   *Extinction:* A project may end because it was successful and achieved its goals, and there is no need for further work. A waste reduction project, an efficiency improvement project, or the introduction of a workflow change may be included in this type of closure since the results of the project are self-sustaining. Another form of extinction is when a project is stopped because it was unsuccessful, organizational objectives changed, or the project was superseded by another of higher priority.

4.   *Starvation:* A project can also be terminated by decreasing its budget, limiting resources, or complete defunding. The reason for starving a project is generally to shadow the failure or non-accomplishment of project goals. Management sometimes uses this approach to avoid embarrassment or direct conflict with other leaders, but it is also used in cases where leadership changes and they shift resources to projects they consider higher priority. Although the original project is never formally ended, it is slowly starved of the resources needed to complete it.

Many companies terminated projects by extinction or starvation due to the poor economy in 2008-2012. Even Google, the "number one" company to work for in America, canceled several projects. They evaluated how popular development projects were with customers and employees, how big a problem they addressed, and whether they were meeting internal performance targets. If they didn't meet those criteria, they were closed. "There's no single equation that describes us, but we try to use data wherever possible," said Jeff Huber, Google's senior vice president of engineering. "What products have found an audience? Which ones are growing?"[1]

It is also important to plan for and execute a smooth transition of the project into normal operations of the company if it is completed. Most projects produce results that are integrated into the existing organizational structure. For example, AHS' VAPR project would require staff to support the database, interfaces, import scripts, and reports after the project was completed. However, recall from the business case in Chapter 3 that the life-cycle cost estimate for the project included no money for work to be done after the project was completed. Why? AHS had a policy whereby any project that could be supported with existing staffing did not have to have their operational expenses budgeted separately.

Regardless of whether or not they identified ongoing operational costs, Jeff and Pat ensured that the work required for transitioning the VAPR results—the database, interfaces, import scripts, reports, and online training system—was completed so that the project results could be transitioned to the appropriate functional teams.

SUMMARY OF CLOSING OUTPUTS

Figure 9-1 summarizes key outputs of project closing by knowledge area, based on the *PMBOK® Guide, Fifth Edition.* Procedures for administrative and contract closure are part of organizational process assets. For example, many organizations require some type of customer acceptance or project completion form. Every project should have procedures to guide closure. Samples of closing procedures and other outputs produced in closing the

VAPR project are provided in this chapter, such as a close-out meeting, project celebration, final project report, transition documents, and a lessons-learned report.

Knowledge area	Closing process	Outputs
Project integration management	Close project or phase	Final product, service, or result transition Organizational process assets updates
Project procurement management	Close procurements	Closed procurements Organizational process assets updates

Figure 9-1. Closing processes and outputs

PROJECT INTEGRATION MANAGEMENT

The last process in project integration management is closing the project or phase. To close a project or phase of a project, you must finish all activities and transfer the completed or canceled work to the appropriate people. The main outputs of closing a project or phase are as follows:

- *Final product, service, or result transition:* Project sponsors are usually most interested in making sure that the final products, services, or results are delivered and transitioned to the appropriate part of the organization. A final project report and presentation are also commonly used during project closing. A sample table of contents from the VAPR project's final report is provided in the next section, as well as part of the transition plan. The section of the final report summarizing project results should also address how well the project met key project metrics. It is important for project teams to set aside time to prepare a good final report and presentation, as these items often receive high visibility.

- *Updates to organizational process assets:* Recall that organizational process assets help people understand, follow, and improve business processes. Examples of organizational process assets include policies and procedures, guidelines, information systems, financial systems, management systems, lessons learned, and historical information. During closing, the project team should update appropriate process assets. They need to ensure that the risk register is updated for the final time, the issues log is updated and closed, and lessons learned are formally reviewed and updated with current information. At the end of the VAPR project, both Jeff's and Pat's teams prepared a formal lessons-learned report, which will serve as an asset for future projects. Remember that lessons learned—like risks and issues—are collected starting on the first day of the project and continue to be collected until project closure. The final lessons-learned report is simply a formal documentation of the lessons considered to be the most influential.

VIDEO HIGHLIGHTS

Some of the most useful lessons learned come from project failures. One very visible, painful project failure occurred in 1986 when the Space Shuttle Challenger exploded only 73 seconds after liftoff, killing all seven astronauts onboard. You can watch CNN's live video of the disaster on YouTube by searching for "Challenger disaster live on CNN." This 25th Space Shuttle mission altered the history of manned space exploration. In 2011, the Associated Press released a video called "Challenger's Lessons Still Echo 25 Years Later." President Ronald Reagan formed a presidential committee which grounded the program, and senior management reconsidered what some people thought was a "gung ho" launch culture. Some of the narrative in this video includes the following:

Roger Laune's, Senior Curate at the Air and Space Museum, stated, "What had failed was the communication process where people at a lower level thought there was a problem, but that did not get to the higher level. So communication is the key thing to change."

Mark Hamrick of the Associated Press said that "Challenger's legacy is still debated today…NASA learned quickly that a launch was anything but routine…Ironically, the legacy of Challenger may be that tragedy produced results that made space travel safer for those who followed."[2]

The Challenger was the 25th space shuttle launch. The final (135th) shuttle launch was on July 8, 2011.

In addition to these two outputs, it is also good practice to hold a close-out meeting and celebrate completion of the project or phase. In closing the VAPR project, Jeff and Pat worked with their teams to prepare a customer acceptance/project completion form, a final report and presentation, a formal review of the transition plan's status (provided as part of the final report), and a lessons-learned report. They also held a project close-out meeting to help transfer knowledge to other people in the organization. Although Phase I completed months prior to Phase II, Pat organized a project closure luncheon for both project teams right after the final project presentation given at the end of Phase II. She used the luncheon to celebrate a job well done. In addition to the teams, both project phase champions and the project sponsor were also invited. Dr. Shoemaker, the sponsor, used the opportunity to thank the project teams for contributing to improving patient outcomes at AHS.

Sample Customer Acceptance/Project Completion Form

As part of project closing, AHS asked the project sponsor to complete a customer acceptance/project completion form. Even if the project had been terminated, the sponsor would still have completed the form to signify the end of the project. Figure 9-2 shows the form that was filled out for the VAPR project. Note that this form refers to completion of the entire project, not just a specific deliverable. Although project sponsors generally depend upon their key stakeholders to review the project work and make recommendations regarding acceptance, the document itself should be completed and signed by the project sponsor.

Customer Acceptance/Project Completion Form
June 30

Project Name: **Ventilator Associated Pneumonia Reduction (VAPR) Project**

Project Manager: Jeff Birdwell & Pat Wager

I (We), the undersigned, acknowledge and accept delivery of the work completed for this project on behalf of our organization. My (Our) signature(s) attest(s) to my (our) agreement that this project has been completed. No further work should be done on this project.

<u>Name</u>	<u>Title</u>	<u>Signature</u>	<u>Date</u>
Marilyn Shoemaker	Chief Nursing Officer	*Marilyn Shoemaker*	June 30

1. **Was this project completed to your satisfaction?**   __X__ Yes   _____ No

2. **Please rate this project on a scale of 1-10, with 10 being the highest.   __10__**

3. **Please provide the main reasons for your satisfaction or dissatisfaction with this project.**

The project met and exceeded my expectations. In my 13 years with this organization, I have never seen caregivers so willing to adopt new technology and change their clinical workflows. I believe one reason for this was because the clinical project phase, Phase II, was led by a nurse who could speak the caregivers' language. Pat did a great job gaining the buy-in of clinical leadership as well as staff nursing and therapists. She and Jeff, the Phase I project manager, worked very well together. Jeff and his team created a solid technology foundation upon which Pat's team could build the clinical aspects of the project.

4. **Please provide suggestions on how our organization could improve its project delivery capability in the future.**

One suggestion would be to train other clinicians, like Pat, to manage clinical projects. Jeff did an excellent job mentoring her during this project, but perhaps formal project training for Pat and other nurse and therapy leaders could help AHS be more successful with clinical projects. Staff from the PMO, like Jeff, could serve as mentors, coaches, and providers of tools and systems to facilitate the management of projects.

Thank you for your input!

Figure 9-2. Sample customer acceptance/project completion form

Sample Final Report

Figure 9-3 provides the table of contents for the final project report for the VAPR project. (The cover page of the report included the project title, date, and team member names.) Notice that the report includes a review of the transition plan and a plan to analyze the effectiveness and benefits of the new VAP reduction system and workflows. Also notice that the final report includes attachments for all the project management and product-related documents. Jeff knew the importance of providing complete final documentation on projects and that the project steering committee would expect a comprehensive final report on such an important project, so he and Pat worked together to create them.

The project team produced a hard copy of the final documentation for the project sponsor and each steering committee member, and they placed an electronic copy on the corporate intranet with the other project archives. Jeff and Pat also gave a final project presentation, which summarized key information in the final project report.

Final Project Report
June 20

Project Name: Ventilator Associated Pneumonia Reduction (VAPR) Project

Table of Contents

1. Project Objectives
2. Summary of Project Results
3. Original and Actual Scope
4. Original and Actual Schedule
5. Original and Actual Budget
6. Project Assessment
7. Transition Summary
8. Lessons Learned Summary

Attachments:
A. Key Project Management Documentation (business case, project charter, etc.)
B. Product-Related Documentation (database information, training documents, etc.)

Figure 9-3. Sample table of contents for a final project report

Sample Transition Document

As mentioned earlier, the life-cycle cost estimate for AHS' VAPR did not include any costs for ongoing maintenance because AHS's policy did not require it for project work that was sustainable with current resources. The VAPR project did not require additional resources to sustain it, so maintenance costs were not identified. However, the project deliverables still had to be transitioned to the appropriate functional teams who ran day-to-day operations. The activities required to transition the project deliverables to functional teams were included in the project schedule, and thus also included in the original project budget. During closing project managers must ensure that the deliverables are properly transitioned and that the functional managers are ready to accept ongoing responsibility for the deliverables. A transition review report is one way to document the review process, and a sample is shown in Figure 9-4.

Transition Review Report
June 20

Project Name: Ventilator Associate Pneumonia Reduction (VAPR) Project

Introduction

The main goal of this project was to develop a new clinical workflow to support IHI Ventilator Bundle compliance at AHS. In order to create the workflow the caregivers required information from our electronic medical record systems that indicate if the IHI bundle is being followed by AHS caregivers. This information required the creation of a database, interfaces, import scripts, and reports that must be maintained daily. AHS IT leadership assured the project sponsor that these technology deliverables could be supported by the current Enterprise Data Warehouse (EDW) team, and thus no ongoing maintenance costs needed to be budgeted.

Transition Status

The EDW team was engaged during Phase I and has been supporting the new deliverables since the bulk of Phase I was completed in January. The helpdesk has been provided a step-by-step guide to answer calls about the new workflows. The VAPR system has been added to the helpdesk ticket system and includes all required contact and escalation information. The online training system for VAPR will be managed as part of the annual hospital training program and has been reviewed and accepted by the clinical training oversight group.

Incomplete Transition Work

The new documented clinical workflows must be incorporated into the nurse educator training program. The clinical training oversight group has accepted responsibility for doing this within 90 days. That work is considered outside the scope of this project.

Figure 9-4. Sample transition review report

Sample Lessons-Learned Report

Instead of asking each member of the VAPR project team to write individual lessons-learned reports, Jeff and Pat decided to use a technique Jeff had used before in which key stakeholders held a sticky-note party to document lessons learned. Key stakeholders met, wrote down all of the lessons they had learned on sticky notes, and then posted them to the wall. Since they had been documenting lessons learned from the start of the project, Jeff wrote these on individual sticky notes prior to the party but kept them hidden until then end of the session, at which time he posted them to the wall as additions to what the team brainstormed.

This approach was a fun, non-accusatory way for everyone to get together and share what they had learned from the project. Jeff later summarized the inputs in a list that everyone could access on the project Web site. In order to continue Pat's project management learning experience, he then asked Pat to use the corporate template to prepare a short lessons-learned report for inclusion in the final documentation for the project, as shown in Figure 9-5. A short summary was also included in the final project report and presentation. Notice the question-and-answer format, which was used for all projects done at AHS. Also notice that the lessons-learned report was finished about two weeks after the project ended to let the staff have a bit of breathing time for reflection.

Lessons-Learned Report
July 18

Project Name: Ventilator Associated Pneumonia Reduction Project
Project Sponsor: Marilyn Shoemaker, RN, Ph.D.
Project Manager: Jeff Birdwell, PMP (Ph I) & Pat Wager, RN (Ph II)
Project Dates: July 1 – June 30
Final Cost: $957,000

1. Did the project meet scope, time, and cost goals?

We met scope and time goals, but we used $20,000 of contingency funds. Costs were still within our goal.

2. What was the success criteria listed in the project scope statement?

The following criteria outlined the project scope and success criteria:

- Project completed by the end of the next fiscal year (June 30)
- Project completed for $980,000 or less.
- Sponsor rating of at least 8/10.
- VAP incidence rate is reduced by 25% within 90 days of go live.
- VAP incidence rate is reduced by 35% within 180 days of go live.
- VAP incidence rate is reduced by 50% within 270 days of go live.

3. Reflect on whether or not you met the project success criteria.

We finished on time and within budget, and our sponsor rating was 10/10. The last three criteria will be analyzed at the time periods specified by the AHS Performance Improvement department with the results provided to the Ops Leadership Team within two weeks of the data collection.

4. In terms of managing the project, what were the main lessons your team learned from this project?

The main lessons we learned include the following:

- Having clinical leadership publicly supporting the project was critical to gaining clinician buy-in.
- Naming an experienced clinician as project manager helped gain clinician buy-in and allowed the project team to have a subject matter expert on the team.
- Experience clinicians who are not experienced project managers can be very successful if coached and mentored by a senior project manager.
- Running a multi-phase project can be very successful if the two project managers are both engaged early in the project and remain engaged as needed.
- Good planning paid off when plans were executed. We spent a fair amount of time developing a good project charter, scope statement, WBS, schedules, and so on. Everyone worked together to develop these planning documents, and there was strong buy-in. We kept the plans up-to-date and made key project information available for everyone on a secure Web site.
- Creativity and innovation are infectious. Many creative and innovative ideas were used on this project. After departments had so much fun making their posters in their work areas, people picked up on the idea of being creative and innovative throughout the project. Everyone realized that training and learning could be enjoyable.
- The project steering committee was very effective, and it was extremely helpful to meet regularly. Having members from different departments at AHS was very important and helped in promoting the training required of caregivers as part of this project.

5. Describe one example of what went right on this project.

Leadership wanted to try using an experience nurse to run the clinical portion of the project but was concerned about her general lack of project management experience. Using the PMO to supply a senior project manager to serve as a coach and mentor helped her be successful. This approach has put AHS into a position where we can develop nurses to manage clinical projects.

6. Describe one example of what went wrong on this project.

Physicians did not support the project from the start. They are naturally resistant to any defined workflow that limits, or even appears to limit, their choices when caring for patients. This response should have been predicted based on past projects.

7. What will you do differently on the next project based on your experience working on this project?
Engage senior clinical leadership earlier in the project in order to avoid the overt and covert initial resistance to this project.

Figure 9-5. Project lessons-learned report

Media Snapshot

Disaster struck the Boston Marathon on April 15, 2013, after two explosions killed three people and injured 282. Three CIOs from hospitals in the area reflected on the how their health IT systems handled this difficult situation.

- Jonathan Teich, MD, chief medical informatics officer for Elsevier and as assistant professor of medicine at Harvard: "There are several aspects to information management in a disaster. As you can imagine, this is a situation full of many more patients with much higher acuity than we're used to, often with types of problems, such as blast injuries, that we train for but do not see very often."

- John Halamka, MD, CIO of Beth Israel Deaconess Medical Center in Boston, a practicing emergency physician and Harvard professor: "From an IT perspective, maintaining a high bandwidth, reliable and secure infrastructure was key. The demand for communication – voice, email, social media and streaming video was very high. The scalability built into the design of all our systems – networks, servers, storage, and client devices – served us well...I was in touch with all my managers and staff by 4 p.m. There were no open IT issues. Aside from the shock and eventual anger we all felt at having this happen in our home town, it was a typical operational day."

- Jim Noga, vice president and CIO Partners HealthCare: Noga said that IT's role was definitely subordinate to the direct care providers. "It is our job to ensure we make available to them the IT resources they need. IT participates in emergency planning exercises and understands the importance of steady-state, assuring the high availability of systems, keeping communications channels open and otherwise staying out of the way. That is our focus during a crisis." [3]

Project Close-Out Meeting and Knowledge Transfer

It is good practice to hold a close-out meeting as a project nears completion or termination. At this meeting, like the kick-off meeting, you should invite key project stakeholders. Some people call this **close-out meeting** a **post-mortem** because it is normally held after the project has died or been put to rest. The project champion should start off the meeting, and the project manager and his/her team should review information like the following:

- The scope, time, and cost goals and outcomes
- The success criteria and results in achieving them
- Major changes that occurred during the project and how they were addressed
- The major lessons learned on the project
- A review of the transition to operations

The project team should also ask for comments and questions from stakeholders. It's important to get other perspectives on how things went. If there are still any issues that need to be addressed, the project manager should follow through on them to successfully close them out.

It is also important to take time to transfer knowledge learned while working on the project. In particular, people who will take over products or results produced as part of the project would need to spend time with project team members so they understand what is involved in detail. In this example, people from IT were actively engaged as part of the project, and they would also be responsible for ongoing maintenance and operations of the VAPR database and reporting system. However, the clinical training department was not heavily involved in the project, and they would be responsible for maintaining the VAPR online training program. The online training program would have to be reviewed with them and transferred to their department for ongoing maintenance.

Jeff and Pat met personally with anyone responsible for maintaining the products or services operationally, primarily to ensure that the functional teams were comfortable picking up the operational aspects of the work. If required they would provide additional support or mentoring on the transitioned project deliverables, even though the project may have technically ended.

Many organizations are working hard to improve the knowledge transfer process, because employee knowledge or human capital is one of their key assets. It is crucial, therefore to make project knowledge transfer a priority, especially if the benefits of a project are not achieved immediately. For example, one of the success criteria for the VAPR project was to reduce the incidence of VAP by 25% within 90 days of implementation. Pat made sure that the Quality Council understood this and other goals so they could monitor the performance of the changes initiated as part of the VAPR project.

> ## Best Practice
>
> Kent Greenes is an expert and consultant on knowledge management. Blogger Dale Arseneault captured the following useful ideas from one of Kent's presentations on best practices in knowledge transfer:
> 1. "Best" or "better" practices are not adopted; they're adapted.
> 2. As Jack Welch said, "You don't have a better or best practice until someone else is using it."
> 3. The learner is important, and making learning easy is critical or people will recreate "good enough."
> 4. Focus on general, broadly applicable practices first, rather than choosing highly specialized practices.
> 5. Do something, see what works, then broaden the scope.
> 6. Peer assistance is a critical tool to begin, and even conclude, the process.
> 7. Uncover success stories, communicate the stories, and assist the learning and adaption processes.
> 8. Facilitation is critical to the process - both the role and the capability.
> 9. Documentation/video/audio artifacts are the starting point for discovery and productive conversation; it is vital to put the people with the learning needs and the people who have the experience together to enable transfer.
> 10. To facilitate discovery of best practices, leverage communities wherever possible.[4]

PROJECT PROCUREMENT MANAGEMENT

The final process in project procurement management is closing procurements, which involves completion of each procurement. The project team should determine if all work required in each contract was completed correctly and satisfactorily and resolve any open items. The team should also update records to reflect final results and archive information for future use. Closing procurements may occur many times during a project, as each contract should be formally closed as the work is completed.

Tools to assist in closing procurements include:

- *Procurement audits*: **Procurement audits** are often performed to identify lessons learned in the entire procurement process. Organizations should strive to improve all of their business processes, including procurement management.

- *Negotiated settlements*: Ideally, any disagreements during procurement will be settled by negotiating between the buyer and seller. Sometimes other methods are required, such mediation, arbitration, or litigation.

- *A records management system*: A **records management system** provides the ability to easily organize, find, and archive documents, such as those related to procurement. It is often an automated system, or at least partially automated, because there can be a large amount of information related to project procurement.

Outputs from closing procurements include closed procurements (such as closed contracts) and updates to organizational process assets. Just as with closing the project or phase, updating organizational process assets includes documentation, historical information, and lessons learned. To close contracts, the buying organization often provides the seller with formal written notice that the contract has been completed. Buyers might also consider the final payment to the seller as the contract closeout. The contract itself should include requirements for formal acceptance and closure.

Healthcare Perspective

Many industries (restaurants, hotels, entertainment parks, etc.) have used themes when designing facilities, but it's a recent trend for healthcare organizations. Children's hospitals, in particular, have begun adopting themed design due to fierce competition and customer expectations, and a memorable interior helps them stand out among their peers. For example, the University of Minnesota Amplatz Children's Hospital in Minneapolis adopted a "Passport to Discovery" theme where each floor has a unique animal, color, and habitat. Patients are issued a "passport" at check-in, and they receive stamps on their passport as they travel through the hospital. The theme also assists in navigation, as the terrazzo floor in the main lobby includes a beautiful compass pattern laid at magnetic north, and anyone with an actual compass could use it to find their way around the hospital.

Tsoi/Kobus & Associates, the design firm for this project, documented several do's and don'ts in their lessons learned for this project:
- Don't be too abstract when selecting your theme.
- Be sensitive of the ages, ethnic, and socioeconomic backgrounds of all users.
- Avoid an unsophisticated or cartoonish approach.
- Don't let the theme upstate the architecture.

"Because we worked closely with the Amplatz Children's Hospital team throughout the design process, our client became the strongest advocate of the 'Passport to Discovery' theme. They made sure that their garage consultant used the correct accent color for each parking level; they coordinated with their various vendors and made sure the storytellers were incorporated on the covers of the wall-mounted CPU units and on the hundreds of clocks throughout the hospital. The result is a space that is integrated down to the last detail…A successful themed hospital interior demands a high level of creativity and self-discipline from interior designers and intense collaboration among different design trades. But the hard work comes with rewards—beautiful spaces for people at their most vulnerable times"[5]

Sample Written Notice of a Closed Contract

Figure 9-7 provides an example of a formal letter that AHS sent to the online training program provider, Greek Geeks, to formally close out their contract. The contract, a service agreement in this case, included a clause stating that written notice would be provided to formally close the agreement. The seller in this particular example also requested that the buyer provide a short performance assessment as part of the closure letter. (See Chapter 6 to review the service agreement and Chapter 5 for the contract statement of work.)

Academic Health Systems Contract Closure Notice
March 8

As described in our service agreement, this letter provides formal notice that the work you were contracted to perform for Academic Health Systems (AHS) has been completed. Greek Geeks developed an online training program to be hosted on AHS' current online training system. Final payment is being processed based on the invoice provided by Greek Geeks.

Pat Wager, the project manager, has provided the following performance assessment for the work provided:

"We were very pleased with the work of Greek Geeks. Members of the firm were professional, knowledgeable, and easy to work with. AHS depended on Greek Geeks to develop an online training program for this important project, and we were extremely happy with the results. On a scale of 1 to 10, you earned a 10!"

Christopher Michaels

By: Christopher Michaels, Contract Specialist
Date: March 8

Figure 9-7. Sample contract closure notice

What Went Wrong?

Everyone seems to agree that it is important to document and share project lessons learned, yet a survey of 961 experienced project managers found that although 62 percent had formal procedures for learning lessons from projects, only 12 percent adhered closely to them.

The Project Management (PM) Perspective research team wanted to discover how organizations capture lessons learned and apply them to new projects. Their findings were very discouraging. Although many tools and processes were in place for capturing lessons-learned information at the end of a project, few organizations bothered to use them.

"End-of-project post-mortems were infrequently and inadequately performed. Project managers cited the usual problems: a lack of time, key people not available, a culture of blame. And, as one interviewee noted, 'Most projects don't have enough budget to support any good closure.'"[6]

ADVICE ON CLOSING PROJECTS

Although project teams do not typically spend much time on closing projects, it is important to do it well. Below are a few words of advice on quickly and successfully closing projects, whether they were successful or not:

- It is important to plan for project closing. There should be deliverables in the WBS, and therefore activities assigned to them, to perform project closing. For example, someone should be assigned the task of reviewing lessons learned and creating one final lessons-learned report. Resources should be assigned to prepare the final project report, presentation, and some type of celebration.

- It will be much easier to close a project if the project team captures lessons learned and other important information required for closing as soon as possible. For example, the project team should have some type of log where everyone can document lessons learned as they occur—starting on the first day of the project. A simple blog would work well for this purpose, or team members could document lessons learned as part of progress reports.

- Project managers should take time to thank their team and other project stakeholders and have some type of closing celebration. Just having a team lunch or informal gathering with refreshments might be appropriate. If it was a big, highly successful project, a more formal celebration and rewards would be appropriate. See the examples in the following *What Went Right?* passage.

What Went Right?

Many project teams go all out to celebrate project closing. For example:

- Popular television shows likes American Idol have great closing shows. For example, in the 2013 season finale, there were performances from Jennifer Hudson, Adam Lambert, Mariah Carey, Keith Urban, and others before announcing the winner, Candice Glover. You can find several video clips of these and other final talent-related shows on the Internet.

- Many viewers get teary eyes watching the last few minutes of Extreme Home Makeover . Ty Pennington and his team of designers, builders, volunteers, friends, family, and neighbors gather to see the new home built quickly for a family in need. Everyone enjoys the tradition of shouting, "Move that bus!"

Of course this chapter would not be complete without a cartoon about closing projects (Figure 9-8). May you never have nightmares about not finishing your projects!

Figure 9-8. Bad dreams about not finishing projects (www.xkcd.com)

CASE WRAP-UP

Pat and Jeff stood in front of the project steering committee. They invited their entire team to give the final presentation to demonstrate that even though this project included two project managers and two teams working on their own phases, it was a group effort that required ongoing collaboration. Although they had several challenges along the way, as all projects do, overall the project was a success. The new training course got positive feedback from the clinicians, the new workflows were implemented with little pushback, and the reporting system provided accurate and timely data. Although it is too early to know if the project work will result in a reduction in the incidence of VAP, the system is now in place to make that happen. Jeff asked his team members to summarize their accomplishments, and then Pat's team followed with theirs. Both Jeff and Pat were proud of how their teams worked together, and it was clear to the steering committee that these staff members were ready to tackle the next challenging project.

CHAPTER SUMMARY

Closing phases or projects involves gaining stakeholder and customer acceptance of the final products and services, and bringing the phase or project to an orderly end. It includes verifying that all of the deliverables are complete. This chapter summarizes the closing processes and key outputs for project integration and procurement management.

Closing outputs related to integration management include final products, services, or result transition and updates to organizational process assets. Sample closing documents for the VAPR project include a final project report, lessons-learned report, transition documents, and customer acceptance/project completion form. It is also good practice to hold a close-out meeting and hold some type of celebration when a project ends.

Closing outputs related to procurement management include closed procurements and updates to organizational process assets. A sample written contract closure notice is provided for the VAPR project.

Helpful advice for closing projects includes planning for closure, documenting lessons learned and other important information as soon as possible, and celebrating project closure.

QUICK QUIZ

1. Which knowledge areas include tasks related to closing?

   A. project scope, time, cost, and quality management

   B. project integration, scope, time, cost, and quality management

   C. project integration and procurement management

   D. all of the knowledge areas

2. Which of the following statements is false?

   A. Even though many projects are canceled before completion, it is still important to formally close any project.

   B. Closing includes verifying that all of the deliverables are complete.

   C. Closing often includes a final presentation and report.

   D. Closing does not include developing a transition plan.

3. Updating documentation and historical information produced by the project in a useful format is part of _____.

   A. updating organizational process assets

   B. archival

   C. closing procurements

   D. lessons learned

4. Answering questions such as, "What will you do differently on the next project based on your experience working on this project?" is part of a _____.

   A. lessons-learned report

   B. customer acceptance/project completion form

   C. written notice of contract closure

   D. transition plan

5. What is the most common reason for closing or terminating a project?

   A. addition

   B. integration

   C. extinction

   D. starvation

6. The _____ should include requirements for formal acceptance and closure of contracts.

   A. project management plan

   B. procurement management plan

   C. contract itself

   D. contract management plan

7. A _____ is another name for a project close-out meeting

   A. celebration

   B. post project

   C. final review

   D. post mortem

8. _____are reviews often performed during contract closure to identify lessons learned in the entire procurement process

   A. Procurement audits

   B. Post mortems

   C. Lessons learned

   D. Knowledge transfers

9. Which of the following was not a lesson learned from the VAPR project?

   A. Having clinical leadership publicly supporting the project was critical to gaining clinician buy-in.

   B. The project steering committee was not very effective

   C. Experience clinicians who are not experienced project managers can be very successful if coached and mentored by a senior project manager.

   D. Running a multi-phase project can be very successful if the two project managers are both engaged early in the project and remain engaged as needed.

10.   Which of the following is not advice for closing projects or phases?

   A.   You don't need to celebrate completing a project, especially if it did not go well.

   B.   You should capture lessons learned as soon as possible, not just at the end of a project

   C.   You should include tasks in the WBS for project closing

   D.   You should assign resources to specific project closing tasks

Quick Quiz Answers

1. C; 2. D; 3. A; 4. A; 5. B; 6. C; 7. D; 8. A; 9. B; 10. A

DISCUSSION QUESTIONS

1.   What is involved in closing projects? Why should all projects be formally closed?

2.   What are the main closing outputs created as part of integration management? Why is it important to create a final project report, presentation, and lessons-learned report?

3.   What are the main topics included in a lessons-learned report?

4.   What is a post-mortem?

5.   What are the main closing outputs created as part of procurement management?

6.   What advice about project closing is most useful to you? What other advice would you add?

EXERCISES

Note: These exercises can be done individually or in teams, in-class, as homework, or in a virtual environment. Learners can either write their results in a paper or prepare a short presentation or video to show their results.

1.   Find an example of a large healthcare project that took more than a year to complete. Describe some of the tasks performed to close the project.

2.   Using the lessons-learned template on the companion Web site, write a lessons-learned report for a project you worked on. If you cannot think of one, interview someone who recently completed a project and write a lessons-learned report on that project.

3.   Compare the lessons-learned template on the companion Web site and one you find from another resource. For example, Microsoft has a Word template for one. Summarize their similarities and differences, citing your references.

4. Find an article or video that provides a good example of closing a healthcare project. Summarize your findings.

5. Watch the videos mentioned in the Video Highlights for this chapter about the Space Shuttle Challenger disaster and lessons learned from it. (See www.healthcarepm.com for the direct links.) Research other articles and videos about the lessons learned from the Challenger and space travel since then. Document your findings and opinions.

TEAM PROJECTS

Note: These team projects can be done in-class, as homework, or in a virtual environment. Learners can either write their results in a paper or prepare a short presentation or video to show their results

1. Your organization is about to complete a project to raise money for an important charity. Assume that there are 1,000 people in your organization. Also, assume that you had six months to raise as much money as possible, with a goal of $100,000. With just one week to go, you have raised $92,000. Prepare a lessons-learned report for the project, using information from your responses to this exercise in previous chapters as well as your creativity to determine what the final outcome was for the project.

2. You are part of a team in charge of a project to help people in your company (500 people) lose weight. This project is part of a competition, and the top "losers" will be featured in a popular television show. Assume that you had six months to complete the project and a budget of $10,000. The project will end in one week, so you and your team are busy closing out the project. Prepare a lessons-learned report for the project, using information from your responses to this exercise in previous chapters as well as your creativity to determine what the final outcome was for the project.

3. Using the information you developed in Team Project 1 or 2, role-play the final project meeting, at which you present the final project presentation to key stakeholders. Determine who will play what role (project manager, team member from a certain department, senior managers, and so on). Be creative in displaying different personalities (a senior manager who questions the importance of the project to the organization, a team member who is very shy or obnoxious).

4. Perform the closing tasks for one of the case studies provided in Appendix B. If you are working on a real team project, create relevant closing documents, such as a final project report and lessons-learned report, using the templates and samples in this chapter as guides. Present your results to the class.

KEY TERMS

close-out — A meeting held at the end of the project.

post-mortem meeting — A term sometimes used for a project close-out meeting since it is held after the project has died or been put to rest.

procurement audits — Reviews often performed during contract closure to identify lessons learned in the entire procurement process.

records management system — A tool that provides the ability to easily organize, find, and archive documents.

END NOTES

[1]Vindu Goel, "How Google Decides to Pull the Plug," The New York Times (February 14, 2009).

[2]Associated Press, "Challengers Lessons Still Echo 25 Years Later," www.youtube.com (January 27, 2011).

[3] Bernie Monegain, "IT key for Boston bombing patients: CIOs from three of Boston's elite hospitals discuss its impact on critical patient care," Healthcare IT News (April 17, 2013).

[4]Dale Arseneault, "Best Practice Knowledge Transfer – Practical Ideas," Reflections on Knowledge Management and Organizational Innovation (January 15, 2008).

[5]Chu Foxlin, "Lessons learned from the new University of Minnesota Amplatz Children's Hospital," Healthcare Design (December 21, 2011).

[6]Blaize Reich, "Lessons Not Learned," Projects @ Work, (October 9, 2008).

Chapter 10

Best Practices in Project Management

LEARNING OBJECTIVES

After reading this chapter, you will be able to:

- Define best practices in general and best practices in project management for healthcare organizations
- Summarize best practices in project management for individuals
- Explain how improving project management maturity can improve project and organizational performance
- Describe research on project management maturity
- Discuss best practices described in this text
- Read final advice about project management

OPENING CASE

After completing the Ventilator Associated Pneumonia Reduction (VAPR) project, Jeff suggested that Pat be asked to join a special task force to work with the new corporate Project Management Office (PMO) recently formed by the CEO, Francis Anthony. Their purpose was to create a repository of project management best practice information and make recommendations on specific ones most useful for the corporation and each division, such as Academic Health Systems (AHS).

The PMO VP, Marie Scott, led the task force. Other members included representatives from each division as well as three other members of the corporate PMO. They were expected to complete their work within two months, and Pat was asked to spend about ten hours per week on this task force. Pat had a good experience as project manager on the VAPR project, but she knew that she had a lot to learn about improving her skills. She was excited to be a part of this team and looked forward to improving the organization's project management capabilities. The rest of the task force was excited to have Pat, a nurse just learning project management, taking part in the task force. They knew her clinical background and recent experience would provide insights they needed.

INTRODUCTION

Many organizations understand the value of project management, yet they struggle to implement it well. There is great value to learning about best practices in project management on a case-by-case basis, but you can also learn a lot by looking at larger studies of best practices. This chapter defines project management best practices and provides information on best practices for organizations and individuals. It also describes how increasing an organization's project management maturity level can improve project and organizational performance.

PMI published a report in 2013 called "Pulse of the Profession." You can download this free report from www.pmi.org as well as a one-page infographic called "The High Cost of Low Performance" and access related reports by other organizations. Of course PMI wants to promote project management, but it is hard to ignore some of the facts provided in their global survey:

- Organizations with high performance in meeting project scope goals, timelines, and budgets risk only $20 million per $1 billion spent, while their less successful peers jeopardize $280 million or fourteen times more for the same $1 billion spent.

- Only 54 percent of respondents say their organizations fully understand the value of project management, and only 6 percent have a project management-related role at the C-level (i.e. CIO, CFO, etc.).
- Since 2008, project success rates have declined ten percentage points. [1]

What Went Right?

It may seem surprising to know that many famous corporations still do not follow very basic project management processes or have just recently adopted them. Below are a few examples of how organizations have benefited from following best practices in project management:

- One of the world's largest rental-car companies, Hertz, just established project management offices in 2007 and developed standard processes for their organization. For example, in order to optimize bus service for customers at Heathrow Airport in London, bus drivers defined project goals and outcomes, analyzed information, established simple milestones, and performed measurements of the scope, time, cost, and customer satisfaction goals of the project. This simple process helped Hertz to greatly improve bus services. "Project management is changing the face of Hertz. It's the toolbox the company has never had before, and it's changing who we are."[2]

- The board of Siemens launched a worldwide initiative to improve its project management. The German electronics group had worked out that half its turnover came from project-like work, and it calculated that if it could complete all of these projects on time and to budget, it would add EURO3 billion ($3.7 billion U.S. dollars) to its bottom line over three years. A key element of the scheme was the introduction of project managers to the company's sales teams to try and temper their more extravagant promises, a move that requires a careful balance between reining them in and killing the deal. [3]

DEFINING PROJECT MANAGEMENT BEST PRACTICES

In order to benefit from best practices in project management, it is important to first define what best practices are. Below are three general definitions of best practices:

- Webster's Dictionary (2007) defined a best practice as "a practice which is most appropriate under the circumstances, especially as considered acceptable or regulated in business; a technique or methodology that, through experience and research, has reliably led to a desired or optimum result."
- Wikipedia (2009) defined a best practice as "the most efficient (least amount of effort) and effective (best results) way of accomplishing a task, based on repeatable procedures that have proven themselves over time for large numbers of people....The idea is that with proper processes, checks, and testing, a desired outcome can be delivered with fewer problems and unforeseen complications."

- Wikipedia (2013) defines a best practice as "a method or technique that has consistently shown results superior to those achieved with other means, and that is used as a benchmark. In addition, a 'best' practice can evolve to become better as improvements are discovered. Best practice is considered by some as a business buzzword, used to describe the process of developing and following a standard way of doing things that multiple organizations can use."

Perhaps you do not think it is a best practice to use a Wikipedia definition in a text book! The point is that there is more than one definition of a best practice, and the concept itself is complex. A best practice for one industry or region may not work in a different one, as you will see later in this chapter. Further, as noted from the two Wikipedia citations, definitions and best practices change over time.

For example, if you are reading this text as part of a course, you should know about best practices for studying and getting good grades in college. There are general best practices that most people might agree on, such as showing up for and paying attention in class, doing homework on time, setting aside time to study and get a good night's rest before exams, and so on. For individual students, however, there might be other best practices that are more effective, and those practices might vary based on the subject and course. Perhaps you need to be part of study group to do well on homework assignments and exams in a particular subject. Perhaps for another class or student you need to study alone in a very quiet location. Perhaps a particular course requires a lot of online participation to get a good grade. Some general best practices might apply, but there are also some that are unique to each person or course.

The following sections describe PMI's view of best practices in project management as well as information from a popular business text on the subject.

Video Highlights

Some people reflect on best practices for leading a good life, especially when they find out they have a terminal disease. For example, millions of people watched "The Last Lecture" by Dr. Randy Pausch, a computer science professor at Carnegie Mellon University who was diagnosed with pancreatic cancer. You can watch a video of the entire lecture and several related videos, including one where Diane Sawyer interviewed Dr. Pausch after he gave his lecture in a segment on ABC News called "Lecture of a Lifetime." At the beginning of the interview, Dr. Pausch says that his mother used to introduce him as a doctor, but not the kind who helps people. Dr. Pausch said that if you wait long enough, other people will show you their good side. He also emphasized how important it is to tell the truth and lead your life the right way. At the end of the interview, Diane Sawyer said that he definitely is the kind of doctor who helps people! The following text was taken from the Web site, lastlecture.com, in June 2012:

"On September 18, 2007, computer science professor Randy Pausch stepped in front of an audience of 400 people at Carnegie Mellon University to deliver a last lecture called 'Really Achieving Your Childhood Dreams.' With slides of his CT scans beaming out to the audience, Randy told his audience about the cancer that is devouring his pancreas and that will claim his life in a matter of months. On the stage that day, Randy was youthful, energetic, handsome, often cheerfully, darkly funny. He seemed invincible. But this was a brief moment, as he himself acknowledged…Randy's lecture has become a phenomenon, as has the book he wrote based on the same principles, celebrating the dreams we all strive to make realities. Sadly, Randy lost his battle to pancreatic cancer on July 25th, 2008, but his legacy will continue to inspire us all, for generations to come."

The Project Management Institute's Definition of Best Practices

The Project Management Institute (PMI) Standards Development Program published the first version of the Organizational Project Management Maturity Model (OPM3) in December 2003 to address the need to bridge the gap between organizational strategy and successful projects. (Maturity models are described in more detail later in this chapter.) OPM3® is a standard developed to provide a way for organizations to measure their organizational project management maturity against a comprehensive set of best practices. The second edition of this document was published in 2008 (the most recent one as of publication of this text).

OPM3®, Second Edition defines **best practices** as "optimal methods, currently recognized within a given industry or discipline, to achieve a goal or objective."[4] It lists hundreds of best practices, which PMI says are achieved through developing and consistently demonstrating their supporting capabilities, as observed through measurable outcomes. **Capabilities** are incremental steps leading up to one or more best practices, and

outcomes are the tangible or intangible results of applying capabilities. A **key performance indicator (KPI)** is a criterion used to determine the degree to which an outcome is achieved.

The first edition of OPM3® provides the following example to illustrate a best practice, capability, outcome, and key performance indicator:

- *Best practice:* Establish internal project management communities

- *Capability (one of four for this best practice):* Facilitate project management activities

- *Outcome:* Local initiatives, meaning the organization develops pockets of consensus around areas of special interest

- *Key performance indicator:* Community addresses local issues

Best practices are organized into three levels: project, program, and portfolio. Within each of those categories, best practices are categorized by four stages of process improvement: standardize, measure, control, and improve. For example, the list that follows contains several best practices listed in OPM3:

- Project best practices:

    o *Project initiation process standardization*—Project initiation process standards are established.

    o *Project plan development process measurement*—Project plan development process measures are established, assembled, and analyzed.

    o *Project scope planning process control*—Project scope planning process controls are established and executed to control the stability of the process.

    o *Project scope definition process improvement*—Project scope definition process problem areas are assessed, process improvement recommendations are collected, and process improvements are implemented.

- Program best practices:

    o *Program activity definition process standardization*—Program activity definition process standards are established.

    o *Program activity sequencing process measurement*—Program activity sequencing process measures are established, assembled, and analyzed.

    o *Program activity duration estimating process control*—Program activity duration estimating process controls are established and executed to control the stability of the process.

    o *Program schedule development process improvement*—Program schedule development process problem areas are assessed, process improvement recommendations are collected, and process improvements are implemented.

- Portfolio best practices:

    o *Portfolio resource planning process standardization*—Portfolio resource planning process standards are established.

    o *Portfolio cost estimating process measurement*—Portfolio cost estimating process measures are established, assembled, and analyzed.

    o *Portfolio cost budgeting process control*—Portfolio cost budgeting process controls are established and executed to control the stability of the process.

Ultimate Business Library Best Practices

In 2003, the Ultimate Business Library published a book called *Best Practice: Ideas and Insights from the World's Foremost Business Thinkers*. This book includes articles by well-known business leaders such as Warren Bennis (author of over 30 books on leadership, including *On Becoming a Leader*), Daniel Goleman (author of *Emotional Intelligence* and other popular books), and Thomas Stewart (editor of the *Harvard Business Review* and author of *Intellectual Capital: The New Wealth of Organizations*).

In the book's introduction, Rosabeth Moss Kanter, a professor at Harvard Business School and a well-known author and consultant, says that visionary leaders know "the best practice secret: Stretching to learn from the best of the best in any sector can make a big vision more likely to succeed."[6] Kanter also emphasizes the need to have measurable standards for best practices. Organizations can measure performance against their own past; against peers; and, even better, against their potential. Kanter suggests that organizations need to continue to reach for higher standards. She suggests the following exercise regimen for business leaders who want to intelligently adapt best practices to help their own organizations:

- Reach high. Stretch. Raise standards and aspirations. Find the best of the best and then use it as inspiration for reaching full potential.

- Help everyone in your organization become a professional. Empower people to manage themselves through benchmarks and standards based on best practice exchange.

- Look everywhere. Go far afield. Think of the whole world as your laboratory for learning.[7]

Media Snapshot

After reviewing many nominations in 2007, the Project Management Institute published a list of twenty-four organizations from around the world that are considered to be outstanding in project management. These organizations apply project management best practices that are fully supported by the entire organizations and have a significant impact on the bottom line. Project management is a core component of their business. Below is an alphabetical list of these organizations and their countries:

- AgênciaClick (Brazil)
- Airports Company South Africa (South Africa)
- Beijing Organizing Committee for the Olympic Games (China)
- Central Federal Lands Highway Division (United States)
- Commonwealth Scientific and Industrial Research Organisation (Australia)
- Fluor Corp. (United States)
- IBM (United States)
- Indra Sistemas S.A. (Spain)
- Infosys Technologies (India)
- Intel Corp. (United States)
- MD Anderson Cancer Center (United States)
- Memphis Managed Care Corp. (United States)
- Missouri State Government (United States)
- Mutual of Omaha (United States)
- National Aeronautics and Space Administration (United States)
- Petrobras (Brazil)
- Saudi Aramco (Saudi Arabia)
- Serasa (Brazil)
- Shell (Netherlands)
- Stork NV (Netherlands)
- Suncorp (Australia)
- TV Guide Interactive (United States)
- Wipro Technologies (India)Workplace Technology Services (Canada)[5]

Note that in 2013 the MD Anderson Cancer Center in Houston, Texas, also earned the No. 1 spot in U.S. News & World Report's annual rankings of the best hospitals for cancer care for the sixth year in a row!

In addition, Robert Butrick, author of *The Project Workout,* wrote an article on best practices in project management for the Ultimate Business Library book. He suggests that organizations need to follow these basic principles of project management:

- Make sure your projects are driven by your strategy. Be able to demonstrate how each project you undertake fits your business strategy, and screen out unwanted projects as soon as possible.

- Use a staged approach. You can rarely plan a project in its entirety. Use progressive steps or stages to project planning, and use the same generic stages for all types of projects. Have gate reviews before starting each stage to revalidate a project and before committing more resources and funding for the project. Place high emphasis on the early stages of a project to reduce risks and decrease time to market.

- Engage your stakeholders. Ignoring stakeholders often leads to project failure. Be sure to engage stakeholders at all stages of a project, and encourage teamwork and commitment at all times.

- Ensure success by planning for it. To help projects succeed, the balance of power often needs to be tipped toward the project and away from line management.

- Monitor against the plan. Everyone working on projects must have guidance, training, and support in creating plans and making project-related decisions. Organizations must develop and follow control techniques for managing risks, issues, scope changes, schedule, costs, and project reviews. Monitoring and forecasting against a plan ensure that everyone is on the same page and prevent unwanted surprises.

- Manage the project control cycle. Monitoring should focus more on the future than on the past. Project managers must continuously check that the project plan is still fit for the purpose of the project and likely to deliver the business benefits on time. Project changes must be managed to ensure that only those enabling project benefits to be realized are accepted. Avoid the dangers of scope creep, and let stakeholders know that project benefits drive the scope.

- Formally close the project: Every project should be closed to make sure that all work ceases, that lessons are learned, and that remaining resources are released for other purposes.[8]

Healthcare Community of Practice Best Practices

PMI's Healthcare Community of Practice published a "List of Project Management Best Practices in a Healthcare Delivery Organization" in 2011. They first defined the goals of the work being performed in healthcare delivery organizations and then listed best practices to meet defined goals.

The key goals of project teams in healthcare delivery organizations include:

1. Clear understanding of the project objectives

2. The project's deliverables are clearly defined

3. Communication of project progress

4. Change management process

5. Resource allocations (identified/approved)

6. System or future state designs clearly understood by sponsor(s) and all stakeholders

7. Risks clearly understood

8. Well planned tests performed

9. Project financial governance

10. Go-Live / Activation activities planned and executed

11. Post project records complete

An example of best practices for the first goal of having a clear understanding of the project objectives include:

a. Expectations clearly defined

b. Purpose clearly defined

      i. product of the project clearly defined

      ii. benefit of the product of the project clearly defined

c. Project objectives expressed in a form easily communicated

d. Project sponsor approves list of objectives in writing

e. Alignment validated with

      i. Strategic plan

      ii. Organizational vision

      iii. Organizational mission

      iv. Organizational disaster recovery plan

      v. System and application refresh plan

This document also suggests that it often a best practice to divide projects into distinct phases so that teams can understand their roles and how their efforts satisfy the requirements of the current phase. [9]

BEST PRACTICES OF INDIVIDUAL PROJECT MANAGERS

Andy Crowe, founder and CEO of Velociteach, wrote a book in 2006 called *Alpha Project Managers: What the Top 2% Know That Everyone Else Does Not*. As the title suggests, an alpha project manager is defined as one who falls in the top two percent of project managers in terms of performance. Project managers were rated by their customers, senior managers, and team members based on their performance in the following areas:

- Setting expectations

- Communicating efficiently and effectively

- Managing issues

- Identifying and managing risks

- Leading the project team

- Meeting the scope, quality, time, and budget baselines for the project

- Managing the procurement process

- Managing changes to the project

- Balancing competing stakeholder needs

- Delivering a product, service, or result that met expectations

For this study, Crowe surveyed 860 project managers who had all been clients/students at Velociteach. Although this was not a scientific study, the aggregate results provide interesting information that can help define best practices for project managers. The 860 project managers, their senior managers, customers, and project team members all answered numerous survey questions. The general format of the questions was as follows: Mark the degree with which you agree with the following statement: Strongly disagree (0%), Somewhat disagree (20%), Neutral (50%), Somewhat agree (75%), Strongly agree (100%). For some questions, the scale was based on the degree of importance, with 100% being the most important.

The 18 people identified as alpha project managers varied most from the other project managers in the following ways:

- *They enjoy their work more than their counterparts.* When asked to mark the degree to which they agreed with the statement: "On the whole, I generally love my job," the alpha average response was 67% while the non-alpha average was only 32%. They also view their jobs more as a career and took 19% more job-related training than the non-alphas (45.1 hours vs. 38.0 hours in the past three years).

- *They believe they have more authority than their counterparts.* When asked to mark the degree to which they agreed with the statement: "I have adequate authority to manage the projects for which I am responsible," the alpha average response was 89% while the non-alpha average was only 47%. It is interesting to note that from senior management's point of view, the alphas and non-alphas had about the same level of organizational authority at about 87%.

- *They believe they can have a personal impact on project success.* When asked to mark the degree to which they agreed with the statement: "What is the importance of your role on your current project," the alpha average response was 96% while the non-alpha average was only 70%. It is interesting to note that the senior managers' response to this question was very close to the project managers for both groups.

- *They are more efficient and effective communicators.* When project managers' customers, senior managers, and team members were asked, "How would you rank this project manager's overall responsiveness to your project-related requests?" (from very ineffective to very effective) the alphas' stakeholders' average response was 88% while the non-alpha average was only 49%. It is also interesting to note that alpha project managers send *fewer* e-mails per day and spend *less* time in meetings than the non-alphas. They know how to prioritize work and focus on what is most important. When the alphas were probed in interviews to understand more about their communication best practices, key traits emerged:

  o *They talk to stakeholders very early in the project and tailor communication to meet their needs.*

  o *They create a communication schedule and stick to it.*

  o *They communicate their messages quickly in a clear and concise manner.*

  o *They create an open communication channel and talk with stakeholders regularly about the topic of communication itself.*

  o *They know that on many projects, communication is the only deliverable stakeholders will receive until the product or service is completed.*

- *They allocate about twice as much time toward project planning.* Alpha project managers spend more time in every process group than their counterparts except for execution, as follows:

  o *Initiating:* 2% vs. 1%

  o *Planning:* 21% vs. 11%

  o *Executing:* 69% vs. 82%

  o *Controlling:* 5% vs. 4%

  o *Closing:* 3% vs. 2%

- *They think it is important for the project manager to be a hands-on manager and a domain expert.* When asked to "Rank the importance of the project manager being a domain expert as a contributor to overall project success," the average alpha response was 94% vs. 68% for the non-alphas.

- *They can get consensus and handle conflicts.* When senior managers and customers were asked "How would you rate this project manager's ability to identify, understand, and satisfy your individual goals for the project," the average alpha response was 92% vs. 64%. When asked a similar question about conflict resolution, the alpha average was 61% vs. 46%.

- *They are managing more strategic projects and understand strategic goals.* When asked "Is your primary project considered highly strategic to your organization," the average alpha response was 60% vs. 41%. When asked, "Can you state your organization's top (three) strategic goals," the average alpha response was 60% vs. 23%.

The results of this study can be interpreted in several ways, especially if you analyze the interview responses, as Crowe does in his book. Some of the areas where alpha project managers are different from non-alpha project managers are based on their attitudes and beliefs, such as enjoying their work, believing they have authority, and believing they can have a personal impact on a project. Most of the other areas, however, are based on best practices which *can be learned*, such as being a good communicator, spending more time on project planning, being a hands-on project manager and a domain expert, being able to get consensus and handle conflict, and understanding and supporting strategic goals.[10]

What Went Wrong?

Many people are "thrown" into the role of project manager. For example, Nick Carson (his name is disguised) was an outstanding technical specialist on a large biotech project. He was working on a crucial project for his small company when the project manager quit. Senior management asked Nick to take over. Nick had never led a project, and he made the mistake of trying to still do his old job while also managing the project.

Nick worked lots of overtime and did actually complete the project, but his senior managers were not happy. Nick never gave them a detailed schedule or understandable status reports. Whenever he talked to them, they could not understand all of the technical detail he focused on. Nick thought he did a great job, so he was amazed when he was offered a severance package to leave the company. He decided he never wanted to manage a project again.

This true story illustrates the fact that many organizations do not do a good job of selecting, training, or mentoring their project managers. Nick was an *accidental project manager*, a common, and unfair, method whereby many technical people become project managers.

PROJECT MANAGEMENT MATURITY

In addition to following best practices, organizations can improve project management performance by using **maturity models**, which are frameworks for helping organizations improve their processes and systems. Maturity models describe an evolutionary path of increasingly organized and systematically more mature processes. Many maturity models have four to six levels, with the first level describing characteristics of the least organized or least mature organizations, and the highest level describing the characteristics of the most organized and mature organizations.

Capability Maturity Model Integration

A popular maturity model is in continuous development at the Software Engineering Institute at Carnegie Mellon University. The Software Engineering Institute (SEI) is a federally funded research and development center established in 1984 by the U.S. Department of Defense with a broad mandate to address the transition of software engineering technology. The **Capability Maturity Model Integration** (CMMI) is "a process improvement approach that provides organizations with the essential elements of effective processes. It can be used to guide process improvement across a project, a division, or an entire organization. CMMI helps integrate traditionally separate organizational functions, set process improvement goals and priorities, provide guidance for quality processes, and provide a point of reference for appraising current processes."[11] Many companies that want to work in the government market have realized that they will not get many opportunities even to bid on projects unless they have a CMMI Level 3.

The capability levels of the CMMI, numbered zero through five, are:

0. *Incomplete*: At this level, a process is either not performed or partially performed. No generic goals exist for this level, and one or more of the specific goals of the process area are not satisfied.

1. *Performed*: A performed process satisfies the specific goals of the process area and supports and enables the work needed to produce work products. Although this capability level can result in improvements, those improvements can be lost over time if they are not institutionalized.

2. *Managed*: At this level, a process has the basic infrastructure in place to support it. The process is planned and executed based on policies and employs skilled people who have adequate resources to produce controlled outputs. The process discipline reflected by this level ensures that existing practices are retained during times of stress.

3. *Defined*: At this maturity level, a process is rigorously defined and the standards, process descriptions, and procedures for a project are tailored from the organization's set of standard processes to suit that particular project.

4. *Quantitatively Managed*: At this level, a process is controlled using statistical and other quantitative techniques. The organization establishes quantitative objectives for quality and process performance that are used as criteria in managing the process.

5.   *Optimizing*: An optimizing process is improved based on an understanding of the common causes of variation inherent in the process. The focus is on continually improving the range of process performance through incremental and innovative improvements.[12]

Project Management Maturity Models

In the late 1990s, several organizations began developing project management maturity models based on the Capability Maturity Model (CMM), an earlier version of CMMI. Just as organizations realized the need to improve their software development processes and systems, they also realized the need to enhance their project management processes and systems for all types of projects. A few of these maturity models include:

- PMI's OPM3, as mentioned earlier, which includes four process improvement stages or levels:

  1.   Standardize

  2.   Measure

  3.   Control

  4.   Continuously improve

- The International Institute for Learning, Inc. uses Kerzner's model, with five levels of project management maturity:

  1.   Common language

  2.   Common processes

  3.   Singular methodology

  4.   Benchmarking

  5.   Continuous improvement

- ESI International's ProjectFRAMEWORK™ is a five-level model:

  1.   Ad-hoc

  2.   Consistent

  3.   Integrated

  4.   Comprehensive

  5.   Optimizing

- Berkeley's Project Management Process Maturity (PM) model includes these five levels:

  1.   Ad-hoc: No project management processes or practices are consistently available, and data is not consistently collected or analyzed

2. Planned: Project management processes, problem areas, and data are informally defined, identified, collected

3. Managed: Formal project planning and control systems and data are managed

4. Integrated: Program management is used, and project management data and processes are integrated and quantitatively analyzed, measured, and stored

5. Sustained: Project management processes are continuously improved and are fully understood, and data is optimized and sustained

Figure 10-1 provides an illustration of the Berkeley model. Each project management maturity model shows a progression from the least mature to most mature level, although the number and title of levels vary somewhat.

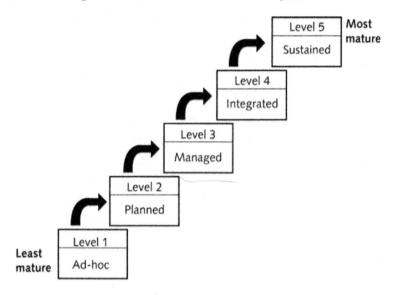

Figure 10-1. Berkeley project management process maturity model

Research on Project Management Maturity

Regardless of the project management maturity model followed, the goal is clear: organizations want to improve their ability to manage projects. Many organizations are assessing where they stand in terms of project management maturity, just as they did for software development maturity with the CMMI maturity model. Organizations are recognizing that they must make a commitment to the discipline of project management to improve project quality and organizational performance.

Ibbs' The Value of Project Management Research

Several studies have proven the value of improving project management maturity to organizations. William Ibbs, a Professor at the University of California at Berkeley, led a PMI-sponsored research study published in 2002 called "The Value of Project Management." After assessing project management maturity using Berkeley's model and reviewing data from 52 companies in the U.S., the researchers made the following conclusions:

- *Companies with more mature project management practices have better project performance.* They deliver projects on time and on budget more often. Less mature companies often miss their schedule targets by 40 percent and their cost targets by 20 percent.

- *Project management maturity is strongly correlated with more predictable project schedule and cost performance.* More mature companies have a schedule performance index (SPI) variation of 0.08 and a cost performance index (CPI) variation of 0.11. Less mature companies have indexes of 0.16 for SPI and CPI. For a $10 million project, this translates into a $1.6 million cost variation.

- *High project management maturity results in lower direct costs of project management.* Companies with a high maturity level spend 6–7 percent of total project costs on project management. Companies with low maturity spent about 11 percent.[13]

Thomas and Mullaly Research on Project Management Value

PMI sponsored another study entitled "Researching the Value of Project Management," which was published in 2008. This 400+-page report summarizes research on 65 organizations. In general, most of the organizations did see value in project management. The researchers stated that they were "extremely comfortable stating unequivocally that project management delivers value to organizations."[14]

It is interesting to note that in this study, unlike the earlier one led by Ibbs, the researchers found that most organizations did not try to quantify the value of project management. They said that measuring ROI "proved extremely elusive." [15] In this study, value focused on measuring project management and satisfaction, alignment, process outcomes, and business outcomes. The authors of this study also found that project management value appears to increase in proportion to the maturity level of the organization. Organizations with a higher level of maturity reported greater levels of intangible value.

This study, as well as the Ibbs' study and many others sponsored by PMI are available for free for PMI members at *www.pmi.org*. You can also keep up-to-date on new developments on the topic of project management value by visiting the Web site *www.valueofpm.com*.

Crawford and Cook-Davies Study on Best Industry Outcomes

In 2012 PMI published another study by Lynn Crawford and Terry Cook-Davies called "Best Industry Outcomes." One purpose of this research was to find best practices and organizational project management outcomes (OPMs) common to different industries by project type, not to specific companies or organizaitons. The researchers addressed questions related to finding the strategic drivers that are characteristic of specific project types and industries, including utilities, IT/telecommunications, engineering/construction, government, financial and business systems, automotive, aerospace/defense, fast moving consumer goods, and pharmaceutical. These industry sectors are listed in order of the mean OPM capabilities found in this study. The researchers also examined outcomes that are most valued based on strategic drivers as well as project management systems and practices associated with strategic drivers and goals.

In the conclusions section of their 152-page report, the authors state, "The presence of patterns between industries…is proven beyond any reasonable doubt…while each industry has evolved its own systems and capabilities in light of its own strategic intentions and drivers, no industry has yet fully developed a suite of systems and capabilities that are sufficiently rounded and robust to produce the OPM outcomes that are necessary to achieve the business success criteria. No industry is without room for improvement." [16]

Customer focus was an important strategic driver across all industries, and execution performance was clearly valued as a success criterion in all sectors. Delivery of a product or service was the most common type of project across all sectors, and meeting time, cost, and resource constraints was a shared challenge. Program management was most ubiquitous across all industries, and quality was also commonly used. The most underrepresented project management concepts or tools included stakeholder management, value management, and organizational change management. All industries were better at achieving cost and schedule outcomes than they were at managing scope and quality, achieving positive trends in productivity, and in implementing strategy.

One interesting finding in this study, among many, was that although the aerospace and defense industry had the highest overall percentage of project management systems in place (followed by IT/telecommunications), they did not use them as frequently or as well as the IT and telecommunications sector. Organizational capabilities were among the lowest of all industry sectors for the aerospace and defense industry, explained by one manager by the desire for engineers to do things their own way. The automotive industry came in last place in terms of overall percentage of project management systems in place, followed by the pharmaceutical industry.

Members of PMI can read this and other PMI-sponsored studies for free from www.pmi.org. Note there are extensions to the *PMBOK® Guide* for the construction industry and for government.

PricewaterhouseCoopers' Study on Boosting Business Performance

As mentioned in Chapter 1, PwC surveyed 200 companies from 30 different countries in 2004 about their project management maturity and found that *over half of all projects fail*. They also found that only 2.5% of corporations consistently meet their targets for scope, time, and cost goals for all types of projects. The survey's main objective, however, was to investigate whether a higher maturity level would provide a higher project performance level. The following conclusions were made by the survey authors:

- *A higher maturity level for an organization enhances overall project performance, not in just one project, but in the overall portfolio of projects.* It makes sense for organizations to develop policies and processes that apply for all types of projects, programs, and project portfolios.

- *Most organizations are not satisfied with their current maturity level.* The total average for survey participants was 2.5 on a 5.0 scale, meaning the organizations use informal processes that are not yet institutionalized. This low maturity level contributes to the high project failure rate.

- *Project failures are often a consequence of organizational aspects over which project managers have little influence.* The top reasons cited for project failure included bad estimates, missed deadlines, scope changes, change in environment, insufficient resources, and change in strategy. Poor quality of deliverables and not adequately defining stakeholders were the least prevalent reasons for project failure.

- *Organizational structure has a big impact on overall project performance.* The higher the alignment between structure and business requirements, the higher the overall project performance. The optimal structure should be based on industry, location, and business objectives. The highest performing companies in terms of project results had a project-oriented or strong matrix structure, giving project managers the most authority and control over resources.

- *Staff development and professional certification enhance overall project performance.* However, more than 60% of the companies surveyed do not regularly offer a development program to their project managers. Investments in project management certification do pay off, and the organizational benefits exceed the costs.

- *A systematic approach to change management is fundamental for superior project performance.* The majority of the best performing and most mature organizations always or frequently apply change management to their projects.

- *Staffing projects with a majority of internal resources as opposed to external resources is a better guarantee of success.* External resources add value when employed in moderation. The highest performance was achieved by using 25% external resources and 75% internal resources.

- *The extent to which project management software is used is correlated to maturity levels.* The lower the maturity level, the more difficulties the organization will have in implementing software. Processes must be established for the software to provide benefits.[17]

In a follow-up study published in 2012, PwC found that project management is gaining ground. Below are key findings from their latest study:

- *Project management maturity levels are on the rise.* 62% of respondents were now at the highest two maturity levels compared to only 21.9% in 2004.

- *Higher maturity yields higher performance.* Organizations have formalized project management processes, especially for scope, quality, and cost management. 66.6% of participants agree that additional change control processes and deliverable controls are in place throughout the project lifecycle to assure quality of project delivery. 62% agree that adoption of quality assurance strategy effectively addresses scope of testing, timing, responsibility, approach, pass/fail criteria, corrective action processes, and sign-off. 57.5% of respondents agree that funds are appropriately allocated to the project, consistent with the project stage, and are only released when board approval has been given.

- *Projects are essential to business success.* When asked why projects were initiated, the main reasons respondents cited were business imperatives (40.2%), revenue generation (30.1%, and cost reduction (10%).

- *Training and staff development in project management has grown drastically.* Approximately 76% of survey respondents indicated that project management training and development opportunities were available, and 67% believed that project management training contributes to business performance.[18]

Best Practice

Staff development and professional certification enhance overall project performance. A company well-known for developing its project managers is IBM.
 	
        After launching an initiative in 1996 to better meet customer needs and ensure a consistent approach to project management, nearly 10,000 IBM employees earned the PMP credential. The company developed the IBM Project Management Center of Excellence to advocate five fundamental steps for every project:
1. Define the scope
2. Ensure top-level sponsorship
3. Establish a vision
4. Manage as a program
5. Communicate successes and lessons learned throughout the organization
        The company created a worldwide project management method designed to be the single, common method for IBM projects and program worldwide. They provide a collection of processes, templates, and tools for all types of project. IBM also provides a nurturing project management community to help employees find mentors, network, develop relationships, and share knowledge. "Through such initiatives, IBM project managers have the ability to take the same training and pursue certification. They use the same terminology, tools and methodology, customized for their own business unit needs," according to Deborah Dell, PMP, operations and support manager at the Project Management Center of Excellence.[19]

SUMMARY OF BEST PRACTICES MENTIONED IN THIS TEXT

As you can see, understanding and applying best practices can help improve the management of projects, programs, portfolios, and entire companies. Several best practices were described throughout this text. Following is a brief summary of some of them:

- Determine how project, program, and portfolio management will work best in your own organization.

- Involve key stakeholders—including shareholders, customers, and employees—in making major decisions. On healthcare projects involving clinical work, be sure to get key clinicians on-board.

- Develop and follow a formal project selection process to ensure projects support business needs.

- Lay the groundwork for projects before they officially start.

- Separate projects by phases when it makes sense to do so. Be sure someone with a clinical background leads clinical project phases.

- Designate a project champion to provide high-level support and participate in key meetings.

- Form a steering committee with key managers from various departments for projects that will cause major organizational change.

- Provide mentoring and training for project managers and other stakeholders.

- Document action items at meetings, and set the next meeting time.

- Document meeting with minutes, focusing on key decisions and action items, and send them out quickly.

- Use more than one approach for creating cost estimates.

- Use formal supplier evaluation procedures to help select sellers.

- Include a detailed statement of work and schedule in contracts.

- Develop and follow a formal change-control process.

- Work with suppliers to ensure that deliverables are produced properly.

- Follow a deliverable acceptance process to verify project scope.

- Be clear and honest in communicating project status information, and share the responsibility for project communications with the entire project team.

- Formally close projects and share lessons learned.

Healthcare Perspective

Diffusion of best practices in healthcare are often measured in decades rather than months. Researchers from the Mayo Clinic shared their recent list of best practices and suggestions for speeding up the process of putting them in place. Some of the Mayo Clinic standardized best practices that were diffused by the end of 2012 include:

- Central Venous Catheter Insertion and Maintenance Practice Standardization
- RN Bedside Rounds (Shift Handoffs)
- Orthopedic Knee and Hip Protocols
- Mortality Management for Deteriorating Patients
- Preventable Harm Metric
- Airway Management–ICU Intubation
- Computerized System for Quality Monitoring
- Value-Based Purchasing Measures Compliance

Mayo Clinic has developed a model of diffusion status tracker, which looks similar to a dashboard for managing a project portfolio. Senior leadership uses this tool to monitor progress on all active best practice projects. "The ability to consistently bring innovations and best practices to scale across entire systems will be a hallmark of the successful health care organizations of the future….Effective managed diffusion of excellence bolsters our most precious possessions: our patients, our esprit de corps, and our reputation."[20]

FINAL ADVICE ON PROJECT MANAGEMENT

Now that you have read this text and discussed project management with others, we hope that you have matured to see project management as a valuable skill for you as an individual and for all types of organizations. The number of projects and their complexity will continue to increase, especially in the healthcare industry, so it is important to understand, apply, and improve the state of project management.

The knowledge and experience we have gained working on and managing projects continues to help us in our careers and in our personal lives. Kathy Schwalbe was fortunate to step into a project management role very early in her career as a U.S. Air Force officer. Her first real job at the age of 22 was as a project manager, and her organization followed a very disciplined approach to project, program, and portfolio management. She has held several job titles at different organizations since then—systems analyst, senior engineer, technical specialist, information technology management consultant, independent consultant, college professor, and now author and publisher. All of these jobs included working on or managing projects. As a wife and mother of three, she can also attest to the fact that project management skills help in planning and executing personal activities (weddings, birthday parties, vacations, moves, fundraisers, and so on) and in dealing with the joys and challenges of everyday life. When people ask Kathy how she can do so much and still seem so relaxed, she notes that using good project management definitely helps.

Dan Furlong had a very different career path. He began his career as a software developer and was given an opportunity to manage a project when his manager was out for an extended period of time due to health issues. Dan found that he enjoyed the planning as much as he did the executing part of software development, and apparently his organization thought he was a good manager as they assigned him the role of project leader. Dan managed the software development efforts for a manufacturing company, then after a dozen years he moved into healthcare. Like Kathy, and most experienced project managers, Dan has had a series of titles and roles over the years (software developer, senior analyst, project leader, project manager, business systems manager, software development manager, special projects manager, project management officer, etc.). In addition to currently serving as the PMO in an academic medical center, Dan is also an author, speaker, small business owner, and adjunct faculty member at multiple universities. He is also a father of three sons and finds that his results-oriented nature helps him successfully juggle his many commitments.

This book would not be complete without one final cartoon, as shown in Figure 10-2. In project management and life in general, it helps to follow best practices and also keep a sense of humor.

Figure 10-2. Use best practices in the proper context! (www.xkcd.com)

CASE WRAP-UP

Pat Wager learned a lot about her company and best practices in project, program, and portfolio management working on the best practices task force. She loved being paid to read books and articles on the subject, and the whole team worked well together. They developed a new section on the corporate Intranet with project management best practice information, and due to Pat's engagement they were able to better account for the special needs of the clinicians. Because most workers and customers were now using smart phones and tablets, they also developed a free application people could download to their mobile devices to access key information.

Marie Scott encouraged Pat to share some of the task force's findings as well as lessons learned on the VAPR project in an article and presentation at a large, international conference. Marie wanted Pat and Jeff to present together, and they were both excited about the opportunity. Even though Pat's department did not have funds budgeted for this trip, Marie offered to pay for it out of the corporate PMO's budget. Pat began to wonder why other clinicians don't use project management more often when they implement change, and she committed to herself that she was going to help change that.

CHAPTER SUMMARY

Many organizations study and apply best practices to improve their ability to manage projects, programs, and portfolios. PMI developed the Organizational Project Management Maturity Model (OPM3) to help organizations assess and improve their project management maturity. OPM3® lists hundreds of best practices organized by project, program, and portfolio management. The Ultimate Business Library published *Best Practices*, which provides advice on best practices to follow for managing projects and organizations in general. PMI's Healthcare Community of Practice has also developed a list of best practices for managing projects in a healthcare delivery organization.

Individual project managers can also use best practices to improve their performance. Andy Crowe did a study to help understand best practices of alpha project managers, or the top 2%. A few findings include the fact that alpha project managers spend much more time on planning and enjoy their jobs more than other project managers.

A maturity model is a framework for helping organizations improve their processes and systems. Several organizations are using project management maturity models to help improve their project management processes and systems. Several studies, including those by Ibbs, Thomas and Mullaly, Crawford and Cook-Davies, and PricewaterhouseCoopers, show the benefits of improving project management maturity.

This text also describes several best practices in managing projects, programs, and portfolios. A summary list is provided in this chapter.

Project management is a valuable skill for individuals and organizations. As the number of projects and their complexity continue to increase, it is important to understand, apply, and improve the discipline of project management.

QUICK QUIZ

1. _____ are optimal methods, currently recognized within a given industry or discipline, to achieve a goal or objective.

   A. Benchmarks

   B. Key performance indicators

   C. Capabilities

   D. Best practices

2. The Project Management Institute initially published the _____ in December 2003 to address the need to bridge the gap between organizational strategy and successful projects.

   A. Organizational Project Management Maturity Model (OPM3)

   B. Best Practices Report

   C. Alpha Project Managers Guide

   D. Project Management Process Maturity (PM)² model

3. The Project Management Institute defines best practices in each of the following areas except _____.

   A. projects

   B. programs

   C. project personnel

   D. portfolios

4. Organizations can measure performance against their own past; against peers; and, even better, against _____.

   A. profits

   B. potential

   C. revenues

   D. the future

5. Alpha project managers represent the top _____.of project managers based on performance.

    A. 1%

    B. 2%

    C. 5%

    D. 10%

6. Which of the following is a trait of alpha project managers?

    A. They spend more time on execution than other project managers.

    B. They spend more time in meetings than other project managers.

    C. They send fewer emails than other project managers.

    D. They make more money than other project managers.

7. Which of the following is true regarding studies on the value of project management and project management maturity?

    A. The PMI-sponsored study by Ibbs (2002) found that companies with a high maturity level spend less money on project management than companies with a low maturity.

    B. The PMI-sponsored study by Thomas and Mullaly (2008) found that companies focus even more on measuring the ROI or tangible benefits of project management.

    C. The PMI-sponsored study by Crawford and Cook-Davies found that several industries have reached an optimal level of organizational project management maturity.

    D. The PricewaterhouseCoopers study found that the higher the maturity level, the more difficulties the organization will have in implementing software.

8. Which of the following statements is true based on recent studies of project management maturity done by PricewaterhouseCoopers and PMI?

    A. The average project management maturity level in organizations continues to decline.

    B. Higher project management maturity yields higher performance.

    C. Project success rates have increased ten percentage points since 2008.

    D. Most people do not believe that project management training contributes to business performance.

9. Which of the following is not a best practice listed in this text?

    A. Determine how project, program, and portfolio management will work best in your own organization.

    B. Involve key stakeholders—including shareholders, customers, and employees—in making major decisions.

    C. Develop and follow a formal project selection process to ensure projects support business needs.

    D. Don't spend time or money on projects before they officially start.

10. What is the main message of the final cartoon in this chapter in the section on final advice on project management?

    A. Follow best practices, and keep a sense of humor.

    B. Don't invest too much in the stock market.

    C. Always back up your hard drive.

    D. Don't waste your time playing video games.

Quick Quiz Answers

1. D; 2. A; 3. C; 4. B; 5. B; 6. C; 7. A; 8. B; 9. D; 10. A

DISCUSSION QUESTIONS

1. What is a best practice in general? Give examples of best practices in an area unrelated to project management, such as nutrition, exercise, or child rearing.

2. Why should organizations identify and use best practices? What are the main categories of best practices developed as part of OPM3? What does PMI's Healthcare Community of Practice suggest as best practices for project teams in healthcare delivery organizations?

3. What are some of the things that alpha project managers do differently from other project managers?

4. What is a project management maturity model? What benefits have studies shown from increasing project management maturity levels in organizations?

5. Do you believe that developing and applying project management skills can help most individuals and organizations, especially those working in healthcare? Justify your response.

EXERCISES

Note: These exercises can be done individually or in teams, in-class, as homework, or in a virtual environment. Learners can either write their results in a paper or prepare a short presentation or video to show their results.

1.   Review the project management best practices presented in this chapter or describe several used in an organization you are familiar with. Select any two of them and describe how each practice could help improve project management. Include examples of how they could be applied to real project situations in the healthcare industry.

2.   Read PMI's "Pulse of the Profession" report published in March 2013. Summarize key information in the document and your opinion of it.

3.   Skim PMI's latest version of OPM3 or the Healthcare Community of Practice list of best practices. Summarize key information in the document and your opinion of it.

4.   Interview an experienced project manager about best practices he or she has used on an individual and organizational level. Document your findings.

5.   Search for articles and research done in the past three years regarding best practices in project management. What do you think about the quality of what you found? Summarize the findings of least two articles and one research study.

6.   Watch the video mentioned in the Video Highlights where Diane Sawyer interviews Dr. Randy Pausch. Watch at least one other video about the lecture (or the entire lecture itself) and review the Web site www.thelastlecture.com. Summarize some of the advice Dr. Pausch gives and your opinions of it.

TEAM PROJECTS

Note: These team projects can be done in-class, as homework, or in a virtual environment. Learners can either write their results in a paper or prepare a short presentation or video to show their results.

1.   Read one of the reports or books listed in the Endnotes. Summarize key information in this document and your opinions of it.

2.   Research two or three different project management maturity models in more detail, such as those described in this chapter. Several include a sample or free assessment you can take to determine your organization's maturity level. Summarize the results as well as other information about the maturity models.

3.   Based on your team's experiences on your class project and your work experiences, describe what you believe are the most useful best practices for project management. Be sure to include specific examples that describe the best practices you include.

KEY TERMS

best practices — Optimal methods, currently recognized within a given industry or discipline, to achieve a goal or objective.
capabilities — The incremental steps leading up to one or more best practices.
key performance indicator (KPI) — A criterion used to determine the degree to which an outcome is achieved.
maturity model — A framework for helping organizations improve their processes and systems.
outcomes — The tangible or intangible results of applying capabilities.

END NOTES

[1]Project Management Institute, Inc. "Pulse of the Profession" (March 2013)).
[2]Boyd. L. (2008, June) Switching Gears, PM Network (June, 2008).

[3]Mary Evans, "Overdue and Over Budget, Over and Over Again," Economist.com (June 9, 2005).

[4]Project Management Institute, Inc., Organizational Project Management Maturity Model (OPM3) Knowledge Foundation, Second Edition (2008), p 39.

[5]Sarah Fister Gale, "Outstanding Organizations 2007," PM Network (October 2007).

[6]Ultimate Business Library, *Best Practice: Ideas and Insights from the World's Foremost Business Thinkers*. Cambridge, MA: Perseus Publishing (2003), p. 1.

[7]Ibid., p. 8.

[8]Ibid.

[9]PMI's Healthcare Community of Practice, "List of Project Management Best Practices in a Healthcare Delivery Organization," Project Management Institute (September 16, 2011).

[10]Andy Crowe. Alpha Project Managers: What the Top 2% Know That Everyone Else Does Not, Velociteach press, Atlanta, GA (2006).

[11]Software Engineering Institute, "What is CMMI," Carnegie Mellon (*http://www.sei.cmu.edu/cmmi/general/general.html*) (January 2007).

[12]CMMI Product Team, "CMMI® for Development, Version 1.2," CMU/SEI-2006-TR-008ESC-TR-2006-008 (August 2006).

[13]William Ibbs, and Justin Reginato, "Quantifying the Value of Project Management," Project Management Institute (2002).

[14]Janice Thomas and Mark Mullaly, "Researching the Value of Project Management," PMI, (2008), p. 349.

[15]Ibid., p. 246.

[16]Crawford, Lynn and Terry Cook-Davies, "Best Industry Outcomes," Project Management Institute (2012).

[17]PricewaterhouseCoopers, "Boosting Business Performance through Programme and Project Management" (June 2004).

[18]PricewaterhouseCoopers, "Insights and Trends: Current Portfolio, Programme, and Project Management Practices" (2012).

[18]Sarah Fister Gale, "Outstanding Organizations 2007," PM Network (October 2007), p. 12.

[20]James A. Dilling, BSIE, CMPE; Stephen J. Swensen, MD, MMM; Michele R. Hoover, MEd; Gene C. Dankbar, MSIE;Amerett L. Donahoe-Anshus, MA; M. Hassan Murad, MD, MPH; Jeff T. Mueller, MD, "Accelerating the Use of Best Practices: The Mayo Clinic Model of Diffusion," The Joint Commission Journal on Quality and Patient Safety. Volume 39 Number 4 (April 2013)

APPENDIX A:

Brief Guide to Microsoft Project 2013

Note: This guide was written using the free trial of Project 2013 Professional and Windows 7. Your screens may appear slightly different. You can download a free trial of Project 2013 Professional from **www.microsoft.com/project**. Also note that Microsoft does now provide a cloud-based tool now called Project Online available for a monthly fee.

Visit the free companion Web site at **www.intropm.com**. You can download the files mentioned in this text, access additional resources (including videos on using Project 2013 and other tools), purchase this text as a pdf file, and download older versions of this guide (for Project 2007 and 2010) for free.

I would like to thank Dave Klempke and Matt VanZant, adjunct instructors at Augsburg College in Minneapolis, for reviewing this appendix.

INTRODUCTION

There are hundreds of project management software products on the market today. Gartner estimated the project and portfolio management (PPM) software market to be over $1 billion in 2011, and it continues to grow. Unfortunately, many people who own PPM software have no idea how to use it. It is important to understand basic concepts of project management, such as creating a work breakdown structure, determining task dependencies, and so on before making effective use of this software. Many project teams still use spreadsheets or other familiar software to help manage projects. However, if you can master a good project management software tool, it can really help in managing projects. This appendix summarizes basic information on project management software in general. It also provides a brief guide to using Microsoft Office Project 2013 Professional (often referred to as Project 2013), the latest version of the most widely used PPM software.

PROJECT MANAGEMENT SOFTWARE REVIEWS

Figure A-1 provides a screen shot showing the top ten project management software products based on a June 2009 review by TopTenReviews™. That was the last year that a review was provided of non-online PPM software. Most PPM tools now offer totally online versions, including Project 2013. The products listed in the top ten include:

1. Microsoft Project
2. MindView
3. Project KickStart
4. RationalPlan Multi Project
5. FastTrack Schedule
6. Service Desktop Pro
7. Milestones
8. MinuteMan
9. FusionDesk Professional
10. VIP Team To Do List

Notice that Microsoft Project is number one on the list. Also notice its steep price back in 2009 of over $500 for a single user. Remember that students can purchase Microsoft Project and other software at greatly reduced rates from sites such as www.journeyed.com. You can also download a free trial of Project 2013 Professional (not Project Online, which cost $45 per user per month without an annual subscription, as of April 2013) and other software products or access them remotely via the Internet with your school's software license. Check with your school's IT department for more information.

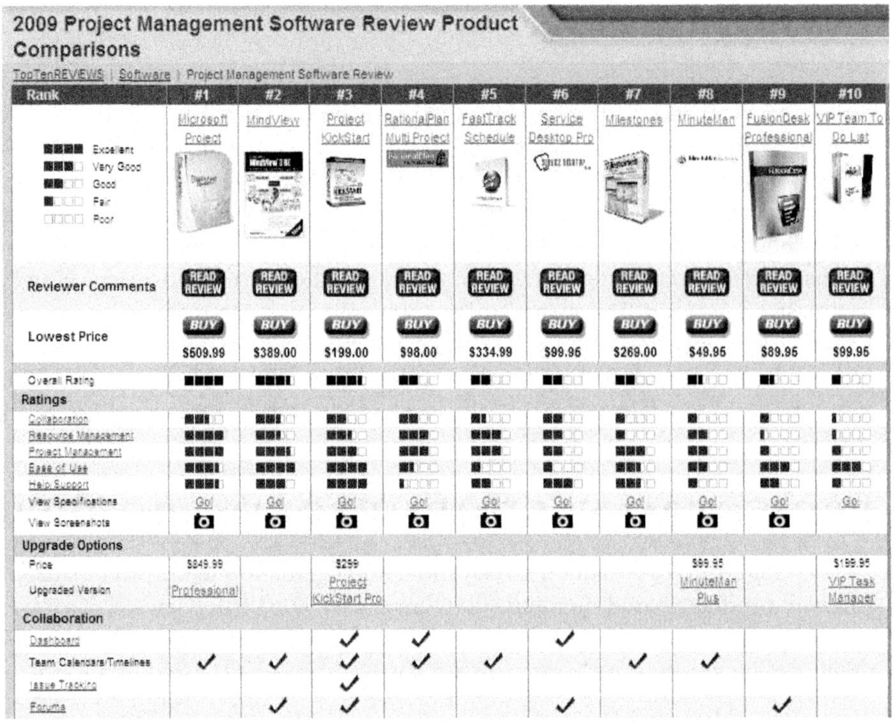

2009 Project Management Software Review Product Comparisons

TopTenREVIEWS | Software | Project Management Software Review

Rank	#1	#2	#3	#4	#5	#6	#7	#8	#9	#10
Excellent / Very Good / Good / Fair / Poor	Microsoft Project	MindView	Project KickStart	RationalPlan Multi Project	FastTrack Schedule	Service Desktop Pro	Milestones	MinuteMan	FusionDesk Professional	VIP Team To Do List
Reviewer Comments										
Lowest Price	$509.99	$389.00	$199.00	$98.00	$334.99	$99.96	$269.00	$49.95	$89.95	$99.95
Overall Rating										
Ratings										
Collaboration										
Resource Management										
Project Management										
Ease of Use										
Help/Support										
View Specifications	Go!	Go!	Go!	Go!	Go!	Go!	Go!	Go!	Go!	Go!
View Screenshots										
Upgrade Options										
Price	$849.99		$299					$99.95		$199.95
Upgraded Version	Professional		Project KickStart Pro					MinuteMan Plus		VIP Task Manager
Collaboration										
Dashboard			✓	✓		✓				
Team Calendars/Timelines	✓	✓	✓	✓	✓		✓	✓		
Issue Tracking			✓							
Forums		✓	✓			✓			✓	

Figure A-1. Top ten project management software product comparisons

Below are descriptions of the criteria for comparing the software products:

- **Collaboration:** How information and issues are communicated with project team members, including email, conference calls, meetings, web-based locations and more. Collaboration should be easy to use.
- **Resource Management:** Project management software should manage and control the resources needed to run a project, such as people, money, time and equipment.
- **Project Management:** The process, practice and activities needed to perform continuous evaluation, prioritization, budgeting and selection of investments are key. Proper project management capabilities provide the greatest value and contribution to the strategic interest of your company.
- **Ease of Use:** All project management software has a learning curve, but the best have functions that are easy to find and simple enough for anyone to use from Day 1, Project 1.
- **Help/Support:** Project management software should offer a comprehensive user guide and help system. The manufacturer should provide email addresses or telephone numbers for direct answers to technical questions.[1]

In addition to reviewing project management software in general, TopTenReviews™ also compared online products in a separate category. These products require an Internet connection for use. Figure A-2 lists the top ten results for 2013. The top ten products listed include:

1. Clarizen

2. Genius Project

3. Daptiv

4. Tenrox

5. Celoxis

6. Project Insight

7. AtTask

8. EPM Live

9. Liquid Planner

10. Easy Projects.net

TopTenReviews™ only listed online project management tools in 2013, and their review was done before Microsoft's Project Online was released. Tools in this list provide the ability to create Gantt charts, numerous reports and views, project dashboards, and integrate with Microsoft Project files. See End Note 2 or visit the Web sites for any of these products and use a free trial version. Also note that there are many other tools available.

BASIC FEATURES OF PROJECT MANAGEMENT SOFTWARE

What makes project management software different from other software tools? Why not just use a spreadsheet or database to help manage projects?

You can do a lot of project management planning and tracking using non-project management software. You could use a simple word processor to list tasks, resources, dates, and so on. If you put that information into a spreadsheet, you can easily sort it, graph it, and perform other functions. A relational database tool could provide even more manipulation of data. You can use email and other tools to collaborate with others.

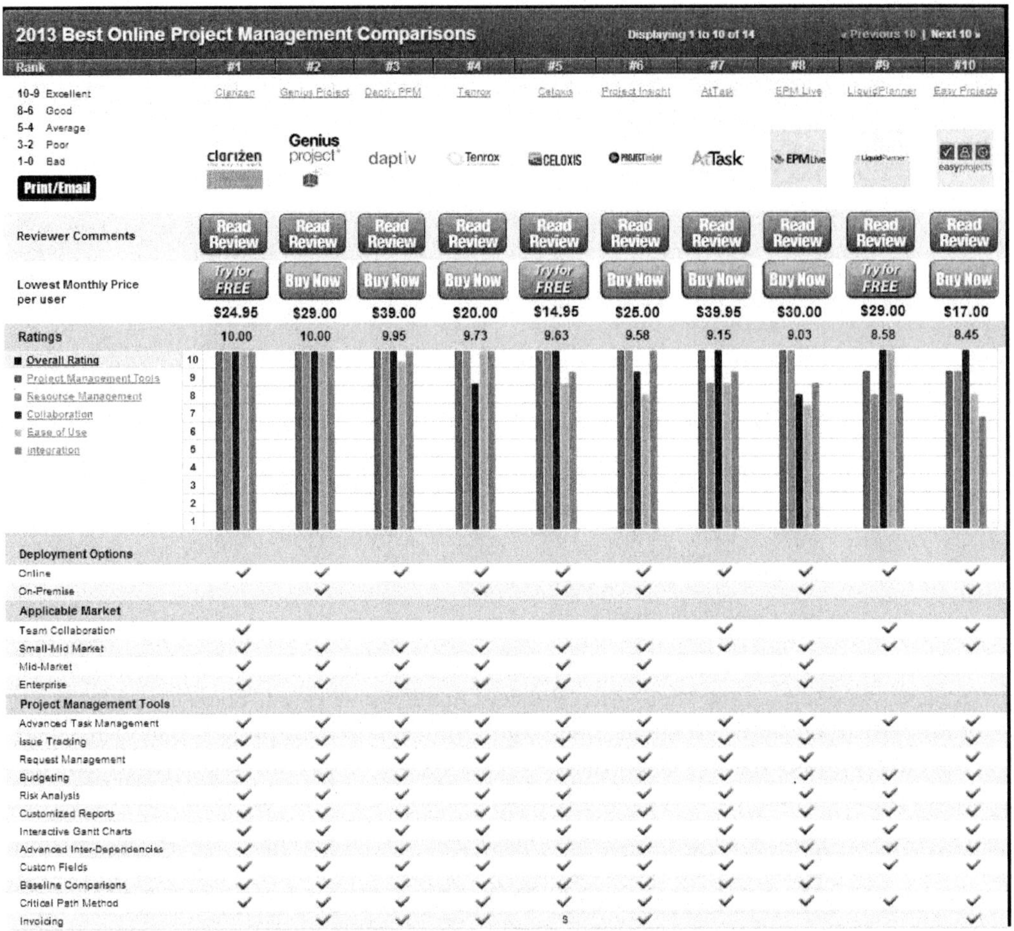

Figure A-2. Top ten online project management product comparisons[2]

However, project management software is designed specifically for managing projects, so it normally includes several distinct and important features not found in other software products:

- *Creating work breakdown structures, Gantt charts, and network diagrams*: A fundamental concept of project management is breaking down the scope of the project into a work breakdown structure (WBS). The WBS is the basis for creating the project schedule, normally shown as a Gantt chant. The Gantt chart shows start and end dates of tasks as well as dependencies between tasks, which are more clearly shown in a network diagram. Project management software makes it easy to create a WBS, Gantt chart, and network diagram. These features help the project manager and team visualize the project at various levels of detail.

- *Integrating scope, time, and cost data*: The WBS is a key tool for summarizing the scope of a project, and the Gantt chart summarizes the time or schedule for a project.

Project management software allows you to assign cost and other resources to tasks on the WBS, which are tied to the schedule. This allows you to create a cost baseline and use earned value management to track project performance in terms of scope, time, and cost in an integrated fashion.

- *Setting a baseline and tracking progress*: Another important concept of project management is preparing a plan and measuring progress against the plan. Project management software lets you track progress for each task. The tracking Gantt chart is a nice tool for easily seeing the planned and actual schedule, and other views and reports show progress in other areas.

- *Providing other advanced project management features*: Project management software often provides other advanced features, such as setting up different types of scheduling dependencies, determining the critical path and slack for tasks, working with multiple projects, and leveling resources. For example, you can easily set up a task to start when its predecessor is halfway finished. After entering task dependencies, the software should easily show you the critical path and slack for each task. You can also set up multiple projects in a program and perform portfolio management analysis with some products. Many project management software products also allow you to easily adjust resources within their slack allowances to create a smoother resource distribution. These advanced features unique to project management are rarely found in other software tools.

As you can see, there are several important features that are unique to project management software that make them worth using. Next you'll learn what's new in Project 2013 and how to use basic features.

WHAT'S NEW IN PROJECT 2013

If you are familiar with Project 2010 or earlier version, it may be helpful to review some of the new features in Project 2013.

- *Improved reports*: With Project 2013, you can create professional reports and add pictures, charts, animation, and links to clearly share project status information. An entirely new set of pre-installed reports are available, including burndown reports, a popular chart used for agile projects. The earned value chart is also much easier to create.
- *New collaboration features*: You can stay in touch with team members by getting progress updates, asking questions, or having strategy discussions, all without leaving Project 2013. You can hover over a name and start an IM session, video chat, email, or phone call. You must have Lync 2010 or later installed to take advantage of this feature.
- *Task paths*: You can now highlight any task and see its task path. All of the task's predecessor tasks show up in one color, and all of its successor tasks show up in another color.

- *Extended dates*: You can set task and project dates up to 12/31/2149.
- *Shared meetings*: If you export Project 2013 reports, timelines, or data to other Office programs, you can use the new sharing feature to join online meetings, share your PowerPoint slides, Word documents, Excel spreadsheets, and OneNote notes from any supported device, even if Office isn't installed.
- *Cloud storage*: You can easily save files to your own SkyDrive or to your organization's shared site. From there you can access and share your files from Project 2013 and other Office applications. Note that Project Online is delivered through Office 365 and used totally online.
- *Easy access*: If you have <u>Project Online</u>, Windows 7 (or later), and an internet connection, you can access a full version of Project from any location, similar to the new Office applications.

Next, you will learn some basic information about Project 2013 and explore the main screen elements and Help facility.

USING PROJECT 2013

Before you can use Project 2013 or any project management software effectively, you must understand the fundamental concepts of project management, such as creating work breakdown structures (WBS), linking tasks, entering duration estimates, assigning resources, and so on. The purpose of this text is to provide specific instructions for using Project 2013 Professional. Consult Microsoft's Web site for detailed information on other products and other resources to help you understand project management concepts.

Before You Begin

This appendix assumes you are using Project 2013 with Windows 7 (or later) and are familiar with other Windows-based applications. Check your work by reviewing the many screen shots included in the steps, or by using the solution files that are available for download from the companion Web site for this text or from your instructor.

> **NOTE:** *You need to be running Windows 7 or later to use Project 2013, a 1 Ghz or greater x86/x64 processor with SSE2 instruction set, 1 GB RAM (32 Bit) / 2 GB RAM (64 Bit), and an up-to-date browser. Certain features require internet connectivity.* You can read more detailed system requirements and download a free trial from www.microsoft.com/project. Students can purchase a full version from sites like www.journeyed.com at a discount. Many colleges and universities provide the software to students either on campus or through remote access. If you can use remote access, the main requirement is internet connectivity. Check with your instructor for details. You might also want to pay for monthly access to Project Online.

This appendix uses a fictitious project—Project A+—to illustrate how to use the software. The WBS for Project A+ uses the five project management process groups as level 2 items (initiating, planning, executing, monitoring and controlling, and closing).

Standard deliverables under each of those process groups are included. Each section of the appendix includes hands-on activities for you to perform.

NOTE: To complete some of the hands-on activities in the appendix, you will need to download files from the companion Web site for this text (www.intropm.com) to your computer. When you begin each set of steps, make sure you are using the correct file. Save the files you create yourself in a different folder so you do not write over the ones you download.

In addition, you will create the following files from scratch as you work through the steps:

- mywbs.mpp

- myschedule.mpp

You will also use the following file to create a hyperlink:

- stakeholder register.doc

Using the 60-day trial of Project 2013

If you plan to download the free trial, perform the following steps:
1. Go to www.microsoft.com/project and click on the **Try** button under Project Professional 2013.
2. Enter your account information. You do need a Microsoft account. It used to be called a Windows Live account, so you may already have one if you set it up for Xbox 360, SkyDrive, Office 2013, Office 365 or other items. If you do not have a Microsoft account, set one up for free.
3. Install Project 2013. The installation for Project 2013 is a bit different from past installations. Microsoft has you download some software (an image file) and then burn it to a CD or hard drive. You then run the software to install the 60-day trial. Be sure to save the product key Microsoft provides and enter it when prompted, and select the automatic upgrade. The trial software is run through Microsoft's online environment, similar to Office 365.

Next you will learn how to start Project 2013, review the Help facility and a template file, and begin to plan Project A+.

Overview of Project 2013

The first step to mastering Project 2013 is to become familiar with the major screen elements and the Help facility. This section describes each of these features.

Starting Project 2013 and Getting Started

To start Project 2013:

1. *Open Project 2013.* There are slightly different methods for opening Project 2013 depending on your operating system. For example, in Windows 7, click the **Start** button on the taskbar, and then click **Project 2013** or type it in the search bar. Alternatively, a shortcut or icon might be available on the desktop; in this case, double-click the icon to start the software.

2. *Review the Get Started feature.* Click on **Get Started**, as shown in the upper right section of Figure A-3.

Figure A-3. Project 2013 initial options – access Get Started

3. *Start the introduction.* Click **Create**, and then click **Start**, as shown in Figure A-4.

Figure A-4. Project 2013 Get Started introductory screen

4. *Review the "4 simple steps" Microsoft lists for using Project 2013*. Review the first step, called Schedule your work, as shown in Figure A-5. Review the other steps by clicking **Next**, as shown in Figures A-6-A-8.

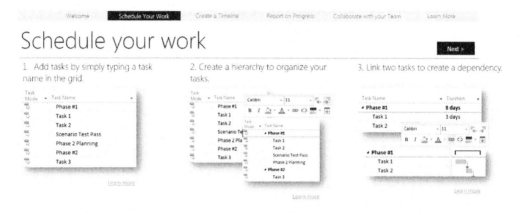

Figure A-5. Schedule your work screen

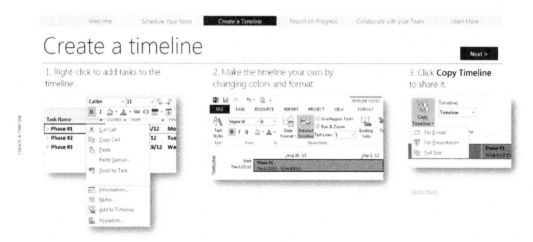

Figure A-6. Create a timeline screen

Figure A-7. Report on progress screen

Figure A-8. Collaborate with your team screen

5. *Explore Help features.* The last screen of Getting Started, **Learn More**, as shown in Figure A-9, provides links to the <u>Project 2013 Getting Started Center</u> (which includes a short video on what's new that is worth watching) and the <u>Project blog</u>. The help feature (question mark in the upper right of the screen) also includes a lot of helpful resources.

Welcome   Schedule Your Work   Create a Timeline   Report on Progress   Collaborate with your Team   Learn More

Keep going. There are lots more new features and ways to work in Project.

See the Project 2013 Getting Started Center

Visit the Project blog

Try out the new features

Figure A-9. Learn More screen

Understanding the Main Screen Elements

To open a blank file:

1. *Open a blank file.* Click the **File** tab, **New**, and then click the first option, **Blank Project.**

2. *Examine the main screen.* Review the main screen elements, as shown in Figure A-10. Look at some of the elements of the screen.

   - The Ribbon, tabs, and Quick Access toolbar are similar to other Office applications.

   - The timeline view is displayed below the ribbon.

   - The default manual scheduling for new tasks is on the lower left of the screen. You can click that option to switch to automatic scheduling.

   - The default view is the Gantt chart view, which shows tasks and other information as well as a calendar display. You can access other views by clicking the View icon on the far left side of the ribbon.

   - The areas where you enter information in a spreadsheet-like table are part of the Entry table. For example, you can see entry areas for Task Name, Duration, Start, Finish, and Predecessors.

   - You can make the Entry table more or less wide by using the Split bar. When you move the mouse over the split bar, your cursor changes to the resize pointer. Clicking and dragging the split bar to the right reveals columns for Resource Names and Add New columns.

   - The first column in the Entry table is the Indicators column. The Indicators column displays indicators or symbols related to items associated with each task, such as task notes or hyperlinks to other files. The second column displays if a task is manually or automatically scheduled, as described later in this appendix.

- The file name displays centered at the top of the screen. When you open a Blank Project after starting Project 2013, it opens a new file named Project1, which is shown in the title bar. If you open a second Blank Project, the name will be Project2, and so on, until you save and rename the file.

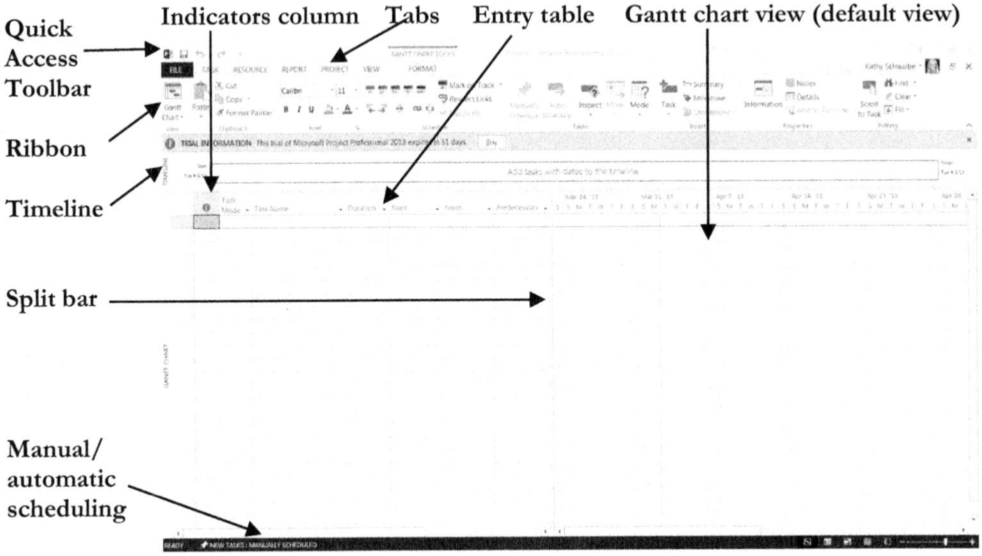

Quick Access Toolbar

Indicators column   Tabs   Entry table   Gantt chart view (default view)

Ribbon

Timeline

Split bar

Manual/ automatic scheduling

Figure A-10. Project 2013 main screen

Using Project Help and the Project Web Site

To access information to help you learn how to use Project 2013:

1. *Access Project Help.* Click on the **question mark/help icon** on the upper side of the ribbon. The Project Help screen displays, as shown in Figure A-11. Remember that this feature requires an Internet connection.

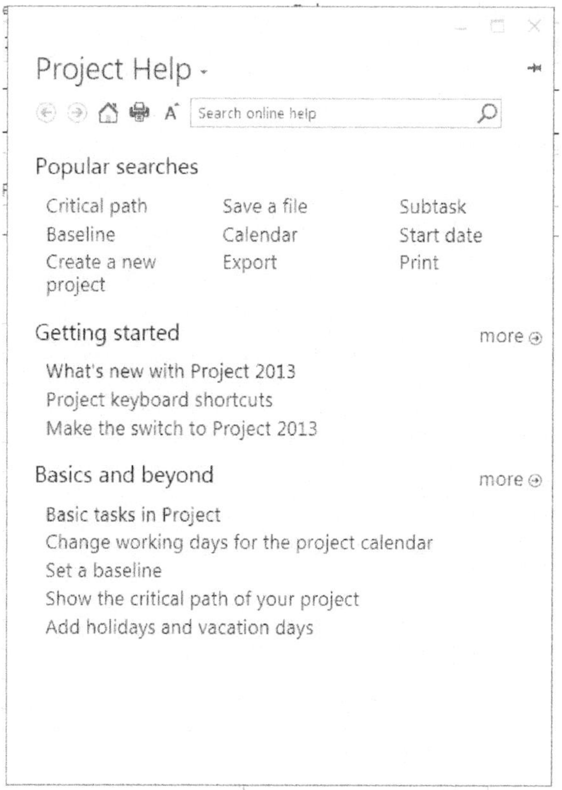

Figure A-11. Topics under Project help

2. *Explore various help topics* Click the Project Help link called **"What's new with Project 2013."** Microsoft provides short videos, steps, templates, articles, and other features to help you learn to use this powerful software. Watch the short video, read the other information on the page, and explore links for more help.

3. *Close Project 2013.* Click the **Close icon** (X in the upper right of the screen) to exit Project 2013.

Many features in Project 2013 are similar to ones in other Windows programs. For example, to collapse or expand tasks, click the appropriate symbols to the left of the task name. To access shortcut items, right-click in either the Entry table area or the Gantt chart. Many of the Entry table operations in Project 2013 are very similar to operations in Excel. For example, to adjust a column width, click and drag between the column heading titles.

Next, you will get some hands-on experience by opening an existing file to explore various screen elements. Project 2013 comes with several template files, and you can also access templates from Microsoft Office Online or other Web sites.

EXPLORING PROJECT 2013 USING AN EXISTING FILE

To open a template file and adjust Project 2013 screen elements:

1. *Open Project 2013 and select the Customer Service template file.* Click the **Start** button on the taskbar, select **Project 2013**, click **Customer Service**, and then click **Create**. These screen shots were taken on **April 3, 2013**, so you can enter that date if you like. Your screen should resemble Figure A-12. (Note: If you cannot find the template, you can download it from www.intropm.com and open it. To open an existing file, click the **File tab**, then select **Open**, and browse to find the file.)

2. *Widen the Task Name column.* Move the **cursor** between the Task Name and Duration columns, and then **double-click** to widen the Task Name column so all of the text shows in one line.

3. *Move the Split Bar.* Move the **Split Bar** to the right so the entire Task Name column text is visible, but not the Duration column. The default table view is the Entry table.

4. *View the first Note*: Move your mouse over the yellow **Notes** symbol in the Indicators column for Task 1 to read it. You can insert notes by any task.

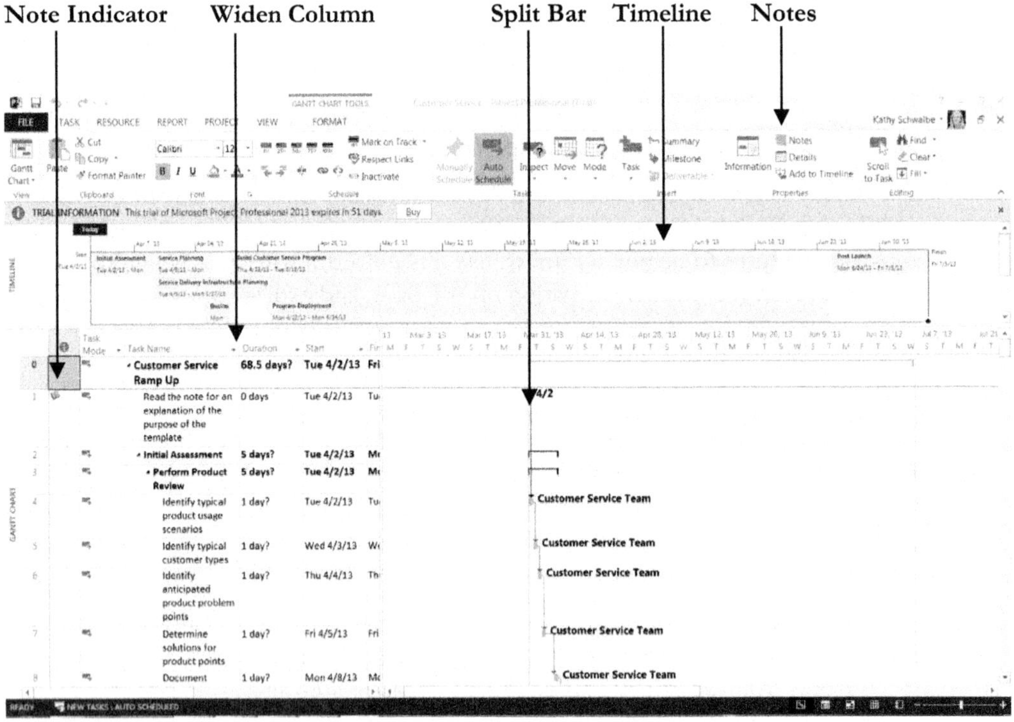

Figure A-12. Customer Service template file

To show different WBS levels:

1. *Select Outline Level 1 to display WBS level 2 tasks.* Click the **View** tab and then the **Outline** button's list arrow, and then click **Outline Level 1**. Notice that only the level 2 WBS items display in the Entry table. The black bars on the Gantt chart represent the summary tasks. Recall that the entire project is normally referred to as WBS level 1, and the next highest level is called level 2.

2. *Adjust the timescale.* Click the **Zoom out** button (minus sign) on the left side of the Zoom slider on the lower left of the screen, as shown in Figure A-13. Notice the milestone task in row 143 indicating the project completion date. Recall that the black diamond symbol on a Gantt chart shows milestones.

3. *Expand a task.* Click the **expand symbol** to the left of **Task 2**, Initial Assessment, to see its subtasks. Click the **collapse symbol** to hide its subtasks. Experiment with expanding and collapsing other tasks and resizing other columns.

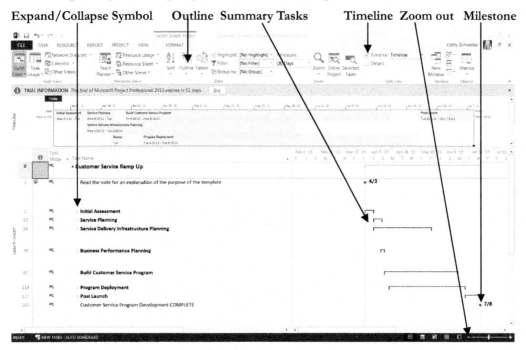

Figure A-13. Showing part of the WBS on the Gantt chart

4. *View all tasks.* Click **Outline** button and select **All Subtasks** to see all of the items in the Task Name column again.

5. *Remove the Timeline.* Click the **Timeline checkbox** on the Ribbon to unselect it. Click it again to display it.

6. *Close the file without saving.* Click the **Close icon** in the upper right of the window, and select **No** when prompted to save the file.

Project 2013 Views

Project 2013 provides many ways to display or view project information. In addition to the default Gantt chart, you can view the network diagram, calendar, and task usage views, to name a few. These views allow you to analyze project information in different ways. The View tab also provides access to different tables that display information in various ways. In addition to the default Entry table view, you can access tables that focus on data related to areas such as the Schedule, Cost, Tracking, and Earned Value.

To access and explore different views:

1. *Explore the Network Diagram for the Customer Service file.* Open the **Customer Service** file again. Click the **Network Diagram** button under the View tab, and then move the **Zoom slider** on the lower right of the screen all the way to the left. Your screen should resemble Figure A-14. Critical tasks display in red.

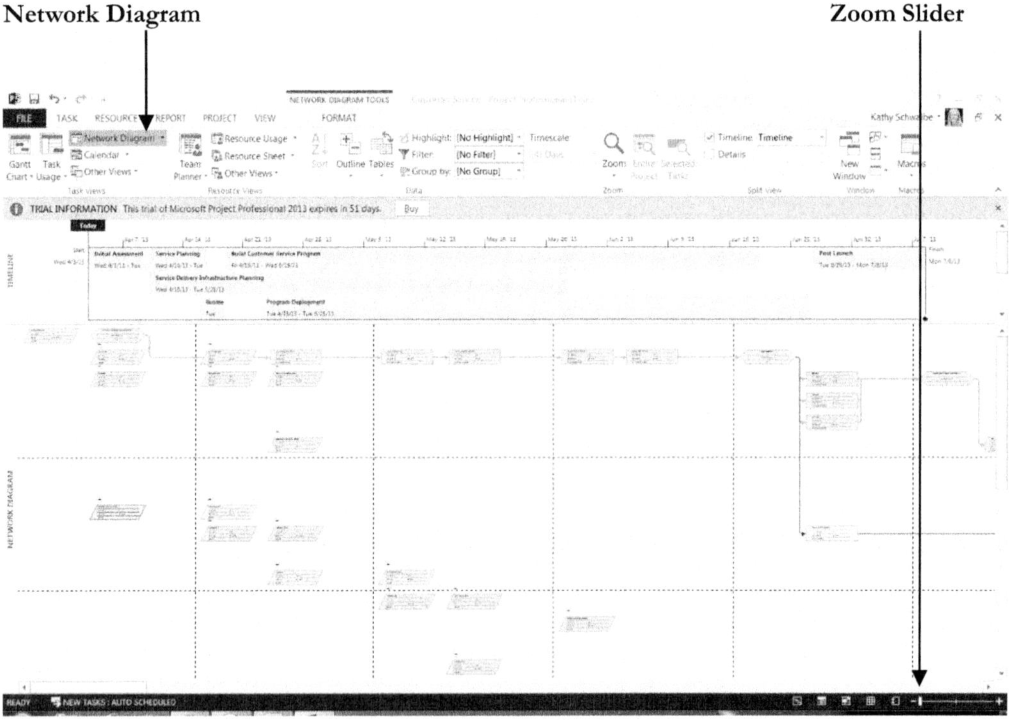

Figure A-14. Network diagram view of Customer Service file

2. *Explore the Calendar view.* Click the **Calendar** button (under the Network Diagram button). Notice that the screen lists tasks each day in a calendar format.

3. *Change the table view.* Click the **Gantt Chart** button on the ribbon, click the **Tables** button under the View tab, and then click **Schedule**. Figure A-15 shows the table view options.

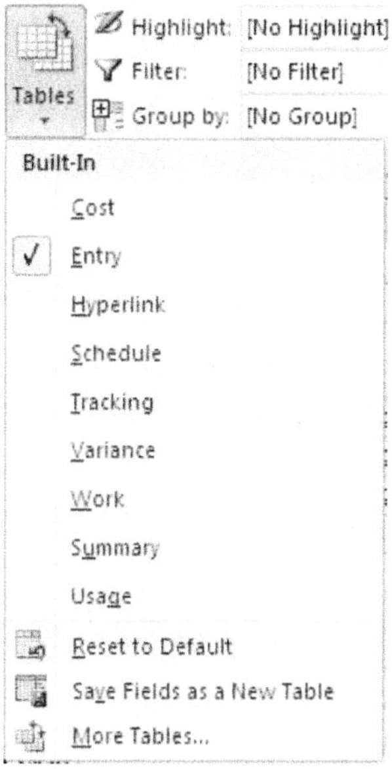

Tables
☑ Highlight: [No Highlight]
▼ Filter: [No Filter]
⊞ Group by: [No Group]

Built-In

    Cost

✓   Entry

    Hyperlink

    Schedule

    Tracking

    Variance

    Work

    Summary

    Usage

    Reset to Default

    Save Fields as a New Table

    More Tables...

Figure A-15. Table view options

4. *Examine the Schedule table and other views.* Select the **Schedule** table view and move the **Split bar** to the right to review the Total Slack column. Notice that the columns in the table to the left of the Gantt chart, as shown in Figure A-16, now display more detailed schedule information, such as Late Start, Late Finish, Free Slack, and Total Slack. Remember that you can widen columns by double-clicking the resize pointer to the right of that column. You can also move the split bar to reveal more or fewer columns. Experiment with other table views, then return to the **Entry** table view.

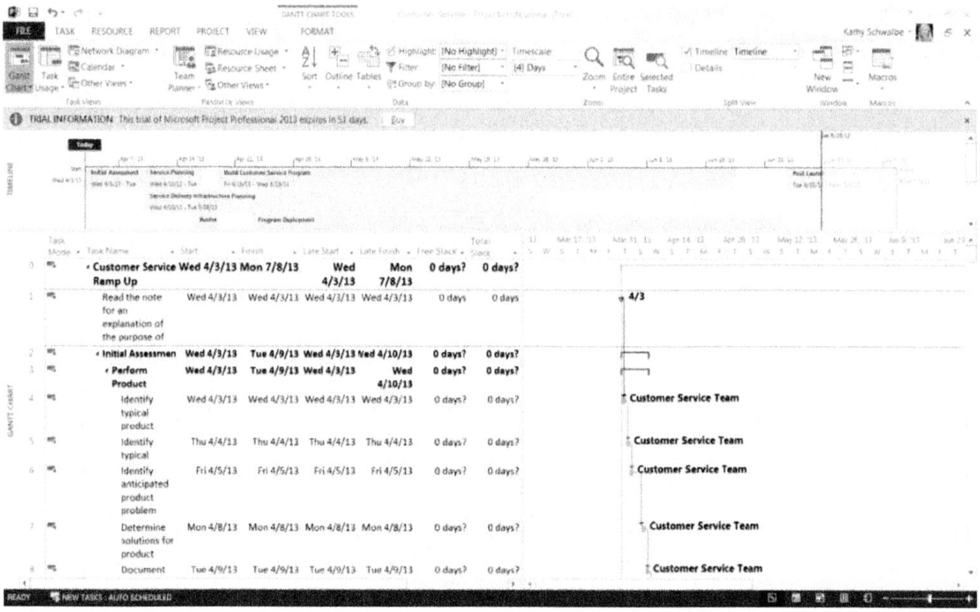

Figure A-16. Schedule table view

Project 2013 Reports

Project 2013 provides many ways to report project information as well. In addition to traditional reports, you can also prepare visual reports, with both available under the Report tab. Note that the visual reports often require that you have other Microsoft application software, such as Excel and Visio. Project 2013 automatically formats reports for ease of printing.

To access and explore different reports:

1. *Explore the Reports feature.* Click the **Report** tab to see the variety of reports available in Project 2013.

2. *View the Project Overview report.* Click **Dashboards**, and then double-click **Project Overview**. Review the report and new options on the ribbon, as shown in Figure A-17.

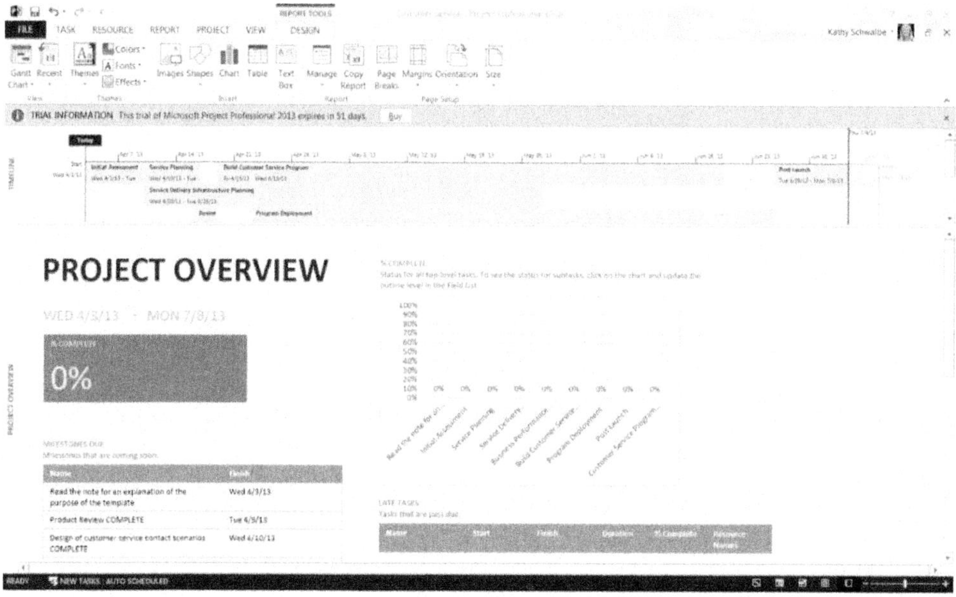

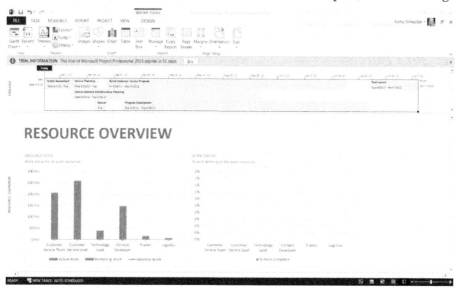

Figure A-17. Project Overview report

3. *Open the Resource Overview report.* Click the **Report** tab again, click **Resources**, and then click **Resource Overview**. Review the report, as shown in Figure A-18.

Figure A-18. Resource Overview report

4. *Examine the report and experiment with others.* Click on the **Report** tab, click **In Progress**, and then click **Critical Tasks** to display the Critical Tasks report, as shown in Figure A-19. Examine other reports.

5. *Return to the Gantt chart.* Click the **View** tab, and then click on **Gantt Chart** to return to the Gantt chart view. You can close the file without saving it if you wish to take a break.

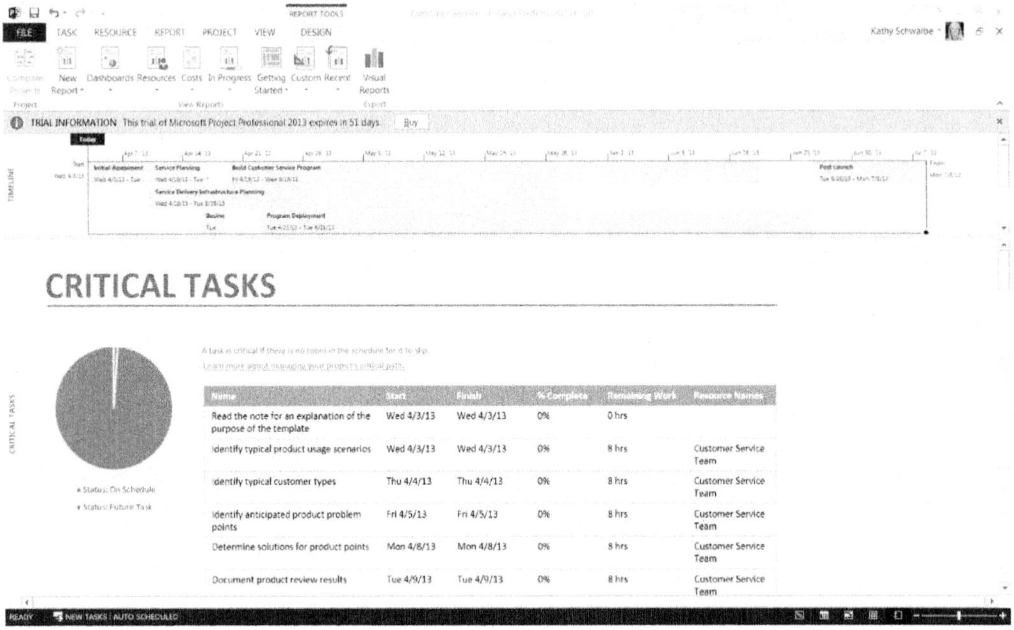

Figure A-19. Critical tasks report

Project 2013 Filters

Project 2013 uses a relational database to filter, sort, store, and display information. Filtering project information is very useful. For example, if a project includes thousands of tasks, you might want to view only summary or milestone tasks to get a high-level view of the project by using the Milestones or Summary Tasks filter from the Filter list. You can select a filter that shows only tasks on the critical path if that is what you want to see. Other filters include Completed Tasks, Late/Overbudget Tasks, and Date Range, which displays tasks based on dates you provide. As shown earlier, you can also click the Show button on the toolbar to display different levels in the WBS quickly.

To explore Project 2013 filters:

1. *Access filters.* Click the **View** tab, if necessary, and make sure the Customer Service file is in the Gantt Chart: Table Entry view. Click the **Filter list arrow** (under the Data group), as shown in Figure A-20. The default filter is No Filter, which shows all tasks.

Filter list arrow

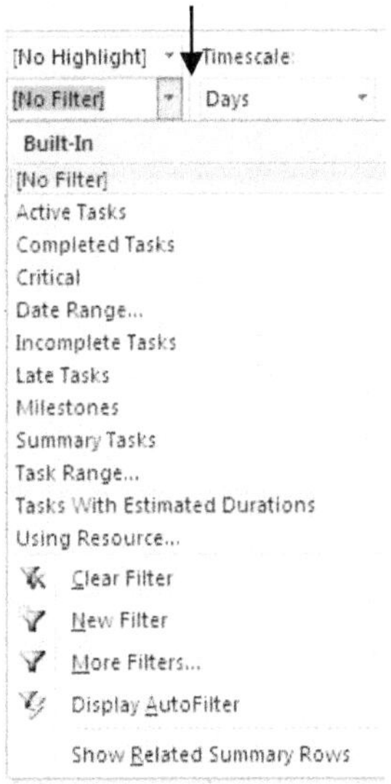

Figure A-20. Using a filter

2. *Filter to show milestones.* Click **Milestones** in the list of filters. Notice that the Gantt chart only shows the summary tasks and milestones for the project. Your screen should resemble Figure A-21. Recall that milestones are significant events.

3. *Show critical tasks.* Select **No Filter** from the Filter list box to reveal all the tasks in the WBS again. Click the **Filter** list arrow, and then click **Critical Tasks**. Now only the critical tasks appear in the WBS. Experiment with other filters.

4. *Close the file.* When you are finished reviewing the Customer Service file, click **Close** from the File tab or click the **Close** button. Click **No** when asked if you want to save changes.

5. *Exit Project 2013.* Click the **Close** button for Project 2013.

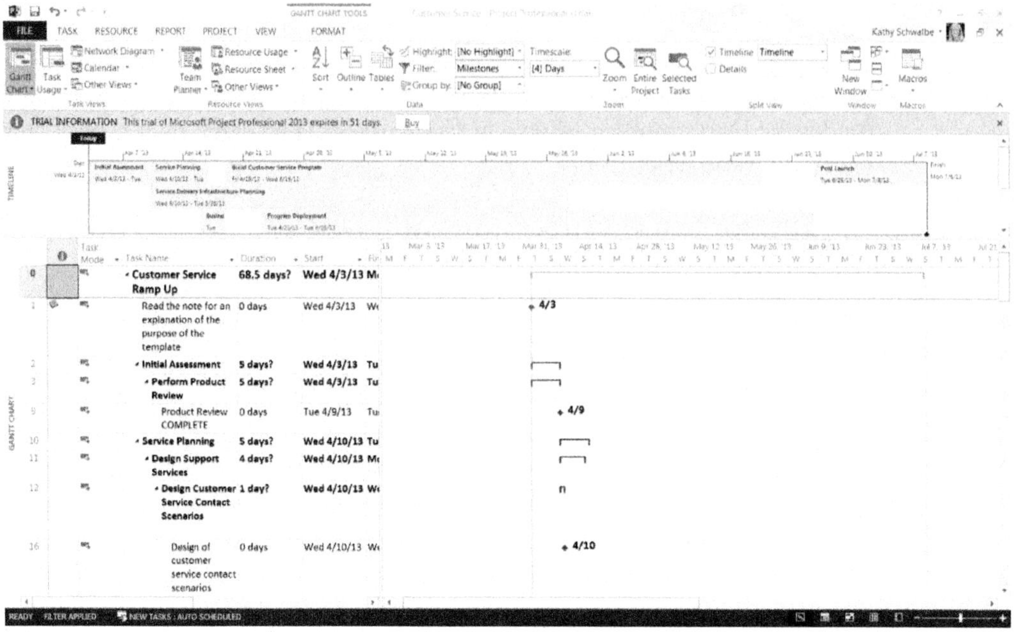

Figure A-21. Milestones filter applied

Now that you are familiar with the main screen elements, views, reports, and filters, you will learn how to use Project 2013 to create a new file.

CREATING A NEW FILE AND ENTERING TASKS IN A WORK BREAKDOWN STRUCTURE

To create a new Project 2013 file, you must first name the project, enter the start date, and then enter the tasks. The list of tasks and their hierarchy is the work breakdown structure (WBS). The file you create could be used for a class project which lasts approximately three months. It uses the project management process groups to reinforce use of several project management deliverables described in this text. You could modify this file to meet your specific needs.

NOTE: In this section, you will go through several steps to create a new Project 2013 file named mywbs.mpp. If you want to download the completed file to check your work or continue to the next section, a copy of mywbs.mpp is available on the companion Web site for this text at www.intropm.com. Try to complete an entire section of this appendix (entering tasks in a work breakdown structure, developing the schedule, and so on) in one sitting to create the complete file.

Creating a New Project File

To create a new project file:

1.   Create a blank project. Open Project 2013 and click on **Blank Project**. A blank project file opens with a default filename of Project1, Project2, and so on. (If Project 2013 is already open and you want to open a new file, click the **File** tab, select **New**, and then **Blank Project**.)

2.   Open the Project Information dialog box. Click the **Project** tab, and then click **Project Information** to display the Project Information dialog box, as shown in Figure A-22. This dialog box enables you to set dates for the project, select the calendar to use, and view project statistics. The project start date will default to the current date. Note that in Figure A-22 the file was created on 4/3/13 and a Start date of 9/9/13 was entered.

NOTE: All dates are entered in month/day/year or American format. You can change the date format by selecting Options from the File tab. Click the date format you want to use in the Date Format box under the General settings. You can also customize the Ribbon, change default currencies in the display, and so on under Project Options.

3.   Enter the project start date. In the Start date text box, enter **9/9/13**. Setting your project start date to 9/9/13 will ensure that your work matches the results that appear in this appendix. Leave the Current date and other information at the default settings. Click **OK** or press Enter.

4.   *Enter advanced project properties.* Click the **File** tab, and then click **Info**. Click **Project Information** on the right side of the screen, and then click **Advanced Properties**. Enter **Project A+** for the title, if you want to change the title. You can also enter a subject, author, and other information as desired. Click the **left arrow** at the top left of the screen to go back to the previous screen.

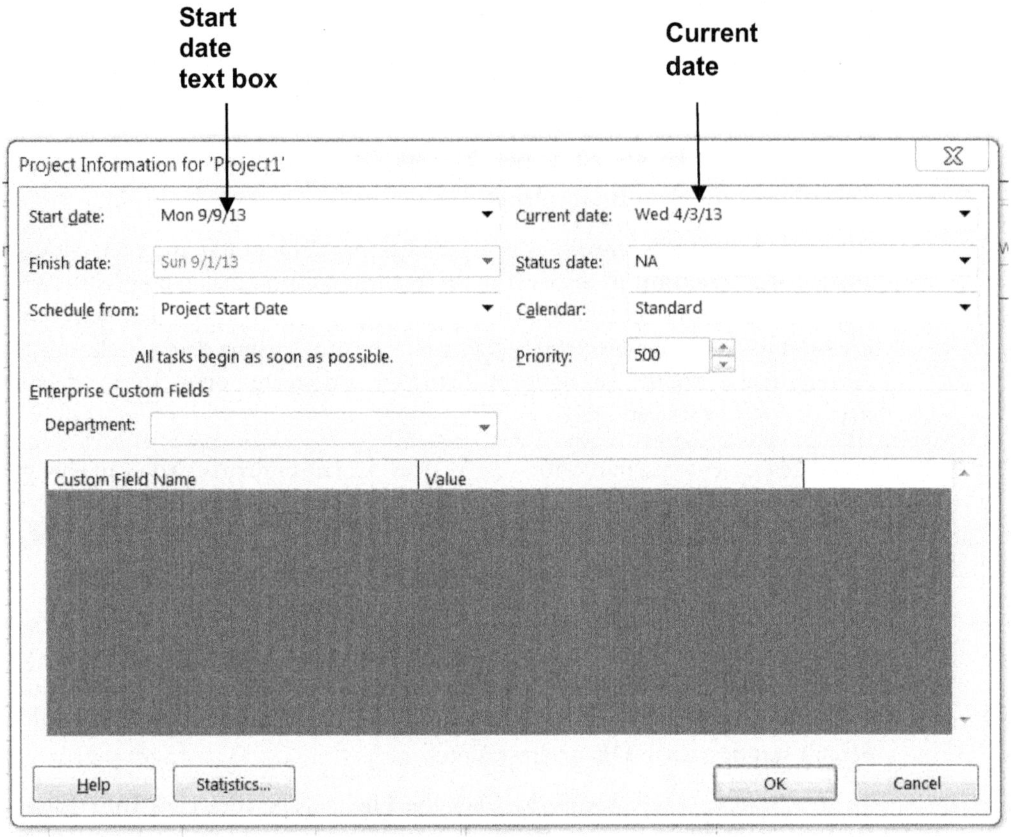

Start date text box

Current date

Figure A-22. Project information dialog box

Creating a Work Breakdown Structure Hierarchy

As mentioned earlier, a work breakdown structure (WBS) is a fundamental part of project management. Developing a good WBS takes time, and it will make entering tasks into the Entry table easier if you develop the WBS first. For this example, you will use the project management process groups as the level 2 items and add some key deliverables and milestones under each one. You will use the information in Figure A-23 to enter tasks. Note that Microsoft Project uses the term tasks instead of deliverables or activities or milestones, so it is also used in this appendix.

1. Initiating	16. Deliverable 2
2. Stakeholder identification	17. Deliverable 3
3. Stakeholder register completed	18. Deliverable 1 completed
4. Stakeholder management strategy completed	19. Deliverable 2 completed
5. Project charter	20. Deliverable 3 completed
6. Project charter completed	21. Monitoring and Controlling
7. Kickoff meeting	22. Actual hours tracking
8. Kickoff meeting completed	23. Project documents updates
9. Planning	24. Progress report 1
10. Schedule	25. Progress report 2
11. Gantt chart completed	26. Team review meetings
12. Scope statement	27. Closing
13. Initial scope statement completed	28. Final project report
14. Executing	29. Final project presentation
15. Deliverable 1	30. Project completed

Figure A-23. Task list for Project A+

To develop a WBS for the project:

1. *Enter task names.* Enter the 30 items in Figure A-23 into the Task Name column in the order shown. To not have the text wrap, click on the **Format** Tab, click **Column Settings**, and then click **Wrap Text** to turn it off. Do not worry about durations or any other information at this time. Type the name of each item into the Task Name column of the Entry table, beginning with the first row. Press **Enter** or the **down arrow** key on your keyboard to move to the next row.

HELP: If you accidentally skip a row, highlight the task row, right-click, and select Insert Task. To edit a task entry, click the text for that task, and either type over the old text or edit the existing text. Entering tasks into Project 2013 and editing the information is similar to entering and editing data in an Excel spreadsheet. You can also easily copy and paste text from Excel or Word into Project, such as the list of tasks.

---

2.   *Adjust the Task Name column width as needed.* To make all the text display in the Task Name column, move the mouse over the right-column gridline in the **Task Name** column heading until you see the resize pointer , and then click the **left mouse** button and drag the line to the right to make the column wider, or double-click to adjust the column width automatically.

This WBS separates tasks according to the project management process groups of initiating, planning, executing, controlling, and closing. These categories will be the level 2 items in the WBS for this project. (Remember the whole project is level 1.) It is a good idea to include all of these process groups because there are important deliverables that must be done under each of them. Recall that the WBS should include *all* of the work required for the project. In the Project A+ WBS, the WBS will be purposefully left at a high level (level 3). You will create these levels, or the WBS hierarchy, next when you create summary tasks. For a real project, you would usually break the WBS into even more levels and then enter activities to provide more details to describe all the work involved in the project. For example, each deliverable would probably have several levels, activities, and milestones under it. You can review other Project 2013 template files or other sources for more information.

Creating Summary Tasks

After entering the items listed in Figure A-23 into the Entry table, the next step is to show the WBS levels by creating summary tasks. The summary tasks in this example are Tasks 1 (initiating), 9 (planning), 14 (executing), 21 (monitoring and controlling), and 27 (closing). You create summary tasks by highlighting and indenting their respective subtasks.

To create the summary tasks:

1.   *Select lower level or subtasks.* Highlight **Tasks 2** through **8** by clicking the cell for Task 2 and dragging the mouse through the cells to Task 8.

2.   *Indent subtasks.* Click the **Indent Tasks** button on the Ribbon under the Schedule group of the Task tab (or press Alt + Shift + right arrow) so your screen resembles Figure A-24. After the subtasks (Tasks 2 through 8) are indented, notice that Task 1 automatically becomes boldface, which indicates that it is a summary task. A collapse symbol appears to the left of the new summary task name. Clicking the collapse symbol (filled triangle sign) will collapse the summary task and hide the subtasks beneath it. When subtasks are hidden, an expand symbol (unfilled triangle sign) appears to the left of the summary task name. Clicking the expand symbol will expand the summary task. Also, notice that the symbol for the summary task on the Gantt chart has changed from a blue to a black line with arrows indicating the start and end dates. The Task Mode has also changed to make this task Automatically scheduled. You'll learn more about this feature later. For now, focus on entering and indenting the tasks to create the WBS.

Expand or collapse symbols by
Summary tasks   Indent Task   Summary task symbol

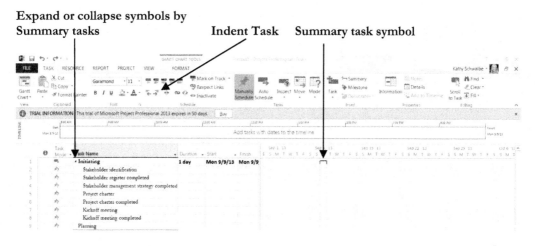

Figure A-24. Indenting tasks to create the WBS hierarchy

3.   *Create other summary tasks and subtasks.* Create subtasks and summary tasks for the other process groups by following the same steps. Indent **Tasks 10** through **13** to make Task 9 a summary task. Indent **Tasks 15** through **20** to make Task 14 a summary task. Indent **Tasks 22** through **26** to make Task 21 a summary task. Indent **Tasks 28** through **30** to make Task 27 a summary task. Widen the Task Name column to see all of your text, as needed.

TIP: To change a task from a subtask to a summary task or to change its level in the WBS, you can "outdent" the task. To outdent the task, click the cell of the task or tasks you want to change, and then click the Outdent Task button (the button just to the left of the Indent Task button). You can also press Alt + Shift + Right Arrow to indent tasks and Alt + Shift + Left Arrow to outdent tasks.

Numbering Tasks

To display automatic numbering of tasks using the standard tabular numbering system for a WBS:

1.   *Show outline numbers.* Click the **Format** tab, and then click the **Outline Number checkbox** under the Show/Hide group. Project 2013 adds the appropriate WBS numbering to the task names.

2.   *Show project summary task.* Click the Project Summary checkbox just below the Outline Number checkbox. Scroll to the top of the file to see that a new task, Project A+, the title of the project, has been added under row 0. Your file should resemble Figure A-25.

Outline Number and Project Summary Task Check Boxes

Outline Numbers   **Project Summary Task**

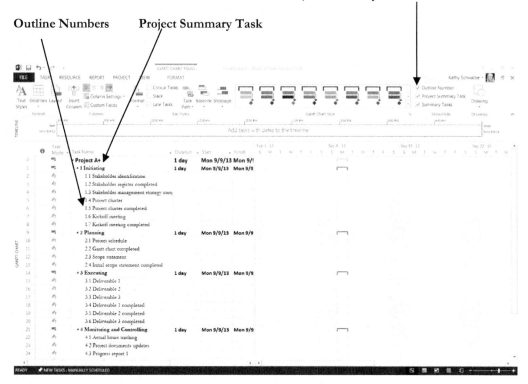

Figure A-25. Adding automatic outline numbers and a project summary task

Saving Project Files Without a Baseline

An important part of project management is tracking performance against a baseline, or approved plan. It is important to wait until you are ready to save your file with a baseline because Project 2013 will show changes against a baseline. Since you are still developing your project file for the Project A+ project, you want to save the file without a baseline, which is the default way to save a file. Later in this appendix, you will save the file with a baseline. You will then enter actual information to compare planned and actual performance data.

To save a file without a baseline:

1. *Save your file.* Click the **File** tab and then click **Save**, or click the **Save** button on the Quick Access toolbar.

2. *Enter a filename.* In the Save dialog box, type **mywbs** in the File name text box. Browse to the location in which you want to save the file, and then click **Save**. Remember that you can move the Split bar to show more or fewer columns.

3. *Close Project 2013.* Click the Close icon to exit Project 2013.

HELP: If you want to download the Project 2013 file mywbs.mpp to check your work or continue to the next section, a copy is available on the companion Web site for this text at www.intropm.com.

DEVELOPING THE SCHEDULE

Many people use Project 2013 for its scheduling features. The first step in using these features, after inputting the WBS for the project, is to change calendars, if needed, and then enter durations for tasks or specific dates when tasks will occur. You must also enter task dependencies in order for schedules to adjust automatically and to do critical path analysis. After entering durations and task dependencies, you can view the network diagram, critical path, and slack information.

Calendars

The standard Project 2013 calendar assumes that working hours are Monday through Friday, from 8:00 a.m. to 5:00 p.m., with an hour for lunch from noon until 1:00 p.m. In addition to the standard calendar, Project 2013 also includes a 24 Hours calendar and Night Shift calendar. The 24 Hours calendar assumes resources can work any hour and any day of the week. The Night Shift calendar assumes working hours are Monday through Saturday, from 12:00 a.m. to 3:00 a.m., 4:00 a.m. 8 a.m., and 11 p.m. to 12 a.m. You can create a different base calendar to meet your unique project requirements.

To create a new base calendar:

1. *Open a new file and access the Change Working Time dialog box.* With Project 2013 open, click the **Project** tab, and then click the **Change Working Time** button under the Properties group. The Change Working Time dialog box opens, as shown in Figure A-26.

2. *Name the new base calendar.* In the Change Working Time dialog box, click **Create New Calendar**. The Create New Base Calendar dialog box opens. Click the **Create new base calendar** radio button, type **Fiscal** as the name of the new calendar in the **Name** text box, and then click **OK**.

3. *Change the fiscal year start.* In the Change Working Time dialog box, click **Options** at the bottom of the screen. Change the **fiscal year** to start in **October** instead of January. Review other options in this screen, and then click **OK twice**.

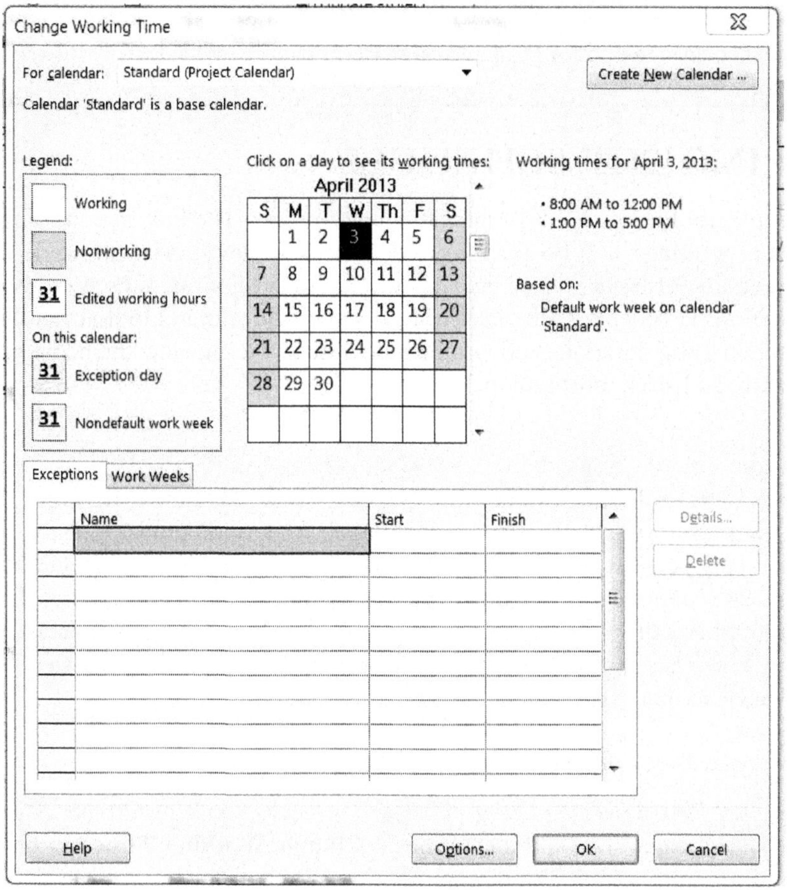

Figure A-26. Change Working Time dialog box

You can use this new calendar for the whole project, or you can assign it to specific resources on the project.

To assign the new calendar to the whole project:

1.   Open the Project Information dialog box. Click the **Project** tab, and then click the **Change Working Time** button.

2.   Select a new calendar. Click the **For calendar** list arrow to display a list of available calendars. Select your new calendar named **Fiscal** from this list, and then click **OK**.

To assign a specific calendar to a specific resource:

1.   Assign a new calendar. Click the **View** tab, and then click the **Resource Sheet** button under the Resource Views group. Type **Adam** in the Resource Name column, press **Enter**, and then select the word **Adam**.

2. *Select the calendar.* Click the cell under the **Base** column that says **Standard** on the right part of the screen for Adam. Click the list arrow to display the options, and then select **Fiscal** as shown in Figure A-27.

Resource Name ▼	Type ▼	Material ▼	Initials ▼	Group ▼	Max. ▼	Std. Rate ▼	Ovt. Rate ▼	Cost/Use ▼	Accrue ▼	Base ▼
Adam	Work		A		100%	$0.00/hr	$0.00/hr	$0.00	Prorated	Fiscal

Figure A-27. Changing calendars for specific resources

3. *Block off vacation time.* Double-click the resource name **Adam** to display the Resource Information dialog box, and then click the **Change Working Time** button, located on the General tab in the Resource Information dialog box. You can block off vacation time for people by selecting the appropriate days on the calendar and marking them as nonworking days. Click **OK** to accept your changes, and then click **OK** to close the Resource Information dialog box.

4. *Close the file without saving it.* Click the **Close** box, and then click **No** when you are prompted to save the file.

Entering Task Durations

Recall that duration includes the actual amount of time spent working on an activity plus elapsed time. Duration does not equal effort. For example, you might have an activity that you estimate will take one person 40 hours of effort to complete, but you allow two weeks on a calendar for its duration. You can simply enter 2w (for two weeks) in the Duration column for that activity (called a task in Project 2013).

Manual and Automatic Scheduling

If you have used earlier versions of Project, you probably noticed that when you entered an item in the Task Name column, it was automatically assigned a duration of one day, and Start and Finish dates were also automatically entered. This is still the case in Project 2013 if you use automatic scheduling for a task. If you use manual scheduling, no durations or dates are automatically entered. The other big change with manual scheduling is that summary task durations are not automatically calculated based on their subtasks when they are set up as manually scheduled tasks. Figure A-28 illustrates these differences. Notice that the Manual subtask 1 had no information entered for its duration, start, or finish dates. Also note that the duration for Manual summary task 1's duration is not dependent on the durations of its subtasks. For the automatic summary task, its duration is dependent on its summary tasks, and information is entered for all of the durations, start, and end dates. You can switch between automatic and manual scheduling for tasks in the same file, as desired, by changing the Task Mode.

Task Mode	Task Name	Duration	Start	Finish	February 21			March 7			March 21	
					S	T	M	F	T	S	W	S	T
	⊟ Manual summary task 1	4 wks	Thu 2/25/10	Wed 3/24/10								
	Manual subtask 1											
	Manual subtask 2	2 wks										
	⊟ Automatic summary task 1	15 days	Thu 2/25/10	Wed 3/17/10								
	Automatic subtask 1	1 wk	Thu 2/25/10	Wed 3/3/10								
	Automatic subtask 2	2 wks	Thu 3/4/10	Wed 3/17/10								

Figure A-28. Manual versus automatic scheduling

When you move your mouse over the Task Mode column (shown in the far left in Figure A-28) Project 2013 displays the following information:

- A task can be either Manually Scheduled or Automatically Scheduled.
- Manually Scheduled tasks have user-defined Start, Finish and Duration values. Project will never change their dates, but may warn you if there are potential issues with the entered values.
- Automatically Scheduled tasks have Start, Finish and Duration values calculated by Project based on dependencies, constraints, calendars, and other factors.

Project Help provides the following example of using both manual and automatic scheduling. You set up a preliminary project plan that's still in the proposal stage. You have a vague idea of major milestone dates but not much detail on other dates in various phases of the project. You build tasks and milestones using the Manually Scheduled task mode. The proposal is accepted and the tasks and deliverable dates become more defined. You continue to manually schedule those tasks and dates for a while, but as certain phases become well-defined, you decide to switch the tasks in those phases to the Automatically Scheduled task mode. By letting Project 2013 handle the complexities of scheduling, you can focus your attention on those phases that are still under development.

Duration Units and Guidelines for Entering Durations

To indicate the length of a task's duration, you normally type both a number and an appropriate duration symbol. If you type only a number, Project 2013 automatically enters days as the duration unit. Duration unit symbols include:

- d = days (default)
- w = weeks
- m = minutes
- h = hours
- mo or mon = months
- ed = elapsed days
- ew = elapsed weeks

For example, to enter two weeks for a task's duration, type 2w in the Duration column. (You can also type wk, wks, week, or weeks, instead of just w.) To enter four days for a task's duration, type 4 or 4d in the Duration column. You can also enter elapsed times in the Duration column. For example, 3ed means three elapsed days, and 2ew means two elapsed weeks.

You would use an elapsed duration for a task like "Allow cement to dry." The cement will dry in exactly the same amount of time regardless of whether it is a workday, a weekend, or a holiday. Project's default calendar does not assume that work is done on weekends. You will learn to change the calendar later in this appendix.

It is important to follow a few important rules when entering durations:

- To mark a task as a milestone, enter 0 for the duration. You can also mark tasks that have a non-zero duration as milestones by checking the "Mark task as milestone" option in the Task Information dialog box on the Advanced tab. You simply double-click a task to access this dialog box. The milestone symbol for those tasks will appear at their start date.

- You can enter the exact start and finish dates for activities instead of entering durations in the automatic scheduling mode. To enter start and finish dates, move the split bar to the right to reveal the Start and Finish columns. You normally only enter start and finish dates in this mode when those dates are certain.

- If you want task dates to adjust according to any other task dates, do not enter exact start and finish dates. Instead, enter durations and then establish dependencies to related tasks.

- To enter recurring tasks, such as weekly meetings, select Recurring Task from the Task button under the Task tab, Insert group. Enter the task name, the duration, and when the task occurs. Project 2013 will automatically insert appropriate subtasks based on the length of the project and the number of tasks required for the recurring task.

- Project 2013 uses a default calendar with standard workdays and hours. Remember to change the default calendar if needed, as shown earlier.

Next, you will set task durations in the file that you created and saved in the previous section. If you did not create the file named mywbs.mpp, you can download it from the companion Web site for this text.

Use the information in Figure A-29 to enter durations. The Project 2013 row number is shown to the left of each task name in the table.

Task Row	Task Name	Duration
2	Stakeholder identification	1w
3	Stakeholder register completed	0
4	Stakeholder management strategy completed	0
5	Project charter	1w
6	Project charter completed	0
7	Kickoff meeting	3d
8	Kickoff meeting completed	0
10	Project schedule	5d
11	Gantt chart completed	0
12	Scope statement	8d
13	Initial scope statement completed	0
15	Deliverable 1	3w
16	Deliverable 2	5w
17	Deliverable 3	6w
18	Deliverable 1 completed	0
19	Deliverable 2 completed	0
20	Deliverable 3 completed	0
24	Progress report 1	0
25	Progress report 2	0
28	Final project report	4d
29	Final presentation	4d
30	Project completed	0

Figure A-29. Task durations

Entering Task Durations

To enter task durations:

1. *Enter the duration for Task 2.* Open the mywbs file, and move the split bar to the right, if needed, to reveal the Duration, Start, and Finish columns. Click the **Duration** column for row 2, Stakeholder identification, type **1w**, and then press **Enter**. Notice that the duration for the first task, Initiating, also changed since it is a summary task and is an Automatically scheduled task, as shown in the Task Mode column. When you created summary tasks earlier, Project changed their scheduling mode to Automatic. Also notice that the Start and Finish date for Task 2 remain blank, since that task is a Manually scheduled task.

2. *Enter the duration for Task 3.* In the **Duration** column for row 3, Stakeholder register completed, type **0**, and then press **Enter**. Remember that a task with zero duration is a milestone. Notice the milestone or diamond symbol next to the date 9/9 that appears on the Gantt chart, as shown in Figure A-30. Adjust the Task Name column width to see all of the text, and use the Zoom slider on the bottom right of the screen to change the length of the Gantt chart bars.

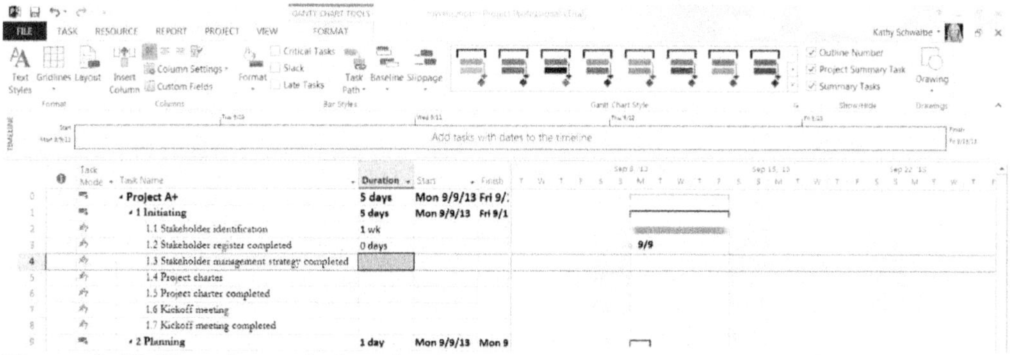

Figure A-30. Entering task durations

3. *Make all tasks Automatically scheduled tasks.* To save time because you do want most of the tasks to be automatically scheduled, select all of the tasks by clicking the **Task Name** column heading, and then click the **Auto Schedule** button under the **Task** tab, Tasks group. Most of the durations change to 1.

4. *Enter remaining task durations.* Continue to enter the durations using the information in Figure A-29 or Figure A-31. Do not enter durations for tasks not listed in the figure. Notice that the Planning Wizard dialog box displays when you make the same entry several times in a row, such as after task 20. Click OK to close the dialog box. You can adjust the column widths and Zoom, if desired.

Task Name	Duration	Start	Finish	13 Sep 1, '13 Sep 8, '13 Sep 15, '13 Sep 22, '13 Sep 29, '13 Oct 6, '13 Oct 13, '13
1.6 Kickoff meeting	3 days	Mon 9/9/13	Wed 9/11/13	
1.7 Kickoff meeting completed	0 days	Mon 9/9/13	Mon 9/9/13	9/9
4 2 Planning	8 days	Mon 9/9/13	Wed 9/18/13	
2.1 Project schedule	5 days	Mon 9/9/13	Fri 9/13/13	
2.2 Gantt chart completed	0 days	Mon 9/9/13	Mon 9/9/13	9/9
2.3 Scope statement	8 days	Mon 9/9/13	Wed 9/18/13	
2.4 Initial scope statement completed	0 days	Mon 9/9/13	Mon 9/9/13	9/9
4 3 Executing	30 days	Mon 9/9/13	Fri 10/18/13	
3.1 Deliverable 1	3 wks	Mon 9/9/13	Fri 9/27/13	
3.2 Deliverable 2	5 wks	Mon 9/9/13	Fri 10/11/13	
3.3 Deliverable 3	6 wks	Mon 9/9/13	Fri 10/18/13	
3.4 Deliverable 1 completed	0 days	Mon 9/9/13	Mon 9/9/13	9/9
3.5 Deliverable 2 completed	0 days	Mon 9/9/13	Mon 9/9/13	9/9
3.6 Deliverable 3 completed	0 days	Mon 9/9/13	Mon 9/9/13	9/9
4 4 Monitoring and Controlling	1 day	Mon 9/9/13	Mon 9/9/13	
4.1 Actual hours tracking	1 day	Mon 9/9/13	Mon 9/9/13	
4.2 Project documents updates	1 day	Mon 9/9/13	Mon 9/9/13	
4.3 Progress report 1	0 days	Mon 9/9/13	Mon 9/9/13	9/9
4.4 Progress report 2	0 days	Mon 9/9/13	Mon 9/9/13	9/9
4.5 Team review meetings	1 day	Mon 9/9/13	Mon 9/9/13	
4 5 Closing	4 days	Mon 9/9/13	Thu 9/12/13	
5.1 Final project report	4 days	Mon 9/9/13	Thu 9/12/13	
5.2 Final project presentation	4 days	Mon 9/9/13	Thu 9/12/13	
5.3 Project completed	0 days	Mon 9/9/13	Mon 9/9/13	9/9

Figure A-31. Entering more durations

5. *Insert a recurring task above Task 26, Team meetings.* Click **Team review meetings** (Task 26) in the Task Name column to select that task. Click the **Task** tab, and click the **Task** button drop-down box under the Insert group, and then click **Recurring Task**. The Recurring Task Information dialog box opens.

6. *Enter task and duration information for the recurring task.* Type **Team review meetings** as the task title in the Task Name text box. Type **15min** in the Duration text box. Select the **Weekly** radio button under Recurrence pattern. Make sure that **1** is entered in the **Recur every** list box. Select the **Thursday** check box. In the Range of recurrence section, type **9/12/13** in the Start text box (or select it with the drop-down calendar), click the **End by** radio button, and then type **12/5/13** in the End by text box (or select it in the calendar), as shown in Figure A-32. The new recurring task will appear above Task 26, Team review meetings, when you are finished. **Delete task 40**, Team review meetings, by right clicking anywhere in row 40 and selecting Delete Task.

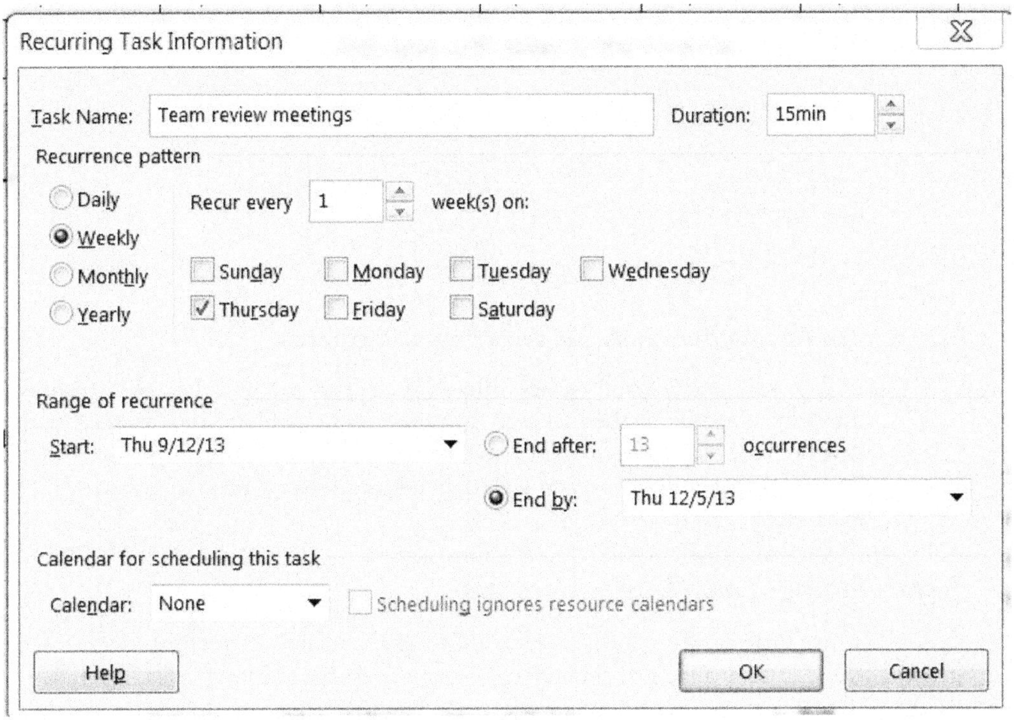

Recurring Task Information   ✕

Task Name: Team review meetings   Duration: 15min

Recurrence pattern

○ Daily   Recur every 1   week(s) on:

● Weekly

○ Monthly   ☐ Sunday   ☐ Monday   ☐ Tuesday   ☐ Wednesday

○ Yearly   ☑ Thursday ☐ Friday   ☐ Saturday

Range of recurrence

Start: Thu 9/12/13   ▼   ○ End after: 13   occurrences

                                        ● End by: Thu 12/5/13   ▼

Calendar for scheduling this task

Calendar: None   ▼   ☐ Scheduling ignores resource calendars

Help   OK   Cancel

Figure A-32. Recurring task information dialog box

> **TIP:** You can also enter a number of occurrences instead of an End by date for a recurring task. You might need to adjust the End by date after you enter all of your task durations and dependencies. Remember, the date on your computer determines the date listed as Today in the calendar.

7.   *View the new summary task and its subtasks.* Click **OK**. Project 2013 inserts a new Team review meetings subtask in the Task Name column. To collapse the recurring task, click the **collapse symbol.** Move your mouse over the Recurring Task symbol in the Indicator column for row 26 to read the note about it occurring 13 times. Notice that the recurring task appears on the appropriate dates on the Gantt chart.

8.   *Adjust the columns displayed and the timescale.* Move the **split bar** so that only the Task Name and Duration columns are visible. If needed, increase the Duration column's width so all of the text is visible. Click the **Zoom Out** button on the Zoom slider in the lower left of the screen to display all of the symbols in the Gantt chart. Your screen should resemble Figure A-33.

	❶	Task Mode	Task Name	Duration	Start	Finish	13	Jul 21, 13	Aug 11, 13	Sep 1, 13	Sep 22, 13	Oct 13, 13	Nov 3, 13	Nov 24, 13
17		⇒	3.3 Deliverable 3	6 wks	Mon 9/9/13	Fri 10/18/13								
18		⇒	3.4 Deliverable 1 completed	0 days	Mon 9/9/13	Mon 9/9/13			◆ 9/9					
19		⇒	3.5 Deliverable 2 completed	0 days	Mon 9/9/13	Mon 9/9/13			◆ 9/9					
20		⇒	3.6 Deliverable 3 completed	0 days	Mon 9/9/13	Mon 9/9/13			◆ 9/9					
21		⇒	⊿ 4 Monitoring and Controlling	63.03 days	Mon 9/9/13	Thu 12/5/13								
22		⇒	4.1 Actual hours tracking	1 day	Mon 9/9/13	Mon 9/9/13								
23		⇒	4.2 Project documents updates	1 day	Mon 9/9/13	Mon 9/9/13								
24		⇒	4.3 Progress report 1	0 days	Mon 9/9/13	Mon 9/9/13			◆ 9/9					
25		⇒	4.4 Progress report 2	0 days	Mon 9/9/13	Mon 9/9/13			◆ 9/9					
26	♺	⇒	**4.5 Team review meetings**	60.03 days	Thu 9/12/13	Thu 12/5/13								
40		⇒	⊿ 5 Closing	4 days	Mon 9/9/13	Thu 9/12/13								
41		⇒	5.1 Final project report	4 days	Mon 9/9/13	Thu 9/12/13								
42		⇒	5.2 Final project presentation	4 days	Mon 9/9/13	Thu 9/12/13								
43		⇒	5.3 Project completed	0 days	Mon 9/9/13	Mon 9/9/13			◆ 9/9					

Figure A-33. All task durations and recurring task entered

9. *Save your file and name it.* Click **File** on the Menu bar, and then click **Save As**. Enter **myschedule** as the filename, and then save the file to the desired location on your computer or network. Notice that all of the tasks still begin on 9/9/13. This will change when you add task dependencies. Keep this file open for the next set of steps.

Establishing Task Dependencies

To use Project 2013 to adjust schedules automatically and perform critical path analysis, you *must* determine the dependencies or relationships among tasks. There are several different methods for creating task dependencies: using the Link Tasks button, using the Predecessors column of the Entry table or the Predecessors tab in the Task Information dialog box, or clicking and dragging the Gantt chart symbols for tasks with dependencies. You will use the first two methods in the following steps.

To create dependencies using the Link Tasks button, highlight tasks that are related and then click the Link Tasks button under the Task tab, Schedule group. For example, to create a finish-to-start (FS) dependency between Task 1 and Task 2, click any cell in row 1, drag down to row 2, and then click the Link Tasks button. The default type of link is finish-to-start. In the Project A+ file, you will also set up some other types of dependencies and use the lag option to set up overlaps between dependent tasks.

> **TIP:** To select adjacent tasks, click and drag the mouse to highlight them. You can also click the first task, hold down the Shift key, and then click the last task. To select nonadjacent tasks, hold down the Control (Ctrl) key as you click tasks in order of their dependencies.

When you use the Predecessors column of the Entry table to create dependencies, you must manually enter the information. To create dependencies manually, type the task row number of the preceding task in the Predecessors column of the Entry table. For example, Task 3 has Task 2 as a predecessor, which can be entered in the Predecessors column, meaning that Task 3 cannot start until Task 2 is finished. To see the Predecessors column of the Entry table, move the split bar to the right. You can also double-click on the task, click the Predecessors tab in the Task Information dialog box, and enter the predecessors there.

Next, you will enter the predecessors for tasks as indicated. You will create some dependencies by manually typing the predecessors in the Predecessors column, some by using the Link Tasks button, and the remaining dependencies by using whichever method you prefer.

To link tasks or establish dependencies for Project A+:

1. *Display the Predecessors column in the Entry table.* Move the split bar to the right to reveal the full Predecessors column in the myschedule.mpp file you saved in the previous section. Widen the Task Name or other columns, if needed.

2. *Highlight the cell where you want to enter a predecessor, and then type the task number for its predecessor task.* Click the **Predecessors cell for Task 3**, Stakeholder register completed, type **2**, and press **Enter**. Notice that as you enter task dependencies, the Gantt chart changes to reflect the new schedule. Also notice that several cells become highlighted, showing the Visual Change Highlights feature of Project 2013.

3. *Enter predecessors for Task 4 and view the Task Path.* Click the **Predecessors cell for Task 4**, type **2**, and press **Enter**. Click the **Format** tab, and then click the **Task Path** button under the Bar Styles group. Experiment with the options to highlight Predecessor, Driving Predecessors, Successors, and Driven Successors, and then click Remove Highlighting.

4. *Establish dependencies using the Link Tasks button.* To link Tasks 5 and 6, click the **task name for Task 5** in the Task Name column and drag down through **Task 6**. Then, in the **Task** tab, click the **Link Tasks** button (looks like a chain link) under the Schedule group. Notice that the result is the same as typing 5 in the Predecessors column for Task 6, as shown in Figure A-34.

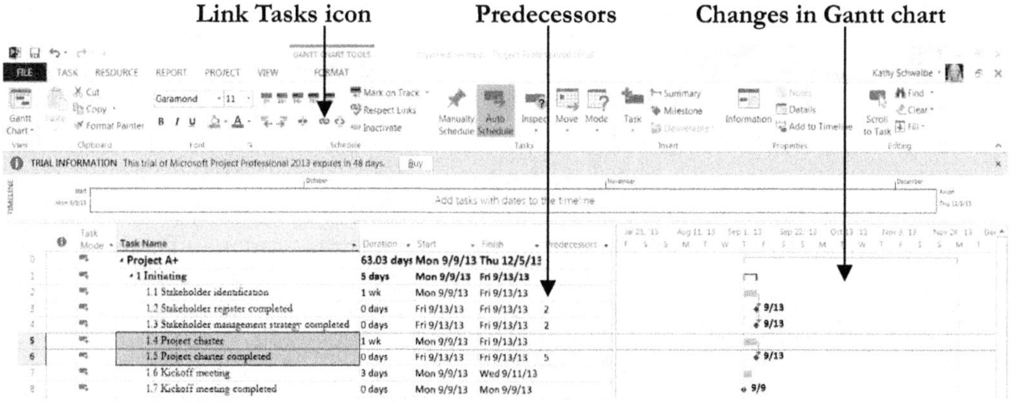

Figure A-34. Entering predecessor

5. *Enter dependencies and lag time using the Task Information dialog box.* Double-click on the **Task Name** for **task 5**, Project charter, and then click on the **Predecessors tab** in the Task Information dialog box. Click in the cell under Task Name, and

then click the **Task Name** down arrow and select **Stakeholder identification**. Click the **Type** drop down arrow to see the various types of dependencies. For this task, you will keep the default type of finish-to-start. Click the **Lag drop down arrow**, then **type -50%** and press **Enter**. (Lag means there is a gap between tasks, and lead or negative lag means there is an overlap). Your screen should resemble Figure A-35. Click **OK** to close the dialog box. Notice that the Predecessor column for task 5 displays 2FS-50%, meaning there is a finish-to-start relationship with task 2 and a lag of -50%, meaning the task can start when task 2 is 50% completed.

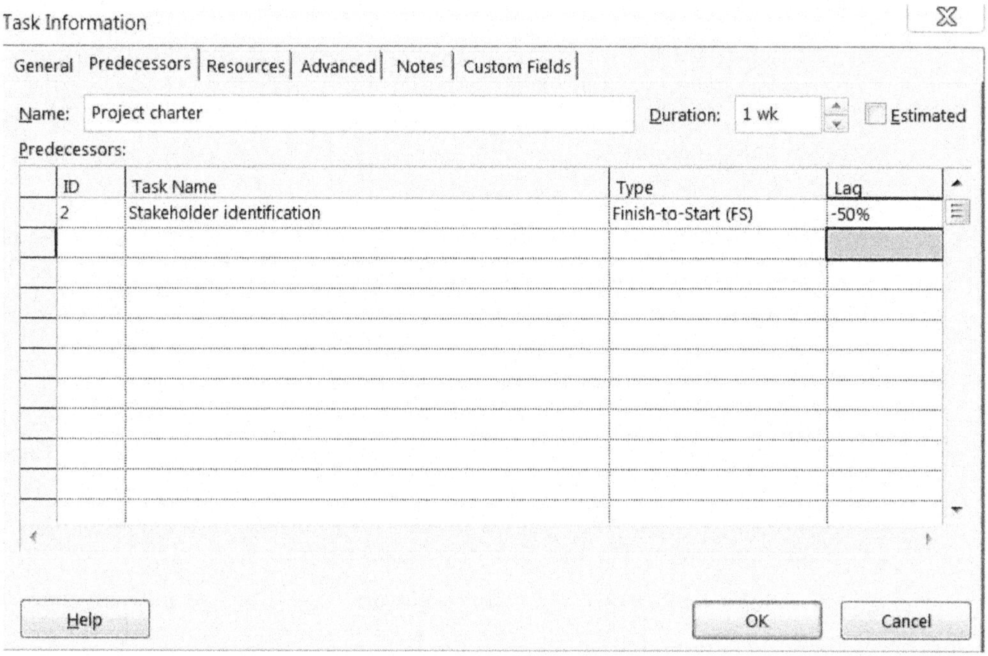

Task Information				⌧
General	Predecessors	Resources	Advanced	Notes	Custom Fields

Name: Project charter   Duration: 1 wk   ☐ Estimated

Predecessors:

ID	Task Name	Type	Lag
2	Stakeholder identification	Finish-to-Start (FS)	-50%

Help   OK   Cancel

Figure A-35. Entering predecessor information using the task information dialog box

6.   *Enter remaining dependencies.* **Link the other tasks** by either manually entering the predecessors into the Predecessors column, by using the Link Tasks button, or using the Task Information dialog box. Use the information in Figure A-36 to make your entries, being careful to leave some of the predecessors blank, as shown. If you have entered all data correctly, the project should end on 12/6, or December 6, 2013.

Task Row	Task Name	Predecessors
3	Stakeholder register completed	2
4	Stakeholder management strategy completed	2
5	Project charter	2FS-50%
6	Project charter completed	5
7	Kickoff meeting	2,6
8	Kickoff meeting completed	6,7
9	Planning	
10	Schedule	5,12FS-50%
11	Gantt chart completed	10
12	Scope statement	5
13	Initial scope statement completed	12
14	Executing	
15	Deliverable 1	12
16	Deliverable 2	18
17	Deliverable 3	18
18	Deliverable 1 completed	15
19	Deliverable 2 completed	16
20	Deliverable 3 completed	17
21	Monitoring and Controlling	
22	Actual hours tracking	2
23	Project documents updates	3
24-40	Progress Report 1 through Closing	
41	Final project report	18,19,20
42	Final presentation	18,19,20
43	Project completed	41,42

Figure A-36. Predecessor information for Project A+

7.   *Adjust several dates.* You know that you have to deliver the two progress reports on specific dates. Click on the **Start dates for Tasks 24 and 25** and change those dates to October 10 and November 7. Also change the **Finish dates for tasks 22 and 23 to December 4** to make those dates more realistic. Project 2013 will display a yellow warning symbol to remind you that you are changing default dates, which is fine in these examples.

8.   *Review the file.* If needed, click the **Zoom Out** button on the Zoom slider to adjust the timescale so all of the information shows on your screen. When you finish, your screen should resemble Figure A-37. Double-check your screen to make sure you entered the dependencies correctly.

		Task Mode	Task Name	Duration	Start	Finish	Predecessors
0			**Project A+**	**64.5 days**	**Mon 9/9/13**	**Fri 12/6/13**	
1			**1 Initiating**	**10.5 days**	**Mon 9/9/13**	**Mon 9/23/13**	
2			1.1 Stakeholder identification	1 wk	Mon 9/9/13	Fri 9/13/13	
3			1.2 Stakeholder register completed	0 days	Fri 9/13/13	Fri 9/13/13	2
4			1.3 Stakeholder management strategy completed	0 days	Fri 9/13/13	Fri 9/13/13	2
5			1.4 Project charter	1 wk	Wed 9/11/13	Wed 9/18/13	2FS-50%
6			1.5 Project charter completed	0 days	Wed 9/18/13	Wed 9/18/13	5
7			1.6 Kickoff meeting	3 days	Wed 9/18/13	Mon 9/23/13	2,6
8			1.7 Kickoff meeting completed	0 days	Mon 9/23/13	Mon 9/23/13	6,7
9			**2 Planning**	**9 days**	**Wed 9/18/13**	**Tue 10/1/13**	
10			2.1 Project schedule	5 days	Tue 9/24/13	Tue 10/1/13	5,12FS-50%
11			2.2 Gantt chart completed	0 days	Tue 10/1/13	Tue 10/1/13	10
12			2.3 Scope statement	8 days	Wed 9/18/13	Mon 9/30/13	5
13			2.4 Initial scope statement completed	0 days	Mon 9/30/13	Mon 9/30/13	12
14			**3 Executing**	**45 days**	**Mon 9/30/13**	**Mon 12/2/13**	
15			3.1 Deliverable 1	3 wks	Mon 9/30/13	Mon 10/21/13	12
16			3.2 Deliverable 2	5 wks	Mon 10/21/13	Mon 11/25/13	18
17			3.3 Deliverable 3	6 wks	Mon 10/21/13	Mon 12/2/13	18
18			3.4 Deliverable 1 completed	0 days	Mon 10/21/13	Mon 10/21/13	15
19			3.5 Deliverable 2 completed	0 days	Mon 11/25/13	Mon 11/25/13	16
20			3.6 Deliverable 3 completed	0 days	Mon 12/2/13	Mon 12/2/13	17
21			**4 Monitoring and Controlling**	**60.03 days**	**Thu 9/12/13**	**Thu 12/5/13**	
22			4.1 Actual hours tracking	1 day	Wed 12/4/13	Wed 12/4/13	2
23			4.2 Project documents updates	1 day	Wed 12/4/13	Wed 12/4/13	3
24			4.3 Progress report 1	0 days	Thu 10/10/13	Thu 10/10/13	
25			4.4 Progress report 2	0 days	Thu 11/7/13	Thu 11/7/13	
26			**4.5 Team review meetings**	**60.03 days**	**Thu 9/12/13**	**Thu 12/5/13**	
40			**5 Closing**	**4 days**	**Mon 12/2/13**	**Fri 12/6/13**	
41			5.1 Final project report	4 days	Mon 12/2/13	Fri 12/6/13	18,19,20
42			5.2 Final project presentation	4 days	Mon 12/2/13	Fri 12/6/13	18,19,20
43			5.3 Project completed	0 days	Fri 12/6/13	Fri 12/6/13	41,42

Figure A-37. Project A+ file with durations and dependencies entered

9.   *Preview and save your file.* Click the **File** tab, and then select **Print** to preview and print your file. Click **Page Setup**, and then click the option to **Fit to 1** so it will print on one page, as shown in Figure A-38. Be careful before printing any Project 2013 files so you do not waste a lot of paper. When you are finished, click **Save** to save your file again. Keep the file open for the next set of steps.

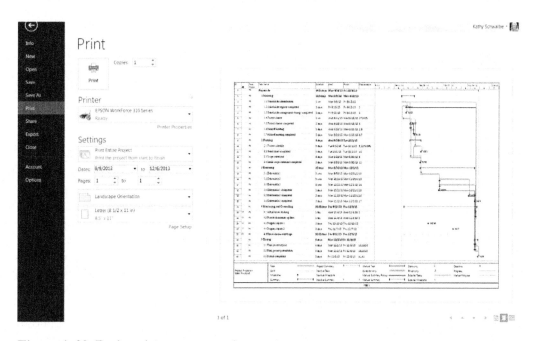

Figure A-38. Project A+ set up to print on one page

Gantt Charts, Network Diagrams, and Critical Path Analysis

Project 2013 shows a Gantt chart as the default view to the right of the Entry table. As described earlier in this text, network diagrams are often used to show task dependencies. This section explains important information about Gantt charts and network diagrams and describes how to make critical path information more visible in the Gantt Chart view.

Because you have already created task dependencies, you can now find the critical path for Project A+. You can view the critical tasks by changing the color of those items in the Gantt Chart view. Tasks on the critical path will automatically be red in the Network Diagram view. You can also view critical path information in the Schedule table or by using the Critical Tasks report.

To make the text for the critical path tasks appear in red on the Gantt chart:

1. *Change the critical tasks format.* Using the myschedule.mpp file you previously saved, click the **Format** tab, and then click the **Critical Tasks check box** in the Bar Styles group, as shown in Figure A-39. Notice that the critical tasks display in red in the Gantt chart. You can also quickly change the Gantt Chart Style by clicking one of those options.

Critical Tasks check box

Figure A-39. Formatting critical tasks

2. *View the network diagram.* Click the View tab, and then click the **Network Diagram** button under the Task Views group Click the **Zoom Out** button on the Zoom slider several times and watch the view change. Figure A-40 shows all of the tasks in the Project A+ network diagram. Note that milestone tasks, such as Stakeholder management strategy completed, the fourth box on the top, appear as pointed rectangular boxes, while other tasks appear as rectangles. Move your mouse over that box to see it in a larger view. Notice that tasks on the critical path automatically appear in red. A dashed line on a network diagram represents a page break. You often need to change some of the default settings for the Network Diagram view before printing it. As you can see, network diagrams can be messy, so you might prefer to highlight critical tasks on the Gantt chart as you did earlier for easier viewing.

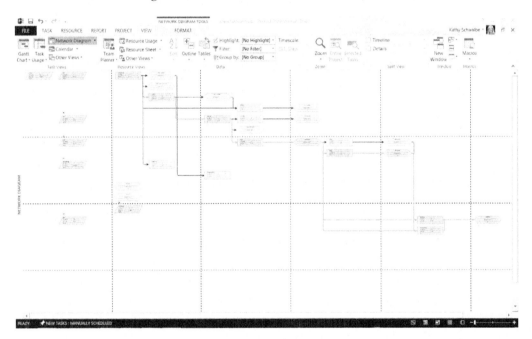

Figure A-40. Network diagram view

3. *View the schedule table.* Click the **Gantt Chart** button under the **View** tab to return to Gantt Chart view. Right-click the **Select All** button to the left of the

Task Mode column heading and select **Schedule**. Alternatively, you can click the **View** tab and click the **Tables** button under the Data group and then select **Schedule**. The Schedule table replaces the Entry table to the left of the Gantt Chart. Your screen should resemble Figure A-41. This view shows the start and finish (meaning the early start and early finish) and late start and late finish dates for each task, as well as free and total slack. Right-click the **Select All** button and select **Entry** to return to the Entry table view.

Select All button   Schedule table

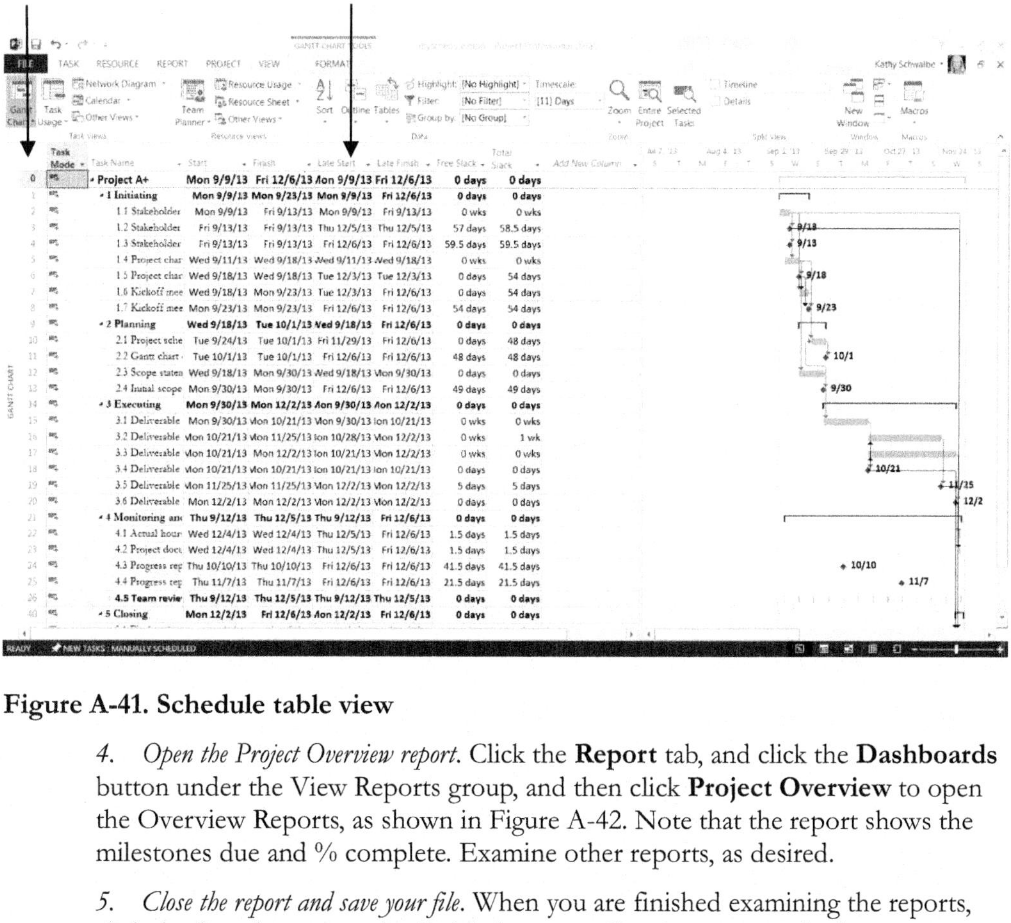

Figure A-41. Schedule table view

4.   *Open the Project Overview report.* Click the **Report** tab, and click the **Dashboards** button under the View Reports group, and then click **Project Overview** to open the Overview Reports, as shown in Figure A-42. Note that the report shows the milestones due and % complete. Examine other reports, as desired.

5.   *Close the report and save your file.* When you are finished examining the reports, click the **Save** button on the Quick Access toolbar to save your final myschedule.mpp file, showing the Entry table and Gantt chart view. Close Project 2013 if you are not continuing to the next section.

PROJECT OVERVIEW

MON 9/9/13 - FRI 12/6/13

% COMPLETE

0%

% COMPLETE
Status for all top-level tasks. To see the status for subtasks, click on the chart and update the outline level in the Field List.

MILESTONES DUE
Milestones that are coming soon.

Name	Finish
Stakeholder register completed	Fri 9/13/13
Stakeholder management strategy completed	Fri 9/13/13
Project charter completed	Wed 9/18/13
Kickoff meeting completed	Mon 9/23/13
Gantt chart completed	Tue 10/1/13
Initial scope statement completed	Mon 9/30/13
Deliverable 1 completed	Mon 10/21/13
Deliverable 2 completed	Mon 11/25/13
Deliverable 3 completed	Mon 12/2/13
Progress report 1	Thu 10/10/13
Progress report 2	Thu 11/7/13

100% 90% 80% 70% 60% 50% 40% 30% 20% 10% 0%

0%   0%   0%   0%   0%

Initiating   Planning   Executing   Monitoring   Closing
and
Controlling

LATE TASKS
Tasks that are past due.

Name	Start	Finish	Duration	% Complete	Resource Names

Figure A-42. Project Overview report

> **HELP:** If you want to download the Project 2013 file myschedule.mpp to check your work or continue to the next section, a copy is available on the companion Web site for this text at www.intropm.com.

Next you will explore some of the cost and resource management features of Project 2013.

PROJECT COST AND RESOURCE MANAGEMENT

Many people do not use Project 2013 for cost or resource management. Some organizations have more established cost management software products and procedures in place, and many people simply do not know how to use the cost or resource management features of Project 2013. However, these features make it possible to integrate total project information more easily. This section offers brief instructions for entering fixed and variable cost estimates, assigning resources to tasks, viewing resource histograms, and entering actual cost and schedule information after establishing a baseline plan. It also explains how to use Project 2013 for earned value management. More details on these features are available in Project Help, online tutorials, or other texts. See other chapters of this text for information on some of these concepts.

Entering Fixed and Variable Cost Estimates

You can enter costs as fixed or variable. Fixed costs include costs like a specific quantity of materials or costs for consultants hired at a fixed cost. Variable costs vary based on the amount of materials or hours people work. On many projects, human resource costs are the largest percentage of total project costs.

Entering Fixed Costs in the Cost Table

The Cost table allows you to easily enter fixed costs related to each task. You will enter a fixed cost of $200 related to Task 15, Deliverable 1.

To enter a fixed cost:

1. *Display the Cost Table view.* Open your Project 2013 file myschedule.mpp, if necessary. Right-click the **Select All** button to the left of the Task Mode column heading and select **Cost**. The Cost table replaces the Entry table to the left of the Gantt chart. **Widen** the Task Name column and then move the **Split bar** to the right, as needed, until you see the entire Cost table.

2. *Enter a fixed cost.* In the **Fixed Cost column for Task 15**, Deliverable 1, type **200** and press **Enter**. Notice that the Total Cost and Remaining Cost columns reflect this entry, and changes are made to the summary task, Executing, as well. Your screen should resemble Figure A-43.

Select All button   Fixed Cost column of cost table

	Task Name	Fixed Cost	Fixed Cost Accrual	Total Cost	Baseline	Variance	Actual	Remaining
0	◢ **Project A+**	$0.00	Prorated	$200.00	$0.00	$200.00	$0.00	$200.00
1	◢ **1 Initiating**	$0.00	**Prorated**	**$0.00**	**$0.00**	**$0.00**	**$0.00**	**$0.00**
2	1.1 Stakeholder identification	$0.00	Prorated	$0.00	$0.00	$0.00	$0.00	$0.00
3	1.2 Stakeholder register completed	$0.00	Prorated	$0.00	$0.00	$0.00	$0.00	$0.00
4	1.3 Stakeholder management strategy completed	$0.00	Prorated	$0.00	$0.00	$0.00	$0.00	$0.00
5	1.4 Project charter	$0.00	Prorated	$0.00	$0.00	$0.00	$0.00	$0.00
6	1.5 Project charter completed	$0.00	Prorated	$0.00	$0.00	$0.00	$0.00	$0.00
7	1.6 Kickoff meeting	$0.00	Prorated	$0.00	$0.00	$0.00	$0.00	$0.00
8	1.7 Kickoff meeting completed	$0.00	Prorated	$0.00	$0.00	$0.00	$0.00	$0.00
9	◢ **2 Planning**	**$0.00**	**Prorated**	**$0.00**	**$0.00**	**$0.00**	**$0.00**	**$0.00**
10	2.1 Project schedule	$0.00	Prorated	$0.00	$0.00	$0.00	$0.00	$0.00
11	2.2 Gantt chart completed	$0.00	Prorated	$0.00	$0.00	$0.00	$0.00	$0.00
12	2.3 Scope statement	$0.00	Prorated	$0.00	$0.00	$0.00	$0.00	$0.00
13	2.4 Initial scope statement completed	$0.00	Prorated	$0.00	$0.00	$0.00	$0.00	$0.00
14	◢ **3 Executing**	**$0.00**	**Prorated**	**$200.00**	**$0.00**	**$200.00**	**$0.00**	**$200.00**
15	3.1 Deliverable 1	$200.00	Prorated	$200.00	$0.00	$200.00	$0.00	$200.00
16	3.2 Deliverable 2	$0.00	Prorated	$0.00	$0.00	$0.00	$0.00	$0.00
17	3.3 Deliverable 3	$0.00	Prorated	$0.00	$0.00	$0.00	$0.00	$0.00

Figure A-43. Entering a fixed cost

Entering Resource Information and Cost Estimates

Several methods are available for entering resource information in Project 2013. The Resource Sheet allows you to enter the resource name, initials, resource group, maximum units, standard rate, overtime rate, cost/use, accrual method, base calendar, and code. Once you have established resources in the Resource Sheet, you can assign those resources to tasks in the Entry table with the list arrow that appears when you click a cell in the Resource Names column. The Resource Names column is the last column of the Entry table. You can also use other methods for assigning resources, such as using the Assign

Resources button or using the split window, which is the recommended approach to have the most control over how resources are assigned because Project 2013 makes several assumptions about resources assignments that might mess up your schedule or costs. Next, you will enter information for three people working on Project A+ and assign them to a few tasks using various methods.

To enter basic information about each person into the Resource Sheet and assign them to tasks using the Entry table and toolbar:

1. *Display the Resource Sheet view.* Click the **View** tab, and then click the **Resource Sheet** button under the Resource Views group.

2. *Enter resource information.* Enter the information from Figure A-44 into the Resource Sheet. The three resources names are **Kathy, Dan, and Scott**. The Std. Rate and Ovt. Rate for Kathy is **40**, and the Std. and Ovt. Rates for Dan and Scott are **30**. Type the information as shown and press the **Tab** key to move to the next field. When you type the standard and overtime rates, you can just type the number, such as 40, and Project 2013 will automatically enter $40.00/hr. The standard and overtime rates entered are based on hourly rates. You can also enter annual salaries by typing the annual salary number followed by /y for "per year." Your screen should resemble Figure A-44 when you are finished entering the resource data.

Resource Name	Type	Material	Initials	Group	Max.	Std. Rate	Ovt. Rate	Cost/Use	Accrue	Base
Kathy	Work		K		100%	$40.00/hr	$40.00/hr	$0.00	Prorated	Standard
Dan	Work		D		100%	$30.00/hr	$30.00/hr	$0.00	Prorated	Standard
Scott	Work		S		100%	$30.00/hr	$30.00/hr	$0.00	Prorated	Standard

Figure A-44. Resource sheet view with resource data entered

TIP: If you know that some people will be available for a project only part time, enter their percentage of availability in the Max Units column of the Resource Sheet. Project 2013 will then automatically assign those people based on their maximum units. For example, if someone can work only 50% of his or her time on a project throughout most of the project, enter 50% in the Max Units column for that person. When you enter that person as a resource for a task, his or her default number of hours will be 50% of a standard eight-hour workday, or four hours per day. You can also enter the number of hours each person is scheduled to work, as shown later.

3. *Assign resources to tasks.* From the **View** tab, select the **Gantt Chart** button under the Task Views group, and then click the **Select All** button and switch back to the **Entry** table. Move the Split bar to reveal the Resource Names column, if needed.

4. *Assign Kathy to task 2, Stakeholder identification.* Click in the **Resource Names** cell for **row 2**. Click the list arrow, click on the **checkbox** by **Kathy**, and then press **Enter** or click on another cell. Notice that the resource choices are the names you

just entered in the Resource Sheet. Also notice that after you select a resource by checking the appropriate checkbox, his or her name appears on the Gantt chart, as shown in Figure A-45. To assign more than one resource to a task using the list arrow, simply select another checkbox. Note that Project 2013 will assume that each resource is assigned full-time to tasks using this method since the task is in automatically schedule mode. Also note that you can use filter by Resource Names to only show tasks assigned to specific resources after you enter the resources.

Filter Resource Names

	Task Mode	Task Name	Duration	Start	Finish	Predecessors	Resource Names
0		⁴ **Project A+**	**64.5 days**	**Mon 9/9/13**	**Fri 12/6/13**		
1		⁴ 1 Initiating	**10.5 days**	**Mon 9/9/13**	**Mon 9/23/13**		
2		1.1 Stakeholder identification	1 wk	Mon 9/9/13	Fri 9/13/13		Kathy
3		1.2 Stakeholder register completed	0 days	Fri 9/13/13	Fri 9/13/13	2	☐ Dan
4		1.3 Stakeholder management strategy completed	0 days	Fri 9/13/13	Fri 9/13/13	2	☑ Kathy
5		1.4 Project charter	1 wk	Wed 9/11/13	Wed 9/18/13	2FS-50%	☐ Scott
6		1.5 Project charter completed	0 days	Wed 9/18/13	Wed 9/18/13	5	

Figure A-45. Resource assigned using the entry table

5. Assign two resources to a task. Click in the **Resource Names** cell for **row 5 (Project charter)**. Click the **list arrow**, then click on the **checkbox by Dan and Kathy,** and then press **Enter**. Notice that both resource names appear in the Resource Names column and on the Gantt chart for this task, and the task duration remains at 1 week.

6.   Change the resource assignments. Click in the **Resource Names** cell for **Task 2**, Stakeholder identification, click the **list arrow**, and add **Dan** as another resource. Notice that when you change an original resource assignment, Project prompts you for how you want to handle the change, as shown in Figure A-46. Click the **Exclamation point** symbol to read your options. In past versions of Project, resource additions would change schedules automatically unless the user entered them a certain way. Now you have much more control of what happens to your schedule and costs. In this case, we do want to accept the default of keeping the duration constant.

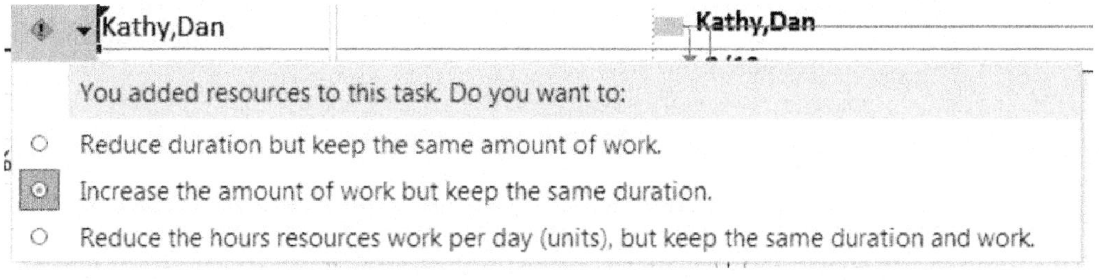

⊕	▾	Kathy,Dan		**Kathy,Dan**

You added resources to this task. Do you want to:

○   Reduce duration but keep the same amount of work.

◉   Increase the amount of work but keep the same duration.

○   Reduce the hours resources work per day (units), but keep the same duration and work.

Figure A-46. Options when additional resources are added to tasks

7. *Review the cost table.* Right-click the **Select All** button to the left of the Task Mode column heading and select **Cost**. Notice that costs have been added to the tasks where you added resources. Project assumes that people are assigned full-time to tasks. It is showing a cost of $2,800 each for Task 2 and Task 5. In the next section, you will see how to control resources entries even more. First, right-click the **Select All** button to the left of the Task Mode column heading and select **Entry** to return to the Entry table.

To control resource and work assignments using the Resource details window:

1. *Open the Resource Form.* Notice the **red symbols in the Indicator columns** for rows/tasks 2 and 5. Move your mouse over the symbol to read the message about resources being overallocated. Click the Task Name for row 2, Stakeholder identification, click the **Resource** tab, and then click on the **Details** button under the Properties group. A Resource Form is displayed at the bottom of the screen, as shown in Figure A-47. Project 2013 assumes every task is assigned full-time, so since Kathy is scheduled on two tasks on the same day, it says she is overallocated.

> **TIP:** You can right-click on the lower screen to review see additional forms/views. You can click the Select All button at the top right of the screen to view different tables at the top of the screen. You want to make sure that resource and work hour assignments do not adjust your schedules in ways you did not intend.

2. *Make tasks 2 and 5 manually scheduled.* Click the **Select All** button and switch to the **Entry table**. Click the drop-down in the **Task Mode** column for Tasks 2 and 5 to make them **manually scheduled**. When you assigned resources, Project 2013 assumed they were working full-time or 40 hours per week on each task. Because these two tasks have days that overlap, there is an overallocation. You do not expect each resource to work that many hours, so you can change them by using the Resource Form.

3. *Change the number of Work hours.* Select Task 2, **Stakeholder identification** in the top window, and then click the **Work** column in the Resource Form window for **Kathy** in the lower part of your screen. Type **10h**, press **Enter**, and again type **10h** and press **Enter** for the next task, Task 5, Project charter, and then click the **OK** button. Click Next to see Dan's Resource Form, as shown in Figure A-47.

Task mode indicator   Change # work hours

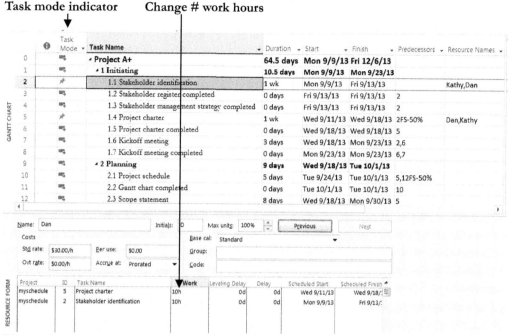

Figure A-47. Changing Work hours for tasks

4.   Enter additional work hours and review the Gantt chart. Change Dan's work hours to **10h for Tasks 2 and 5** as well. Notice in the Gantt chart that the duration for Tasks 2 and 5 are still one week. The overallocation indicator should now disappear because the number of hours has been reduced from the default of 8 hours per day, or 40 hours for a 5-day task. To remove the Resource Form, click **Details** on the Ribbon under the Resource tab.

5.   Examine the new cost information. Click the Select All button, and then click **Cost** to view the Cost table. Tasks 2 and 5 each show only $700 for Total Cost.

6.   Close the file without saving it. Close the file, but do not save the changes you made.

Using the Team Planner Feature

Another way to assign resources and reduce overallocations is by using the Team Planner feature. Assume you have two people assigned to work on a project, Brian and Cindy, as shown in Figure A-48. Notice that Brian is assigned to work on both Task 1 and Task 2 full-time the first week. Therefore, Brian is overallocated. Cindy is scheduled to work on Task 3 full-time the second week, and Task 4, also scheduled for the second week, is not assigned yet.

Overallocation indicator

Figure A-48. Overallocated resource

You can click on the Team Planner view under the View tab to see a screen similar to the top section of Figure A-49. Notice that Brian has both Tasks 1 and 2 assigned to him at the same time. These tasks and Brian's name display in red to show the overallocation. Cindy is assigned Task 3 the following week, and Task 4 is unassigned. By simply clicking and dragging Task 4 straight up so it is under Brian in Week 2 and Task 2 straight down so it is under Cindy in Week 1, you can reassign those tasks and remove Brian's overallocation, as shown in the bottom section of Figure A-49. Many people will appreciate the simplicity of this feature, first introduced in Project 2010!

Before moving tasks in the Team Planner View:

Resource Name	Unscheduled Tasks	Apr 7, '13								Apr 14, '13							Apr 21, '13							Apr 28, '13		
		T	F	S	S	M	T	W	T	F	S	S	M	T	W	T	F	S	S	M	T	W	T	F	S	S	M
▲ Brian											Task 1															
											Task 2															
Cindy																		Task 3							
Unassigned Tasks: 1																										
																		Task 4							

After moving tasks in the Team Planner View:

Resource Name	Unscheduled Tasks	Apr 7, '13								Apr 14, '13							Apr 21, '13							Apr 28, '13		
		T	F	S	S	M	T	W	T	F	S	S	M	T	W	T	F	S	S	M	T	W	T	F	S	S	M
Brian											Task 1							Task 4								
Cindy											Task 2							Task 3								
Unassigned Tasks: 0																										

Figure A-49. Adjusting resource assignments using the Team Planner feature

Entering Baseline Plans, Actual Costs, and Actual Times

After entering information in the Task Name column, establishing task durations and dependencies, and assigning costs and resources, you are ready to establish a baseline plan. By comparing the information in your baseline plan to actual progress during the course of the project, you can identify and solve problems. After the project ends, you can use the baseline and actual information to plan similar, future projects more accurately. To use Project 2013 to help control projects and view earned value information, you must establish a baseline plan, enter actual costs, and enter actual durations. In the next series of steps you will use a new file called tracking.mpp that you downloaded from the companion Web site for this text (www.intropm.com).

To save a file as a baseline and enter actual information:

1.   *Open the file called tracking.mpp.* The file should be showing the Cost table view. Notice that this short project was planned to start on January 7, 2013 and end on February 13 of the same year, have three resources assigned to it, and cost $11,200. Click the **Project** tab, click the **Set Baseline** button under the Schedule group, and click **Set Baseline**, as shown in Figure A-50.

Select All button   **Set Baseline**

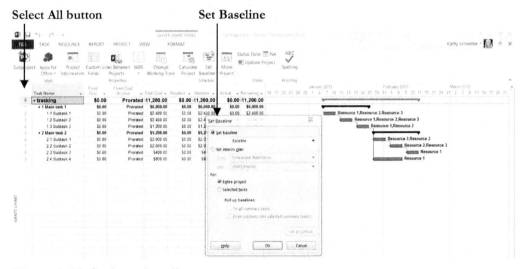

Figure A-50. Saving a baseline

2.   *Save the file as a baseline.* Examine the **Set Baseline** dialog box. Click the drop-down arrow to see that you can set up to ten baselines. Accept the default to save the entire project. Click **OK**. Notice that the Baseline column changes to blue.

3.   *Display the Tracking table.* Click the **Task** tab, right-click the **Select All button** and then click **Tracking** to view the tracking table. Move the split bar to the right to reveal all of the columns in the table, if needed. Move your mouse over each tracking button in the Ribbon in the top line of the Schedule group to see what it does. Your screen should resemble Figure A-51

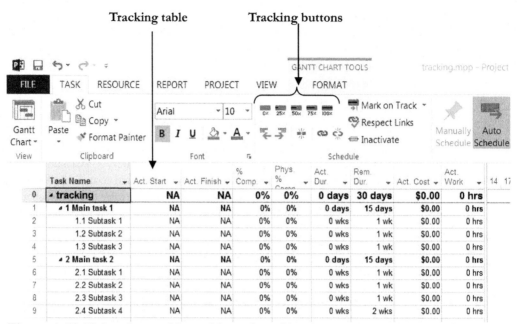

Figure A-51. Using the tracking table and tracking buttons

4. *Mark Tasks 2 through 4 as 100% complete.* Click the Task Name for Task 2, **Subtask 1 under Main task 1**, and drag down through Task 4 to highlight those tasks. Click the **100% Complete** button on the Ribbon. The columns with dates, durations, and cost information should now contain data instead of the default values, such as NA or 0. The % Comp. column should display 100%. Adjust column widths if needed. Your screen should resemble Figure A-52. Notice that the Gantt chart bars for those three tasks now have a black line through them.

Task Name	Act. Start	Act. Finish	% Comp.	Phys. % Comp.	Act. Dur.	Rem. Dur.	Act. Cost	Act. Work		January 2013														February 2013								
▲ tracking	Mon 1/7/13	NA	38%	0%	25 days	1.75 days	$6,000.00	320 hrs																						
▲ 1 Main task 1	Mon 1/7/13	Fri 1/25/13	100%	0%	15 days	0 days	$6,000.00	320 hrs																						
1.1 Subtask 1	Mon 1/7/13	Fri 1/11/13	100%	0%	1 wk	0 wks	$2,400.00	120 hrs		Resource 1,Resource 2,Resource 3																				
1.2 Subtask 2	Mon 1/14/13	Fri 1/18/13	100%	0%	1 wk	0 wks	$2,400.00	120 hrs				Resource 1,Resource 2,Resource 3																	
1.3 Subtask 3	Mon 1/21/13	Fri 1/25/13	100%	0%	1 wk	0 wks	$1,200.00	80 hrs					Resource 1,Resource 2																
▲ 2 Main task 2	NA	NA	0%	0%	0 days	15 days	$0.00	0 hrs																					
2.1 Subtask 1	NA	NA	0%	0%	0 wks	1 wk	$0.00	0 hrs								Resource 2,Resource 3													
2.2 Subtask 2	NA	NA	0%	0%	0 wks	1 wk	$0.00	0 hrs									Resource 2,Resource 3												
2.3 Subtask 3	NA	NA	0%	0%	0 wks	1 wk	$0.00	0 hrs										Resource 1										
2.4 Subtask 4	NA	NA	0%	0%	0 wks	2 wks	$0.00	0 hrs									Resource 1											

Figure A-52. Tracking table information

5. *Enter actual completion dates for Task 6.* Click the Task Name for Task 6, **Subtask 1 under Main task 2**, click the **Mark on Track drop-down**, and then click **Update Tasks.** The Update Tasks dialog box opens. For Task 6, enter the Actual Start date as **1/28/13** (the same as the Current Start date) and the Actual Finish date as **2/11/13** (ten days later than the Current Finish date), as shown in Figure A-53. Click **OK.** Notice how the information in the tracking sheet has changed.

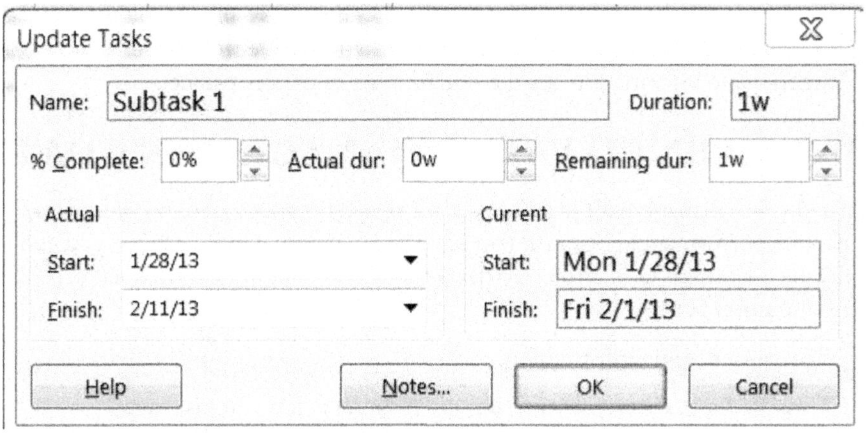

Figure A-53. Update Tasks dialog box

6.   *View the Tracking Gantt chart.* Click the drop-down arrow on the far left of the screen where it says Gantt chart, and then click **Tracking Gantt** to quickly switch to that view. Move the **split bar** and adjust column widths as needed. Use the **horizontal scroll bar** in the Gantt chart window to the right (move the slider to the left) to see symbols on the Tracking Gantt chart. Use the **Zoom slider** on the lower right of the screen to adjust the timescale so you can see all of the symbols. Your screen should resemble Figure A-54. The blue bar for task 6 shows the actual time you just entered. Notice that the delay in this one task on the critical path has caused the planned completion date for the entire project to slip (now Feb 25 versus Feb 13). Also notice the Indicator column to the far left. The check marks show that tasks are completed.

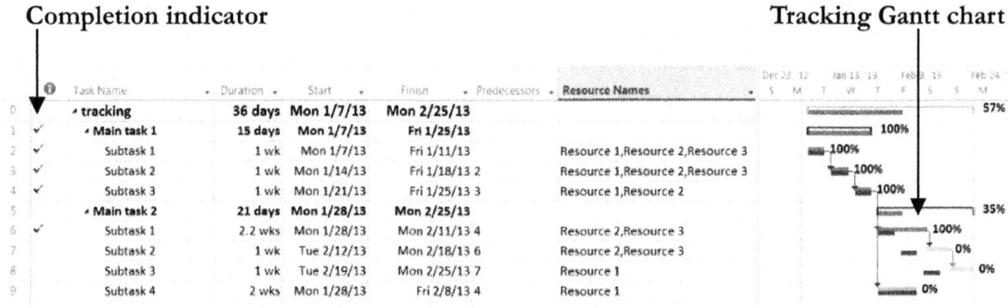

Figure A-54. Tracking Gantt chart view

7.   *Save your file as a new file named myactuals.mpp.* Click **File** on the Menu bar, and then click **Save As**. Name the file **myactuals**, and then click **Save**.

Notice the additional information available on the Tracking Gantt chart. Completed tasks have 100% by their symbols on the Tracking Gantt chart. Tasks that have not started yet display 0%. Tasks in progress, such as Task 5, show the percentage of the work completed (35% in this example). The project summary task bar indicates that the entire project is 57% complete. Viewing the Tracking Gantt chart allows you to easily see your schedule progress against the baseline plan. After you have entered some actuals, you can review earned value information for the initiating tasks of this project.

VIEWING EARNED VALUE MANAGEMENT DATA

Earned value management is an important project management technique for measuring project performance. Because you have entered actual information, you can now view earned value information in Project 2013. You can also view an earned value report using the visual reports feature.

To view earned value information:

1. *View the Earned Value table.* Using the myactuals file you just saved (or downloaded from the companion Web site), click the **Select All** button, select **More Tables,** and double-click **Earned Value**. Move the split bar to the right to reveal all of the columns, as shown in Figure A-55. Note that the Earned Value table includes columns for each earned value acronym, such as PV, EV, AC, SV, CV, etc. Also note that the EAC (Estimate at Completion) is higher than the BAC (Budget at Completion) for Task 6 (and its summary task, Task 5), where the task took longer than planned to complete. Task 0 shows a VAC (Variance at Completion) of ($3,360.00), meaning the project is projected to cost $3,360 more than planned at completion. Remember that not all of the actual information has been entered yet. Also note that the date on your computer must be set later than the date of a completed task for the data to calculate properly.

	Task Name	Planned Value - PV (BCWS)	Earned Value - EV (BCWP)	AC (ACWP)	SV	CV	EAC	BAC	VAC
0	▲ myactuals	$11,200.00	$8,000.00	$10,400.00	($3,200.00)	($2,400.00)	$14,560.00	$11,200.00	($3,360.00)
1	▲ Main task 1	$6,000.00	$6,000.00	$6,000.00	$0.00	$0.00	$6,000.00	$6,000.00	$0.00
2	Subtask 1	$2,400.00	$2,400.00	$2,400.00	$0.00	$0.00	$2,400.00	$2,400.00	$0.00
3	Subtask 2	$2,400.00	$2,400.00	$2,400.00	$0.00	$0.00	$2,400.00	$2,400.00	$0.00
4	Subtask 3	$1,200.00	$1,200.00	$1,200.00	$0.00	$0.00	$1,200.00	$1,200.00	$0.00
5	▲ Main task 2	$5,200.00	$2,000.00	$4,400.00	($3,200.00)	($2,400.00)	$11,440.08	$5,200.00	($6,240.08)
6	Subtask 1	$2,000.00	$2,000.00	$4,400.00	$0.00	($2,400.00)	$4,400.00	$2,000.00	($2,400.00)
7	Subtask 2	$2,000.00	$0.00	$0.00	($2,000.00)	$0.00	$2,000.00	$2,000.00	$0.00
8	Subtask 3	$400.00	$0.00	$0.00	($400.00)	$0.00	$400.00	$400.00	$0.00
9	Subtask 4	$800.00	$0.00	$0.00	($800.00)	$0.00	$800.00	$800.00	$0.00

Figure A-55. Earned value table

2. *View the earned value chart.* Click the **Report** tab, and then click **Costs** under the View Reports group, and then click **Earned Value Report**, as shown in Figure A-56. You can experiment with different report options or click the link to Learn more about earned value, as desired.

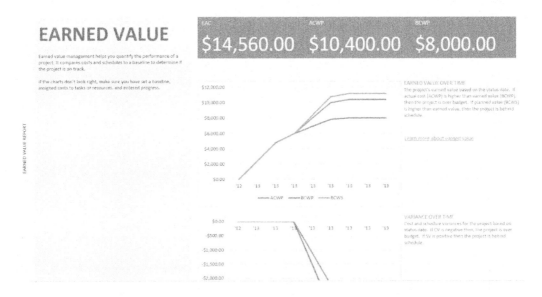

Figure A-56. Earned value report

3. *Close Project 2013 without saving the file*. Click the **File tab**, click **Close**, and select **No** when prompted to save the file. You can also exit Project 2013 and take a break, if desired.

Next you will use a few more features of Project 2013 to help tie your Project to other applications.

INTEGRATING PROJECT 2013 WITH OTHER APPLICATIONS AND APPS FOR OFFICE

Project 2013 provides several features to make it easy to integrate with other applications. For example, you can copy data between Project 2013 and other applications (including the timeline), or you might want to create hyperlinks to project documents created in Word, Excel, PowerPoint, or other applications from within your project files. You can also purchase and add new apps to Project 2013 from Microsoft's Office Store.

Copying Information Between Applications

Most people are familiar with copying information between Office applications. For example, you can highlight a column of data in Excel, select copy, and then select Paste in Project 2013 or other applications. You can also create a new Project 2013 file from an existing Excel file by select New from Excel Workbook. It is also easy to copy a timeline from Project 2013 into another application.

To copy a timeline from Project 2013:

1.   Open another Project 2013 template file. Start Project 2013, and open a template file, such as **Residential Construction**, as shown in Figure A-57. Notice the timeline near the top of the screen.

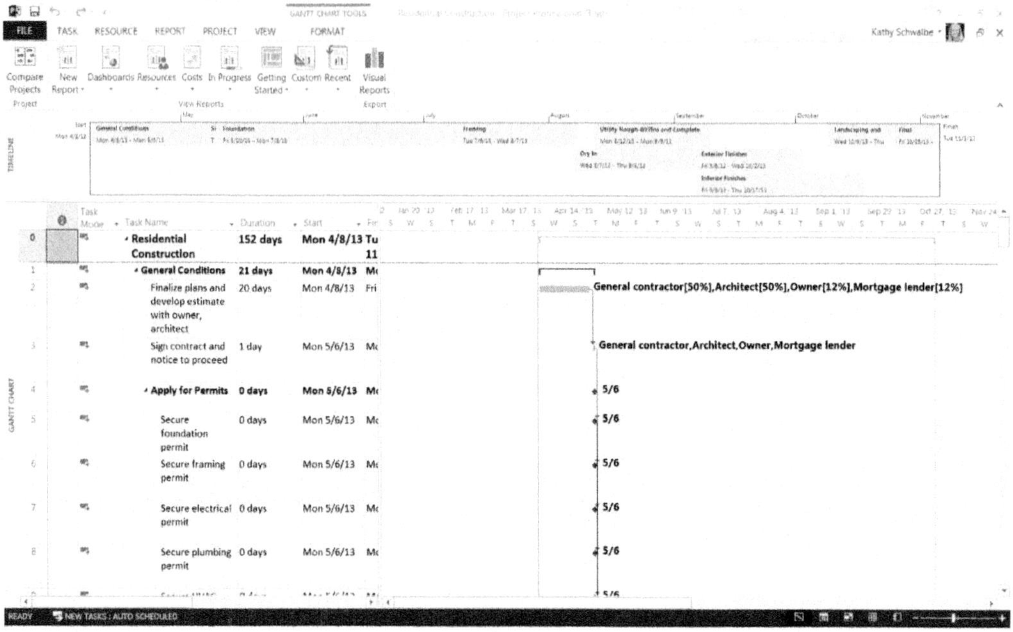

Figure A-57. Residential construction template

2.   Make changes to the Timeline. Move your mouse over the second item on the Timeline called Site Work. **Right-click on Site Work**, and select **Remove from Timeline**.

3.   Open the Insert Hyperlink dialog box. Click on Task 4, **right-click Apply for Permits**, and then click **Add to Timeline**. (Note that this milestone could be worded better to indicate that it has no duration, such as Permit Applications Submitted). Make other adjustments to the Timeline, as desired.

3.   Copy the Timeline into PowerPoint. Click anywhere on the Timeline, and then click the **Copy Timeline button** in the Copy group on the Ribbon, as shown in Figure A-58, and select **For Presentation**.

4.   Copy the Timeline into PowerPoint. Open **PowerPoint**, change the slide layout, add a title to the slide, and change the theme, as desired, and then **right-click** and select **Paste picture**. Your screen should resemble Figure A-59, showing the Project 2013 Timeline in your presentation.

Copy Timeline

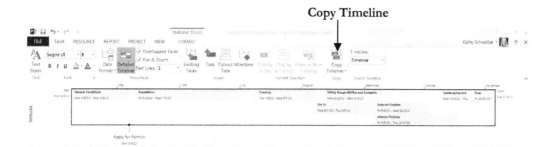

Figure A-58. Copy Timeline

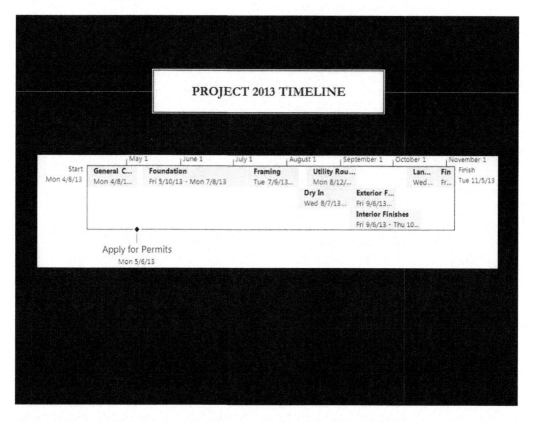

Figure A-59. Timeline copied into PowerPoint

Creating Hyperlinks to Other Files

Some people like to use their Project 2013 file as a main source of information for many different project documents. To do this, you can simply insert a hyperlink to other document files. For example, you can create a hyperlink to the file with the stakeholder register you listed as a milestone in your Task Name column earlier.

To insert a hyperlink within a Project 2013 file:

1.   Open the **myschedule.mpp** file. Use the file you saved earlier or download it from the companion Web site for this text. The Entry table and Gantt Chart view should display.

2.   *Select the task in which you want to insert a hyperlink.* Click the Task Name for Task 3, **Stakeholder register completed**.

3.   *Open the Insert Hyperlink dialog box.* Right-click in that cell, then click **Hyperlink**. The Insert Hyperlink dialog box opens, as shown in Figure A-60. You will have different folders visible based on your computer's directory structure.

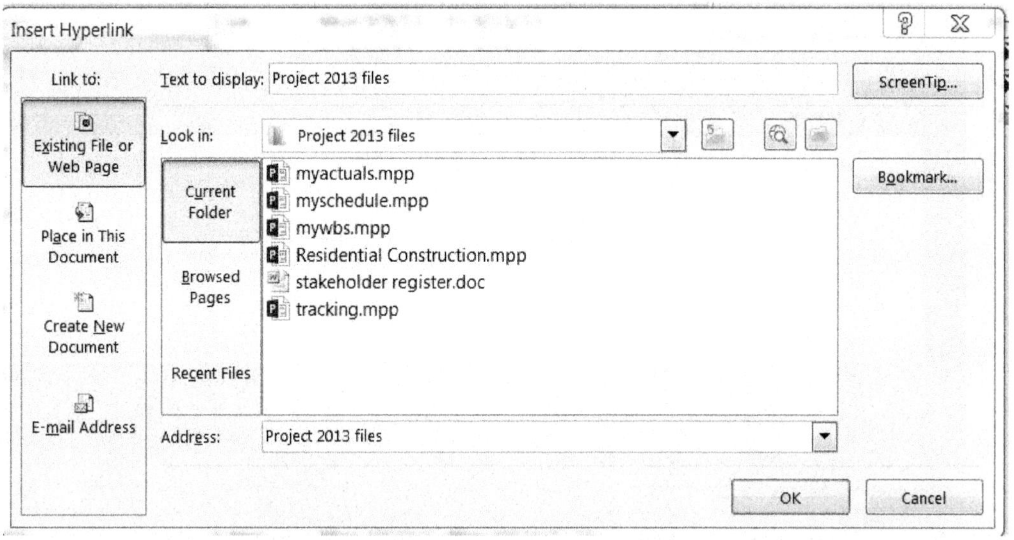

Figure A-60. Insert hyperlink dialog box

4.   *Double-click the filename of the hyperlink file.* Change the **Look in:** information until you find where you have saved the files you downloaded for this appendix. Double-click the Word file named **stakeholder register**, and then click **OK**. A Hyperlink button appears in the Indicators column to the left of the Task Name for Task 3. Move your mouse over the hyperlink button until the mouse pointer changes to the Hand symbol to reveal the name of the hyperlinked file. If you click on it, the file will open.

Using Project 2013 Apps

Microsoft has an Office Store where you can download special apps for Project 2013. New apps are added often.

To explore Project 2013 apps:

1.   *Access the Office Store.* With Project 2013 open, click the **Project** tab, then click the **Apps for Office button** on the left of the Ribbon under the Apps group. The Apps for Office dialog box opens, as shown in Figure A-61.

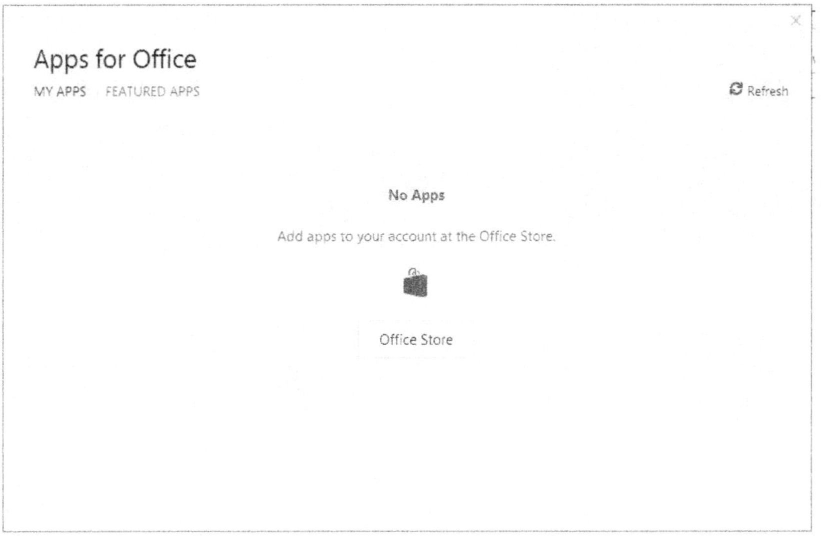

Figure A-61. Apps for Office dialog box

2.   *Explore the Office Store.* Click the **Office Store button**. Your screen should resemble Figure A-62, which shows the apps available on April 6, 2013. Read information about various apps, and add them as desired.

Figure A-62. New Apps for Project on the Office Store (April, 2013)

You have really just touched the surface of Project 2013's powerful features, but you probably know more than most people who have this software! There are several books with more detailed information on using Project 2013 that you can use to learn even more, or you can experiment with the software and Help feature to understand it more.

DISCUSSION QUESTIONS

1.   What are some unique features of project management software?

2.   What are the new features of Project 2013?

3.   How do you create a WBS in Project 2013?

4.   How do you enter task durations and establish dependencies between tasks?

5.   How can you make sure that resource assignments do not mess up your schedule?

6.   How can you use the Team Planner to assign resources and reduce overallocations?

7.   How do you establish a baseline in Project 2013 and enter actual information?

8.   What type of information do you see in the Earned Value table?

9.   How can you copy a Timeline from Project into other applications and access other application files from within Project 2013?

10.   Where can you access apps created for Project 2013?

EXERCISES

1.   To make sure you understand the information in this appendix, perform the steps yourself. Print out the following screens or send them to your instructor, as directed:

   a.   The adjusted Customer Service file as shown in Figure A-13.

   b.   The Schedule table view for the Customer Service file, similar to Figure A-16.

   c.   The Customer Service file filtered to show only milestones, similar to Figure A-21.

   d.   The mywbs file with automatic outline numbers and a project summary task, similar to Figure A-25.

   e.   Create a new Project file called generic-wbs that shows the WBS for a generic project. Make the main categories phase 1, phase 2, phase 3, and phase 4. Include at least four tasks and one milestone under each of these main categories, using meaningful, fictitious names for them. Enter 0 for the duration of the milestones, but do not enter any durations for the other tasks. Be sure to indent tasks and show the outline numbers before printing or submitting the file. Note: If you are doing a project for your class, you can use data for that project instead.

2.   Continue performing the steps in this appendix, starting with the section called Developing the Schedule. Print out the following screens or send them to your instructor, as directed:

   a.   The myschedule file with durations and dependencies entered, similar to Figure A-38.

   b.   The earned value table, similar to Figure A-55.

   c.   Continue performing the steps, even if you do not have to print out more screens. Write a one-to-two page paper describing the capabilities of Project 2013 and your opinion of this software. What do you like and dislike about it?

3.   Use some of the information in the body of the text *An Introduction to Project Management* or *Healthcare Project Management* (or find a sample WBS and Gantt chart on your own). Enter the WBS into Project 2013 to practice your Project 2013 skills.

   a.   Review one of the sample WBSs provided in Chapter 4 (or that you find elsewhere). Indent tasks and use the automatic numbering feature. Print out or submit your file.

   b.   Use the information in Chapter 4 under the section called Developing the Project Schedule to create the Gantt chart for Project X. Also create the network diagram for Project X. Make sure both will print out on one page each, then print or submit them to your instructor. Assume the start date was 6/9/09, or June 9, 2009, to make your results match the screen shots in Chapter 4. (Or use a similar project you find elsewhere).

   c.   Make up actual information for Project X (or a similar project). Assume some tasks are completed as planned, some take more time, and some take less time. View and then print out or submit the tracking Gantt chart.

4.   If you are doing a team project as part of your class or for a project at work, use Project 2013 to create a detailed file describing the work you plan to do for the project.

   a.   Create a detailed WBS, including several milestones, estimate task durations, link tasks, add tasks to the timeline, and enter resources and costs, assign resources, and so on. Save your file as a baseline and print it out send it to your instructor, as desired.

   b.   Track your progress on your team project by entering actual cost and schedule information. Create a new baseline file if there have been a lot of changes. View earned value information when you are halfway through the project or course. Continue tracking your progress until the project or course is finished. Print or submit your Gantt chart, Project Summary report, Earned Value table, and relevant information to your instructor.

   c.   Write a two- to three-page report describing your experience. What did you learn about Project 2013 from this exercise? How do you think Project 2013 helps in managing a project? You may also want to interview people who use Project 2013 for their experiences and suggestions.

END NOTES

[1]TopTenREVIEWS™, "Project Management Software," (http://project-management-software-review.toptenreviews.com) (accessed June 17, 2009).

[2]TopTenREVIEWS™, "Best Online Project Management Comparisons," (http://online-project-management-review.toptenreviews.com/) (accessed April 7, 2013).

Appendix B:
Resources

NOTE: You can find Appendix B in its entirety on the companion Web site for this text at www.healthcarepm.com. Instructors should contact the author (schwalbe@augsburg.edu) to gain access to a secure instructor site.

Appendix B summarizes resources you can use to expand your understanding of project management, and updates will be added as needed. You will find a listing of the template files (and be able to download them all in one compressed file), detailed case studies, information on project management simulation software and MindView Business software, the files used for Appendix A on Project 2013, resources mentioned in the text, project management certification information, and links to additional resources related to project management. Feel free contact the authors at schwalbe@augsburg.edu with any questions or suggestions.

GLOSSARY

accepted deliverable – a verified deliverable that has been reviewed by the stakeholders during the validate scope process and accepted as meeting their needs.

activity – A distinct, scheduled portion of work performed during the course of a project .

activity attributes — Information that provides schedule-related information about each activity, such as predecessors, successors, logical relationships, leads and lags, resource requirements, constraints, imposed dates, and assumptions related to the activity.

activity list — A tabulation of activities to be included on a project schedule.

activity-on-arrow (AOA) approach, or the **arrow diagramming method (ADM)** — A network diagramming technique in which activities are represented by arrows and connected at points called nodes to illustrate the sequence of activities.

actual cost (AC) — The total direct and indirect costs incurred in accomplishing work on an activity during a given period.

agile — Popular software development method that use an iterative workflow and incremental delivery of software in short iterations.

analogous estimates, or **top-down estimates** — The estimates that use the actual cost of a previous, similar project as the basis for estimating the cost of the current project.

balanced scorecard — A methodology that converts an organization's value drivers to a series of defined metrics.

baseline — A starting point, a measurement, or an observation that is documented so that it can be used for future comparison; also defined as the original project plans plus approved changes.

benchmarking — The process of generating ideas for quality improvements by comparing specific project practices or product characteristics to those of other projects or products within or outside of the performing organization.

best practices — Optimal methods, currently recognized within a given industry or discipline, to achieve a goal or objective.

bid — A document prepared by sellers providing pricing for standard items that have been clearly defined by the buyer.

blogs — Easy-to-use journals on the Web that allow users to write entries, create links, and upload pictures, while allowing readers to post comments to particular journal entries.

bottom-up estimates — Cost estimates created by estimating individual activities and summing them to get a project total.

budget at completion (BAC) — The approved total budget for the project.

buffer — Additional time to complete a activity, added to an estimate to account for various factors.

burst — An occurrence when two or more activities follow a single node on a network diagram.

business case — A document that provides justification for investing in a project.

capabilities — The incremental steps leading up to one or more best practices.

cash flow — Benefits minus costs, or income minus expenses.

cause-and-effect diagrams — Also called fishbone or Ishikawa diagrams, these diagrams can assist in ensuring and improving quality by finding the root causes of quality problems.

champion — A senior manager who acts as a key proponent for a project.

change log — A document that lists each project change, its effect on project constraints, and if the change is approved or not.

checklist — A list of items to be noted or consulted.

close-out — A meeting held at the end of the project.

closing processes — The actions that involve formalizing completion and acceptance of the project or phase and bringing it to an orderly end.

collaborating mode — The conflict-handling mode where decision makers incorporate different viewpoints and insights to develop consensus and commitment.

communications management plan — A document that guides project communications.

compromise mode — The conflict-handling mode that uses a give-and-take approach to resolve conflicts.

conformance to requirements — The process of ensuring that the project's processes and products meet written specifications.

confrontation mode — The conflict-handling mode that involves directly facing a conflict using a problem-solving approach that allows affected parties to work through their disagreements.

contingency plans — The predefined actions that the project team will take if an identified risk event occurs.

contingency reserves or **contingency allowances** — The funds held by the project sponsor that can be used to mitigate cost or schedule overruns if known risks occur.

contract statement of work (SOW) — A document that describes the goods or services to be purchased.

contracts — The mutually binding agreements that obligate the seller to provide the specified products or services, and obligate the buyer to pay for them.

control chart — A graphical display of data that illustrates the results of a process over time.

cost baseline — A time-phased budget that project managers use to measure and monitor cost performance.

cost-reimbursable contract — A contract that involves payment to the seller for direct and indirect actual costs.

crashing — A technique for making cost and schedule trade-offs to obtain the greatest amount of schedule compression for the least incremental cost.

critical chain scheduling — A method of scheduling that takes limited resources into account when creating a project schedule and includes buffers to protect the project completion date.

critical path — The series of activities that determine the *earliest* time by which the project can be completed; it is the *longest* path through the network diagram and has the least amount of slack or float.

critical path method (CPM), or **critical path analysis** — A network diagramming technique used to predict total project duration.

deliverable — A product or service produced or provided as part of a project.

dependency, or **relationship** — The sequencing of project activities.

de-scoping, — A schedule compression technique where you remove deliverables that are ancillary to the primary project objectives in order to reduce the project timeline

directives — The new requirements imposed by management, government, or some external influence.

discount factor — A multiplier for each year based on the discount rate and year.

discount rate — The rate used in discounting future cash flows.

discretionary costs — costs that organizations have discretion in deciding whether to fund them.

discretionary dependencies — The dependencies that are defined by the project team.

duration — The actual amount of time spent working on an activity *plus* elapsed time.

earned value (EV) — An estimate of the value of the physical work actually completed.

earned value management (EVM) — A project performance measurement technique that integrates scope, time, and cost data.

effort — The number of workdays or work hours required to complete a activity.

empathic listening — The process of listening with the intent to understand by putting yourself in the shoes of the other person.

estimate at completion (EAC) — A forecast of how much the project will cost upon completion.

ethics — A set of principles that guide our decision making based on personal values of what is "right" and "wrong".

executing processes — The actions that involve coordinating people and other resources to carry out the project plans and produce the deliverables of the project.

external dependencies — The dependencies that involve relationships between project and non-project activities.

extrinsic motivation — A motivation that causes people to do something for a reward or to avoid a penalty.

fallback plans — The plans that are developed for risks that have a high impact on meeting project objectives, and are put into effect if attempts to reduce the risk are not effective.

fast tracking — A schedule compression technique where you do activities in parallel that you would normally do in sequence.

Federal Acquisition Regulation (FAR) — Regulation that provides uniform policies for acquisition of supplies and services by executive agencies in the U.S.

feeding buffers — Additional time added before activities on the critical path that are preceded by non-critical-path activities.

fitness for use — The ability of a product to be used as it was intended.

fixed-price or **lump-sum contract** — A type of contract that involves a fixed price for a well-defined product or service.

flowcharts — The graphic displays of the logic and flow of processes that help you analyze how problems occur and how processes can be improved.

forcing mode — The conflict-handling mode that involves exerting one's viewpoint at the potential expense of another viewpoint.

forecasts —Reports that predict future project status and progress based on past information and trends.

Gantt charts — A standard format for displaying project schedule information by listing project activities and their corresponding start and finish dates in a calendar format.

groupthink — The conformance to the values or ethical standards of a group.

histogram — A bar graph of a distribution of variables.

initiating processes — The actions to define and authorize new projects and project phases as well as identifying those who will be impacted by the project.

integrated change control — The process of identifying, evaluating, and managing changes throughout the project's life cycle.

internal rate of return (IRR) — The discount rate that results in an NPV of zero for a project.

intrinsic motivation — A motivation that causes people to participate in an activity for their own enjoyment.

Invitation For Bid (IFB) – A procurement document used to solicit quotes from potential sellers when the specifications are clearly identified by the buyer and the seller is selected based primarily on price. Unlike an RFP, potential sellers have little or no input regarding solutions or approaches to solutions with an IFB. Sometimes used interchangebly with RFQ.

issue — a matter under question or dispute that could impede project success.

issue log — a tool used to document, monitor, and track issues that need to be resolved for effective work to take place.

key performance indicator (KPI) — A criterion used to determine the degree to which an outcome is achieved.

kick-off meeting — A meeting held at the beginning of a project so that stakeholders can meet each other, review the goals of the project, and discuss future plans.

lag — when an activity requires a gap in time before it can start

lead — when an activity can overlap a preceding one

leader — A person who focuses on long-term goals and big-picture objectives, while inspiring people to reach those goals.

make-or-buy analysis — The process of estimating the internal costs of providing a product or service and comparing that estimate to the cost of outsourcing.

management reserves — Funds held for unknown risks.

manager — A person who deals with the day-to-day details of meeting specific goals.

mandatory dependencies — The dependencies that are inherent in the nature of the work being performed on a project.

Maslow's hierarchy of needs — A hierarchy that states that people's behaviors are guided or motivated by a sequence of needs (physiological, safety, social, esteem, and self-actualization).

maturity model — A framework for helping organizations improve their processes and systems.

merge — A situation when two or more nodes precede a single node on a network diagram.

methodology — A plan that describes how things should be done to manage a project.

metric — A standard of measurement.

milestone — A significant event on a project.

mind mapping — A technique that uses branches radiating out from a core idea to structure thoughts and ideas.

mirroring — The matching of certain behaviors of the other person.

monitoring and controlling processes — The actions taken to measure progress toward achieving project goals, monitor deviation from plans, and take corrective or preventative action to match progress with plans and customer expectations.

multitasking — When a resource works on more than one activity at a time.

Murphy's Law — If something can go wrong, it will.

Myers-Briggs Type Indicator (MBTI) — A popular tool for determining personality preferences.

net present value (NPV) analysis — A method of calculating the expected net monetary gain or loss from a project by discounting all expected future cash inflows and outflows to the present point in time.

network diagram — A schematic display of the logical relationships among, or sequencing of, project activities.

node — The starting and ending point of an activity on an activity-on-arrow network diagram.

nondiscretionary costs — costs that organizations must fund to stay in business

opportunity cost of capital — The return available by investing the capital elsewhere.

organizational process assets — Policies and procedures related to project management, past project files, and lessons-learned reports from previous, similar projects.

outcomes — The tangible or intangible results of applying capabilities.

overallocation — When more resources than are available are assigned to perform work at a given time.

parametric modeling — A technique that uses project characteristics (parameters) in a mathematical model to estimate project costs.

Pareto chart — A histogram that can help you identify and prioritize problem areas.

Parkinson's Law — Work expands to fill the time allowed.

payback period — The amount of time it will take to recoup, in the form of net cash inflows, the total dollars invested in a project.

phase — A a distinct project cycle that produces deliverables.

phase gating — A process whereby project leadership reviews progress on a project after each phase to determine if it should move on to the next phase.

planned value (PV) — That portion of the approved total cost estimate planned to be spent on an activity during a given period.

planning processes — The actions that involve devising and maintaining a workable scheme to ensure that the project meets its scope, time, and cost goals as well as organizational needs.

portfolio — A collection of projects or programs and other work that are grouped together to facilitate effective management of that work to meet strategic business objectives.

post-mortem meeting — A term sometimes used for a project close-out meeting since it is held after the project has died or been put to rest.

precedence diagramming method (PDM) — A network diagramming technique in which boxes represent activities.

process — A series of actions directed toward a particular result.

procurement audits — Reviews often performed during contract closure to identify lessons learned in the entire procurement process.

program — A group of projects, subprograms, or program activities managed in a coordinated way to obtain benefits not available from managing them individually.

Program Evaluation and Review Technique (PERT) — A network analysis technique used to estimate project duration when there is a high degree of uncertainty about the individual activity duration estimates.

program manager — A person who provides leadership and direction for the project managers heading the projects within the program.

progress reports — Reports that describe what the project team has accomplished during a certain period.

project — A temporary endeavor undertaken to create a unique product, service, or result.

project buffer — The additional time added before a project's due date to account for unexpected factors.

project charter — A document that formally recognizes the existence of a project and provides a summary of the project's objectives and management.

project dashboard — A graphic screen summarizing key project metrics.

project management — The application of knowledge, skills, tools, and techniques to project activities to meet the project requirements.

Project Management Institute (PMI) — International professional society for project managers.

project management knowledge areas — Project integration management, scope, time, cost, quality, human resource, communications, risk, and procurement management.

project management office (PMO) — An organizational entity created to assist project managers in achieving project goals.

project management plan — A document used to coordinate all project planning documents and to help guide a project's execution and control.

project management process groups — Initiating, planning, monitoring and controlling, and closing.

Project Management Professional (PMP) — Certification provided by PMI that requires documenting project experience, agreeing to follow the PMI code of ethics, and passing a comprehensive exam.

project management tools and techniques — Methods available to assist project managers and their teams; some popular tools in the time management knowledge area include Gantt charts, network diagrams, critical path analysis, and project management software.

project manager — The person responsible for working with the project sponsor, the project team, and the other people involved in a project to meet project goals.

project organizational chart — A graphical representation of how authority and responsibility is distributed within the project.

project portfolio management — The grouping and managing of projects and programs as a portfolio of investments that contribute to the entire enterprise's success.

project sponsor — The person who provides the direction and funding for a project.

PRojects IN Controlled Environments (PRINCE2) — A project management methodology with eight process groups developed in the U.K.

proposal — A document in which sellers describe what they will do to meet the requirements of a buyer.

quality — The degree to which a set of inherent characteristics fulfill requirements.

quality assurance — The activities related to satisfying the relevant quality standards for a project.

quality audit — A structured review of specific quality management activities that helps identify lessons learned, which could improve performance on current or future projects.

RACI charts — A type of responsibility assignment matrix that shows **R**esponsibility, **A**ccountability, **C**onsultation, and **I**nformed roles for project stakeholders.

rapport — A relationship of harmony, conformity, accord, or affinity.

rate of performance (RP) — The percentage of actual work completed divided by the percentage of work planned to have been completed at any given time.

Rational Unified Process (RUP) framework — A project management methodology that uses an iterative software development process that focuses on team productivity and delivers software best practices to all team members.

records management system — A tool that provides the ability to easily organize, find, and archive documents.

Request for Proposal (RFP) — A document used to solicit proposals from prospective suppliers for products or services that are complex in nature, high in value, or which may be met with a variety of solutions or approaches by the seller. Price is typically not the primary determining factor with an RFP.

Request for Quote (RFQ) — A document used to solicit quotes or bids from prospective suppliers for the purchase of limited quantities of goods, commodity goods, or products/services with known specifications. Sometimes used interchangeably with an IFB.

required rate of return — The minimum acceptable rate of return on an investment.

requirement — A condition or capability that must be met or possessed by a system, product, service, result, or component to satisfy a contract, standard, specification, or other formal document.

requirements management plan — A plan that describes how project requirements will be analyzed, documented and managed.

requirements traceability matrix (RTM) — A table that lists requirements, various attributes of each requirement, and the status of the requirements to ensure that all of them are addressed.

resource histogram — A column chart that shows the number of resources required for or assigned to a project over time.

resource leveling — A technique for resolving resource conflicts by delaying tasks.

resource loading — The amount of individual resources an existing schedule requires during specific time periods.

responsibility assignment matrix (RAM) — A matrix that maps the work of the project as described in the WBS to the people responsible for performing the work.

return on investment (ROI) — (Benefits minus costs) divided by costs.

risk — An uncertainty that can have a negative or positive effect on meeting project objectives.

risk events — The specific, uncertain events that may occur to the detriment or enhancement of the project.

risk register — A document that contains results of various risk management processes, often displayed in a table or spreadsheet format.

root cause — The real or underlying reason a problem occurs.

run chart — A chart that displays the history and pattern of variation of a process over time.

scatter diagram — A diagram that helps show if there is a relationship between two variables.

scope baseline — The approved project scope statement and its associated WBS and WBS dictionary.

scope creep — The tendency for project scope to continually increase.

scope validation — The formal acceptance of the completed project deliverables by the customer or designated stakeholders.

short list — A list of the top three to five suppliers created to reduce the work involved in selecting a source.

Six Sigma — A comprehensive and flexible system for achieving, sustaining, and maximizing business success; uniquely driven by close understanding of customer needs, disciplined use of facts, data, and statistical analysis, and diligent attention to managing, improving, and reinventing business processes.

slack or **float** — The amount of time an activity may be delayed without delaying a succeeding activity or the project finish date.

slipped milestone — A milestone activity that was actually completed later than originally planned.

smoothing mode — The conflict-handling mode that de-emphasizes or avoids areas of differences and emphasizes areas of agreement.

staffing management plan — A plan that describes when and how people will be added to and taken off of a project.

stakeholder analysis — A a technique for analyzing information to determine which stakeholders' interests to focus on and how to increase stakeholder support throughout the project.

stakeholder register — A document that includes details related to the identified project stakeholders

stakeholders — People involved in or affected by project activities.

standard — A document that describes best practices for what should be done to manage a project.

status reports — Reports that describe where the project stands at a specific point in time.

strategic planning — The process of determining long-term objectives by analyzing the strengths and weaknesses of an organization, studying opportunities and threats in the business environment, predicting future trends, and projecting the need for new products and services.

SWOT analysis — Analyzing Strengths, Weaknesses, Opportunities, and Threats.

synergy — The concept that the whole is equal to more than the sum of its parts.

systems — Sets of interacting components working within an environment to fulfill some purpose.

systems analysis — A problem-solving approach that requires defining the scope of the system to be studied, and then dividing it into component parts for identifying and evaluating its problems, opportunities, constraints, and needs.

systems approach — A holistic and analytical approach to solving complex problems that includes using a systems philosophy, systems analysis, and systems management.

systems management — Addressing the business, technological, and organizational issues associated with creating, maintaining, and modifying a system.

systems philosophy — An overall model for thinking about things as systems.

systems thinking — A holistic view of an organization to effectively handle complex situations.

task – Work that is done in support of operational, functional, or project performance. Tasks are not part of the schedule (activities are shown on the schedule). Tasks include many management functions such as things done to manage the team, run a production line, or build relationships.

team contract — A document created to help promote teamwork and clarify team communications.

template — A file with a preset format that serves as a starting point for creating various documents so that the format and structure do not have to be re-created.

Theory of Constraints (TOC) — A management philosophy that states that any complex system at any point in time often has only one aspect or constraint that is limiting its ability to achieve more of its goal.

three-point estimate — An estimate that includes an optimistic, most likely, and pessimistic estimate.

time-and-material contract — A type of contract that is a hybrid of both a fixed-price and cost-reimbursable contract.

***to*-complete performance index (TCPI)** — The cost performance that must be achieved on the remaining work in order to meet a specified goal, such as the BAC or EAC.

tracking Gantt chart — A Gantt chart that compares planned and actual project schedule information.

triggers — The indicators or symptoms of actual risk events.

triple constraint — Balancing scope, time, and cost goals.

Tuckman model — A model that describes five stages of team development (forming, storming, norming, performing, and adjourning).

verified deliverable — A deliverable that has been completed and checked for correctness as part of quality control.

weighted scoring model — A technique that provides a systematic process for basing project selection on numerous criteria.

withdrawal mode — The conflict-handling mode that involves retreating or withdrawing from an actual or potential disagreement.

work breakdown structure (WBS) — A deliverable-oriented grouping of the work involved in a project that defines the total scope of the project.

work breakdown structure (WBS) dictionary — A document that describes detailed information about WBS deliverables, sub-deliverables, and work packages.

work package — A deliverable at the lowest level of the WBS, where it can be appropriately assigned to and managed by a single accountable person.

workarounds — The unplanned responses to risk events.

INDEX

CPSIA information can be obtained
at www.ICGtesting.com
Printed in the USA
LVOW02s0422210916

505458LV00002B/50/P